CW00920404

Caves and Karst
of the
Yorkshire Dales

Edited by

Tony Waltham and David Lowe

British Cave Research Association

Caves and Karst of the Yorkshire Dales

Copyright © British Cave Research Association

Published by British Cave Research Association,
The Old Methodist Chapel, Great Hucklow, Buxton SK17 8RG, UK
www.bcra.org.uk/bookshop
publications-sales@bcra.org.uk
BCRA is a UK registered charity, number 267828

All rights reserved. No part of this book may be reprinted or reproduced or utilised
in any form or by any electronic, mechanical or other means, including photocopying
and recording, subject to statutory exception, or by any information storage or retrieval
system, without permission in writing from the publisher.
Copyright on the texts, photographs and drawings resides with the respective authors,
and copyright of the design and layout is owned by BCRA.

Editors: Tony Waltham and David Lowe
Graphics and artwork: Tony Waltham
Photograph preparation: Jerry Wooldridge
Design and layout: Tony Waltham and David Lowe

ISBN 978-0-900265-46-4 (paperback)
ISBN 978-0-900265-47-1 (hardback)

Published 2013

Printed by John Browns, Nottingham

Cover photographs:
Front: above: Kilnsey Crag, Wharfedale (Tony Waltham)
below: High-level passage in Boreham Cave (Clive Westlake)
right: Shaft in Hurnel Moss Pot (John Forder)
Back: above: Ingleborough and pavements on Scales Moor (Tony Waltham)
below: Pool in the main streamway of Lancaster Hole (Paul Deakin)
Frontispiece: Hole in the Wall, Gordale Scar (Tony Waltham)

Caves and Karst of the Yorkshire Dales

Volume 1

The Chapters

Volume 2

Contents

Volume 2 of *Caves and Karst of the Yorkshire Dales* is primarily an e-book.

Its chapters are essentially overviews of the known caves within each area, dale or fell; these summarise the main features of the caves and their geomorphology, but they are not exhaustive descriptions that approach the details and passage descriptions within available guidebooks.

Production as an e-book in a series of individual chapter files means that any one chapter can be up-dated whenever major revision is needed following significant discoveries of cave passages. As these chapters will evolve in parallel with the exploration of the caves, the authors may change on subsequent versions.

Chapters will be published on-line as and when each is completed, and the first versions will appear throughout 2013 and 2014.

The chapter files are available on the web pages of the British Cave Research Association at bcra.org.uk .

A paper edition of Volume 2 will be published when all its component chapters are completed.

Preface

The British Cave Research Association has a double interest in the Yorkshire Dales. Perhaps first as the major area within Britain for sport caving, cave exploration and cave study. But also for the magnificent glaciokarst landscapes of the Dales and the vital role that the caves, in particular their dateable stalagmites, make to regional studies of landscape evolution.

This book covers both the descriptive and the scientific aspects of both the caves and the karst landforms of the Dales. Its writing and editing have then had the double target of maintaining sound academic standards in its data recording and also of presenting its material in a style that is readable and comprehensible by the non-specialist. It is the first in a series of new books that will cover the caves and landfoms of all the main karst areas within Britain.

The book has no comprehensive glossary, as readers are directed to the *Dictionary of Karst and Caves*, which is published within the BCRA Cave Studies Series, and was compiled by the two editors of this volume. A few chapters have their own mini glossaries for acronyms and terms that may be unfamiliar to some readers.

Locations of caves and landforms are not described in detail within the text, but the comprehensive Index to Localities contains the National Grid References of all named sites.

Acknowledgements

Credit goes to Phil Murphy for initiating the project to produce this book as a successor to the BCRA's earlier volume *Limestones and Caves of North-West England*, which had been published in 1974 and was long out of print and out of date. Together with David Judson, he gathered authors for various chapters, and they established the broad structure of the book, based largely on the 1974 volume. However, the huge advances in scientific studies of the Dales caves meant that the project grew like Topsy, and grew beyond their means, so they eventually handed over to the present editors. Their initial work is recognised with gratitude, and they remain as contributing authors on chapters within the two volumes into which the project has expanded.

The editors offer their thanks to the many colleagues and friends who have contributed to the preparation of this book in various ways, and to whom due credit is afforded.

Some authors have been with the project from its initiation, while others were invited to join at later stages. Sincere thanks are due to all the authors, as it is they who have provided the material that has made the book both possible and worthwhile.

All chapters have been peer reviewed, and the referees are thanked for their helpful comments. Tim Atkinson, Vanessa Banks, Dave Brook, Andrew Chamberlain, Tony Cooper, John Cordingley, Silvia Dacre, Andy Farrant, Trevor Faulkner, Trevor Ford, Helen Goldie, John Gunn, Ric Halliwell, Alan King, Harry Long, Terry O'Connor, Hannah O'Regan, Martyn Pedley, Richard Shaw, Mike Simms, Graeme Swindles, Chris Thomas, John Thorp, Heather Viles, Paul Wood and Steve Worthington are all thanked for their reviews of individual chapters.

Special thanks are due to four colleagues who have given extensive support that has gone well beyond the call of duty, namely Harry Long and John Cordingley with their encyclopaedic knowledge of the Dales and its caves, John Thorp with his great knowledge of the cave palaeontology and archaeology, and Trevor Faulkner with his archival knowledge of the scientific literature. Also, many thanks to Andrew Rigby who has astutely guided the book into its final printing.

Numerous friends have generously contributed photographs to the book, many in response to request lists sent round by the editors. Thanks are due to all of them; credits for all photographs are given in the captions, though only initials are cited where the credit is to either the chapter authors or the volume editors. Sincere gratitude is also accorded to Jerry Wooldridge, who improved, adjusted and balanced all the photographs where appropriate, and thereby greatly reduced the workload of the editors.

Diagrams and artwork have largely been provided by the chapter authors and then re-worked into house style, with sources credited in the captions where appropriate.

Cave surveys are the work of innumerable cavers, frequently in very cold and very wet conditions underground. Without their efforts, there would be no database for the scientific studies. The many individual cavers are credited by their club names on surveys of specific caves, but the area maps that show numerous caves are compiled from multiple sources and credit is due to too many to name.

Tony Waltham and David Lowe

Contents

CHAPTER 1

The Yorkshire Dales

Tony Waltham and David Lowe

White limestone scars terracing the hillsides, great expanses of bare limestone pavement, streams that sink into the ground, deep pothole shafts peppering the high benches, and the extensive networks of caves passages that lie beneath the fells. These are just some elements of the Yorkshire Dales karst. Though not the only significant karst terrain in Britain, it has more than its share of the best developed and best known limestone landforms. The Dales region has the country's longest cave system and the greatest expanses of glaciokarst, whereas the deepest cave and the largest gorge lie elsewhere. A combination of the spectacular and the beautiful makes the limestone country of the Dales strikingly significant in terms of its geomorphology and its landscape values.

Karst is just one element of the terrain that characterises the Yorkshire Dales. The limestone scars and the steep-sided glaciated valleys combine to make the area one of the most scenic parts of England. Its National Park extends over an area about 40 km square, with the landscapes of its southern half dominated by limestone outcrops. The area, commonly known simply as the Dales, is a distinctive block within the central Pennine Hills, with its rivers draining to both the west and east coasts of England.

Though the karst region is generally referred to as the Yorkshire Dales, it includes the Ease Gill valley that lies in tiny slices of both Lancashire and Cumbria; this therefore lies outside the National Park, which keeps within the county boundary (Fig. 1.5). The surface karst in Ease Gill is largely unspectacular but it overlies multiple complex cave systems that have now been linked to become part of the Three Counties Cave System (named as such because it also extends beneath the county boundary into Yorkshire). At times the less formal and more relaxed term, the Dales, is perfect to describe what many would claim is the finest area of karst and caves in Britain.

Geography of the Dales

Within the Yorkshire Dales, the more spectacular and extensive karst, and most of the larger caves, are contained within an area known as the Craven Uplands. This is the belt of limestone country that is dominated by the Three Peaks of Ingleborough, Pen-y-ghent and Whernside and also extends eastwards to Malham and Wharfedale. Wide limestone benches lie at altitudes around 400m and summits rise above the karst to about 700m. Towards the southwest the Uplands overlook the Craven Lowlands, which generally lie below 200m, and the margin between the two areas is the great step in the terrain marking the line of the Craven Faults.

The Yorkshire Dales, by Tony Waltham and David Lowe
Tony Waltham: Nottingham; tony@geophotos.co.uk
David Lowe: Nottingham; drdjlowe@yahoo.co.uk
Chapter 1, pages 1–10 in Caves and Karst of the Yorkshire Dales,
edited by Tony Waltham and David Lowe.
Published 2013 by the British Cave Research Association,
978-0-900265-46-4 and at www.bcra.org.uk

Geology of the limestone

The Craven Uplands are just the southern, slightly upturned edge of the Askrigg Block, an ancient geological structure that has helped to define the elements within the landscape of the Yorkshire Dales. This largely fault-bounded block is a positive feature that has been upstanding relative to its neighbouring terrain for a substantial part of geological time. It still stands high above the Craven Lowlands towards the southwest, but its other boundaries are more subdued. In the north it is bounded by faults that cross the Pennines through the lower ground of the Stainmore Gap, its western edge is also faulted, where adjacent higher ground includes the Howgill Fells, and in the east the edge of the Block dips gently away beneath younger rocks beyond Nidderdale.

Perhaps the most significant aspect of the Askrigg Block's history is that around 350 million years ago, in Carboniferous times, it formed a shallow shelf sea that was almost surrounded by deeper-water basins. Carbonates were deposited on that shelf to form the limestones that are now host to most of the caves and karst of the Dales. Along the southern margins of the Askrigg Block, a thick limestone

Figure 1.1. Ingleborough standing above the limestone benches that are interrupted by Chapel-le-Dale and Kingsdale (TW).

Figure 1.2. Stalactites in Pippikin Pot (photo: Mark Shinwell).

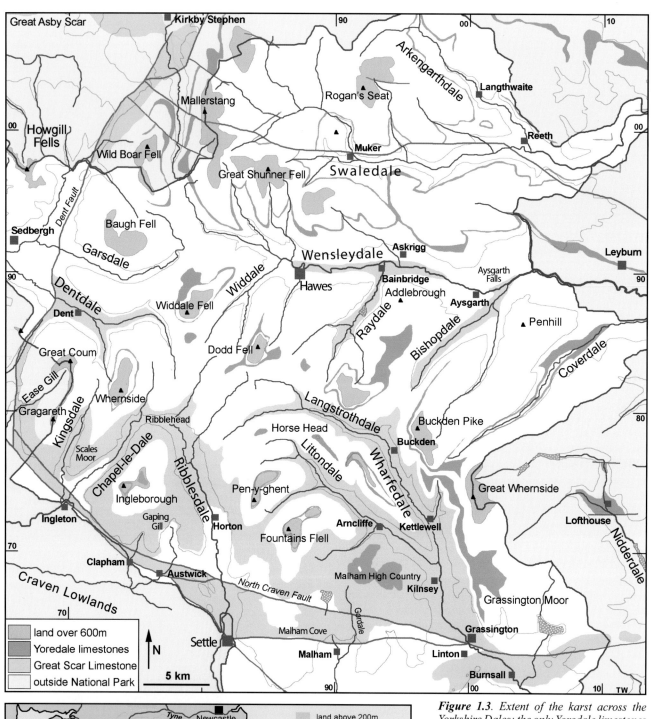

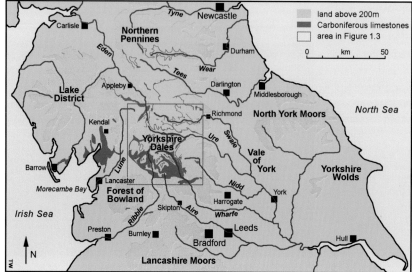

Figure 1.3. Extent of the karst across the Yorkshire Dales; the only Yoredale limestones marked are those with significant caves and karst; all the marked outcrops are of the Main Limestone, except across Grassington Moor, Nidderdale and Coverdale (Middle Limestone) and on the Malham High Country (where the lower Yoredale limestones are contiguous with the Great Scar Limestone); contours are at 300m and 600m.

Figure 1.4. Location of the Yorkshire Dales astride the north-south chain of the Pennine Hills, within the heart of northern England; the areas of Carboniferous limestone marked are only those with significant known karst.

Figure 1.5 (opposite). Limestone pavements on the main benches around Ingleborough, with Pen-y-ghent rising in the distance (TW).

The Great Scar Limestone

The major karst landforms and most of the larger cave systems in the Yorkshire Dales are developed on and within a major unit of strong, largely pale-coloured limestone that is informally known as the *Great Scar Limestone*. Though this unit is readily recognisable in terms of its related geomorphology, it is less clearly defined in geological terms. This is because, although it everywhere includes the formally-defined Great Scar Limestone Group, it locally extends upwards to take in one or more of the younger limestone beds that lie within the Yoredale Group.

Within the Dales, the Great Scar Limestone Group presents a consistent and distinctive appearance. In contrast there is considerable lateral and stratigraphical variation within the lower part of the overlying Yoredale Group, reflecting the changing and contrasting environments in which its original sediments were deposited. In its classic form a typical Yoredale cyclothem includes basal marine limestone, overlain in turn by marine shale, sandstone, seatearth and coal. However, in some areas the clastic rocks are virtually absent, and one or more of the Yoredale limestone beds can be in continuity with each other and with the underlying Great Scar Limestone Group.

The Carboniferous Limestone stratigraphy is described in Chapter 2, but within subsequent chapters the terms *Great Scar Limestone* or *the limestone* are used to refer to the Great Scar Limestone Group along with whichever overlying limestone beds exhibit similar lithologies and are essentially in continuity. Across the western Dales this includes the Lower Hawes Limestone, which is everywhere lithologically similar to the underlying limestones. Farther east the informal *Great Scar Limestone* unit includes some or all of the Lower Hawes, Upper Hawes, Gayle and Hardraw Scar limestone beds, reflecting the absence of significant intervening

shale and sandstone. In the diagram below, the geomorphological unit that contains the main elements of the Dales karst and caves is enclosed by the pale blue background. On Grassington Moor this extends up to the Middle Limestone to recognise that streams sinking into this limestone at Mossdale Caverns and Langcliffe Pot pass through intervening shales and sandstones to enter the underlying Great Scar Limestone (see Chapter 7). The Girvanella Bed is a generally-thin nodular limestone that forms a marker band near the top of the main limestone sequence (see Chapter 2)

This informal use of the term *Great Scar Limestone* is intended to provide a sensible approach to describing the broad geological context of the karst geomorphology without the need to become immersed in the finer details of stratigraphy. The diagram shows the formal stratigraphical names, which are derived from the Sedbergh area, and relates these to names that are more recognisable and applicable to the limestones that contain the Dales' main karst and caves on the southern part of the Askrigg Block.

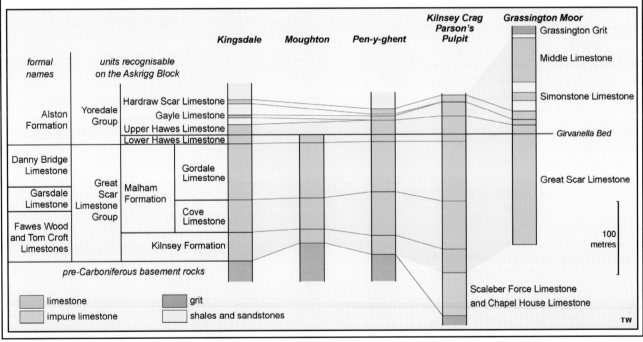

sequence is exposed, and this hosts the main areas of the Craven Uplands karst that are centred on Ingleborough and Malham. Farther north on the tilted block these beds lie buried beneath younger rocks.

Most of the Dales karst and caves have formed on and within the Great Scar Limestone, which takes its name from the rock scars along the sides of all the Craven Dales, from Kingsdale across to Wharfedale. This limestone is largely a pale grey or cream in colour, but it weathers to a white surface patina that makes it so very distinctive as a landscape feature. It is generally between 150 and 200m thick, and hosts all the deeper caves. Above the Great Scar Limestone, the Yoredale Group is a mixed rock sequence dominated by impermeable shales. These gather the run-off from rainfall and snowfall to form streams that flow into the caves in the Great Scar. The Yoredale sequence also includes another set of limestone beds. Though nowhere more than about 50m thick individually, these Yoredale limestones contain their own caves and support their own karst, notably in the northern dales where the Great Scar Limestone is buried deep beneath the surface.

Complications occur locally, where some of the Yoredale limestones are contiguous with the Great Scar Limestone, notably in and around Wharfedale, and the geomorphological unit that forms the karst does not match any single term that is geologically correct (see box). The geological map and key in Figure 1.5 are simplified to indicate the areas of limestone outcrop that can be distinguished by their karst geomorphology.

Climate

The climate of the Yorkshire Dales is temperate and oceanic, dominated by frontal systems and associated depressions that sweep in from the southwest and provide copious amounts of relief rainfall when they meet the Craven Uplands. Weather records from the Malham Tarn Field Centre (Burt and Horton, 2003) are reasonably representative for most of the Dales karst, and provide a 40-year sequence of data (Table 1.1). Temperatures rise to daily means of only around 15°C through the summer months of June to September, and ground frosts strike on nearly half the nights of the year. Snow lies on the fells for an average of 35 days of each winter, but for longer on the summits, and for less time on the dale floors where it rarely persists for longer than a week.

Figure 1.6. Wharfedale in winter (TW).

Figure 1.7. On pasture in Ribblesdale, sheep walk past a reed-filled shakehole where water drains into the limestone beneath (TW).

On average, every other day in the Dales can be described as rainy, with more than a millimetre of precipitation, and the rainfall is spread very evenly through the year. The weather over the Dales karst can hardly be described as harsh, but it is a notable event when cave streams either drop to levels that open sumps or decline in flow to give the cave divers good visibility in placid waters; and summer storms always bring the risk of major flooding underground.

Countryside

Grassland dominates the landscape of the Yorkshire Dales. The wide-open fells, broken by limestone scars but with only rare stands of trees, create much of the character of the Dales. Even the dale floors are dominated by a mixture of rough pasture and nurtured meadows, with very little that goes under the plough. The open grassland dictates the style of farming, almost entirely devoted to hill sheep and cattle, but it also owes much to the sheep that have grazed it for thousands of years and remain very effective at keeping down any growth of shrubs and trees. Adding to the character of the grasslands are the dry stone walls, built of local limestone or sandstone, which form dense networks on every dale floor and continue more widely spaced over even the highest fells.

Though the farming has a major visual impact on the landscape of the Dales, it provides only a foundation to the Dales economy. The largest part of the economy is related to tourism in and around the many villages and small towns within the Yorkshire Dales National Park. The Park encompasses most but not all of the karst, and its major visitor attractions include some of the karst landforms. Malham Cove and Gordale Scar earn 'honey-pot' status with

Mean annual air temperature		6.9°C
Mean coldest month	January	1.5°C
Mean warmest month	August	13.0°C
Lowest recorded temperature	(February 1986)	−13.0°C
Highest recorded temperature	(August 1990)	28.2°C
Nights per year with ground frost		145
Mean annual rainfall		1502.4 mm
Mean wettest month	December	167.0 mm
Mean driest month	May	90.6 mm
Wettest recorded month	(October 2000)	328.9 mm
Driest recorded month	(April 1980)	2.5 mm
Rainy days (>1 mm rainfall) per year		180

Table 1.1. Selected statistics of the climate recorded at Malham Tarn between 1961 and 2000 (after Burt and Horton, 2003).

Figure 1.8. The open expanse of grassland on a loessic soil over the limestone, in Dowkabottom, above Littondale (TW).

Figure 1.9. Hardraw Force, the highest of the many waterfalls in Wensleydale (TW).

the numbers of people they attract on a fine summer weekend. Waterfalls are always an attraction, and the Dales have many, nearly all formed where streams cascade over strong beds of limestone. There are also three show caves, White Scar Cave, Ingleborough Cave and Stump Cross Caverns, each with its own character, for those who wish to venture underground in relative comfort. But there is far more to the Dales, and the combination of stone-built villages dating from the 1700s, dry-stone walls tracing up the dalesides, and the wild open fells above provides some of the most visually pleasing countryside in Britain. The National Park thrives on the proceeds of its undoubted scenic value (Waltham, 2007).

Mining, mainly for lead ore, was a major industry, in Swaledale and Wharfedale in particular, but a peak of activity around 1800, when the miners found their way into some significant caves, declined to nothing at all after about 1980. Its place in the local economy has been taken only in part by quarrying, both for limestone and for the older

Quaternary chronology

As many Quaternary events are diachronous, dates in the table on the right are best estimates from a variety of sources that are applicable to a timeline for the Yorkshire Dales. All dates are in years counted back from 2000 (so expressed as b2k) derived from the Greenland ice cores back to about 48 ka and then from correlations with radiometrically dated lavas and tephras. Calibrated carbon years are effectively the same, as they are linked to the ice-core years but are expressed as years before 1950. Ages in uncalibrated carbon years are younger by about 1600 years at 12 ka and by about 3500 years at around 40 ka. MIS are Marine Isotope Stages (see Chapter 3). There is ongoing debate over the cold phases of the 'Wolstonian', as the type locality may be of a different age, but no better names have yet been agreed for these intervals.

A chronology of the late Quaternary, in the table below, has dates in years BC or AD, or in thousands of years BP (meaning Before Present at the year 2000). The starts of the archaeological periods are diachronous, and these quoted are applicable to the Yorkshire Dales. The last glaciation of the Dales region extended over about 27–16 ka, but was diachronous between valleys and uplands during both advance and retreat.

MIS	start	British terms	other terms	
1	11.7	Holocene		
2	27.5	Late Devensian	Weichselian, Würm	Late Pleistocene
3	59		Upton Warren IS	
4	73	Middle Devensian	cold	
5a	77		Brimpton IS	
5b	90	Early Devensian	cold	
5c	100		Chelford IS	
5d	114	Early Devensian	cold	
5e	126	Ipswichian	Eemian	
6	186	Late 'Wolstonian'	Saalian, Riss	Middle Pleistocene
7	245		Aveley IG	
8	303	Middle 'Wolstonian'		
9	339		Purfleet IG	
10	362	Early 'Wolstonian'		
11	423	Hoxnian	Holsteinian	
12	478	Anglian	Elsterian, Mindel	
13	540			
20–14	814	Cromerian		Early Pleistocene
62–22	1750	Beestonian	Bavelian, Günz	
	2588	Pleistocene start		

MIS	start	stage	sub-divisions	archaeology
1		Holocene	Neoglacial = Little Ice Age : AD 1500 – 1800 Medieval Climatic Optimum : AD 900 – 1300 Atlantic : 8.0 – 5.0 ka	Medieval Period AD 400 Romano-British Period AD 100 Bronze Age 2600 BC Neolithic 3900 BC Mesolithic 9600 BC
	11.7		Pre-Boreal and Boreal : 11.7 – 8.0 ka	
2		Late Devensian	Loch Lomond Stadial = Younger Dryas : 12.8 – 11.7 ka Windermere Interstadial = Lateglacial Interstadial : 14.7 – 12.9 ka Last Glacial-Interglacial Transition : 14.7 – 11.7 ka	Palaeolithic from about 45 ka
	27.5		Last Glacial Maximum = Dimlington Stadial : 26 – 19 ka	

Figure 1.10. Landsat image of the southern part of the Askrigg Block, in false colour; the more lush plant cover, notably along the cultivated land of the dale floors, shows as brown, and forestry plantations show as dark brown; some of the bare limestone shows in a pale blue tint. As the sun direction is from the south, the north sides of the hills and the south sides of the valleys are in deep shadow. In this image, Ribblesdale lies top to bottom down the centre, with the triangular mass of Ingleborough on its left; Barbondale is in the top left corner; Littondale and Wharfedaleare on the right and converge just off the image.

and generally harder rocks that lie beneath it in Chapel-le-Dale and Ribblesdale. The number of quarries has declined, but the few large survivors are important employers, and the remaining limestone quarries have little impact on the karst. Extraction of water-worn rockery stone from the limestone pavements was destructive in the past, but this has now ceased completely.

Geomorphology of the Dales

Most of the karst landforms that now occur in the Dales limestones have developed their recognisable morphological features within about the last million years. The same applies to most of the caves, which were no more than very narrow fissures when their evolution is traced back more than the same million years or so. The history of both the surface landforms and the caves therefore spans much of the Quaternary, when the Dales landscape evolved by fluvial erosion that was interrupted by multiple interludes of glacial activity. The chronology of the Quaternary (see box on the previous page) is now reasonably well constrained, not least by the data that have been derived from datable stalagmites in the Dales caves (see Chapter 10).

The dales themselves are fine examples of glaciated troughs with U-shaped profiles that are closest to perfection in Chapel-le-Dale and Wharfedale. However they were occupied by discrete valley glaciers only for short periods during growth and decay of the ice sheets. For much longer periods, ice covered the entire area of the Yorkshire Dales, and ice erosion on the limestone benches above the dales left the bare rock surfaces that were subsequently etched by erosion to become limestone pavements. Elsewhere, the ice deposited and then over-ran thick layers of rock debris and shaped it into the distinctive mounds that are the drumlin fields; those around Ribblehead are among the best developed and best known in Britain, purely as glacial features, unrelated to the karst. Meltwater also provided a powerful erosional force, both beneath the ice sheets and during each phase of deglaciation, and the gorges that it carved have survived in the limestone terrains where they have not been degraded by subsequent fluvial erosion. The impact of the Quaternary ice sheets is apparent throughout the landscape, and the pavements, gorges, dolines and caves combine to create within the Yorkshire Dales a glaciokarst of international significance.

Figure 1.11. Kettlewell village, on the floor of the glaciated trough of Wharfedale, seen from the limestone bench on its east flank (TW).

Figure 1.12. The drumlins at Ribblehead, seen beyond the track of the Settle to Carlisle railway that traverses the Dales karst (TW).

Caves in the Dales

With nearly half the total number of caves currently recorded in Britain, and nearly half the combined length of known cave passage, the Yorkshire Dales karst is a notable cave region. Most of the major caves are in the western half of the Craven Dales (Fig. 1.15), compared to fewer in the east and hardly any known caves in the largest block of limestone, northeast of Malham Tarn. Though depths reached in the Dales caves appear insignificant on a world scale (Georgia's Krubera is nearly ten times as deep), the longest (the Three Counties Cave System) is about number 25 in a list of the world's longest caves. The Dales caves have atmosphere and appeal; their clean-washed streamways descending staircases of waterfall shafts offer sheer spectacle, as well as sport that can be both challenging and enjoyable. And where the active stream caves intersect old and abandoned high-level passages, a caver can walk through silent galleries some of which are beautifully decorated by calcite stalactites and stalagmites.

Many of the Dales caves are known as potholes, or just as pots. Both terms refer primarily to a cave that opens on the surface as a vertical shaft, whereas many that are entered through roughly horizontal passages are named as caves. Confusingly, some caves continue with deep underground

Figure 1.14. Cow Pot, an open pothole 23m deep from daylight, first descended by the Yorkshire Ramblers in 1899 (photo: Mark Shinwell).

Figure 1.13. Main streamway in Lancaster Hole (photo: Paul Deakin).

shafts and some potholes have extensive passages below their entrance shafts; the name of a feature is no indication of its overall dimensions, but generally refers only to the nature of its entrance. And many others of the great Dales cave systems are just named as holes, which is purely descriptive, avoids any inferences about depth, and casts no aspersions on the spectacular qualities of their underground passages.

Figure 1.15. Locations of some of the more important caves in the Dales, including most but not all of the longer and deeper systems; at the western end of the karst, all the caves from Bull Pot (of the Witches) to Large Pot are now parts of the Three Counties Cave System.

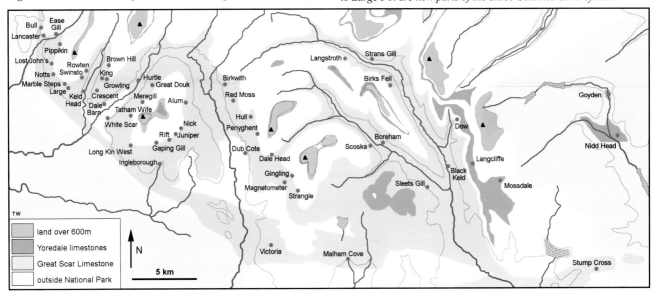

Exploration of the caves

Excepting the opening up of Ingleborough Cave in 1837 (Craven, 1999), serious underground exploration in the Dales began only in 1892, when members of the Yorkshire Ramblers' Club enjoyed a golden age, needing only to walk up onto the pristine limestone benches to descend innumerable open potholes and caves (Craven, 2007). This burst of activity was prompted partly by the fact, a shock to local pride, that the great shaft of Gaping Gill was first descended completely by a passing Frenchman in 1895. However, with heavy rope ladders and no private cars, every weekend's caving was a major expedition, journeying out from their home town of Leeds. Only after 1918 were many more clubs formed, each to provide the team effort and the then essential pool of expensive equipment. Notable were the Craven Pothole Club, the Bradford Pothole Club and the British Speleological Association, with the latter eventually making the lion's share of major discoveries, including some caves that were seriously challenging to explore, especially with the equipment available at the time (Craven, 2001).

The same clubs continued activities after 1945, and were joined by many others. The Northern Pennine Club and the Northern Cave Club each began long series of notable and difficult explorations, while the Red Rose Cave and Pothole Club began a protracted and productive involvement with the caves of Ease Gill. The most successful new club was the University of Leeds Speleological Association, which since the 1960s has made numerous spectacular discoveries and also set new standards in producing the cave surveys that are an invaluable scientific output from sporting cavers.

Huge improvements in diving equipment and the introduction of single rope techniques have revolutionised caving to the extent that major new discoveries continue to be made within the Dales. Members of the Cave Diving Group have explored vast lengths of underwater cave passage behind the main resurgences. Meanwhile, no longer needing to rely upon club funds to provide expensive equipment, many cavers have taken to working with groups of friends. One such group, the Misty Mountain Mud Mining Corporation, specialises in digging out the mud and debris that have choked many cave passages over time, and their major success has been in forging some of the missing links that finally made the Three Counties Cave System a reality. This and all the other major caves in the Dales are described and discussed in Volume 2 of this book.

Figure 1.16. Stalagmites in Pippikin Pot, Leck Fell, of the type invaluable for dating by their content of uranium isotopes (TW).

Cave research

Beyond the cave surveys that are produced by every team that discovers a new cave and are invaluable as a basis for various scientific studies, there has been relatively little systematic research within the Dales caves. This is partly because their potentially cold, wet and hostile environment is not conducive to slow and painstaking observation and recording. Archaeological excavations and biological collecting are generally the least restrained because they mostly take place in the entrance zones. The exception in terms of research deep in caves has been the collecting of suitable stalagmite samples for radiometric dating. Laboratory analysis of specific isotopes produced during uranium decay has provided reference age values that have supported establishment of an outline cave development chronology (see Chapters 7 and 10). Scope for future research lies in applying improved and novel dating techniques, and in studying the stable isotopes within stalagmites in order to elucidate data on palaeoclimates. Alongside the laboratory work, detailed geological and geomorphological mapping in some of the larger but slightly more accessible cave systems will continue to provide the evidence required to interpret the evolution of the caves and the surface landforms.

None of the techniques of isotope science, or the results of their application, was available when the predecessor of this volume was published nearly 40 years ago (Waltham, 1974). That so much has changed, and that so much progress

Figure 1.17. Straw stalactites in the half-submerged tube of Boreham Cave's high-level passage, discovered by, and still only accessible to, cave divers (photo: Dave Ryall).

has been made, warranted the preparation of this book. Not only has cave research advanced to new levels of vision and understanding, but the output of chronological data has given caves, in the Dales and elsewhere, a greater prominence in wider studies of the evolution of Britain's landscapes.

Karst adjacent to the Dales

Whereas the Yorkshire Dales region is the prime concern of this book, there are significant caves and karst landforms in many adjacent limestone areas.

The Yoredale limestones continue northwards beyond the Dales and thicken along the Northern Pennines, where they form long narrow outcrops along the flanks of major valleys (Fig. 1.5). The more important of their scattered caves merit a Chapter in Volume 2.

West of the Pennines, Carboniferous limestones form the bedrock in a large area on and around the Arnside peninsula, on the eastern side of Morecambe Bay, but the greater proportion of this is lowland covered by thick glacial and alluvial sediments. Karst is developed only in and on fault-bounded blocks of higher ground, where the limestone pavements include many that are extensive and particularly well developed (see Chapter 5). Between some of the pavements, wetlands floor basins with underground drainage that distinguishes them as the only poljes in Britain (Gale, 1981, 1984, 2000) and maze caves were developed at past water tables in their marginal limestone bluffs (Ashmead, 1974; Waltham et al., 1997). On the north side of the bay, the limestones of Furness are notable for large karstic collapse features known as sops that were filled with high-grade iron ore, which has been extracted in its entirety (Rose and Dunham, 1977; Moseley, 2010); a few small caves lie in the flanks of the various limestone hills (Brook et al., 1994). On both sides of the bay, small caves have yielded important bone deposits and other archaeological material (Smith, 2012; Wilkinson et al., 2011).

The same limestones extend northwards as an incomplete fringe around the older rocks of the Lake District (Fig. 1.2). South of Appleby, the low escarpment of Great Asby Scar has the most extensive of many well-developed limestone pavements (Waltham et al., 1997). There are just a few caves recorded along the narrow discontinuous outcrop towards the northwest, and also in limestone around Whitwell in the Forest of Bowland (Brook et al., 1994).

Figure 1.19. A newly collapsed doline on the gypsum at Ripon, in the Vale of York (TW).

East of the Pennines, karst landforms are developed to a limited scale on various units of younger and weaker rocks. The narrow escarpment of Permian dolomitic limestone, extending from south of Harrogate to north of Darlington, has small-scale underground drainage on its dip slope, and Smeaton Pot and Farnham Cave have the longest known passages (Gibson et al., 1976; Lowe, 1978; Speight, 1987). At Knaresborough, the same limestone is cut through by the River Nidd gorge, which contains tufa springs known as the Petrifying Well and some adjacent cave dwellings (Cooper and Burgess, 1993). Permian gypsum, in beds with a parallel outcrop just to the east of the dolomitic limestone, have few visible karst features, except where subsiding and collapsing dolines have caused major damage to buildings and infrastructure, notably in Ripon (Cooper, 1986, 2005).

Across the Vale of York, the ooidal limestones of the Late Jurassic Corallian Group have the best of the karst features in the North York Moors. Beneath the floor of Bransdale, Excalibur Pot has more than 1600m of passages, including a long streamway and multiple high-levels (Douthwaite and Ewles, 2010). It is the only long cave currently known

Figure 1.18. Limestone pavement at Holmepark Fell, one of many extensive pavements east of Morecambe Bay (photo: Simon Webb).

Figure 1.20. The stream passage in Excalibur Pot, in the Jurassic limestones of the North York Moors (photo: Gary Douthwaite).

Figure 1.21. The Main Chamber the Gaping Gill Cave System with Fell Beck in full flood forming an unusually large waterfall from daylight (photo: Paul Deakin).

beneath the Moors, but is probably indicative of many more caves yet to be discovered in the Corallian limestones. The nearby Kirkdale Cave, developed at a similar horizon, has a small maze of abandoned bedding passages, which gained significance when Ipswichian bone deposits were excavated from them (Boylan, 1981; McFarlane and Ford, 1998). Farther west, the scarp edges of the Hambleton Hills, also formed in Jurassic rocks, are noted for their many Windypits, with vertical shafts that descend into deep and long fissures and rift passages; however these are primarily landslip fissures where dissolutional enlargement has been minor or negligible (Cooper et al., 1976; Gibbs and Stewart, 2003; Murphy and Lundberg, 2008.).

The Chalk surface of the Yorkshire Wolds has a well developed fluviokarst with numerous dry valley systems (Waltham et al., 1997), but no caves are recorded within it, other than sea caves, most notably at Flamborough Head.

Though the eastern part of Yorkshire contains a host of contrasting karst landforms within its various soluble rocks, none compares to the spectacular glaciokarst and extensive cave systems of the Dales.

References

Ashmead, P, 1974. The caves and karst of the Morecambe Bay area. 201-226 in Waltham, *op. cit.*

Boylan, P J, 1981. A new revision of the Pleistocene mammal fauna of Kirkdale Cave, Yorkshire. *Proc. Yorks. Geol. Soc.*, **43**, 253-280.

Brook, D, J Griffiths, M H Long and P F Ryder, 1994. *Northern Caves 3: The Three Counties System and the North-west.* Dalesman: Lancaster, 287pp.

Burt, T P and B P Horton, 2003. The climate of Malham Tarn. *Field Studies*, **10**, 635-652.

Cooper, A H, 1986. Subsidence and foundering of strata caused by the dissolution of Permian gypsum in the Ripon and Bedale areas, North Yorkshire. *Geol. Soc. Spec. Publ.*, 22, 127-139.

Cooper, A H, 2005. Remediation of a sinkhole over gypsum in Ripon, UK. 272-276 in T Waltham, F Bell and M Culshaw, *Sinkholes and Subsidence*, Springer: Berlin.

Cooper, A H and I C Burgess, 1993. Geology of the country around Harrogate. *Mem. Brit. Geol. Surv.*, Sheet 62.

Cooper, R G, P F Ryder and K R Solman, 1976. The North Yorkshire windypits: a review. *Trans. Brit. Cave Res. Assoc.*, **3**, 77-94.

Craven, S A, 1999. A history of cave exploration in the Northern Pennines, United Kingdom, up to 1838. *Cave Karst Science*, **26**, 53-59.

Craven, S A, 2001. The British Speleological Association (1935–1973) and its founder Eli Simpson: with particular reference to activities in the northern Pennines of England. *Cave Karst Science*, **28**, 99-112.

Craven, S A, 2007. History of cave exploration in the Northern Pennines of England: the work of the clubs 1892–1945. *Cave Karst Science*, **34**, 23-32.

Douthwaite, G and M Ewles, 2010. Excalibur's hidden secrets. *Descent*, 213, 20-22.

Gale, S J, 1981. The geomorphology of the Morecambe Bay karst and its implications for landscape chronology. *Zeitschrift Geomorphologie*, **25**, 457-469.

Gale, S J, 1084. Quaternary hydrological development in the Morecambe Bay karst, northwest England. *Norsk Geografisk Tidsskrift*, **38**, 185-192.

Gale, S J, 2000. *Classic landforms of Morecambe Bay.* Geographical Association: London, 48pp.

Gibbs, J and R Stewart, 2003. *Moorland caver: a guide to the caves and windypits of the North Yorkshire Moors.* JMG: Cleveland, 76pp.

Gibson, R, M Bliss and R Shackleton, 1976. Caves of the Magnesian Limestone. *J. Yorks. Subterranean Soc.*, 1, 9-22.

Lowe, D J, 1978. Farnham Cave, a rift cave in the Magnesian Limestone. *Trans. Brit. Cave Res. Assoc.*, **5**, 23-28.

McFarlane, D A and D C Ford, 1998. The age of the Kirkdale Cave palaeofauna. *Cave Karst Science*, **25**, 3-6.

Moseley, M, 2010. The metalliferous mines of Cartmel and south Lonsdale. *British Mining* (Northern Mines Research Society), 89, 104pp.

Murphy, P J and J Lundberg, 2008. Uranium series dates from the Windypits of the Noth York Moors: implications for late Quaternary ice cover and the timing of speleogenesis. *Earth Surface Processes Landforms*, **34**, 305-313.

Rose, W C C and K C Dunham, 1977. Geology and hematite deposits of South Cumbria. *Econ. Mem. Geol. Surv. G. B.*, Sheet 58.

Smith, I R, 2012. Kirkhead Cavern, Kent's Bank Cavern and Whitton's Cave near Allithwaite: geology, sediments and archaeology. 98-102 in H J O'Regan, T Faulkner and I R Smith (eds), *Cave Archaeology and Karst Geomorphology in North West England: Field Guide.* Quaternary Research Association: London.

Speight, A, 1987. Smeaton Pot. *Caves and Caving*, 35, 33-35.

Waltham, A C (ed.), 1974. *Limestones and Caves of North-west England.* David and Charles (for British Cave Research Association): Newton Abbot, 477pp.

Waltham, T, 2007. *The Yorkshire Dales Landscape and Geology.* Crowood: Marlborough, 224pp.

Waltham, A C, M J Simms, A R Farrant and H S Goldie, 1997. *Karst and Caves of Great Britain.* Chapman & Hall (for Joint Nature Conservation Committee): London, 358pp.

Wilkinson, D M, H J O'Reagan and J Thorp, 2011. Dogs, scouts and cavers: a history of archaeological excavation at Dog Hole Cave, Haverbrack, Cumbria, UK. *Cave Karst Science*, **38**, 125-130.

Figure 1.22. The main passage in Sleets Gill Cave is dry and abandoned except when it fills to the roof in times of flood; its size may be taken as an indication that there are many more caves awaiting discovery in the great block of limestone between Malham and Littondale (TW).

CHAPTER 2

Geology of the limestones

Colin Waters and David Lowe

Cave systems in the Yorkshire Dales occur predominantly within the rock unit known as the Great Scar Limestone Group (Fig. 2.1). This Group, which is restricted in extent to northern England, was deposited during the early Carboniferous, ranging from Tournaisian to Visean age, about 359 to 330 million years ago (Table 2.1; Gradstein *et al.,* 2012; Waters and Condon, 2012). Britain then lay close to the Equator and the area now including the Dales was submerged beneath warm, clear tropical seas. These waters had rich and diverse communities of corals, brachiopods, crinoids, bivalves and algae colonising the sea-bed, and free-swimming ammonoids (coiled molluscs, commonly referred to as goniatites). Their lime-rich remains accumulated on the sea-bed, were bored by organisms or broken by wave and current activity, to produce carbonate sands, silts and muds, which, with time, lithified to form limestone.

Early Carboniferous tectonic plate movement resulted in a broadly north–south stretching of the continental crust beneath the area that is now Britain. This resulted in a series of crustal blocks forming topographical highs (horsts) and basinal lows (grabens), which greatly influenced the distribution and thickness of subsequent limestone deposition. One such structural high, the Askrigg Block, underlies the Yorkshire Dales (Figs 2.3 and 2.4), where the Great Scar Limestone beds were deposited in shallow waters on top of older basement rocks. Sedimentation into the basins adjacent to the Askrigg Block led to development of rocks of deeper-water facies including mudstones and thinner bedded limestones, some of which are slightly older than the Great Scar Limestone.

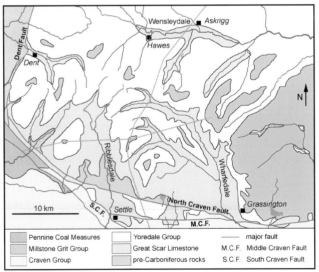

Figure 2.1. Main features of the Craven Dales geology. The green lines show the approximate profiles of the cross-sections shown in Figures 2.4 and 2.5.

Geology of the limestones, by Colin Waters and David Lowe,
Colin Waters, British Geological Survey; cnw@bgs.ac.uk
David Lowe, Nottingham; drdjlowe@yahoo.co.uk
Chapter 2, pages 11–28 in **Caves and Karst of the Yorkshire Dales**,
edited by Tony Waltham and David Lowe.
Published 2013 by the British Cave Research Association,
978-0-900265-46-4 and at www.bcra.org.uk
Colin Waters publishes with the permission of the Executive Director of the British Geological Survey.

Lower Palaeozoic basement

The Carboniferous rocks lie unconformably on a basement comprising sedimentary rocks, largely of Lower Palaeozoic age (Fig. 2.2; Aitkenhead, *et al.,* 2002; Barnes *et al.,* 2006), along with the Wensleydale Granite, which was proved in the Raydale Borehole (Fig. 2.3). Most of the basement rocks are confirmed as of Ordovician or Silurian age. However, data relating to the structural history of the Ingleton Group (north of Ingleton and around Douk Gill in Ribblesdale) suggest a Precambrian origin rather than the Ordovician age indicated by meagre fossil evidence (Soper and Dunning, 2005).

Lower Palaeozoic sedimentary rocks crop out over Barbon and Middleton Fells immediately west of the Dent Fault and to the north, in the Howgill Fells, as well as forming inliers in several valleys from Kingsdale in the west as far as Malham in the east (Fig. 2.3). Both Dakyns (1876) and Raistrick (1931) considered it probable that Silurian bedrock also underlies alluvial deposits near Chapel House Lodge, Kilnsey, in Wharfedale. However, despite the evidence of abundant Silurian erratics being confined to the drift deposits of only a short stretch of the valley between Chapel House Lodge and Burnsall, no definitive proof of this sub-drift basement outcrop – such as a borehole – has been obtained.

Basement rock types include sandstones, siltstones and mudstones, with some limestones, ranging in age mainly from 475 to 420 million years old. They were folded, weakly metamorphosed and locally strongly cleaved during Acadian deformation, about 400 million years ago, before being uplifted and eroded to produce the land surface over which the Carboniferous seas subsequently transgressed. The unconformity between the Carboniferous beds and the underlying basement rocks is well exposed at many places, including Foredale and Thornton Force (Fig. 2.2).

Figure 2.2. Sub-horizontal limestones and basal conglomerate of the Holkerian Cove Limestone overlie sub-vertical 'slates' of the Ingleton Group at Thornton Force in Kingsdale (TW).

Buried beneath some 500m of Carboniferous rocks southeast of Hawes, the Wensleydale Granite batholith is inferred to be about 450 Ma old, on consideration of its textural and geochemical similarities with undoubted Ordovician granites of the Lake District (Millward, 2006). Thus, the granite was not intruded into the Carboniferous limestone succession, but through Ordovician and older rocks before the earliest beds of the Carboniferous were laid down around a hundred million years later. Following intrusion of the granite, Silurian rocks were deposited across parts of the area before the entire Lower Palaeozoic succession and the granite were uplifted and then denuded, producing a landscape with significant local relief prior to

the start of limestone deposition. The basement ridges and troughs inherited from this relief (discussed also in Chapter 8) now form the floor of the limestone karst, but are known only from limited exposures. Some of the largest basement landscape features are recognisable between Ribblesdale and Crummack Dale (see box below), where they have significant influence upon the direction of underground drainage (Soper and Edwards, 2012).

Although heavily fractured and generally moderately well cleaved, the Lower Palaeozoic succession as a whole is impermeable and is commonly accepted as forming the ultimate limit for the downward movement of groundwater passing through the overlying limestone.

Basement topography and basal conglomerate

Deposition of the Yorkshire Dales limestones began when the Dinantian sea first transgressed an irregular topography of folded and faulted Lower Palaeozoic rocks that form the basement of the Askrigg Block. Along the southern edge of the Block the landscape included locally steep-sided troughs and ridges reflecting the contrasting resistance to erosion of the different basement lithologies. During the Dinantian the Block was subsiding gently towards the north before merging into the Stainmore Basin, and in the south the Craven Fault System formed steep drops into the adjacent Craven Basin. Eastwards the Block probably extended and sloped gently towards the present Vale of York (Aitkenhead *et al.*, 2002) but details are hidden beneath overlying younger rocks. Westwards the topography stepped up into still-higher, fault-guided basement uplands across the Dent Fault, the step limiting Dinantian transgression in this direction.

About 360 million years ago water levels rose and the sea that occupied the Craven and Stainmore basins began to encroach onto lower parts of the Block. Deposits from the first (Courceyan) transgression are few and poorly known in the southern Dales, where much of the Stockdale Farm Formation, proved only in boreholes, is of this age. If similar beds were deposited where local palaeo-depressions reached the Block margins, they were subsequently removed by erosion. Localised sandy and dolomitic beds, some deposited during the second (Chadian) transgression, occur in the Ravenstonedale arera and were proved in the Raydale Borehole, but across most of the southern Dales no Chadian rocks are known.

A distinctive and locally unique red-tinged conglomerate bed exposed at the entrance to Dub Cote Cave, southeast of Horton in Ribblesdale, might be of similar age and mode of origin to fan conglomerates (Dunham and Wilson, 1985) that crop out near Sedbergh. A thin mudstone bed containing freshwater fossils, uncovered in a quarry west of Horton (Garwood and Goodyear, 1924), is probably the oldest Carboniferous bed preserved in the area. It occupies a palaeo-depression in the Silurian basement rocks and is overlain by a thin bed of black marine limestone, also presumed to be much older than the overlying Great Scar Limestone Group. It is unknown whether the Dub Cote conglomerate is the same age as these beds, or whether it marks the base of the younger Great Scar Limestone Group.

Across most of the southern Dales the third major (Arundian) transgression failed to submerge all of the Block's high points. Reworked rock debris was incorporated into basal conglomerates – basement rock clasts in a limestone matrix – that are widespread, though not ubiquitous. Exposures south of Pen-y-ghent and in Crummack Dale are grey, with clasts generally far smaller and more-angular than those seen in the reddish Dub Cote conglomerate. Even-larger clasts, including rounded boulders and cobbles, occur at Thornton Force in Kingsdale (Fig. 2.2). Where exposed or seen in boreholes south of the North Craven Fault, conglomeratic basal beds of the Chapel House Limestone, the oldest part of the Great Scar sequence, are also grey, with basement rock clasts. Conglomeratic limestones higher in this unit confirm that a hinterland providing clastic rock debris survived locally well into Arundian times.

At Nappa Scars in Crummack Dale, a basal conglomerate 2m thick, with rounded clasts, overlies the steeply-dipping Ordovician basement rocks. Just a few metres above, a coarser, locally-derived slide-breccia includes large angular blocks of Ordovician slaty siltstone (Waltham, 2005). Up-valley at Austwick Beck Head, the basal beds change character laterally. On the beck's northern bank the basal limestone is virtually pebble-free, lying directly on Ordovician mudstones. The southern bank exposes a conglomeratic bed more than a metre thick, with well-rounded Ordovician mudstone pebbles and cobbles in a limestone matrix (Waltham, 2005).

Except for the Dub Cote exposure, most Dales basal conglomerates are Arundian. However, at this time a few areas remained above water, and deposition of the Kilnsey Formation failed against these local highs. This is well shown on both sides of Crummack Dale, where the mid-Holkerian Cove Limestone overlies a west–east basement ridge, with the older Kilnsey Formation present only north and south of the ridge. Continuations of this ridge underlie other locations where Arundian and early Holkerian rocks are absent and mid-Holkerian beds overlie the basement, as at Silverdale and Fountains Fell. Another basement-high that lacks Arundian limestones extends towards Malham from the west, probably reflecting contemporaneous movement of the nearby North Craven Fault.

Elsewhere the base of the Great Scar Limestone is not notably conglomeratic, though thick mudstones interbedded with muddy limestones near the base of the Kilnsey Formation show that fine-grained clastic debris still existed, at least in southern areas, and that some basement highs remained above sea level. At White Scar Cave there is no basal conglomerate as such, reflecting its location across a debris-free basement ridge that is exposed in the floor of the cave (Waltham, 1977). Nevertheless, interbeds of shale, sandstone and conglomeratic-limestone in the lowest 15m of the limestone sequence indicate that a source of clastic rock material lay close by.

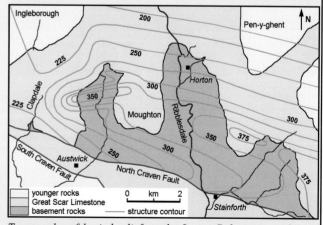

Topography of buried relief on the Lower Palaeozoic rocks and unconformity at the base of the limestone, based on outcrop data in Crummack Dale and Ribblesdale. Depth to the unconformity beneath upper Clapdale is unknown, so this interpretation is taken no farther west (largely after Soper and Edwards, 2012).

Limestones of the Ravenstonedale Group

The earliest Carboniferous rocks deposited within the district belong to the Ravenstonedale Group (Waters and Davies, 2006; Waters *et al.*, 2007; Dean *et al.*, 2011). This succession is thickest (about 380m) in the Stainmore Trough, north of the Dales, where the type locality is located, but it thins markedly towards the south over the Askrigg Block (Fig. 2.5). Though there are no significant outcrops in the Dales area, a buried limestone succession about 150m thick, ranging from Chadian to early Holkerian age, was proved by the Raydale Borehole 6 km southeast of Hawes.

Deposition on the northern part of the Askrigg Block occurred following early Visean sea-level rise and transgression, with the succession located marginal to the more open and deeper marine conditions in the Stainmore Trough at the time. The Raydale Dolostone and Penny Farm Gill formations comprise interbedded dolostone, limestone, siltstone and sandstone, deposited in a shallow marine, intertidal and supratidal environment. Between the two, the Marsett Formation is a succession of alluvial sandstones and conglomerates. Rocks of the Ravenstonedale Group are overlain by the beds of the Great Scar Limestone Group, with component formations as described for the northern part of the Askrigg Block (Fig. 2.6).

The Stockdale Farm Formation, which is present on the southern margins of the Askrigg Block and proved in boreholes near Settle (Arthurton *et al.,* 1988), comprises lithologies similar to those present within the Ravenstonedale Group, but including anhydrite, deposited on an alluvial plain and marginal marine flats subject to periodic desiccation and fluctuating salinity. Its upper surface is deeply fissured, probably representing a significant non-sequence and palaeokarst, overlain by Arundian beds belonging to the Chapel House Limestone Formation.

Depositional texture recognisable					Depositional texture not recognisable
Original components not bound together during deposition				Components bound together during deposition	
Contains mud (clay and fine silt)			Lacks mud and is grain-supported		
Mud supported		Grain supported			
< 10% grains	> 10% grains				Crystalline carbonate
Mudstone	**Wackestone**	**Packstone**	**Grainstone**	**Boundstone**	

Table 2.2. *Classification of carbonate rocks according to their depositional texture, as used in Table 2.3 (Dunham, 1962)*

Glossary

argillaceous: sediment or rock made up of silt- and/or clay-sized rock or mineral particles (smaller than 0.625mm), and commonly containing clay minerals.

batholith: large, commonly dome-shaped, body of igneous rock, formed when magma from the Earth's mantle intrudes into the crust and solidifies, generally deep beneath the contemporary surface.

benthic: aspects relating to the bottom of a body of water, such as the bed of a lake or the ocean floor.

bentonite: clay-rich rock commonly formed by decomposition of volcanic tuff, in which case it tends to be potassium-rich, with high levels of the clay-mineral illite, and known as K-bentonite.

bioclastic: largely composed of the remains of dead organisms.

biostrome: sedimentary rock, generally bedded, that is built up of the remains of marine organisms, so includes shell beds and reefs.

bioturbated: sediment or rock that is disturbed or restructured by moving or burrowing organisms.

connate: connate fluid is trapped in pores during sediment deposition and subsequently expelled as the buried sediment is transformed into rock.

facies: pronounced *fashease*, the characteristics of a rock unit that reflect conditions and environment of deposition.

fenestral fabric: also called 'birdseye structure' – rock fabric with distinctive inclusions (fenestrae) of sparry calcite; a diagnostic feature of many porcellanous limestones.

hade: the angle of inclination of a fault, vein or joint measured from the vertical.

inlier: an outcrop of older rocks completely surrounded by younger rocks, due to erosion, structural effects or a combination of the two.

unconformity: a geological surface that represents a significant depositional break and/or period of erosion between the rock successions below and above.

Current international terminology					Worldwide		Former British terminology; some names/ranks still in informal use		
Regional Substage	Regional Stage	Stage (Age)	Subseries (Subepoch)	Series (Epoch)	System (Period)	Date Ma	Subsystem	Series (Epoch)	Regional Stage
		Asselian		Cisuralian	**Permian**	298.9		Lower (Early) Permian	Autunian
Stephanian C	Stephanian	Gzhelian	Upper (Late) Pennsylvanian	Pennsylvanian	Carboniferous	303.7	Upper Carboniferous	Stephanian	Not divided
Stephanian B									
Barruelian		Kasimovian				307.0			
Cantabrian									
Asturian	Westphalian	Moscovian	Middle (Mid) Pennsylvanian			315.2		Westphalian	Westphalian D
Bolsovian									Bolsovian
Duckmantian									Duckmantian
Langsettian							Silesian		Langsettian
Yeadonian	Namurian	Bashkirian	Lower (Early) Pennsylvanian					Namurian	Yeadonian
Marsdenian									Marsdenian
Kinderscoutian									Kinderscoutian
Alportian									Alportian
Chokierian						323.2			Chokierian
Arnsbergian		Serpukhovian	Upper (Late) Mississippian	Mississippian		330.9		Visean	Arnsbergian
Pendleian									Pendleian
Brigantian							Lower Carboniferous		Brigantian
Asbian	Visean	Visean	Middle (Mid) Mississippian				Dinantian		Asbian
Holkerian									Holkerian
Arundian									Arundian
Chadian						346.7			Chadian
Courceyan	Tournaisian	Tournaisian	Lower (Early) Mississippian			358.9		Tournaisian	Courceyan

Table 2.1. *Comparison of Carboniferous geological time and chronostratigraphical units (not to scale) currently approved internationally (left side) and those in common use in the British Isles (right side); geological time ranks are shown in bracketed italics where they differ. Modified from Waters et al., 2011; dates of Stage bases from Gradstein et al., 2012.*

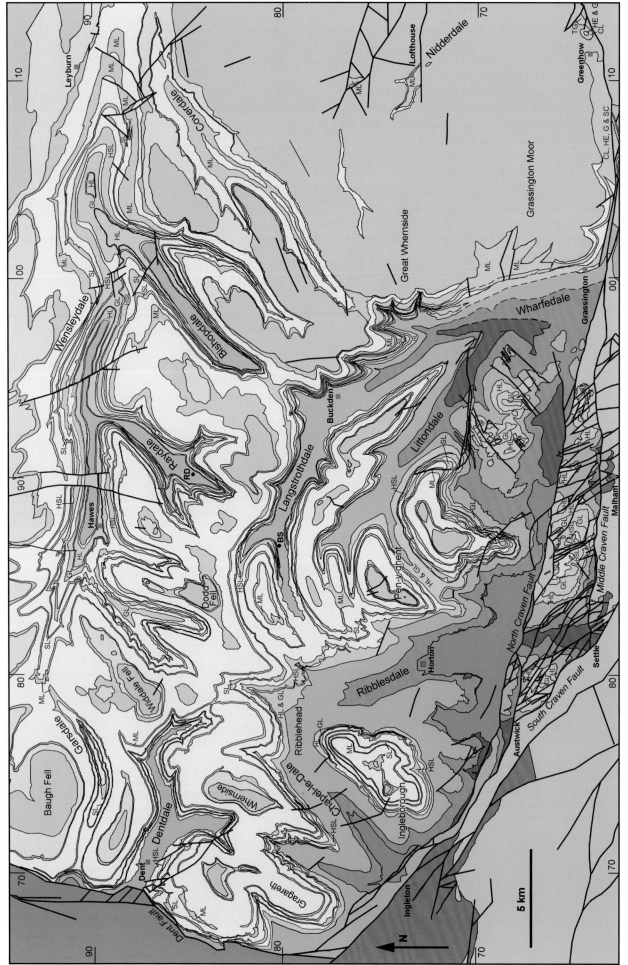

Figure 2.3. Generalised bedrock geology of the southern part of the Yorkshire Dales, which contains the majority of the area's caves and karst landforms; see key and index map to 1:50,000 British Geological Survey maps on facing page (simplified and rationalised from maps of the British Geological Survey). Acronyms for the Yoredale limestones are expanded in Figure 2.18.

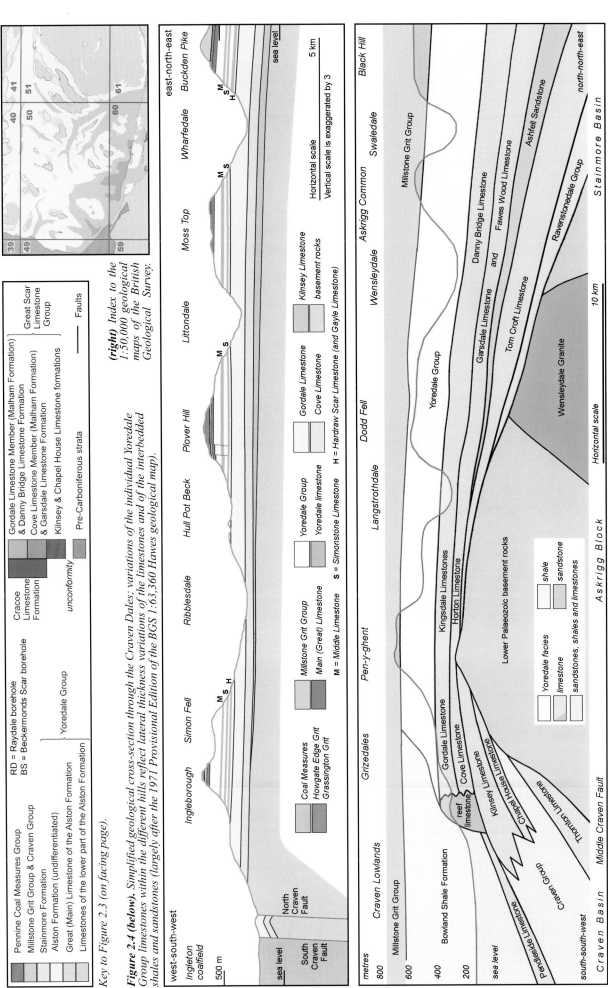

Key to Figure 2.3 (on facing page).

Pennine Coal Measures Group
Millstone Grit Group & Craven Group
Stainmore Formation
Alston Formation (undifferentiated)
Great (Main) Limestone of the Alston Formation
Limestones of the lower part of the Alston Formation

Gordale Limestone Member (Malham Formation) & Danny Bridge Limestone Formation
Cove Limestone Member (Malham Formation) & Garsdale Limestone Formation
Kilnsey & Chapel House Limestone formations

Cracoe Limestone Formation
Great Scar Limestone Group

Pre-Carboniferous strata
unconformity
Faults

RD = Raydale borehole
BS = Beckermonds Scar borehole
Yoredale Group

(right) Index to the 1:50,000 geological maps of the British Geological Survey.

Figure 2.4 (below). Simplified geological cross-section through the Craven Dales; variations of the individual Yoredale Group limestones within the different hills reflect lateral thickness variations of the limestones and of the interbedded shales and sandstones (largely after the 1971 Provisional Edition of the BGS 1:63,360 Hawes geological map).

Figure 2.5. Diagrammatic profile showing the main units of the Lower Carboniferous sequences across the Askrigg Block. This profile is on a line about 45° anticlockwise from that in Figure 2.4. The red line represents an approximate profile of the present topography; added purely for the purpose of relating the geology to the hills and dales; elevations at the left end of the section are displaced relative to actual values because the effects of the Craven Faults are ignored to keep the stratigraphical units intact (largely after Aitkenhead et al., 2002).

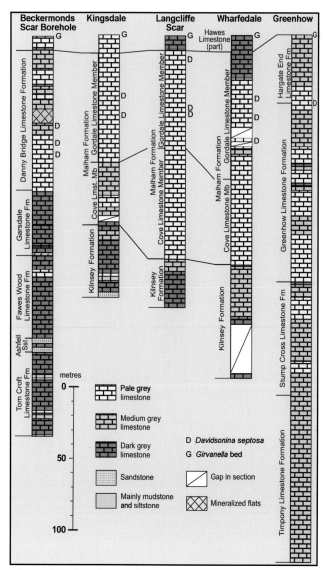

Figure 2.6. *Correlation of stratigraphical sections of the Great Scar Limestone Group (adapted from Dunham and Wilson, 1985).*

Figure 2.7. *The Stebden Hill (left) and Butter Haw Hill reef knolls, with the grit edge of Cracoe Fell beyond (TW).*

Great Scar Limestone Group

The thick limestone sequence across much of the southern Yorkshire Dales has long been known informally as the Great Scar Limestone (George *et al.,* 1976). This term has now been defined formally and applied more widely across northern England (Waters and Davies, 2006; Waters *et al.,* 2007; Dean *et al.,* 2011). Most of the major Dales cave systems occur within this limestone. Present as far west as the Isle of Man, and right across the Alston and Askrigg blocks, the Great Scar Limestone Group includes many locally-defined formations, with distinct nomenclatures applied to isolated successions on the various horst and tilt-block highs.

Even within the area of the Askrigg Block several different schemes have evolved (Dunham and Wilson, 1985) and despite attempts at rationalisation, three separate nomenclatures persist (Figs 2.6 and 2.9). In the south the terms Horton Limestone and Kingsdale Limestones (George *et al.,* 1976) have largely been superseded by, in ascending order, Chapel House Limestone, Kilnsey and Malham formations (Arthurton *et al.,* 1988). Apron knoll reefs grew along the Block's southern margin from late Holkerian to early Brigantian times (Figs 2.7 and 2.8). Formerly referred to as Marginal Reef Limestones of the Malham Formation (Arthurton *et al.,* 1988), these are now assigned to the Cracoe Limestone Formation (Dean *et al.,* 2011).

Formation	Member	Grey colour	Grain size	Lithology (major)	Lithology (subordinate)	Bedding	Thick (m)
NORTH ASKRIGG BLOCK							
Danny Bridge Limestone		Pale to mid		Wackestone	Packstone, mudstone and minor grainstone; palaeokarstic surfaces overlain by bentonitic clays, palaeosols		102–168
Garsdale Limestone		Dark		Wackestone with bands of porcellanous calcilutite	Interbedded sandstone and siltstone, thin mudstone beds and rare thin coals		41–58
Fawes Wood Limestone		Mid to dark		Grainstone and packstone	Silty or stylolitic partings and some porcellanous micrites		55–80
Tom Croft Limestone		Mid to dark	Medium and coarse	Grainstone with peloids, shelly debris, crinoid fragments and variable amounts of dolomite	Thin basal limestone breccia with siltstone and quartz pebbles	Poor	60–80
SOUTH ASKRIGG BLOCK							
Cracoe Limestone		Mid and mid-pale	Highly variable	Organic boundstones to packstones and wackestones	Megabrecciation and neptunian dykes (crinoid- and mudstone-filled)	Massive to weak	>100
Malham Formation	Gordale Limestone	Mid-pale to very pale	Fine and medium	Bioclastic packstones and wackestones, commonly pseudobrecciated	Cross-bedded grainstones, thin conglomerates; clay beds above palaeokarstic surfaces	Thick to very thick	70–94
	Cove Limestone	Pale to very pale	Medium and coarse	Bioclastic and peloidal packstones and grainstones	Micrites ('Porcellanous Bed'), variably fenestral; clay beds above palaeokarstic surfaces	Massive to weak	72–114
Kilnsey Formation	Scaleber Quarry Lst	Mid and mid-dark	Fine to coarse	Bioclastic packstones and grainstones	Mudstone interbeds; bands and nodules of black chert	Thin and thick	29–134
	Scaleber Force Lst	Dark	Fine to coarse	Packstones	Wackestones, mudstone interbeds	Thin to thick	22–61
Chapel House Limestone		Mid to mid-pale	Medium and coarse	Calcarenite, oolitic grainstones. Locally extensively dolomitized	Basal conglomerates; siltstone, sandstone and mudstone laminae; dolomicrites and fenestral or algal lime-mudstones; argillaceous wackestones	Well-bedded	33–56
GREENHOW INLIER							
Hargate End Limestone		Dark or mid	Medium to very coarse	Crinoidal limestone	Chert is present, especially near the top	Well-bedded	46
Greenhow Limestone		Pale	Fine to medium	Sparry grainstone, locally peloidal and crinoidal	Clay beds above palaeokarstic surfaces	Thick to very thick	120
Stump Cross Limestone		Pale brown to pale	Fine and medium	Limestone	Variably dolomitic in its lower part	Poor	84
Timpony Limestone		Mid to dark	Fine	Limestone	Chert nodules in the upper part; shale partings in the lower part	Very thin to thick	>120

Table 2.3. *Dales Great Scar Limestone Group lithologies; the main cavernous limestones are shaded pale blue (after Dean et al, 2011).*

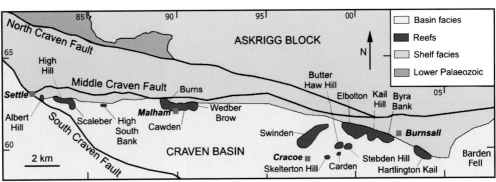

Figure 2.8. Outcrops of the main Visean knoll-reefs within the Craven Reef Belt. During the mid-Carboniferous, rocks of basinal facies (Bowland Shale Formation) were deposited over a continuous apron reef, parts of which have since been exhumed, revealing knolls as relics of the pre-Namurian land surface (modified and extended from Aitkenhead et al., 2002).

These terms apply only to the condensed succession laid down on the southern Askrigg tilt-block high. As the sequence passes northwards towards the Stainmore Trough, facies changes necessitate an additional classification (Dunham and Wilson, 1985), comprising, in ascending order, the Tom Croft Limestone, Ashfell Sandstone, Fawes Wood Limestone, Garsdale Limestone, and Danny Bridge Limestone formations (Figs 2.6 and 2.9). No geochemical data yet exist for these rocks, but it is likely that the Danny Bridge Limestone is of high purity, whereas the Garsdale, Fawes Wood and Tom Croft limestones are probably less pure (Harrison et al., 1991).

The Great Scar Limestone succession is up to about 280m thick where little of it is exposed in the northern part of the Dales but is recorded in the Beckermonds Scar Borehole in Langstrothdale (Fig. 2.6); it decreases to a thickness of about 190m at the southern margin of the Askrigg Block around Settle. The Group as a whole comprises limestone, typically well-washed, bioclastic and highly bioturbated with crinoid banks and shelly or coral biostromes; these were all deposited in an open, shallow-water marine environment. Thin basal

beds are commonly conglomeratic (see box on p.12), with angular or rounded pebbles and cobbles of local Lower Palaeozoic rock types in a carbonate matrix. Colour, nature of bedding and grain-size variations are the key criteria that allow the component formations and members to be recognised at outcrop and in boreholes (Tables 2.1 and 2.2).

As is common with other Visean platform areas of the British Isles, the group shows a trend from dark or mid grey Arundian to Holkerian carbonates (including the Kilnsey, Tom Croft Limestone, Fawes Wood Limestone and Garsdale Limestone formations) to pale grey late Asbian limestones (principally the Danny Bridge, Malham and Greenhow Limestone formations). Major palaeokarstic bedding surfaces overlain by thin mudstones (shales), indicating periodic temporary emergence related to minor depositional cyclicity (Waltham, 1971). Larger-scale cycles in the Dales limestone sequences, and throughout Britain, have been described as mesothems (Ramsbottom, 1973). These were considered to be the result of sea-level changes, and the boundaries of each of these major cycles are recognised as widespread disconformities in shelf areas.

Figure 2.9. The approximate correlations of former and current lithostratigraphical unit names within the Great Scar Limestone Group and the lower (mostly Brigantian) part of the Yoredale Group. Horizontal colour bands show the extent of rock units laid down during each major cycle (formerly Regional Stages, now Regional Substages) of the Dinantian and the basal Namurian (see also Table 2.1). Note that until recently the base of the Pendleian was drawn below the Great/Main Limestone. Horizons of two marker beds, the algal Girvanella (Nodular) Bed and the Porcellanous Bed, are shown only for areas where their occurrence is confirmed. Geological remapping around Greenhow is not yet complete; hence the current validity of the limestone unit names shown (based on Dunham and Stubblefield, 1945) is unconfirmed, particularly the Stump Cross Limestone, drawn with dashed boundaries.

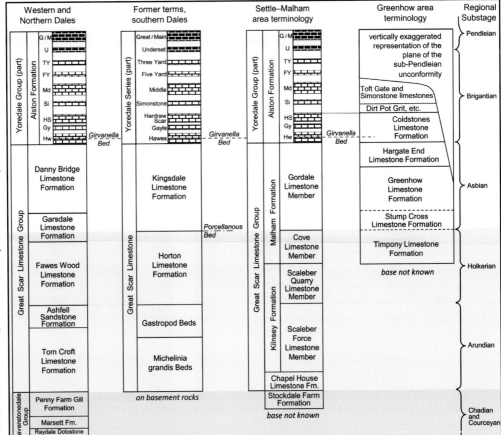

Figure 2.10. *Palaeokarstic surface overlain by a thin clay bed, within the ?Greenhow Limestone near Greenhow (CW).*

Figure 2.12. *Girvanella Bed, exposed between the Lower and Upper Hawes limestones in Pen-y-ghent Gill (TW).*

Many Asbian shelf carbonate sequences display repeated shallowing-upward cycles, which commonly culminate in palaeokarstic surfaces (Fig. 2.10) formed during emergence (Walkden, 1987). There is also a progressive increase in minor cycle thickness from 1–5m in the early Asbian to greater than 10m in the early Brigantian, and a concomitant trend towards deeper water sedimentation of the rocks at the cycle bases (Walkden, 1987).

Thin mudstone and siltstone interbeds can occur at any interval within the Great Scar Limestone Group. The mudstone beds, many of which are commonly described as shales, may be laterally persistent, and range in thickness from a few centimetres to more than 2m (Fig. 2.11), as in Shale Cavern in Lost John's Cave (Waltham, 1971). They formed by slow accumulation of a limited supply of clastic debris from distant land areas entering the carbonate-dominated depositional basin during pauses or reductions in limestone deposition. Sandstones and siltstones had a similar but generally more local origin. The thicker mudstones are mainly related to major cycle boundaries (Ramsbottom, 1973; George *et al.,* 1976), or to longer-than-average breaks between minor cycles, and they tend to occur above palaeokarstic surfaces (Fig. 2.10).

Locally the thickness of mudstone beds can be exaggerated due to the strong relief of an underlying palaeokarst. This is clearly displayed part way down the Double Bucket shaft in Notts Pot and in the Lancaster Hole Main Drain (Fig. 2.11).

These beds may include bentonite-rich clays, derived mainly as airborne fallout from distant explosive volcanicity, resembling, but less abundant than, Derbyshire's clay wayboards (Walkden, 1972; Ford, 1977). In North Wales similar beds are considered to be residual soils or palaeosols derived from subaerial alteration of wind-blown volcanic debris (Somerville, 1979).

Some Dales mudstone beds include seatearths with fossil rootlets, also related to palaeokarstic activity, probably augmented by volcanic fallout, or related to other aeolian, loessic deposits. A few are also associated with thin coals, as exposed in and adjacent to 3-Ways Chamber in Notts Pot, and in the Coal Hole Inlet of Short Drop Cave. Thin muddy coal seams occur elsewhere, with examples reported at Douk Gill and Brants Gill (probably the same horizon) and at a higher horizon above Ringle Mill Cave in Ribblesdale (Dyson, 1969). The stratigraphical level of the Meal Bank Coal, close to the South Craven Fault near Ingleton, remains equivocal. A position midway between the *Girvanella* Nodular Bed (Figs 2.6 and 2.12) and a band rich in *Davidsonina (Cyrtina) septosa* high in the Gordale Limestone Member was claimed by Turner (1968), suggesting a possible correlation with the Notts Pot Coal, at the boundary between the Lower Hawes and Gordale limestones. Superficially this appears to disagree with measurements and relationships discussed by Garwood

Figure 2.11. *A significant shale bed exposed in the Main Drain of Lancaster Hole also infills well-marked palaeokarstic channels in the underlying limestone (TW).*

Figure 2.13. *The Porcellanous Bed, well exposed as the striking pale coloured horizon along the north wall of the Main Chamber in Gaping Gill (photo: Jeff Cowling).*

Limestone cycles and the Porcellanous Bed

Porcellanous limestone beds characterise carbonate deposition under regressive conditions, when areas initially covered by a shelf sea become hyper-saline, shrink and dry-up due to evaporation. Because such environments are unfavourable to most marine life, resultant rocks lack coarse fossil debris and typically comprise precipitated calcite mud (hence another common name, 'calcite-mudstone'). In the Yorkshire Dales one particular bed, known as the Porcellanous Bed, provides a widespread and readily mappable marker (Garwood and Goodyear, 1924). Limestones above and below the Porcellanous Bed horizon differ markedly in their properties and appearance, and were known as the Horton Limestone below and the Kingsdale Limestones above (George *et al.*, 1976).

In Juniper Gulf the Porcellanous Bed (centre) is c. 500 mm thick, with open inception voids clearly visible above and below. The axis of this imposing shaft is guided by a sub-vertical strike-slip fault (TW).

Recognition of depositional cyclicity within the Great Scar Limestone by Schwarzacher (1958) was endorsed by Doughty (1968), though subsequently there was uncertainty about the wider validity of their ideas (Arthurton *et al.*, 1988). Meanwhile, a model of medium-scale cyclicity (Ramsbottom, 1973) explained the discrete fossil assemblages long recognised within the 'coral-brachiopod' zones of the British Carboniferous Limestone. On a depositional shelf the zonal sequence does not represent a single, smooth evolutionary pathway. Instead it records faunal changes that are isolated fragments of an overall evolutionary trend, separated by gaps corresponding to long periods of non-deposition.

Within the Dales, the Porcellanous Bed represents just one aspect of sedimentation towards the end of the Holkerian Substage, near the top of the Horton Limestone. Where fully developed it comprises the deposits of a period of regression during which calcite-mud settled gently through shallow, largely undisturbed, water – commonly envisaged as a lagoon – that had become isolated as the sea retreated. If desiccation of the lagoon had became total, the Porcellanous Bed would have been followed in ascending order by thinner beds of dolomite-mudstone, gypsum, bittern salts and halite. Such beds are absent in the Dales, probably because the lagoons were re-invaded by the sea, or it could be that these highly soluble rocks were deposited and subsequently removed, perhaps by the effects of karstic dissolution and subaerial erosion before the Asbian marine transgression and deposition of the Kingsdale Limestones.

It is unlikely that the Holkerian limestones in the Dales were deposited on a planar surface formed when older sediment had filled and removed irregularities in the pre-Carboniferous landmass. Irregularities of the basement topography were not overtopped by transgressing seas until part way through the Holkerian. Allowing for variable deposition (reflecting different water depths) and differential compaction, there was probably still some sea-floor relief at the close of the Holkerian. So, withdrawal of the sea was irregular. Some areas lacked lagoons, elsewhere lagoons shrank or drained quickly leaving little in the way of regressive deposits. There are virtually no lagoonal deposits within what would have been a belt of steep submarine topography near the shelf margin south of the North Craven Fault. In both situations the Porcellanous Bed is locally absent.

Superimposed upon the broader relationships are the effects of minor depositional changes, perhaps related to regional tectonic adjustments, to localised movements of the Askrigg Block, or even to Milankovitch cycles of global climate change (see Chapter 3). Short, sharp sea-level oscillations or fluctuations as the major cycle closed led to development of two porcellanous beds, as exposed on the west side of Kingsdale; elsewhere several thin porcellanous beds occur. Whether the Porcellanous Bed is single, multiple or locally absent, the rocks close to the Holkerian cycle boundary provide an inception horizon that has influenced cave development throughout the Dales (see Chapter 8).

and Goodyear (1924). Accepting this current uncertainty, if the Meal Bank Coal correlates with the Notts Pot Coal, then both seams also correlate with the Salt Lake Mudstone bed that is traced at outcrop round much of Ingleborough (Turner, 1968).

The limestones of the Great Scar Limestone Group also include a number of marker horizons. Porcellanous limestone bands are distinctive lime-mudstones (micrites) with fenestral fabrics that occur mainly within intervals of the Fawes Wood Limestone and Garsdale Limestone formations in western areas and the equivalent upper part of the Cove Limestone Member in the southeast. Historically, the distinctive Porcellanous Bed (Fig. 2.13; see box above), which is well exposed in Gaping Gill Main Chamber (Glover, 1974), was chosen to mark the boundary between the Horton Limestone and the overlying Kingsdale Limestones. This marker can be traced fairly reliably, albeit locally discontinuously, through the southern Dales area from Ease Gill across into upper Wharfedale. Elsewhere, beds

of comparable age contain several porcellanous limestone beds of similar appearance. The possibility of confusion led to use of the terms Horton Limestone and Kingsdale Limestones, separated at the Porcellanous Bed, being discontinued and replaced by the Cove and Gordale limestones (parts of the Malham Formation), which can be mapped on the basis of their gross lithology, bedding characteristics and distinctive landforms (Arthurton *et al.*, 1988).

Lower in the succession the laterally equivalent Kilnsey and Fawes Wood Limestone formations contain beds with Holkerian coral assemblages that include distinctive colonies of *Lithostrotion (Nematophyllum) minus*. Higher in the succession the *Davidsonina (Cyrtina) septosa* bands, marked by discrete concentrations of drifted brachiopods and corals, commonly with oncolitic (algal) coatings (Arthurton, *et al.*, 1988), occur predominantly within the Gordale Limestone in the southeast and within the corresponding Danny Bridge Limestone farther west and north (Fig. 2.6).

Geological research and mapping

Nineteenth century pioneers of geology, including John Phillips, Adam Sedgwick (who was born at Dent) and John Marr, provided early descriptions of the geology of the district. The first systematic mapping across the entire area was carried out by the Geological Survey (now the British Geological Survey) at 1:10,560 scale during the late 1800s. Much of the terminology applied to the rock succession has changed since then, but over most of the area the general stratigraphical relationships drawn out on early Geological Survey maps remain broadly valid. However, mapping of local geological structures was less detailed, and only major fault lines and mineral veins were mapped routinely. More recent geological mapping in some parts of the district and observations made during cave exploration have confirmed that many more faults are present (see maps below). Since the early mapping within the district by the Geological Survey there has been continued local investigation.

Classic early works on the Lower Palaeozoic rocks by King and Wilcockson (1934) and on the limestones in the southern part of the area by Garwood and Goodyear (1924) remained as benchmarks for many years, before their findings were further revised. Re-mapping by the Geological Survey has covered only the Settle (Sheet 60) and Kirkby Lonsdale (Sheet 49) areas, though maps covering the Hawes (Sheet 50) and Masham (Sheet 51) areas have been reconstituted to take account of the latest data. No modern BGS mapping exists for the Pateley Bridge (Sheet 61) area but, at the time of writing, resurvey is underway. Geological mapping by Dunham and Stubblefield (1945) provided a local understanding of the stratigraphy and structure of part of the Pateley Bridge area, in the vicinity of Greenhow. A comprehensive summary of the stratigraphy, structure and mineralisation of the Askrigg Block as a whole was provided by Dunham and Wilson (1985).

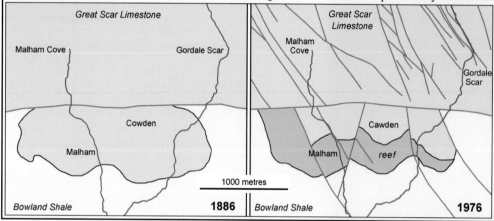

Example of progress in mapping the geology, based on the area around Malham and Gordale. Left: 1886 mapping taken from 1:10,560 Yorkshire County Sheet 133) picks out the Middle Craven Fault and a broad stratigraphy. Right: 1976 mapping derived from 1:10,560 sheets SD86SE and SD96SW. The stratigraphy as shown is simplified for clarity but the highly complex fault pattern revealed by the modern mapping is retained. Place names as on source maps. (Generalised from maps of the British Geological Survey).

Succession in the Craven Dales

The Chapel House Limestone Formation is exposed only in the core of a minor anticline in Ribblesdale (Murray, 1983), but is proved in boreholes elsewhere (Arthurton *et al.*, 1988). It includes a basal conglomerate with clasts of local Lower Palaeozoic rock, and the higher limestones also contain scattered rock clasts, thin mudstones and dolomitic siltstone beds (Table 2.1). Hence, the formation (Table 2.4) has a low to medium purity overall (Murray, 1983).

Above this the Kilnsey Formation forms most of Kilnsey Crag, up to the base of the main overhang (Fig. 2.14). It is typified by dark to medium-pale grey, thick- to thin-bedded, bioclastic limestone with mudstone beds and partings. Its lower Scaleber Force Limestone Member is relatively muddy with low-purity limestones, compared to the higher-purity, Scaleber Quarry Limestone Member above (Table 2.4).

Figure 2.14. At Kilnsey Crag the Scaleber Force Limestone Member (Kilnsey Formation) appears pale brown at the cliff foot; the the main face and overhang are Scaleber Quarry Limestone Member, and the Cove Limestone Member (Malham Formation) caps the crag (CW).

Figure 2.15. Malham Cove, Type Section for the Cove Limestone Member (Malham Formation). These rocks overlie the top of the Kilnsey Formation just below water level at the foot of the cliff, where Malham Beck emerges from Malham Cove Rising (the unit boundary is a major inception horizon). The rest of the unit, with few bedding planes, forms the cliff up to and including the 6m bed forming the main overhang. The base of the more thinly-bedded Gordale Limestone Member overlies the overhanging 6m bed, and is marked by the obvious grassy strips on both wings of the Cove (TW).

	Chapel House Limestone Formation	Kilnsey Formation		Malham Formation		Stump Cross Limestone	Greenhow Limestone	Hargate End Limestone	Alston Formation		
		Scaleber Force Limestone Member	Scaleber Quarry Limestone Member	Cove Limestone Member	Gordale Limestone Member				Lower Hawes Limestone	Upper Hawes and Gayle limestones	Hardraw Scar Limestone
Mean values, *weight percent*											
CaCO₃	92.68	87.91	94.57	98.57	99.18	99.30	99.11	95.71	97.00	90.00	84.37
MgO	1.61	1.98	2.31	0.66	0.26	0.22	0.13	0.16	0.76	2.60	1.27
SiO₂	2.32	5.38	0.24	0.08	0.26	0.00	0.00	1.10	0.60	2.70	9.82
A1₂O₃	0.61	1.35	0.15	0.13	0.23	0.00	0.00	0.87	0.30	0.80	2.00
Na₂O	0.01	0.03	0.01	0.01	0.00	0.03	0.07	0.07	0.01	0.01	0.05
K₂O	0.17	0.28	0.04	0.04	0.05	0.00	0.00	0.02	0.06	0.16	0.35
P₂O₅	0.01	0.01	0.01	0.01	0.01	0.00	0.00	0.02	0.02	0.07	0.06
F	0.01	0.02	0.00	0.00	0.01	0.11	0.09	0.11	0.01	0.01	0.03
SrO	0.04	0.08	0.04	0.01	0.17	–	–	–	0.04	0.08	0.14
Fe₂O₃	0.32	0.75	0.12	0.04	0.08	0.04	0.02	0.05	0.24	0.45	0.87
parts per million											
MnO	275	247	224	126	150	300	300	100	320	511	490
Cu	0	1	2	1	0	7	6	8	2	1	3
Pb	1	3	4	1	0	13	16	12	3	1	1
Zn	23	17	19	9	8	32	24	42	45	26	23
Purity classification											
Maximum	2	3	1	1	1	—	—	—	1	2	2
Minimum	5	5	4	2	3	—	—	—	4	5	5
Mean	3	4	2	1	1	1	1	3	2	4	4

***Table 2.4.** Representative analyses of the major limestone units within the southern Dales karst; the CaCO₃ values are calculated from the CaO values in the original dataset (reworked from Murray, 1983).*

The overlying Malham Formation comprises a sequence of very high-purity limestones (Table 2.4), with only traces of silica, pyrite and clay minerals (Murray, 1983). Named after Malham Cove, the lower Cove Limestone Member, forms the lowermost 74m of the cliff, with a strong spring emerging from a submerged cave passage at or very close to the unit's base (Fig. 2.15). Typically this member is a pale grey to very pale grey, massive to weakly-bedded limestone (Table 2.1), tending to form a landscape with grassy slopes and few scars, except for a 6m-thick bed at the top of the unit (Fig. 2.15) that forms extensive scars (Arthurton *et al.*, 1988). The upper Gordale Limestone Member, named after Gordale Scar (Fig. 2.16), caps Malham Cove, forming extensive limestone pavements at slightly higher level. This member is medium-pale to very pale grey, well-bedded limestone, with beds typically a metre or so thick. Its stronger beds form major scar features and extensive limestone pavements across the southern part of the Dales (Fig. 2.17).

Apron knoll reefs are developed along the southern margin of the Askrigg Block, located south of the Middle Craven Fault, occurring in a roughly west–east tract extending 20 km eastwards from Settle to Burnsall (Figs 2.3 and 2.8). This reef facies is recognised as the Cracoe Limestone Formation (Dean *et al.*, 2011). Although principally comprising massive boundstones (Table 2.2), these reef limestones are commonly well-jointed and fractured with abundant ferruginous staining. The limestones are typically of very high purity, downgraded by localised replacement of calcite by silica and dolomite (Murray, 1983). Elsewhere, secondary dolomite and silica have replaced limestones, particularly in the Chapel House Limestone, Cracoe Limestone and Malham formations close to the North and Middle Craven faults (Murray, 1983).

In the past, rocks of the Great Scar Limestone Group have been exploited widely as roadstone, building stone and, especially, walling-stone. Limestone is still quarried at a few sites across the Dales, these days mainly for use as concrete aggregate. The strongest limestones within the Great Scar Limestone of the Dales are within the Chapel House Limestone and the Scaleber Force Limestone (Murray, 1983).

***Figure 2.16.** The approach to Gordale Scar from the south. Above the grassy slopes in the middle distance the uppermost 6m-thick bed of the Cove Limestone is overlain by the more thinly bedded Gordale Limestone Member. As at Malham Cove, the boundary is marked by grassy ledges, some supporting trees and bushes, and minor faulting causes small local steps (CW).*

***Figure 2.17.** Limestone pavement formed on one of the lower beds of the Gordale Limestone Member above Malham Cove (CW).*

Limestones of the Greenhow inlier

Local names are applied to limestones in several inliers near Greenhow in the southeastern Askrigg Block (Figs 2.6 and 2.9), which cannot yet be equated unequivocally with those elsewhere. The succession, in ascending order, comprises the Timpony Limestone, Stump Cross Limestone, Greenhow Limestone and Hargate End Limestone formations.

In the Greenhow inliers (Dunham and Stubblefield, 1945), the lowermost Timpony Limestone comprises mid to dark grey, fine-grained limestone with chert nodules towards the top (Table 2.1). The overlying Stump Cross Limestone, named after the caves within it, consists of pale brownish grey and pale grey, fine-grained limestone. Above this, the dominantly pale grey Greenhow Limestone, is marked by up to 15 mudstone bands and prominent palaeokarstic surfaces. Scars are a conspicuous feature, as on the Gordale Limestone to the west. The Hargate End Limestone is dominantly dark grey or grey crinoidal limestone with its base taken at a notable *Davidsonina septosa* band, closely resembling the upper part of the Gordale Limestone and the approximately equivalent Kingsdale Limestones farther west (Fig. 2.9). The Stump Cross and Greenhow limestones have a generally high chemical purity, whereas the purity of the Hargate End Limestone is more variable (Table 2.4) with up to 3% in total of silica, alumina and iron (Harrison *et al.*, 1991).

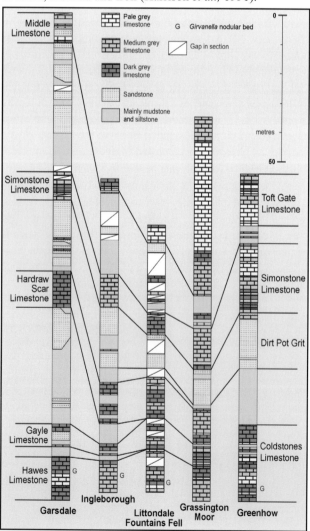

Figure 2.18. Yoredale Group beds between the Hawes and Middle limestones (adapted from Dunham and Wilson, 1985).

Limestones in the Yoredale Group

The Great Scar Limestone Group is overlain by beds of the Yoredale and Millstone Grit groups, the latter typically capping prominent hills above 400m, including the three peaks of Pen-y-ghent, Whernside and Ingleborough. Historically, the Yoredale Series was re-named the Wensleydale Formation (George *et al.*, 1976) for the Askrigg Block. Subsequent correlation of the succession across the wider northern England region led to its formal redefinition as the Yoredale Group. In this district the component Alston and Stainmore formations are of broadly Brigantian and Pendleian age respectively (Waters and Davies, 2006; Waters *et al.*, 2007; Dean *et al.*, 2011). Typically the Alston Formation includes thicker limestones than those within the Stainmore Formation, and those of the former contain most of the cave systems known in Wensleydale, Swaledale and east of Wharfedale.

The Group typically comprises upward-coarsening cycles (referred to as cyclothems) of basal thin, laterally extensive marine limestone, marine shale (locally bioturbated) and thin sandstone, topped at many sites with argillaceous or sandy seatearth and an overlying coal (Fig. 2.18). Thin, or locally thick, developments of chert and shaley chert overlie the limestone beds in some areas. The lithological cyclicity produces the marked terraced or stepped topography typical of the Yoredale Group (Fig. 2.19), with stronger limestones and sandstones forming terraces and steep scarp slopes, between slacks formed by softer, poorly exposed mudstones. Characteristically, the limestones are dark to very dark grey, thin-bedded and bioclastic to biomicritic, with a restricted benthic fauna and rare ammonoids. Most of the sandstones are pale grey, fine- to medium-grained and quartzose to feldspathic. The limestone nomenclature, correlations, and cyclothem thicknesses for the Askrigg Block are summarised in Figure 2.18. Limestones of the lower part of the Alston Formation, up to the Middle Limestone, contain significant active caves, including the extensive Mossdale Caverns and Langcliffe Pot systems beneath the eastern flank of Wharfedale. There are many short stream caves and also extensive maze cave systems within the Underset Limestone and the Great (Main) Limestone (at the top of the Alston Formation) in Wensleydale and Swaledale. The latter limestone extends northwards across the Alston Block and contains the long stream cave of Fairy Holes in Weardale.

Figure 2.19. Characteristic step-like topography on the north side of Fountains Fell, viewed across Pen-y-ghent Gill. Yoredale Group cyclothems, reflected by vegetation changes, occupy the slope from just below the pavements, formed within the Hawes Limestone, and below the summit ridge of Howgate Edge Grit (TW).

A widespread feature of the Hawes Limestone at the base of the Alston Formation limestones is a nodular horizon still known commonly as the *Girvanella* Bed, though the distinctive nodules pruduced by a combination of the alga *Girvanella* and a calcareous foraminifer (*Nebecularia*) are now referred to as *Osagia* (Fig. 2.12). This distinctive bed was formerly adopted as marking the top of the Kingsdale Limestones (George *et al.*, 1976), on the grounds that lithologically the Lower Hawes Limestone resembles the underlying beds of the Great Scar Limestone Group rather than the overlying Yoredale Group beds. In fact the bed does mark a distinct change from high-purity, pale- to mid-grey wackestones and packstones (Table 2.4) below the band (the main part of the Lower Hawes Limestone) to low-purity, mid- to dark-grey wackestones and packstones above (Upper Hawes and Gayle limestones), the latter being more typical of the Yoredale Group (Murray, 1983). The upper division has higher contents of silica, pyrite and clay minerals.

The cycle above the Gayle Limestone includes the Hardraw Scar Limestone (Figs 2.18 and 2.20), which is up to 15m thick. This generally comprises mid-dark to dark grey, muddy, crinoidal packstones and wackestones, locally interbedded with mudstone, with chert nodules common in the upper part. It has a high clay component and is widely silicified (Murray, 1983). Approaching the southeastern part of the Askrigg Block, across the Malham High Country and Lower Wharfedale, the Hawes, Gayle and Hardraw Scar limestones lose all or part of their intervening clastic beds; around Greenhow the limestones amalgamate to form the Coldstones Limestone (Figs 2.9 and 2.18).

The top of the Alston Formation is marked by the top of the geographically widespread Great Limestone. Its name derives from its extent on the Alston Block, but farther south it is still commonly known as the Main Limestone, its original name on the Askrigg Block. It is the youngest Yoredale limestone of significant thickness, and is Pendleian rather than Brigantian in age (Fig. 2.9). The overlying Stainmore Formation is present below the unconformity at the base of the Grassington Grit to the north of a line approximately from Horton in Ribblesdale in the west to Masham in the east (Dunham and Wilson, 1985). In contrast with the Alston Formation, the Stainmore Formation is generally associated with relatively thin, muddy and siliceous limestones. A notable exception is the Crow Limestone, which comprises up to 23m of limestone, cherty limestone and chert. The cyclothems commonly include dark grey chert beds, such as the Main, Richmond and Crow cherts. Reflecting the prevailing northerly dip, most of the Alston Formation and older formations are generally deeply buried in northern areas. Thus, the higher limestones, down to and including the Great (Main) Limestone, contain most of the cave systems known in Wensleydale and farther north.

Within the quarrying trade limestones that take a polish for ornamental use are known as marbles. Being unmetamorphosed they are not true marbles. Several notable examples in the Alston Formation include the generally mid- to dark-grey Dent Marble, formerly quarried from beds including the Underset Limestone above Dentdale, and the dark grey Nidderdale Marble, from a quarry in the Middle Limestone near Lofthouse. Both are well-known for an abundance of white crinoid fossils in their darker matrix.

Figure 2.20. A typical mid-grey, partly muddy Yoredale limestone, the Hardraw Scar Limestone, with interbeds of darker grey shale, exposed in Pen-y-ghent Gill. Here, as elsewhere in the area, these beds include classic fossil build-ups (biostromes) rich in brachiopods such as Productus latissimus *(TW).*

Millstone Grit

The Millstone Grit Group caps many of the peaks in the Dales area, and forms the extensive upland of Grassington Moor between Wharfedale and Nidderdale (Figs 2.1 and 2.3). The group is typified by cyclic successions of quartz-feldspathic sandstone, grey mudstone, thin coal and prominent seatearths (Dunham and Wilson, 1985). Goniatite-bearing marine shales, typical of the group in the southern Pennines, are uncommon on the Askrigg Block. Marine deposits of mostly Kinderscoutian age comprise thin, near-shore, calcareous sandstones with a benthic fauna of brachiopods, crinoids and bryozoans, but lacking goniatites. However, the main feature-forming, thick sandstones are typically fluviatile, with distributary channel palaeoflows towards the south or southwest. Some seatearths might have resulted from prolonged periods of emergence.

The Millstone Grit Group ranges from Pendleian to Yeadonian age (Table 2.3). The base is marked by a slightly angular intra-Pendleian unconformity, resulting in the group resting on increasingly older parts of the Stainmore and Alston formations towards the south. This unconformity is overlain by the Grassington Grit, a sandstone-dominated succession up to 60m in thickness, which rests on numerous Yoredale limestones (Fig. 2.9) and acts as an important catchment that feeds some of the larger cave sinks. This is particularly evident on Pock Stones Moor, part of Barden Fell (Fig. 2.8), where large interstratal subsidence hollows (Fig. 2.21) have developed in a thickness of more than 50m of Grassington Grit (Hudson, 1937), possibly located above an unproven buried limestone knoll reef.

Figure 2.21. One of several large interstratal dolines developed in the Grassington Grit of Pock Stones Moor, Barden Fell (CW).

Geological structure

To the south the Askrigg Block is bounded by the Craven Fault System (Figs 2.1 and 2.3), comprising three major elements with large southward downthrows. The North Craven Fault is a complex of sub-parallel fractures that probably dip steeply to the south with throws of about 160m in the Malham Formation (Arthurton et al., 1988). Northwards a belt of small faults, anticlines and synclines trends more or less parallel to the main fault line (Fig. 2.22). The South Craven Fault throws more than a kilometre at Ingleton where it separates the Westphalian Pennine Coal Measures Group rocks of the small Ingleton Coalfield from the Block's limestone successions. Its throw decreases to about 700m along the Giggleswick Scar fault-line scarp, south of which it is more complex, extending southeastwards into the Craven Basin. The Middle Craven Fault diverges from the South Craven Fault near Settle It has a steep to moderate southerly dip (down to 45°) and within the Malham Formation it throws about 300m. Displacements on the Middle Craven Fault influenced sedimentation during Visean times, in particular associated with development of the Cracoe Limestone Formation apron reef (Figs 2.7 and 2.8). Many lesser fractures are orientated sub-parallel to the three Craven faults (Figs 2.22 and 2.23).

Vertical to steeply west-dipping fractures of the Dent Fault System form the Askrigg Block's western margin (Figs 2.1, 2.3 and 2.22). During the Carboniferous the fractures acted as normal faults but, due to reactivation, now show net reverse (down-east) displacement of the basement rocks (Aitkenhead et al., 2002). Cumulative effects were to push the older rocks of the Howgill Fells against and over the Block's Carboniferous sequence. Folds near the Dent Fault, either sub-parallel or at an acute angle to the main faults, tend to be monoclinal with sub-vertical east-facing limbs (Moseley, 1973).

The eastern limit of the block is poorly defined, because it lies at depth beneath Permian to Cretaceous strata. As the block had a strong tilt, raised to the south, the northern margin of the Askrigg Block is also difficult to define as successions broadly thicken northwards into the Stainmore Trough (Fig. 2.5). A more pronounced thickening occurs to the north of the Stockdale Fault, beneath Swaledale.

On the Askrigg Block, the Carboniferous strata appear relatively undeformed (Fig. 2.22). Though regionally the beds dip gently towards the north and east there are many broad, open fold flexures. Dips on the limbs of these are generally so gentle that they are not readily apparent to the naked eye, and their presence can be detected only by detailed mapping. Generally the plunging axes of these gentle folds lie west–east or northwest–southeast, sub-parallel to the major faults forming the southern margin of the block. Examples can be recognised across the limestone outcrops, notably on Leck Fell and in Kingsdale, Crummack Dale and Ribblesdale. On either side of Ease Gill, in the area between the Dent and Craven fault zones, the courses of various major stream caves (see Chapter 8) suggest that the trends of various minor fold axes might swing from being sub-parallel to the Dent Fault in the west to being sub-parallel to the North Craven Fault farther east.

In addition to the gentle open folds, steep dips are present adjacent to the Dent Fault, notably at Bull Pot of the Witches, and also close to the North Craven Fault on the southern side of Gragareth near Tow Scar. Elsewhere, over-steepened dips that reflect frictional drag during fault movement occur locally along the lines of some lesser fractures. Dips of up to 10° are preserved in pavement exposures adjacent to the Hurnel Moss Fault near Gaping Gill, and local dips up to 35° probably indicate an unnamed fault-line from near P5 on the Allotment southwards towards Clapham Bottoms.

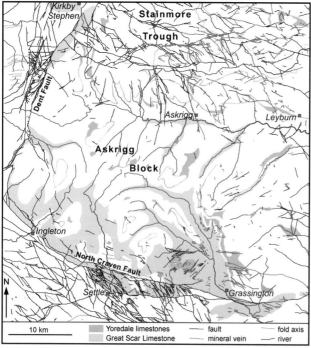

Figure 2.22. *Distribution of mapped faults, veins and folds across the Askrigg Block; an apparent absence of faults in the centre of the Block is at least partly a reflection of the paucity of recent mapping away from marginal and mineralised areas (based on data from the British Geological Survey).*

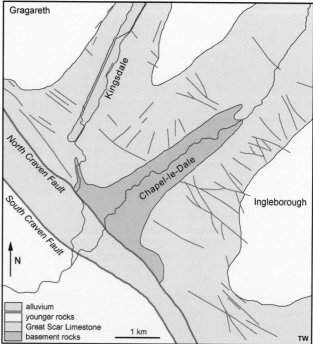

Figure 2.23. *Major fractures within the Great Scar Limestone of Chapel-le-Dale and Kingsdale (based upon aerial photograph interpretation and underground observations). Most are probably strike-slip faults with negligible vertical displacement, but others may be major joints opened by stress release after valley incision.*

Joints and faults within the Askrigg Block

Across the entire Dales, the limestones and other strata are affected by minor faults either as single fractures or zones of sub-parallel fractures. Some of these are marked by the development of large cave features, of which Gaping Gill Main Chamber (Fig. 2.13) and the shaft complex of Notts Pot are among the more obvious examples. Such faults may also be associated with sulphide mineralisation, especially those around Grassington and Greenhow in the south and many more in the Wensleydale to Swaledale area.

Many underground features are clearly related to faults, not all of which are recognised at the surface. Examples include those at Growling Hole, Spectacle Pot, Tatham Wife Hole, Meregill Hole, Long Kin East, Diccan Pot and Hull Pot. Because few of these show any vertical displacement, most have been referred to as 'master joints', but it is likely that they are sub-vertical strike-slip faults with displacements that are parallel to the bedding and so not easily recognised. The structures that guide caves, particularly where they form deep shafts, can cut through many individual beds, in contrast to the more limited vertical range associated with most joints (see Chapter 8).

At Hull Pot (Fig. 2.24) hardly any vertical offset is apparent on a fracture trending WNW–ESE, but this fault shows significant shearing and shattering of the limestone at both ends of the open cavity, and small cubes of galena are present in some of the sheared rock. This seemingly insignificant fracture has not only guided development of the Pot's 18m-deep surface feature, but also the adjacent 32m-deep underground shaft. Eastwards of Hull Pot the fracture passes beneath thick superficial deposits, but its assumed continuation underlies a deep, conical subsidence doline that dries out and refills to form a small tarn at apparently random intervals. Farther west the same fault – or perhaps a separate fracture on the same trend – influenced the location of Cross Pot and Jackdaw Hole. Cross Pot is a single 26m vertical shaft from the surface, formed where the fault is intersected by another, more or less perpendicular, fracture. The known ramifications of Jackdaw Hole slightly farther west are shallower but more complex, with one splay of the fault showing a vertical displacement of less than 30 cm.

Many other fractures guiding cave development might likewise be secondary wrench, tear or strike-slip faults that developed to dissipate the effects of far more substantial movements within the Askrigg Block's bounding fault zones (Garwood and Goodyear, 1924). If so, the most significant fault movements are lateral; vertical displacement is apparent only locally, where the fault trend lies closer to the dip direction. In the northern and southeastern parts of the Dales (Fig. 2.22) numerous mineral veins tens of metres in vertical extent, but with no observable vertical displacement are probably of similar origin. The corollary is that lack of recognition of such fractures in the central part of the Block reflects the likelihood that mineralising brines did not penetrate far beyond its margins and so the fractures remain largely unmineralised. The vein systems of Grassington Moor are dominated by strike-slip faults, and lateral fault dislocations with horizontal slickensides have also been reported in the Greenhow workings and in the nearby Hell Hole (Peachey, 2012).

Figure 2.24. The 18m-deep chasm of Hull Pot (viewed towards the west) has formed along a set of sub-vertical, strike-slip fractures such as the one in the left (southern) wall (photo: Phil Murphy).

Away from mineralised areas and large potholes, surface evidence of minor faulting is difficult to recognise, particularly where there is a thick cover of drift deposits, as on Casterton and Leck fells. Around Malham, however, a tract between the North and Middle Craven faults is largely drift-free, and two sets of minor faults are present. Both sets include faults with small hades and generally small vertical throws, with or without lateral movement. One set trends around SW–NE, typically with vertical displacements of no more than a few metres. The second set is more pronounced, with a dominant NW–SE trend and throws that reach 90m, as at Attermire Scar (Arthurton *et al.,* 1988; Fig. 2.25).

Whether closely or widely spaced, joints form if rigid rock beds crack when gently folded, and they are ubiquitous across the Dales limestone. Drift-free limestones display prominent sub-vertical joint-sets of NW–SE and SW–NE orientation in the west and south, swinging to N–S and W–E orientations in the east (Moseley, 1973). Other mixed joint-sets and secondary wrench faults parallel the trends of the major faults. Together these joint-sets (and parallel faults) guide the grikes that separate the residual limestone clints to produce the well-known limestone pavements of the Yorkshire Dales (Fig. 2.17; see also Chapter 5).

As with minor faults, some joints, whether they cut a single limestone bed or extend vertically through several beds, are important guides of underground drainage routes. They form sub-vertical links between conduits and passages guided by lithological features, and hence have considerable influence on cave development geometry (see Chapter 8).

Figure 2.25. The col followed over the horizon by the drystone wall below Attermire Scar marks the course of a major NW–SE fault, with a vertical displacement of about 90m (TW).

Figure 2.26. Gill Heads Mine – entrances and open workings on the Gill Heads Vein in Trollers Gill; last worked for fluorspar, the mine closed in the early 1980s (photo: Lloyd Llewellyn).

Minerals and mining

The Northern Pennine Orefield stretches from the headwaters of the Tyne in the north to the Craven Fault Zone in the south and the Askrigg Block contributes rather more than one third of this area (Dunham, 1948; Dunham and Wilson, 1985). The mineral deposits are more or less confined to the Carboniferous rocks, but processes that led to mineralisation potentially began before the limestone succession was fully emplaced (see Chapter 8). Mineral deposition was largely via the agency of hydrothermal waters, rich in dissolved minerals, entering and interacting with the Carboniferous rocks. Such waters have four possible sources: juvenile water from crustal igneous magma, water from sub-crustal (mantle) sources, resurgent metamorphic water, and connate and sub-vadose groundwater (Dunham and Wilson, 1985). The last of these appears to have been dominant, as hot mineral-rich brines expelled from the Stainmore Trough in the north and the Craven Basin in the south, were driven into the fissured rocks on the adjacent edges of the Askrigg Block (Heyl *et al.,* 1974; Rogers, 1978).

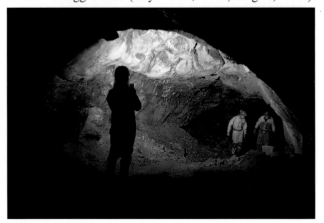

Figure 2.27. Thick sediment and breakdown in an ancient phreatic tunnel within Pikedaw Calamine Caverns (photo: John Forder).

A secondary driving mechanism could have involved regional convection related to reheating of deeply buried granite intrusions. However, isotopically homogeneous brines responsible for the atypical style of mineralisation in the folded rocks of the Greenhow–Skyreholme area were probably at least partly of igneous juvenile origin (Mitchell and Krouse, 1971).

By far the dominant ore mineral found and exploited across the Dales was galena (lead sulphide), commonly associated with small amounts of copper, zinc and iron minerals, plus traces of silver and antimony. Generally these minor components would not repay the cost of concentration, though as many mines approached the end of their viability in the late 19th century some silver was recovered at about 20 sites across the Dales. Probably it proved worthwhile at only two of these, the Braithwaite and West Burton mines above Wensleydale, and at Buckden Gavel above Wharfedale (Dunham and Wilson, 1985).

Sphalerite (zinc sulphide) was second in abundance across the Dales as a whole. Everywhere it was in far smaller quantities than galena, with its best recorded development associated with the Whitaside and Apedale vein systems beneath the Wensleydale–Swaledale interfluve southeast of Gunnerside. Copper and iron sulphides, as well as various complex mixtures, largely occurred as inclusions within the dominant minerals, and were nowhere sufficiently concentrated to repay separation. Many secondary minerals, derived from the primary deposits, generally as a result of oxidation, were found in mines across the Dales, but nowhere in economic quantities (Dunham and Wilson, 1985).

Everywhere the ore minerals were accompanied by various non-metallic or gangue minerals. Calcite (calcium carbonate), baryte (barium sulphate) and fluorite (calcium fluoride) were most common and widespread, but quartz (silicon dioxide), dolomite (calcium-magnesium carbonate) and witherite (barium carbonate) were recorded locally, along with minor quantities of other minerals. At least initially, the gangue minerals were treated as waste and, after separation from the metal ores, were left in the mine spoil heaps.

Across the Dales the economically workable mineral occurrences were known collectively as oreshoots. These fall into four broad types: veins (or rakes), scrins, pipes and flats (or floats or flots) (Dunham and Wilson, 1985).

Veins (Fig. 2.22) are essentially planar mineral bodies, commonly layered or zoned, that were emplaced within fault fissures, most of which are sub-vertical and with only small vertical displacements, the Gill Heads Vein exposed in Trollers Gill near Greenhow being fairly typical (Fig. 2.26). Exceptionally, fault-hosted veins such as the Friarfold Vein in Swaledale, show vertical movements of 30m or more, but most fault-veins probably reflect lateral (strike-slip or wrench) movement that is not readily observable. Many mineral veins occur in zones of sub-parallel, *en echelon* or splaying faults, so related mines commonly form complex underground networks. On the northern side of Swaledale a swathe of worked veins more than a kilometre wide extends for 20 km. Friarfold Vein was the longest single oreshoot, containing a mineralised zone that was 2m wide for more than 4 km of its length.

Narrow veins were known as scrins. Generally these relate to vertical fractures, many of which may be strike-slip faults with nil or negligible displacement, and commonly they occur in sub-parallel sets. Whether scrins were worked or left untouched depended largely upon their position and relationship to other, more substantial, mineral deposits.

Most pipes appear to have formed along the junction of two intersecting fractures, or a fracture and a bedding plane (Dunham and Wilson, 1985). These authors claimed that caverns encountered in some mines post-date mineralisation, and they did not accept the possibility of mineralisation into pre-existing karstic voids, an option recognised in similar contexts in the Derbyshire Peak District (Ford, 2010). It remains feasible that some dissolutional voids, perhaps falling outside normally accepted definitions of caves, pre-dated primary mineral emplacement (see Chapter 8).

Considered as a single type, flats, floats or flots are described as replacement deposits following the bedding at specific horizons (Dunham and Wilson, 1985). Whether these are specific named beds, such as the Great (Main) Limestone, or specific types of bed, such as coarse-grained limestones, is unclear. Whereas flats essentially follow the bedding, an assumption (Dunham and Wilson. 1985) that they formed by rock replacement rather than by infilling pre-existing voids might be flawed, at least locally. The supposedly synonymous terms 'flot' and 'float' were also applied by miners to *ex situ* fragments of vein material or to masses of ore found among rock breakdown debris and within clay deposits in pre-existing cavities intersected by the mines. Some flot-ore undoubtedly derives from flat deposits, but some might represent breakdown and collapse of vein, scrin and pipe ore-bodies when enclosing rock is removed by dissolution and physical breakdown.

A totally different type of cave-related mineral deposit was found at Pikedaw (Fig. 2.27), west of Malham. In the late 18th century, miners working limited copper ore deposits (Fig. 2.28) beneath Pikedaw Hill broke into large, old, natural caves The floors of three spacious chambers contained thick layers of smithsonite, a zinc carbonate that was then known as calamine. After sinking a shaft directly into their Calamine Caverns, the miners simply dug out more than 5000 tonnes of zinc ore. Origins of this unique deposit remain uncertain, but some stalactitic mineral was precipitated chemically, whereas the dominant powdery sediment had probably been eroded and redeposited by a cave stream.

Currently there is no mineral mining beneath the Dales. Fluorite was the last mineral to be mined. Former lead mines west of Greenhow were redeveloped in the 1960s, with new stopes supplying mineral to a small separation plant, but available reserves and output were limited. The last working mine was Gill Heads (Fig. 2.26) in Trollers Gill where, after an earlier history as a lead mine, fluorite was extracted sporadically between the 1920s and the early 1980s. Also during the 20th century, when demand grew for both baryte and fluorite for use as industrial raw materials, some mineral was obtained by reworking the waste material from abandoned lead mines. Dumps at the Old Gang site (off Arkengarthdale) and around Yarnbury (above Grassington) were reworked sporadically until the 1980s.

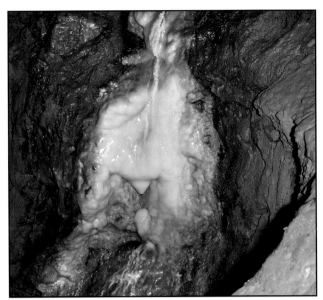

Figure 2.28. Blue calcite flow in Wizards Chasm, not far from the Pikedaw Calamine Caverns west of Malham. The mineral has not been analysed, but its colour probably reflects inclusion of a copper silicate gel within the calcite lattice (photo: Dave Hodgson).

Despite the present lack of mining activity, minerals emplaced within the limestones and adjacent beds have played a major role in the Dales economy in the past. The origin and nature of the mineral deposits are also significant to various cave and karst development issues. Across the entire Dales area some of the mine workings encountered natural caverns, as at Stump Cross and Mongo Gill in the Greenhow area or in the workings associated with the Turf Pits mines beneath Grassington Moor (Dunham and Wilson. 1985). Farther north, several remarkable stratigraphically-constrained maze cave complexes were entered at sites within limestone beneath the Wensleydale–Swaledale interfluve, most notably via the workings of the Devis Hole Mine (Fig. 2.29) (Harrison, 2012).

Figure 2.29. The 20m-diameter First Cavern, part of the Horn's Workings Cave Series in the Devis Hole Mine, is a large natural cave, appreciably modified by miners in their search for flot ore. The roof and upper walls comprise black chert beds, probably the Main Chert, but possibly including younger chert beds, lying above pale brown strata of the Main Limestone. The friable nature of the cherty beds has resulted in significant roof collapse, which was a major problem for 19th century miners (photo: John Dale).

Superficial deposits

Unconsolidated Quaternary deposits, formerly more widely known as drift, variably obscure bedrock geology across the Dales. In valley bottoms and on valley flanks, locally-thick till (boulder clay) and glaciofluvial sand and gravel deposits formed in response to a late Devensian glaciation, with its acme about 18,000 years ago, and its associated deglaciation events (Chapter 3). Ice moved mainly south or east across the Dales, enlarging major valleys such as Ribblesdale and Wharfedale, and deepening lesser valleys such as Kingsdale. Landslides are a typical feature of the steeper valley sides incised into weaker rocks of the Yoredale Group (Fig. 2.30). A blanket of post-glacial to Recent peat deposits is developed extensively across the upland areas (Chapter 12).

Whereas glacial tills and outwash, hill peat and a variety of soils blanket much of the Dales terrain, the stark exposures of Great Scar Limestone provide the most conspicuous features of the landscape. The many eye-catching scars and the wide expanses of limestone pavement are quintessential elements of the glaciokarst of the Yorkshire Dales.

References

Aitkenhead, N and 6 others, 2002. *British Regional Geology: the Pennines and adjacent areas*. British Geological Survey: Nottingham.

Arthurton, R S, E W Johnson and D J C Mundy, 1988. Geology of the country around Settle. *Mem. Brit. Geol. Surv. Sheet 60.*

Barnes, R P, M J Branney, P Stone and N H Woodcock, 2006. The Lakesman Terrane: the Lower Palaeozoic record of the deep marine Lakesman Basin, a volcanic arc and foreland basin. 103–129 in P J Brenchley and P F Rawson (eds), *The Geology of England and Wales*. Geological Society: London.

Dakyns, J R, 1876. On Silurian erratics in Wharfedale. *Proc. Yorks. Geol. Polytech. Soc., 6, 159.*

Dean, M T, M A E Browne, C N Waters and J H Powell, 2011. A lithostratigraphical framework for the Carboniferous successions of Northern Great Britain (onshore). *British Geological Survey Research Report, RR/10/07. 174pp.*

Doughty, P S, 1968. Joint densities and their relation to lithology in the Great Scar Limestone. *Proc Yorks. Geol. Soc., 36, 479–512.*

Dunham, K C, 1948. The geology of the Northern Pennine Orefield: Volume 1, Tyne to Stainmore. *Mem. Geol. Surv. G.B.*

Dunham, K C and C J Stubblefield, 1945. The stratigraphy, structure and mineralization of the Greenhow mining area, Yorkshire. *Q. J. Geol. Soc., 100, 209–268.*

Dunham, K C and A A Wilson, 1985. Geology of the North Pennine Orefield: Volume 2, Stainmore to Craven. *Econ. Mem. Brit. Geol. Surv.. HMSO: London.*

Dunham, R J, 1962. Classification of carbonate rocks according to depositional texture. *Mem. Amer. Assoc. Petroleum Geol., 1, 108–121.*

Dyson, N, 1969. The Meal Bank coal seam and its influence on cave development. *Bradford Pothole Club Bulletin, 5(6), 16–18.*

Ford, T D (Ed.), 1977. Limestones and Caves of the Peak District. Geo Abstracts: Norwich, 469pp

Ford, T D, 2010. Derbyshire pipe veins – deep-seated speleogenesis? *Cave Karst Science, 37(1), 9–22.*

Garwood, E J and E Goodyear, 1924. The Lower Carboniferous succession in the Settle district and along the line of the Craven faults. *Q. J. Geol. Soc., 80, 184–273.*

George, T N and 6 others, 1976. A correlation of Dinantian rocks in the British Isles. *Geol. Soc. Spec. Rep., 7, 87pp.*

Glover, R R, 1974. Gaping Gill – some underground controls of development. Part 2: The Porcellanous Band and its control of passage levels. *Craven Pothole Club Journal, 5(2), 58–65.*

Gradstein, F M, J G Ogg, M Schmitz and G Ogg (eds), 2012. *The Geologic Time Scale 2012.* Elsevier: Oxford.

Harrison, D J, J H Hudson and B Cannell. 1991. Appraisal of high-purity limestones in England and Wales. A study of resources, needs, uses and demands. Part 1 Resources. *Brit. Geol. Surv. Tech. Rep., WF/90/10, 1–241.*

Harrison, T, 2012. Phreatic maze caves, Grinton Moor, Swaledale, UK: survey of the Devis Hole Mine Caves. *Cave Karst Science, 39, 59–62.*

Heyl, A V, G P Landis and R E Zartman, 1974. Isotopic evidence for the origin of Mississippi Valley-type mineral deposits. *Economic Geology, 69, 992–1006.*

Hudson, R G S, 1937. The Millstone Grit succession of the Simonseat Anticline, Yorkshire. *Proc. Yorks. Geol. Soc., 23, 319–349.*

King, W B R and W H Wilcockson, 1934. The Lower Palaeozoic Rocks of Austwick and Horton-in-Ribblesdale. *Q. J. Geol. Soc., 90, 7–31.*

Millward, D, 2006. Caledonian intrusive rocks of northern England and the Midlands. 147–154 in P J Brenchley and P F Rawson (eds), *The Geology of England and Wales*. Geological Society: London.

Mitchell, R H and H R Krouse, 1971. Isotopic composition of sulphur and lead in galena from the Greenhow – Skyreholme area, Yorkshire, England. *Economic Geology, 66, 243–251.*

Moseley, F, 1973. Orientations and origins of joints, faults and folds in the Carboniferous limestones of N.W. England. *Trans. Cave Res. Gp., 15, 99–106.*

Murray, D W, 1983. The limestone and dolomite resources of the country around Settle and Malham, North Yorkshire (with notes on the hard-rock resources of the Horton-in-Ribblesdale area). *Mineral Assessment Report Inst. Geol. Sci., 126, 31pp.*

Peachey, I, 2012. The geological structure of the Skyreholme anticline and its relationship to speleogenesis and post glacial surface morphology [abstract]. *Cave Karst Science, 39, 42.*

Raistrick, A, 1931. The glaciation of Wharfedale, Yorkshire. *Proc. Yorks. Geol. Soc., 22, 9–30.*

Ramsbottom, W H C, 1973. Transgressions and regressions in the Dinantian: a new synthesis of British Dinantian stratigraphy. *Proc. Yorks. Geol. Soc., 39, 567–607.*

Rogers, P J, 1978. Fluid inclusion studies on fluorite from the Askrigg Block. *Trans. Inst. Min. Metall., 87, B107–117.*

Schwarzacher, W, 1958. The stratification of the Great Scar Limestone in the Settle district of Yorkshire. *Liverpool Manchester Geol. J., 2, 124–142.*

Somerville, I D, 1979. Minor sedimentary cyclicity in late Asbian (Upper D$_1$) limestones in the Llangollen district of North Wales. *Proc. Yorks. Geol. Soc., 42, 317–341.*

Soper, N J and F W Dunning, 2005. Structure and sequence of the Ingleton Group, basement to the Central Pennines of northern England. *Proc. Yorks. Geol. Soc., 55, 241–261.*

Soper, J and G Edwards, 2012. Speleogenesis and the sub-Carboniferous unconformity on the Askrigg Block [abstract]. *Cave Karst Science, 39, 42.*

Turner, J S, 1968. A note on the Meal Bank coal horizon around Ingleborough. *Trans. Leeds Geol. Ass., 7, 265–268.*

Walkden, G M, 1972. The mineralogy and origin of interbedded clay wayboards in the Lower Carboniferous of the Derbyshire Dome. *Geol. J., 8, 143–160.*

Walkden, G M, 1987. Sedimentary and diagenetic styles in late Dinantian carbonates of Britain. 131–155 in J Miller, A E Adams and V P Wright (eds), *European Dinantian Environments. Geological Journal Special Issue 12.*

Waltham, A C, 1971. Shale units in the Great Scar Limestone of the southern Askrigg Block, *Proc. Yorks. Geol. Soc., 38, 285–292.*

Waltham, A C, 1977. Cave development at the base of the limestone in Yorkshire. *Proc. 7th Int. Cong. Speleology., Sheffield, 421–423.*

Waltham, T, 2005. Yorkshire Dales: excursion report. *Mercian Geologist, 16, 144–147.*

Waters, C N and D J Condon, 2012. Nature and timing of Late Mississippian to Mid-Pennsylvanian glacio-eustatic sea-level changes of the Pennine Basin, UK. *J. Geol. Soc., 169, 37–51.*

Waters, C N and S J Davies, 2006. Carboniferous: extensional basins, advancing deltas and coal swamps. 173–223 in P J Brenchley and P F Rawson (eds), *The Geology of England and Wales*. Geological Society: London.

Waters, C N, M A E Browne, M T Dean and J H Powell, 2007. Lithostratigraphical framework for Carboniferous successions of Great Britain (Onshore). *Brit. Geol. Surv. Res. Rep., RR/07/01, 60pp.*

Waters, C N and 18 others, 2011. A revised correlation of Carboniferous rocks in the British Isles. *Geol. Soc. Spec. Rep., 26.*

Figure 2.30. The Falls Foot landslide in beds of the Yoredale Group on the steep upper slope of Ingleborough (TW).

CHAPTER 3

Glaciation and Quaternary evolution

Wishart A Mitchell

Upland areas of the British Isles have complex geomorphological records that reflect the influence of past climate changes, particularly those associated with the successive cold (glacial) and temperate (interglacial) stages of Quaternary time. The spectacular and distinctive landscape of the Yorkshire Dales is no exception, where the greatest impact was by glaciers that developed periodically into larger topographically independent icecaps and ice sheets. These eroded the characteristic U-shaped dales (Fig. 3.1) before extending, on occasions, into surrounding lowlands to merge with ice from other regional centres building into ice sheets across much of the British Isles. However, such ice sheets were present for only part of the 'glacial' stages, and for much longer periods of Quaternary time the Dales area was affected by non-glacial, cold-climate processes associated with periglaciation and the formation of widespread permafrost. Periods of transition between these different climate states were generally short, with landscapes adjusting rapidly to new conditions of erosion and sediment flux. In the Craven district of the Yorkshire Dales, the extensive Carboniferous limestone outcrops have added a distinctive lithological influence to these geomorphological systems, leading to development of the world-famous glaciokarst (see Chapter 4) and the spectacular cave systems (see Chapter 7). Dating of speleothems from these caves forms an extremely important, if undervalued, factor within the wider Quaternary record of the British Isles, and has allowed the development of a long-term terrestrial chronology for the region (see Chapter 10).

It is now appreciated that Quaternary climate changes were both complex and rapid, driven primarily by astronomical forcing of solar radiation in what are now known as Milankovitch cycles (Imbrie and Imbrie, 1979; Siegert, 2001; Lisiecki and Raymo, 2007). Onto these are superimposed internal responses reflecting interactions between the climate, oceans and terrestrial systems (Lang and Wolff, 2011). This has allowed the Late Cenozoic to be divided into a series of glacial and interglacial stages based on the oxygen isotope record derived from deep ocean sediments and formally known as Marine Isotope Stages (MIS) (Fig. 3.2). This continuous signal clearly shows that there have been, during the Quaternary, many more glacial events than are apparent in the discontinuous terrestrial archive. Intensification of glaciation, with the development of larger ice sheets capable of covering extensive lowland areas in the northern hemisphere, occurred after the Middle Pleistocene Transition, at c.780 ka (Mudelsee and Schulz, 1997; Lisiecki and Raymo, 2007). Following this, global climate change

was characterised by 100-ka, precession-driven, orbital cycles (Lisiecki, 2010), with cold stages that lasted roughly 100,000 years, in comparison to shorter interglacial stages of around 15,000 years. The asymmetrical profile of each glacial stage reflects that it takes time for an ice sheet to accumulate, with cold stages characterised by long periods of slow climatic deterioration and ice accumulation under cold periglacial conditions. In contrast, deglaciation from maximum ice sheet positions occurred within extremely short time periods (<6 ka), termed Terminations, which were dominated by rapid environmental changes (Denton et al., 2010). Shorter climatic reversals are also known to occur within each cold stage, causing climatic fluctuations between cold stadial conditions and more temperate interstadial environments.

Ocean-floor sediment cores have also revealed the influence of ocean circulation on climate change and rapid environmental responses. In particular, cores from the North Atlantic have revealed the presence of a number of discrete sedimentary layers of ice-rafted debris (IRD). These are interpreted to indicate that during glaciations, the surface of the North Atlantic was periodically dominated by huge numbers of icebergs formed by significant calving events associated with ice sheet instability, particularly of the large North American Ice Sheet; these are now termed Heinrich Events (Hemming, 2004). As these icebergs melted, they deposited the sediment horizons and formed a surface layer of cold fresh water that shut down the thermohaline circulation and triggered rapid climatic cooling in surrounding land masses (Scourse et al., 2009; Thornalley et al., 2010; Naafs, et al., 2011; Stanford et al., 2011).

Figure 3.1. Littondale, one of the dales that was enlarged by glacial erosion during successive Quaternary glaciations to form the characteristic broad trough incised into the high plateau; seen from the hillside above Halton Gill (photo: Harry Long).

Glaciation and Quaternary evolution, by Wishart Mitchell, University of Durham; w.a.mitchell@durham.ac.uk
Chapter 3, pages 29–64 in **Caves and Karst of the Yorkshire Dales**, edited by Tony Waltham and David Lowe.
Published 2013 by the British Cave Research Association, 978-0-900265-46-4 and at www.bcra.org.uk

The Late Pleistocene palaeoclimate record has also been determined from ice cores drilled through the Greenland and Antarctic ice sheets (Rasmussen *et al.*, 2006, 2008; Jouzel and Masson-Delmotte, 2010). Because there is no bioturbation, as in ocean sediments, the ice cores have yielded an even higher temporal resolution record of climate changes within the last interglacial-glacial-interglacial cycle. They have revealed the existence of a number of shorter Dansgaard-Oeschger cycles of about 1470 years, and have allowed development of a well-dated chronostratigraphy for the last glacial cycle. This identifies a series of Greenland Stadials and Interstadials for the Late Pleistocene through the establishment of the Greenland Ice Core Chronology (GICC05) timescale, into which the rapid climate changes of the last glaciation, its termination and the Last Glacial-Interglacial Transition (LGIT) can be placed (Lowe *et al.*, 2008). This timescale (Fig. 3.3) has now been extended back to 48 ka (Blockley *et al.*, 2012).

Figure 3.2 *(below left). The geological record for multiple glaciations of the British Isles. The oxygen isotope profile on the left shows Marine Isotope Stages (MIS) (even-numbered cold glacial stages with high global ice volume and low global sea-level, and odd-numbered warm interglacial stages with low global ice volume and high sea-levels). On the right, blue bars show the interpreted scale of each glaciation, red bars are inferred from the ice-rafted deposits (after Lee, 2011).*

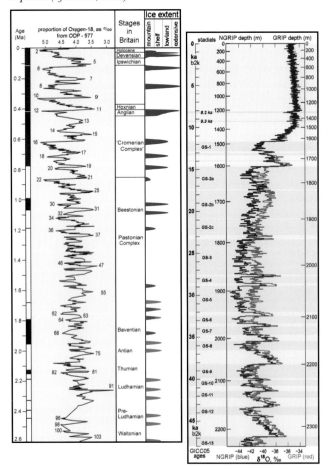

Figure 3.3 *(above right). Timescale of North Atlantic events for the last 48,000 years derived from $\delta^{18}O$ records for the NGRIP and GRIP ice-core records at a 50-year resolution within the GICC05 timescale. Blue indicates Greenland Stadials (GS) numbered from the top; yellow indicates preceding interstadial (GI) with the same number; two short cooling events in the Holocene are also marked at 9.3 and 8.2 ka (after Blockley et al., 2012).*

Definitions and acronyms

Cold-based ice: ice that is frozen to the underlying glacier bed and is below pressure melting point, so that it moves little and has negligible erosional impact on the landscape.

Diffluent: divergent flow causing erosion of new glacial troughs where the pre-glacial valleys cannot cope with increased ice mass.

GICC05 (*Greenland Ice Core Chronology 2005*): a new timescale for the Late Pleistocene and Holocene based on a high resolution chronostratigraphy by counting back annual ice layers and modelling the ice cores, particularly NGRIP; counted back from 2000 AD (hence b2k), so differs from radiocarbon dates that are expressed before 1950.

Ice cores: cores of ice drilled out of ice sheets and glaciers to establish long undisturbed records. Because the ice builds up annually, the resultant stratigraphy provides a high-resolution record of climate change.

Ice stream: a linear zone of rapid ice flowing at an order of magnitude faster than surrounding ice. Due to their fast flow, ice streams are zones of enhanced erosion and are often associated with deep glaciated troughs. They are the important parts of an ice sheet in the transfer of mass from source areas to ice margins.

Ice-rafted debris (*IRD*): sediment, mostly of sand size, recovered from ocean floor sediments deposited from melting icebergs.

Last Glacial Maximum (*LGM*): defined conventionally from sea level records as the most recent time of maximum global ice sheet development between 26.5 and 19 ka.

Last Glacial-Interglacial Transition (*LGIT*): the time of rapid climatic change between the last cold stage and the present Holocene Interglacial; formerly known as the Lateglacial period. In the British chronostratigraphy, it is divided into a warm interstadial known as the Lateglacial (or Windermere) Interstadial lasting 14.7–12.9 ka, and the following return to cold conditions during the Loch Lomond Stadial at 12.9–11.7 ka. Now subdivided with respect to the chronostratigraphy determined from NGRIP and defined by Greenland Stadials (GS) and Interstadials (GI).

Marine Isotope Stages (*MIS*): global chronological sub-division of deep ocean sediment cores based on changes in oxygen isotopes derived from benthic foraminifera, and allowing the establishment of glacial (even numbers) and interglacial (odd numbers) stages.

NGRIP (*North Greenland Ice Core Project*): one of a series of ice cores recovered from the Greenland Ice Sheet, which has been used to establish a global Late Quaternary chronology and palaeoclimatic record.

Periglacial: environment with a severely cold, non-glacial climate, leading to intense frost shattering and the formation of permafrost.

Permafrost: permanently frozen ground in a periglacial regime, capped by an active layer of summer thaw a few metres thick.

Quarrying: a major process of glacial erosion whereby fractures in the bedrock release large blocks that are then removed by entrainment in the basal ice; previously described as ice plucking.

Stadial: sub-division within a stage, marked by intense climatic cooling for a short period of time.

Warm-based ice: ice that is not frozen to the bedrock, but is at pressure melting point so that it is underlain and lubricated by meltwater, thereby allowing faster ice flow and higher rates of glacial erosion.

Although there is no direct evidence for glaciation in northern England during the early part of the Pleistocene, the Dales speleothem record retains important information on climate change that can be correlated to Milankovitch-driven cycles and linked to evidence of ice elsewhere in Britain (Mitchell, 2012a). The underlying premise is that speleothem growth is maximised during warm, wet, interglacial stages when rain water percolated through a soil and vegetation cover. This acidic water enhances dissolution of the limestone and then precipitates calcite due to degassing on contact with cave air (see Chapter 4). Conversely, during

Figure 3.4. Evidence for the Middle to Late Pleistocene glacial cycles from the record of dated speleothems and intervening laminated clays in Victoria Cave, correlated with a normalised marine oxygen isotope curve and the Marine Isotope Stages (MIS) (after Lundberg et al., 2010).

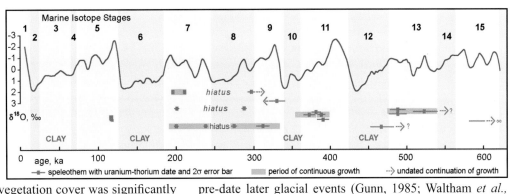

cold glacial stages, when vegetation cover was significantly reduced or eliminated, in association with the formation of permafrost or burial of the caves beneath ice, speleothem growth was retarded or ceased altogether (Atkinson *et al.,* 1978; Gascoyne *et al.,* 1983a, 1983b; Gascoyne and Ford, 1984; Sutcliffe *et al.,* 1985; Baker *et al.,* 1993; Fairchild *et al.,* 2006). More recent research on speleothem ages has been directed towards high-resolution events at shorter timescales, associated with the Dansgaard-Oeschger cycles of the Greenland ice core signal; this suggests a link between temperature, precipitation and solar insolation at sub-Milankovitch timescales (Baker *et al.,* 1995). Little appears to have been published to maximise this potential line of evidence in the Yorkshire Dales (McDermott *et al.,* 2011). Furthermore, it now appears that speleothem growth was able to be maintained even during cooler, but not the coldest, parts of the glacial stages (Mitchell, 2012a; see below).

Uranium–thorium (U–Th) dates determined from a number of cave systems (see Chapter 10) have established that speleothem development can be correlated to the main interglacial periods of the Mid to Late Pleistocene (MIS 13, 11, 9, 7, and 5e) and the Holocene (the present interglacial period, MIS 1), as defined by the oxygen isotope ($\delta^{18}O$) marine record. The longest currently available sequence is from Victoria Cave above Settle (Fig. 3.4), where the earliest finite dates on speleothems point to intermittent growth from c.490 ka onwards (Lundberg *et al.,* 2010; Lord *et al.,* 2012). In addition, laminated clays interstratified within the dated speleothems are interpreted as resulting from glaciation in the vicinity of the cave during MIS 12, 10, 6 and 2. Some uncertainty remains as to whether or not glacial conditions occurred during MIS 8 (see below). Thus, the evidence from the caves forms an important chronological marker for landscape development within the Yorkshire Dales, giving clear evidence of glacial-interglacial cyclicity from the Middle Pleistocene onwards, and into which the glacial record can be constrained in time. In association with the speleothems, many caves acted as sites for local deposition of glacial and glaciofluvial sediments associated with meltwater discharges that would have characterised deglaciation, while also demonstrating that many caves

pre-date later glacial events (Gunn, 1985; Waltham *et al.,* 1997; Ford, 2001; Murphy *et al.,* 2001, 2008). The Yorkshire Dales are, therefore, a critical region in reconstructing the long-term record of palaeoclimate in northern England; their speleothems provide an important and exceptional record of the environmental changes that affected Britain from the mid-Pleistocene to the present (Mitchell, 2012a).

A full assessment of Quaternary events pertinent to understanding specific karst landforms and cave development within the Yorkshire Dales requires palaeoclimatic information from the wider area of the British Isles and the North Atlantic region, in addition to an understanding of the glacial record. Only then can the multiple glaciations that have affected the Dales be placed within the wider context of climatic change, tectonic uplift and geomorphic systems. Particularly important are the wider spatial record and temporal dynamics of the last British-Irish Ice Sheet during the Devensian stage, and the pattern and timing of ice retreat that had such an influence on the texture of the present landscapes of the Dales.

Long-term evolution of the pre-glacial landscape

A conspicuous feature of the Yorkshire Pennines landscape is the extensive series of high-plateau bedrock surfaces between the deeply incised dales, reflecting the survival of pre-glacial surfaces and their selective erosion by former glaciers (Fig. 3.5). Such accordance of summit elevations in upland areas has long been appreciated by geoscientists, and has been explained by erosion and planation independent of the geological structure over long periods of geological time to form peneplains or erosional lowlands that have been subsequently uplifted and dissected (Widdowson, 1997; Goodfellow, 2007). In northern England, explanations of the origins of such planation surfaces have a long pedigree (Belbin, 1985; Huddart and Glasser, 2002). Regrettably, much of this debate has been speculative, and hard facts in terms of genesis and timing of surface formation remain as elusive as ever. Over a long period, the Pennines have been an area of net erosion and denudation, particularly associated with their role as an important regional centre for successive Pleistocene ice sheets.

Figure 3.5. Glaciated terrain of the western Pennines, south from the slopes of Swarth Fell across the plateau surface towards the high remnant summits of Ingleborough, Whernside and Great Coum. Glaciers overdeepened the valleys, including Garsdale in the foreground, where drumlins indicate former ice flow eastwards into Wensleydale (WM).

Periods of tectonic quiescence allowed denudation to form low-relief surfaces. These were interrupted by periods of uplift allowing the formation, at a range of elevations, of planation surfaces that have been tilted and down-warped across many upland areas within the British Isles (Belbin, 1985; Hall and Bishop, 2002; Gordon, 2010; Jarman, 2010). These low-angle relief features, known as palaeic surfaces, form prominent geomorphic markers within many mountain landscapes associated with passive continental margins, notably in Scandinavia (Goodfellow, 2007). They have, however, remained enigmatic in terms of genesis and age, even to being a source of debate regarding their actual existence. Furthermore, it is now appreciated that surface uplift is driven not only by tectonics, but is also a consequence of isostatic compensation due to mass loss by erosion. Thus valley incision into a surface actually triggers subsequent surface uplift with respect to summit elevations, even where there is a decrease in regional mean elevation (Burbank and Anderson, 2001; Staiger et al., 2005). This has been shown to be particularly the case with respect to the impact of glacial erosion, notably ice quarrying, on mountain areas (Thomson et al., 2010; Valla et al., 2011; Iverson, 2012).

Little information is preserved concerning the geological history of the Dales after the end of the Carboniferous (see Chapter 2). Elsewhere in northern England, Mesozoic rocks remain in a number of sedimentary basins that surround the Pennines, but the later Cenozoic is poorly recorded (Kent, 1974; Stone et al., 2010). However, the Cenozoic was an important era with respect to landscape development. It was during this long time interval, from 65 Ma, that plate tectonic activity on a divergent, passive margin associated with the expansion of the Atlantic Ocean, together with far-field influences from the Alpine Orogeny, caused uplift of the land mass that would become the British Isles. However, whereas the overall account is known, the detailed history of uplift is still far from certain; rather, it seems that uplift was intermittent and occurred in a series of pulses due to different tectonic situations, firstly due to the proximity of the Iceland mantle plume and then later because of re-organisation of regional intra-plate stresses around the eastern Atlantic margin (Stoker et al., 2010). In addition, subsidence of the North Sea Basin caused a general tilt from west to east (Kent, 1974). Recent evidence from Scandinavia and Greenland suggest that the formation of uplifted surfaces occurred later in the Neogene than previously thought (Blundell and Waltham, 2009; Japsen et al., 2009, 2011). This is confirmed by apatite fission-track dating from the Eastgate borehole in Weardale, which indicates that uplift associated with the Iceland plume was as recently as Palaeogene (Green et al., 2012).

The present landscape in northern England therefore reflects later responses to on-going, tectonic-erosional coupling. Higher uplift rates in the Pennines can be explained by thermally influenced isostasy related to the presence of underlying granites, but also reflecting underplating and thickening of less-viscous lower crust (Westaway, 2009). Furthermore, uplift may not require an independent tectonic trigger, but may be regarded as a response to erosional isostasy moderated by lower crustal flow due to increased erosion related to climatic cooling following the Pliocene optimum (Green et al., 2012). It seems that continuing uplift

rates of 0.3 mm/year can be proposed from both limited field data and modelling; this is equivalent to 300m within a million years, and explains present elevations of c.800 m by uplift since the Late Pliocene (Westaway, 2009; Westaway et al., 2002). Such uplift in northern Britain is likely to have been accelerated by glacio-isostatic controls associated with crustal depression and rebound connected with ice-sheet loading and unloading during successive glaciations during the Pleistocene, as well as the isostatic rebound associated with differential glacial erosion during such events (Blundell and Waltham, 2009).

In the Yorkshire Dales, distinctive erosion surfaces have been thought to occur at a number of levels, sloping eastwards from the major fault systems that define the western and southern margins of the Askrigg Block, and these were used in the development of a denudation chronology for the area (Hudson, 1933; Sweeting, 1950, 1974; King 1976). Given that many of the 'surfaces' coincide with bedding planes in the Carboniferous rock sequence, their existence has been increasingly questioned and they are better explained as stratimorphs (Waltham, 2012; Waltham and Long, 2011). However, the '1300-foot surface' (at around 400m) around Ingleborough has long been regarded as a good example (Fig. 3.5), and above Malham it may be independent of structure where it cuts across the North Craven Fault (Sweeting, 1950; Clayton, 1981; Waltham, 1990, 2012; see Chapter 4).

Erosion of these tilted and uplifted surfaces in northern England was originally considered to have been initiated by a series of eastward-flowing rivers that acted independently of lithology (Davis, 1895; Trotter, 1929; Kendall and Wroot, 1924; Hudson, 1933; King, 1976). In the Yorkshire Dales, this was thought to be recognised in the drainage pattern of the rivers Swale and Ure, but with a more complex pattern further south where rivers, including the Wharfe and Aire, reflect radial drainage from a structural dome centred over the northwestern Askrigg Block (Hudson, 1933; Palmer, 1967; de Boer, 1974). The topographical asymmetry of the Askrigg Block watershed is also reflected in the drainage pattern of the western Dales associated with the shorter tributaries of the River Lune catchment.

Whereas the denudation chronologies previously proposed are now discredited, there are landscape elements that are difficult to explain without recourse to long-term landscape development. These relict features appear to have been little modified by the passage of ice, with their survival being

Figure 3.6. One of the large dolines that appears to pre-date the Late Devensian glaciation, in the Malham High Country karst (TW).

explained by cold, dry-based ice frozen to the bed so that it protected, rather than eroded, the landscape (Kleman, 1994; Kleman and Stroeven, 1997; Hall and Sugden, 1987; Fabel *et al.*, 2002; Goodfellow, 2007). Of particular note are the large karst dolines at elevations above 450m on the Malham High Country (Fig. 3.6); on the basis of their larger size and more mature morphology, these are regarded as significantly older than the much smaller dolines that have largely formed since the last glaciation (Clayton, 1966; Sweeting, 1972; O'Connor *et al.*, 1974; Gunn, 1985; Vincent, 1996; Goldie and Marker, 2001; Goldie, 2012). This does not mean that these areas were not covered by the ice sheet, but implies that they lay beneath passive, cold-based ice, which allowed preservation of the pre-Devensian landforms. Certain features of the Dales karst landscape may, therefore, have an ancient inheritance (Marker and Goldie, 2007), but no datable sediments or buried soils have yet been found within these depressions to confirm their ages (Goldie, 2012).

Research into other landscapes within the British Isles has also shown that landscape features previously thought to be of pre-glacial, implying Neogene, age may actually be much younger. For example, the Cairngorms form, at about 1300m, the highest low-relief plateau in eastern Scotland and which has been interpreted as a pre-glacial, Pliocene surface (Gordon and Sutherland, 1993; Hall and Phillips, 2006). However, these mountains are also known to have been a major centre for ice dispersal during the Pleistocene. Cosmogenic dates from the impressive tors that stand across the Cairngorm high plateau reveal that they are Mid-Pleistocene in age; however, by extrapolating erosion rates back in time, and taking into account tor burial and preservation under successive cold-based ice sheets, the landscape is thought to have begun to form around 1.3 Ma, thus disproving that they are pre-Quaternary landforms (Phillips *et al.*, 2006; Gordon, 2010). Given that the Cairngorms form the highest planation surface, the implication is that other such surfaces within the British Isles are younger than originally thought and also indicate more denudation than previously envisaged through the Late Cenozoic.

Nevertheless, this does agree with the time range proposed for cave development within the Yorkshire Dales (see Chapter 4). Initiation of the cave systems is thought to be associated with first exposure of the Great Scar Limestone at about 1.3 Ma, estimated from calculations of valley floor incision rates (see Chapter 4) based on a very small number of U-Th dates of old speleothems (Gascoyne *et al.*, 1983a, 1983b). The oldest currently available dated speleothem from the Dales comes from Victoria Cave and has an infinite date of >600 ka (Lundberg *et al.*, 2010).

Ice and landscape development

Global climate change with sufficient temperature cooling to allow expansion of the cryosphere in the Northern Hemisphere began in the Late Pliocene; the first ice-rafted debris in the North Atlantic deep sea record occurred at 2.6 Ma, marking the beginning of the Quaternary Period (Siegert, 2001; Catt *et al.*, 2006; Stone *et al.*, 2010; Lee, 2011; Böse *et al.*, 2012). This initiated an alternating sequence of glacial and interglacial cycles during the Early Pleistocene that were driven at Milankovitch periodicities, with the 41 ka obliquity

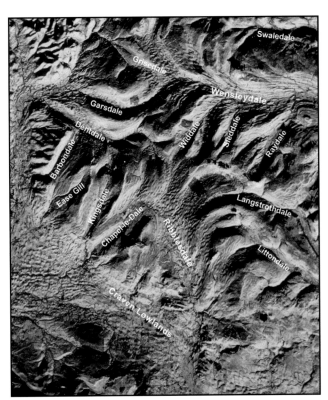

Figure 3.7. Landsat image identifying the main dales of the Craven Uplands on the southwestern corner of the Askrigg Block.

signal being the dominant harmonic (Thierens *et al.*, 2011). It appears that restricted, probably cold-based, ice masses developed over the mountain areas of the British Isles (Fig. 3.2), although the evidence for these is limited and mostly indirect (Clark *et al.*, 2004b; Lee *et al.*, 2012; Böse *et al.*, 2012). These upland areas were landscapes of selective linear glacial erosion and pre-glacial surface preservation, rather than widespread deposition, thereby preventing the establishment of lithostratigraphical sequences. However, some of these early ice sheets and valley glaciers appear to have reached the sea. Ice-rafted debris derived from the British Isles, recorded in marine sediment sequences from offshore northwest Scotland and southwest Ireland, can be dated to the earliest Pleistocene (Stoker *et al.*, 1994; Thierens *et al.*, 2011). In addition, the development of non-glacial, cold-climate processes, with periglacal activity and extensive permafrost, can also have a major impact on alpine and arctic landscape evolution far from any direct glacial influence. Such processes may occur independently of the presence of glacier ice, but are also known to have co-existed and interacted with glaciers (Harris and Murton, 2005; Etzelmüller and Hagen, 2005; Dobinski, 2011).

In the Yorkshire Dales, the most obvious modification of the pre-glacial landscape has been to the palaeo-drainage system (Kendall and Wroot, 1924; Clayton, 1966; Waltham, 1990) and its overprinting by large-scale glacial landforms. Over multiple glacial cycles, glacial erosion has modified the topography, particularly by over-deepening and widening the main valleys to form steep-sided, flat-floored dales with abrupt elevation changes to the plateau (Fig. 3.7). Lithological control can be observed clearly within these troughs, such that slope profiles are more complex than the classical U-shaped form. Limestone and sandstone units within the cyclic rocks of the Yoredale Group have been more resistant to glacier erosion than the interbedded shales, creating stepped cross-profiles within the northern dales (Fig. 3.8), notably in Wensleydale. The style and rate of glacial erosion can also be shown to relate to fracture spacing and strength variations between beds (Duhnforth *et al.*, 2010; Iverson 2012); this can be observed to good effect on the Great Scar Limestone where differential glacier quarrying has formed the terraced scars and benches so characteristic of the southern dales, notably Wharfedale and Chapel-le-Dale (Fig. 3.9), as well as more widely where overlying beds have been removed to create the surfaces that subsequently evolved into the extensive limestone pavements (see Chapter 5). With each successive glaciation, erosion became more focussed along the valleys where the ice was thicker and warmer (at pressure melting point), thereby increasing relative relief with respect to summit plateau elevation, and ultimately leading to the present distinctive landscape of the Dales. This periodic incision has been recorded in the development of the main cave systems at different elevations that reflect erosion and cave abandonment within successive glacial cycles, as incision proceeded with time (see Chapter 4).

Erosion in glaciated regions is primarily controlled by the basal thermal regimes of the glaciers and ice sheets, rather than by slope or elevation, with faster-moving, wet-based ice associated with valley incision, whereas the summit plateaus and interfluves are protected by non-erosive, cold-based ice (Staiger *et al.*, 2005; Kleman and Glasser, 2007). The juxtaposition of pre-glacial landscape elements and deeply incised valleys related to selective glacial erosion is reflected in many present mountain landscapes (Brocklehurst and Whipple, 2002; Brook *et al.*, 2008; Briner *et al.*, 2008; Glasser and Ghiglione, 2009). In such areas, deep glacial troughs are known to have played an important role in ice mass flux out of the ice sheet interior towards the ice margin, thereby controlling the mass balance of the ice sheet and its stability (Briner *et al.*, 2008). Valley modification by glacier ice was highly variable; this depended largely on the relationship of valley trend to ice flow direction, so that many valleys retained their pre-glacial fluvial form

Figure 3.8. A stepped hillside forming the flank of Wharfedale above Cray, created by rock terraces within the sequence of limestones, sandstones and shales of the Yoredale Group (TW).

Figure 3.9. The stepped profile of scars and benches on the side of Chapel-le-Dale, created by differential erosion of stronger and weaker beds within the Great Scar Limestone succession (TW).

in glaciated areas. Furthermore, in many mountain areas, glacier mass flux could not be maintained within pre-glacial valley systems; this resulted in the breaching of secondary cols and the formation of new diffluent troughs (Linton, 1951; Sugden, 1968).

In the Yorkshire Dales, the main valleys are incised more than 400m into the general upland surface, at about 700m, and are characterised by having side slopes and valley heads with slopes >15° (Fig. 3.10). The main troughs are well known because they are the prominent dales. By far the largest is Wensleydale (originally known as Yoredale), the prominent west–east valley where eastward ice flow was focussed along the line of a pre-glacial valley extending to a confluence with the Vale of York at Leeming. During deglaciation, this valley was abandoned by the River Ure which now flows southeastwards to cut through the Permian limestone escarpment at Hackfall Gorge, entering the Vale of York near Boroughbridge (Mitchell and Bridgland, 2011). In the upper part of Wensleydale, the tributary valleys of Snaizeholme and Cotterdale are also glacial troughs, indicating convergence of ice flow from the surrounding high plateaus, both north and south of the main valley (Fig. 3.5). However, the head of the main valley is more complex, with a low, glacial breach forming a wide col at Garsdale Head, linking Wensleydale to upper Garsdale. The northern part of the Ure catchment occupies a larger glacial breach, which forms the spectacular glacial trough of Mallerstang cut by north-flowing ice from an ice centre over Baugh Fell, which converged with south-flowing ice in the Vale of Eden to flow eastwards through Stainmore, a major conduit into eastern England (King, 1976; Mitchell, 1994). This valley is now occupied by the northwards-flowing River Eden, which has captured part of the Ure catchment because of glacial erosion and drumlin formation at Ais Gill (King, 1924; King 1976).

Nothing is known of ice flow patterns during early glaciations. However, from the landforms associated with the last glaciation, it seems that the Yorkshire Dales was

Figure 3.10. The deep and wide glaciated trough of Garsdale, looking westwards and down the valley towards Sedbergh (WM).

an area of complex ice flow, which, at ice sheet maxima, was independent of subglacial topography. Ice centres and divides migrated and even crossed dales, leading to up-valley flow in certain areas (Mitchell, 1994). This can be illustrated by the convergent pattern of drumlins in upper Wensleydale, which indicate that during the last glaciation, Baugh Fell developed a centre with ice divides extending along the present Swale-Ure watershed as well as across Garsdale to allow up-valley ice flow into Wensleydale (Mitchell and Riley, 2006; Mitchell and Hughes, 2012). In the well-developed trough of Mallerstang, to the north of a former ice divide, drumlins around Outhgill (Letzer, 1987) record northwards flow as part of the large drumlin field in the southern Vale of Eden that converges into Stainmore. Thus, the head of Wensleydale demonstrates that the pre-glacial drainage pattern was significantly influenced by glacial erosion, with modification of many major valleys and erosion of new valley systems.

In contrast, valleys that were orientated transverse to ice flow show relatively minimal signs of glacial erosion, and retain a fluvial form. For example, on the west side of Gragareth, Ease Gill occupies a typical fluvial valley where there is little indication that the valley was eroded by ice flowing southwards from Dentdale (Waltham, 2007); similarly the Walden valley was protected from glacial modification when Wharfedale ice was deflected south of Buckden Pike. Other valleys that have maintained an original fluvial form are now deeply incised, as their rivers became adjusted to more effective glacial deepening in the main

valleys that were aligned with ice flow; Pen-y-ghent Gill and Cowside Beck both show this with respect to their outflow into the glacially deepened Littondale (Fig. 3.11).

Ice flow also modified earlier valleys and formed deep troughs along the Dent Fault. The Rawthey valley was enlarged along the western side of Baugh Fell and a diffluent trough formed along the fault in Barbondale by ice unable to vacate lower Dentdale because of greater mass flux down Garsdale and the Rawthey valley (Fig. 3.12). Dentdale was modified into a trough, but the high ground at the head of the dale is problematic in terms of ice source areas. From drumlin distributions associated with the Main Late Devensian glaciation, it would appear that, at some stage, the ice sheet was independent of topography, and formed an ice divide across the middle of Dentdale. This allowed ice to flow up Deepdale and into Kingsdale, eastwards up Dentdale and over into Little Dale and Ribblesdale, as well as across the interfluve into upper Garsdale (Mitchell, 1991a, 1994; see below). Such a pattern is also likely to have occurred during earlier glacial events. However, it is probable that during times of less restricted glaciation, mountain icefields were topographically controlled over the highest plateau areas with outlet glaciers flowing into the different dales. Regrettably, there is no evidence to confirm these earlier patterns of ice flow.

South of Wensleydale, the broad valley pattern is dominated by Ribblesdale and Wharfedale, together with the latter's tributary Littondale (Fig. 3.13). Whereas the River Wharfe flows within a distinct glacial trough, the Ribble, by contrast, occupies a less incised valley eroded

Figure 3.11. The valley of Cowside Beck, off Littondale, was orientated transverse to ice sheet flow that crossed from left to right, infilling it with sediment on the sheltered up-glacier slope. In contrast, the opposite valley side (on the right) has limestone outcrops, including Yew Cogar Scar, related to possible glacial erosion, and subsequent talus development (TW).

Figure 3.12. The diffluent trough of Barbondale, enlarged by ice flow diverted out of Dentdale along the line of the Dent Fault (TW).

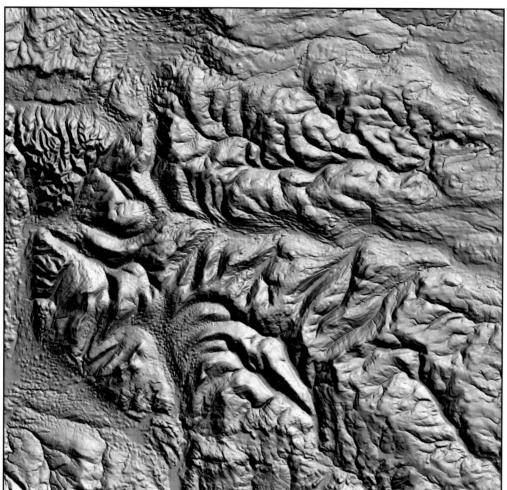

Figure 3.13. Digital Elevation Model of the Askrigg Block showing the major glacial troughs, the drumlin fields in Wensleydale and Ribblesdale as well in the surrounding lowlands, and the limited modification of Swaledale and upper Nidderdale by glacial erosion. The routes of Lake District and Scottish ice, up the Vale of Eden and east across Stainmore, and southeastwards along the Craven Lowlands, are identifiable north and south of the Askrigg Block respectively (base DEM from Land-Form Panorama, Ordnance Survey; Edina Digimaps/JISC).

Figure 3.14. Giggleswick Scar, on the South Craven Fault. This fault-line scarp was accentuated by glacial erosion where ice off the Craven Uplands, as part of a wider flow of ice down Ribblesdale, converged with Craven Lowlands ice that was flowing parallel with the line of the fault (TW).

into the extensive limestone benches of the Craven Uplands that extend from Ingleton eastwards to around Malham (Waltham, 1990). A series of through valleys extending southwards from Dodd Fell towards Pen-y-ghent indicate glacial breaching of the interfluve area between these two river systems at some stage. From the pattern of drumlins associated with the last glaciation, which is particularly well developed in the western part of these valleys, such as at Cam Houses and High Green Field, it is clear that this area formed an important eastern source area of Ribblesdale ice (Mitchell, 2008; Mitchell and Prescott, 2012; see below).

At the western edge of the Ribblesdale ice, Chapel-le-Dale was deeply incised as a separate diffluent trough between Ingleborough and Whernside, suggesting that its width-restricted ice flow was able to be an effective erosional agent leading to localised over-deepening within a wider Ribblesdale ice flow that submerged the entire area (Fig. 3.13) In conclusion, the overall pattern of these large scale polycyclic erosional features indicates that the Yorkshire Dales area was able to generate sufficient ice to form a topographically independent centre that stretched across the high ground from Baugh Fell towards Pen-y-ghent. It is also significant that the glaciated troughs, notably Ribblesdale, are much wider than the present river valleys and that ice flow was continuous across a landscape completely inundated by the ice sheet.

Along the southern edge of the Askrigg Block, the scarp of the Craven Fault Zone separates the Craven Uplands from the Craven Lowlands. Pleistocene ice moved obliquely

across the main faults, so the escarpments were overrun and are largely just broad slopes, unlike the Dent Fault where ice moved along its line and deepened the troughs. The exception is Giggleswick Scar, on the South Craven Fault where it is locally aligned so that ice moved obliquely across it; consequently it is a conspicuous and frequently cited example of a fault-line scarp (Huddart, 2002). Extending for more than 2 km, it forms a step that is up to 100m high between strong limestone to the north and weaker, drift-covered shales and sandstone to the south (Fig. 3.14). The high ground between Settle and Malham also reflects the interaction of lithology and structure, particularly with respect to the fault-guided valley at Victoria Cave and Attermire Scar (Fig 3.15). This 'freshness' may be taken to suggest tectonic activity in Late Cenozoic times, but is more likely due to the lithological contrast across it and to elements

Figure 3.15. Landform development in association with the Middle Craven Fault and Attermire Scar, with the peat bog of Attermire in the foreground (WM).

of quarrying by Devensian ice. However the area is still tectonically active; the Skipton earthquake of Magnitude 4.8 in 1944 was probably caused by movement on the Gargrave Fault, which diverges from the South Craven Fault southeast of the Scar (Versey, 1948).

Also reported from the limestone areas in the Yorkshire Dales are smaller-scale erosional forms that were overridden by Pleistocene ice sheets and glaciers (Sweeting, 1974; see Chapter 4). General reviews of glacier-karst interaction in Canada have produced a classification with respect to the hydrological disruption to karst development due to the presence of glacier ice and permafrost (Ford, 1987). Interaction between ice, and associated meltwater, may destroy, inhibit, preserve and stimulate karst to form a range of landforms and deposits in a range of glacial environmental settings both on the surface and within cave systems (Table 3.1; Chapter 4) This system is further complicated by the presence of ground freezing and the development of permafrost (Ford, 1987, 1993).

Evidence of early glaciations

The first terrestrial stratigraphical evidence in the British Isles for early glaciation can be gleaned from erratics found in river gravel sequences in lowland England; these indicate the former presence of glaciers in the upper river catchments of the Cambrian Mountains (Rose et al., 2001; Catt et al., 2006; Rose, 2009; Lee et al., 2012). Although the timing of these events and correlation to the Marine Isotope Stages (MIS) is poorly known, it is thought that the first significant glaciation occurred during the Baventian cold stage (MIS 68, starting at about 1.87 Ma) with the subsequent glaciations

during MIS 62–54, 54–36, 36, and 22 (Fig. 3.2) (Whiteman and Rose, 1992; Clark et al., 2004b; Lee, 2011; Lee et al., 2012; Böse et al., 2012). Given this information, it would seem likely that the upland areas of northern England would also have supported ice during these early glacial events.

In the British Isles, lithostratigraphical evidence for Middle Pleistocene glaciations is best developed in East Anglia, where there is evidence of multiple glaciations (Lee et al., 2012; Böse et al., 2012). Offshore, on the continental shelf, there is also a more complete sedimentary sequence of ice-rafted debris (Thierens et al., 2011). With respect to the Yorkshire Dales, the evidence is indirect; the evidence of extended ice sheets over southern and eastern England at various times, which were sourced within the British mountains, as demonstrated by evidence from erratic blocks, till geochemistry and plant spores, strongly suggest that the Pennines were an important source area (Rose, 2009; Scheib et al., 2011; Lee et al., 2012). In East Anglia, the oldest direct sedimentological evidence for a British ice sheet is the Happisburgh Till, which has been ascribed to a glaciation during MIS 16 (c.630 ka) (Lee et al., 2004; Rose, 2009), although this date is a matter of on-going controversy (Böse et al., 2012; Lee et al., 2012).

The later Anglian glaciation is widely accepted and constrained to MIS 12 (480–430 ka) by dates from underlying and overlying interglacial deposits (Lee, et al., 2012). This was the most extensive glaciation recorded for the British Isles, diverting the River Thames and destroying or diverting many river systems in lowland England (Rose, 2009). Upland areas of the British Isles, such as the Pennines, would have been completely buried by ice. There have been no attempts to reconstruct the vertical dimensions of the Anglian Ice Sheet; however, surface elevation may have been over 2000m. This is based on distance to the southern ice margin, assuming simplified thermal properties and basal stresses, and comparisons to the reconstructions for the later, smaller, MIS 2 British-Irish Ice Sheet, which has been modelled to have had a surface elevation of c.1500m (Boulton and Hagdorn, 2006; Hubbard et al., 2009). Pennine ice cover is confirmed by the presence of indicator erratics of Carboniferous rocks in the tills ('Older Drift') of the English Midlands (Clark et al., 2004b; Rose, 2009); these may be correlated with tills found in East Anglia (Rose, 2009; Lee et al., 2002, 2012), East Yorkshire and Lincolnshire (Catt, 2007), Derbyshire (Johnson, 1985; Burek, 1991; Aitkenhead et al., 2002; Huddart and Glasser, 2002; Rose, 2009), the Lake District (Stone et al., 2010) and

Effects of glaciers on karst

Destructive
Removal of karren, epikarst and shallow aquifers
Dissection of integrated cave systems by glacial valleys
Infilling of dolines and aggradation of springs
Injection of clastic debris and sediment into caves

Inhibitive
Bedrock shielded from dissolution by carbonate-rich till
Seal and confining of aquifers by clay-rich sediments

Stimulative
Inputs focussed by superimposed glacial streams
Spring elevations lowered by glacial entrenchment
Fissure opening by crustal unloading after deglaciation

Table 3.1. Effects of glaciers on karst terrains (after Ford, 1987).

County Durham (Davies *et al.*, 2011). However, whereas several Middle Pleistocene glacial stages are represented in the geological record, there is still debate regarding the number of tills, their stratigraphical significance and their correlation with the MIS record (Clark *et al.*, 2004b; Rose, 2009; Böse *et al.*, 2012; Lee, *et al.*, 2012).

Within the Craven Dales, the most important speleothem record is currently from Victoria Cave where new uranium-thorium dates support a climatic signal from the Middle Pleistocene (Murphy and Lord, 2003; Lundberg *et al.*, 2010; Lord *et al.*, 2012). A hiatus in flowstone growth between those dating from MIS 13 (c.500 ka) and MIS 11 (c.410 ka) in Victoria Cave is thought to record a major glacial event during MIS 12; this has been correlated with the terrestrial evidence for the Anglian Glaciation. Further evidence is to be found from the presence of laminated clays within the cave; these have been interpreted as reworked loess deposited in glacier-impounded lakes within the cave during glaciations (Lundberg *et al.*, 2010). These clays are interbedded with dated flowstones that are thought to indicate the nearby presence of ice during MIS 12, 10, 6 and 2 but not MIS 8. While the first of these clays can be clearly correlated to the Anglian Glacial Stage, the later event MIS 10 is poorly constrained and un-named in the terrestrial record; certain tills in the English Midlands have been re-interpreted and correlated to MIS 10 (Rose, 2009), and new evidence from the Trent valley demonstrates that the Wragby Till can be ascribed to MIS 8 (White *et al.*, 2010). The presence of a hiatus in one of the speleothem samples from Victoria Cave has been ascribed to MIS 8 (Gascoyne, 1981), but this was to a marine chronology that has since been revised.

The record for glaciation in Victoria Cave, MIS 6, has been previously ascribed to the now discredited 'Wolstonian Stage' of the British stratigraphy (Jones and Keen, 1993; Bowen, 1999; Rose, 2009). Much of the glacial evidence for the 'Wolstonian' is now convincingly correlated to the Anglian Glaciation in MIS 12 or to the MIS 10 event (Lee *et al.*, 2012). Any identification of the MIS 6 glaciation in the East Anglian geological record remains controversial (Böse *et al.*, 2012). An alternative informal name of the

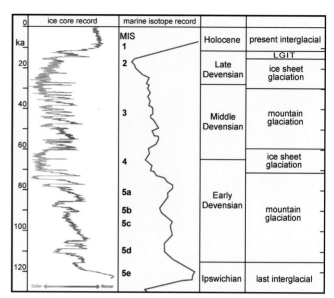

Figure 3.17. Stacked marine oxygen isotope and ice core records for the Devensian Stage of the British climatostratigraphy, with the styles of glaciation (MIS 5d-2); LGIT is the Last Glacial-Interglacial Transition (after Lowe and Walker, 2007; Merritt et al., 2003).

'Tottenhill Glaciation' may be applied to the MIS 6 glacial stage, based on evidence from a quarry of that name (Rose, 2009). However, although the evidence for a glacial event at this time may be unclear in East Anglia, tills further north in eastern England are thought to be of MIS 6 age; these include the Basement Till in Holderness (Clark *et al.*, 2004b; Catt, 2007), Lincolnshire tills (Straw, 1983), weathered tills in the Yorkshire Wolds and South Pennines (Johnson, 1985; Huddart and Glasser, 2002) and basal tills recovered from boreholes in the Cumbrian lowlands (Merritt and Auton, 2000; Stone *et al.*, 2010). Buried glacial deposits in lowland Buchan, in northeast Scotland, have also been ascribed to this cold stage (Merritt *et al.*, 2003), and there is new evidence for MIS 6 ice-rafted debris in glacio-marine sediments offshore from northwest Scotland (Hibbert *et al.*, 2010). Cold conditions in MIS 6, with inferred glaciation, are indicated by the speleothem hiatus at 160–150 ka recorded in a number of Dales caves (Fig. 3.16). Although there is much debate about the southern and eastern extent of the MIS 6 ice sheet, there is sufficient geological information to suggest that there was an ice sheet during this time, and that it covered most of northern England. What it should be called is a matter for discussion.

The climate of the Yorkshire Dales during the succeeding Ipswichian Interglacial was sufficiently warm and temperate for bones of hippopotamus, regarded as the representative animal for this interglacial, to have been preserved in Victoria Cave (Gascoyne *et al.*, 1981; Baker *et al.*, 1993; see Chapter 15) and near Leeds (Cooper and Gibson, 2003). This is reflected in a period of maximum growth in the speleothem record spanning 130–100 ka (Fig. 3.16).

The Last (Devensian) cold stage

In contrast to the limited evidence for earlier Quaternary events, there is an extensive record in the geomorphology, landforms and sediments of the last cold stage in northern England (Johnson, 1985; Huddart and Glasser, 2002; Catt *et al.*, 2006). This cold stage is known to have occurred from

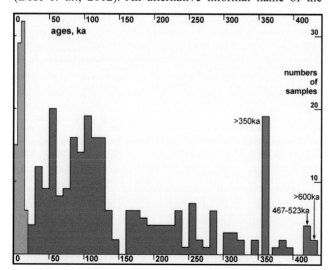

Figure 3.16. Age-frequency distribution for speleothem distribution by uranium–thorium ages, showing growth periods within a number of Craven caves; error bars are ±1σ on dates nearest to the base and top of each speleothem (see Chapter 10 for sources).

the end of the last interglacial (Ipswichian; MIS 5e) at c.115 ka through to the final termination of glacial conditions at the end of MIS 2 at 11.7 ka (Stone *et al.*, 2010). Marine Isotope Stages 5d to 2 cover about 100,000 years, and are collectively known as the Devensian Stage in Britain (Fig. 3.17). The early part of this stage probably did not witness the presence of glaciers; rather, it was a period of declining temperatures that was characterised by periglacial processes operating in a widespread tundra environment, punctuated by the two short, warmer interludes of the Chelford Interstadial, in MIS 5c at around 90 ka, and the Brimpton Interstadial, in MIS 5a at around 70 ka. Uranium–thorium dating from a number of Yorkshire Dales caves reveals a complex climate signal during the early part of the Devensian Stage, with speleothem growth correlated with solar insolation changes at sub-Milankovitch timescales (Baker *et al.*, 1993, 1995). Stump Cross Caverns contain an important record of dated flowstones, and a fauna dominated by wolverine and reindeer has been recovered from the cave to demonstrate that a cold environment had become established by late MIS 5 (c.83 ka). This was much colder than that during the Ipswichian Interglacial, which is characterised by the temperate fauna recorded in Victoria Cave (Sutcliffe *et al.*, 1985).

Glacial conditions occurred during MIS 4 (c.71–59 ka). Evidence from a number of sites in the lowlands adjacent to the Pennines and beyond suggest that glaciers developed in mountain areas during this stadial, along with the expansion of a lowland ice sheet of limited size; however, these sediments are poorly dated and much of the evidence remains equivocal (Worsley, 1991; Jones and Keen, 1993; Ballantyne

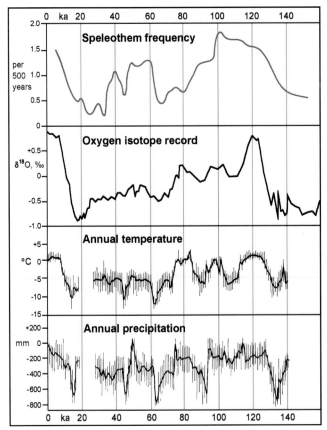

Figure 3.18. Growth frequency curves for speleothems from across northwest Europe correlated with palaeoclimatic events from the marine oxygen isotope record and the pollen record from Grand Pile, France, during the last glacial stage (after Baker et al., 1993).

and Harris, 1994; Huddart and Glasser, 2002; Clark *et al.*, 2004b). Farther afield, diamictons reported from boreholes around Sellafield in west Cumbria have been ascribed to this period (Merritt and Auton, 2000; Stone *et al.*, 2010), as have glacial deposits in east Lincolnshire and Yorkshire (Straw, 1991; Clark *et al.*, 2004b). In northeast Scotland, a number of tills found in lowland Buchan have also been interpreted to be of early Devensian age because of their stratigraphical position (Merritt *et al.*, 2003). Records of ice-rafted debris from offshore northwest Scotland and in the North Sea clearly indicate an extensive glaciation at this time (Hibbert *et al.*, 2010; Carr, 2004; Sejrup *et al.*, 2005, 2009).

The speleothem record (Fig. 3.16) from the Dales caves is ambiguous for the Early Devensian sub-stage, with no definite break in growth that might correlate to a glacial period, though evidence of limited growth clearly reflects cold, periglacial conditions (Gascoyne *et al.*, 1983a, 1983b). A short district-wide hiatus in speleothem growth has been dated to 105 ka, and may mark a rapid but short climatic deterioration (Gascoyne *et al.*, 1983a); however, the reported age-range is wider than the average value, which means these dates require a revised interpretation (Mitchell, 2012a). A review of palaeoclimate from the last interglacial, derived from speleothem dates in northwest Europe, including the Yorkshire Dales, shows a series of peaks and troughs in the frequency of dates that can be correlated with the MIS record (Fig 3.18). This identifies high frequencies of dates from MIS 5 and from the Holocene, with the first major reduction at c.70 ka; this is second only to the reduction that marks the later Last Glacial Maximum, and indicates severe cold climate at a time that may correlate with a glaciation in MIS 4 (Baker *et al.*, 1993).

The Middle Devensian (MIS 3 at 59–27.5 ka) is marked by a complex series of climate oscillations that culminate in the cool, temperate conditions of the Upton Warren Interstadial from 50 to 38 ka (Huddart and Glasser, 2002; Catt *et al.*, 2006; Stone *et al.*, 2010). The MIS 3 stage is reflected in the speleothem record as a period of declining growth rates (Gascoyne *et al.*, 1983a). The growth frequency curves (Fig 3.18) show a number of discrete climatic events that can be correlated to the marine record and to the Grand Pile pollen record in eastern France (Baker *et al.*, 1993). These suggest that MIS 3 can be divided into three units – two periods of enhanced growth (62–49 ka and 42–35 ka) that mark temperate, wet conditions, separated by a short period of below-average growth indicating cold, dry conditions. Declines in growth rates may also reflect the possible existence of permafrost during this period, which is compatible with the discovery of ice-wedge casts in sediments thought to be of this age (Jones and Keen, 1993). Such cold climate is confirmed by various other records, particularly the coleopteran (beetle) record that indicates tundra-like, dry-continental environments at this time (Lowe and Walker, 1997).

The widespread distribution of sites with radiocarbon dates of around 30 ka for organic material beneath till indicates that much of the British Isles was ice-free by this time (Hughes *et al.*, 2011). However, a continued, if minimal, influx of ice-rafted debris to the marine sediments west of Ireland suggests the existence of restricted mountain glaciation during MIS 3 (Hibbert *et al.*, 2010; Chiverrell and Thomas, 2010). The reported absence of dates between 34 and 13 ka (Gascoyne *et al.*, 1983a) and also between 26 and 14 ka (Atkinson *et al.*, 1986) indicate that environmental conditions were not conducive for speleothem growth during the period of maximum Devensian glaciation during MIS 2.

The last British-Irish Ice Sheet

The lowest temperatures reconstructed during the Devensian Stage occurred towards the end of the period during MIS 2, when continental-scale ice sheets reached their greatest extent, in the period known as the Last Glacial Maximum, between 26.5 and 19 ka (P Clark *et al.*, 2009). In the British chronostratigraphy, this is known as the Dimlington Stadial (Rose, 1985). The Main Late Devensian ice sheet was a relatively small ice mass in comparison to others, particularly that over North America. However, the relatively smaller size of the British–Irish Ice Sheet (BIIS) meant that it was highly sensitive to climatic and marine influences, and it was therefore an extremely responsive and dynamic ice sheet. New dating techniques and digital elevation models have allowed revised reconstructions of the extent, thickness and time-transgressive nature of its ice advances and retreats (Bradwell *et al.*, 2008a; Ballantyne, 2010; Hubbard *et al.*, 2009; Chiverrell and Thomas, 2010; McCarroll *et al.*, 2010; Hughes *et al.*, 2011; Clark *et al.*, 2012). These have amended dramatically traditional, spatially-restricted views of the BIIS (Bowen *et al.*, 2002; Boulton and Hagdorn, 2006). Furthermore, high-resolution computer simulations of the ice sheet, baesed on climatic parameters from the NGRIP ice core in Greenland, have shown a highly dynamic model with ice sheet behaviour driven by a series of binge-purge cycles in keeping with the stadial-interstadial record of GICC05 (Hubbard, *et al.*, 2009). These reconstructions show that the ice sheet accumulated mass slowly under stadial conditions, and then rapidly lost mass during warmer interstadials (Hubbard *et al.*, 2009).

It is now believed that, during the Last Glacial Maximum (LGM), the British-Irish Ice Sheet reached the Atlantic shelf edge (Scourse *et al.*, 2009) and coalesced with the Fennoscandian Ice Sheet in the North Sea basin (Sejrup *et al.*, 2005; Bradwell *et al.*, 2008a; Clark *et al.*, 2012); the southern part of the basin was occupied by extended river

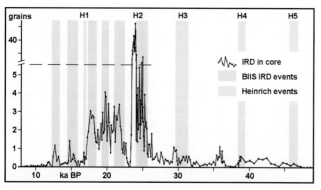

Figure 3.19*. Last glaciation IRD flux resulting from BIIS (British Irish Ice Sheet) activity as recorded from core MD01 2461 from the Porcupine Bank, southwest of Ireland. The grey bars define peaks in IRD activity related to an expanded BIIS ice sheet with marine margins. Heinrich events (H) indicate major inputs of IRD into the north Atlantic from the Laurentide Ice sheet on North America (after Peck et al., 2007; Scourse et al., 2009).*

systems draining much of northern Europe, with a river outlet on the line of the English Channel (Toucanne *et al.*, 2010). Onshore, radiocarbon dates from organic sediments beneath till show that lowland west-central Scotland, close to the former main ice centre, remained ice-free as late as 36.5 ka, although it is likely that there were icefields in the nearby mountains; this constrains the period of ice sheet build-up (Bos *et al.*, 2004: Brown *et al.*, 2006; Finlayson *et al.*, 2010). Marine sedimentary records demonstrate a step-wise increase of ice-rafted debris within the large submarine fans off western Ireland and Scotland dated at 27.4 ka (Hibbert *et al.*, 2010), indicating that the ice sheet had reached the shelf edge by this time (Fig. 3.19). It therefore appears that the last British-Irish Ice Sheet began to develop in the latter part of MIS 3, at a time when climate was deteriorating towards the intense cold of MIS 2 (Hubbard *et al.*, 2009). This major cooling allowed pre-existing ice caps to expand out of the mountains and flow into the surrounding lowlands and off-shore; they coalesced as a single ice sheet that reached its maximum extent over northern Britain around 27 ka (Clark *et al.*, 2012).

Reconstructions of the British–Irish Ice Sheet now portray the ice sheet as having been thick enough to cover, with no nunataks or ice-free areas, all of the land mass of Britain and Ireland north of the well-established ice sheet margin across central England and southern Wales (Catt *et al.*, 2006; Mitchell and Bridgland, 2011; Clark *et al.*, 2012) (Fig. 3.20). Computer-generated reconstructions of the ice sheet, based on ice core temperatures, suggest a range of ice surface elevation values depending on the controlling glaciological factors of basal shear stress, ice temperature and velocity. The suggested elevations these range from >2000m (Boulton and Hagdorn, 2006) to c.1500m (Hubbard *et al.*, 2009; Evans et al., 2009). This would suggest that the Dales ice may have been > 800m thick over the plateau and > 1000m thick over the valleys. However, it is noted that such boundary constraints are difficult to compute within 'forward-marching, time-dependent' models (Hubbard, *et al.*, 2009, p. 764).

Advance of the British–Irish Ice Sheet to its maximum limit is now known to have been asynchronous around its margin, with a highly responsive reaction to changes in mass, and interacting with periods of rapidly rising relative sea level (P Clark *et al.*, 2009). Along the north-western seaboard, the ice sheet reached its maximum extent around 27 ka (Bradwell *et al.*, 2008a), whereas the Irish Sea Ice Stream did not reach its maximum extent, at the Scilly Isles, until after 24.2 ka (Hiemstra *et al.*, 2006; Scourse, 2006; O'Cofaigh and Evans, 2007; Clark *et al.*, 2012). Across northern England, it appears that the maximum ice advance to limits in the Cheshire Lowlands and Vale of York may not have occurred until after 23 ka (Clark *et al.*, 2012), and an even younger advance has been recorded from East Coast ice in Holderness as occurring after 21.7 ka (Bateman *et al.*, 2001). This diachronous behaviour may reflect marine-ice-sheet interactions along the western seaboard of the British Isles, which resulted in increased calving after 23 ka (Scourse *et al.*, 2009). At about the same time, unzipping of the Fennoscandinavian and British ice sheets across the site of the central North Sea (Bradwell *et al.*, 2008a; Hubbard *et*

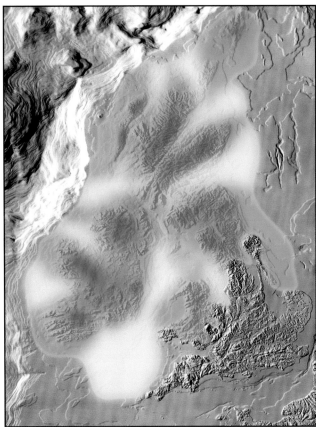

Figure 3.20. Reconstruction of the last British-Irish Ice Sheet, using data from various sources to show the maximum extent of the ice sheet, but not at any one specific time, given the known asynchronous behaviour of different ice sheet sectors. Source areas are darker blue, and possible ice streams are whiter. The eastern boundary is the confluence with the Scandinavian Ice Sheet (after Mitchell and Bridgland, 2011) (DEM from Mountain High Maps).

al., 2009) heralded the beginning of ice sheet self-destruction (Hughes, 2011). Fragmentation and retreat of the British–Irish Ice Sheet continued from about 19 ka through to 14.7 ka with rapid retreat, particularly along marine margins (Hubbard et al., 2009). Retreat of the ice margin into the mountain source areas of both Britain and Ireland was punctuated by still-stands or re-advances along various parts of the margin as ice source areas re-organised on a regional scale. Earliest dates for deglaciation are recorded from many lowland areas, as well as from some of the highest peaks that were exposed at an early stage due to thinning of the ice sheet (Ballantyne, 2010; Hughes et al., 2011).

It is now clear that the ice sheet had multiple source zones centred over the mountain areas of the British Isles, with a major ice divide extending from Ireland to the Scottish Highlands (Evans et al., 2005; Boulton and Hagdorn, 2006; Clark et al., 2012). Ice source areas and their intervening ice divides, originally envisaged as stationary (Boulton et al., 1977, 1985), are now known to be have been dynamic in time and space. Drawdown along marine margins and temporal variations in the importance of competing accumulation areas resulted in the shutdown of some regional ice centres and the associated migration of ice divides (Mitchell, 1994; Boulton and Hagdorn, 2006; Hubbard et al., 2009; Finlayson et al., 2010). As ice cleared from the lowlands, source areas reacted in different ways, with local or regional ice flows switching into ground vacated by ice from more distant

sources (Hubbard et al., 2009; Clark et al., 2012). Thus the present landscape is a suite of glacial landforms, with younger features superimposed on older features to reflect complex flow-switching over short timescales between different ice source areas through the course of a glacial event (Evans et al., 2009).

Research on present day ice sheets, and the now-exposed beds of former ice sheets, has shown that ice streams are characteristic glaciological features defined by linear zones of relatively faster flow (Bennett, 2003). Pleistocene ice streams formed important mass flux conduits that transferred ice towards predominantly marine margins (Stokes and Clark, 1999, 2002; Winsborrow et al., 2010). Their rapid flow reflected critical thermal conditions at the base of the ice sheet, which was at its pressure melting point beneath the temperate, warm-based, ice. In marked contrast, the much slower or immobile ice that formed greater areas of the ice sheet was cold-based, with its basal ice frozen onto the surface of the rock beneath. Subglacial thermal regimes were highly dynamic and changed in time and space; locations of the constraining ice stream were a consequence of interaction between topography, subglacial geology, geothermal heat flux and meltwater routing (Jansson and Glasser, 2005; Kleman and Glasser, 2007). High-resolution satellite imagery and digital elevation models have also allowed better understanding of the large-scale evolution and demise of the British–Irish Ice Sheet, into which regional descriptions and reconstructions can better be assessed (Bradwell et al., 2008a; Evans et al., 2009; Livingstone et al., 2010, 2012).

Identifying the former location of ice streams has been shown to be important in reconstructing ice sheets, as their presence has a direct effect on configuration, thermal character and sediment flux. Using characteristic features of present ice streams, a number of geomorphological features, particularly drumlins and moraines, can be identified and used to establish palaeo-ice stream signatures (Stokes and Clark, 1999). Of particular note are the characteristic convergent flow pattern of drumlin fields, which indicate ice stream accumulation and initiation zones, and the presence of attenuated bedforms that indicate fast flow. The formation of lateral and/or shear moraines have been also been used to define ice stream margins. Reconstructed dimensions shows that length and width of ice streams are in ratio to the size of the former ice sheet (Stokes and Clark, 2002); thus the British–Irish Ice Sheet ice streams were smaller than those identified in the larger ice sheets. Such reconstructions have also required an emphasis on the regional character of the former ice sheet, given that ice stream accumulation zones are commonly an assemblage of numerous converging valleys. This is clearly the case in the Dales, where many of the smaller valleys are but individual components of accumulations into larger ice streams.

Periglacial trimlines, previously thought to define the upper limit of the Main Late Devensian ice sheet in many British and Irish mountains (Ballantyne et al., 1998, 2006, 2008), are now interpreted as internal, thermal divisions between temperate ice and cold ice (Boulton and Hagdorn, 2006; Ballantyne, 2010). This means that the conflict between trimline data, indicating thinner ice, and the offshore evidence

Figure 3.21. East Baugh Fell, with the edge of the high plateau above 600m that formed the main source area of the last ice sheet, seen from the Coal Road above Garsdale Head. Drumlins on the lower moorland slopes, above the cultivated fields, relate to ice flow that was up Garsdale (from the left) and into upper Wensleydale (WM).

for a more expansive, thicker ice sheet is resolved in favour of the latter. However, the trimline may also reflect a major period of internal re-organization of the ice sheet following the Last Glacial Maximum. Cosmogenic dates derived from bedrock or boulders indicate an age of <21 ka for the trimline, assuming it is a single feature (Ballantyne, 2010). However, this period also equates to the first rapid rise in relative sea level and the beginning of deglaciation at c.20 ka (P Clark *et al.,* 2009; Denton *et al.,* 2010). This change in relative sea level would have triggered an acceleration of ice stream velocities in response to increased calving along marine ice margins; this led to drawdown and vertical thinning that formed a series of regional trimlines, prior to the cleaving into separate Irish and British domes at c.19 ka (Hubbard, *et al.,* 2009; Clark *et al.,* 2012).

Devensian glaciation of the Yorkshire Dales

As in previous glaciations, the Yorkshire Dales were enlarged and re-shaped by selective glacial erosion along the major valleys that acted as topographical focus zones for mass transfer of ice and for enhanced erosion by meltwater. Thicker ice within the dales was at pressure melting point, thereby generating a film of water, which was further enhanced by percolation of surface meltwater that had been formed by ablation. This resulted in lubrication of the subglacial interface, whether underlying bedrock or sediments, and so led to enhanced basal flow rates. During the last glaciation, the Dales area was completely submerged by the ice sheet, which flowed independently of topographical influence with ice streams extending over large areas of the uplands and not confined within the dales (Mitchell, 1994; Mitchell and Hughes, 2012). Only during the early stages of glaciation, when the ice was building up over the high plateaus, and subsequently during deglaciation, when topography again guided the pattern of ice recession, did the dales contain alpine-style valley glaciers flowing between rock walls.

The Dales Ice Centre

It has long been established that the western Pennines were able to establish their own ice centre over the extensive high ground (>600m) of Baugh Fell and Wild Boar Fell, around the head of Wensleydale (Fig. 3.21). This was deduced from the evidence of glacial sediments, striations and surface erratics (Goodchild, 1875; Dakyns *et al.,* 1890, 1891; Carvill Lewis, 1894), though the phrase, Dales Ice Centre, was proposed by King in 1976. Similar data showed that adjacent lowlands to the west and south were also crossed by ice that emanated from more distant source areas in southern Scotland and the Lake District, as well as from the Dales (Aveline *et al.,* 1872; Aveline and Hughes, 1888; Tiddeman, 1872). North of the Askrigg Block, the major gap through the Pennines at Stainmore was shown to have been occupied by converging ice from Scotland and the Lake District that was deflected east by local ice over the Howgill Fells and Pennines (Goodchild, 1875). This ice flow is particularly marked by the distinct limit to the distribution of Shap Granite erratics from the eastern Lake District along the southern side of Stainmore, where local Pennine ice was deflected southeastwards into Arkengarthdale. In the Vale of York, ice from the Dales, particularly from Wensleydale (Fig. 3.22), coalesced with ice moving southeastwards through Stainmore and southwards from County Durham to form a large and complex lobe terminating at the moraine ridges at Escrick and York (Carvill Lewis, 1894).

Within the Pennines, striations indicate ice flow down the main valleys, but they also show a more general eastwards flow across the high ground at altitudes of 600–700m (Goodchild, 1875; Dakyns *et al.,* 1891). Early reconstructions of flow directions assumed that the ice was topographically controlled at lower elevations, within the valleys, but was able to flow in different directions in the upper levels; this was required to explain the apparent radial flow pattern that involved ice flowing up certain tributary valleys (Goodchild,

Figure 3.22. The broad sweep of Wensleydale, showing the overall glaciated, streamlined landscape, looking southwards towards Widdale from the Muker road across the drift tail that diverts Hearne Beck (WM).

1875, 1887). The early Geological Survey Memoirs (Aveline and Hughes, 1888; Dakyns *et al.,* 1890, 1891) included regional synthesis and summary of the superficial deposits with an emphasis on the drift, including the first mention of drumlins and drift tails (see below). Problematic striations in upper Garsdale questioned the accepted idea that ice flow was generally down valley and were taken to demonstrate that the ice sheet was able to flow independently of topography, with ice flow across and up pre-existing valleys (Dakyns *et al.,* 1891). At that time, ice sheet reconstructions tended to focus on the idea of a large single dome covering northern Britain, and down-played the evidence for local ice centres as features of deglaciation.

With major land-based ice sheets across northern Britain established in concept, attention became focussed on detailed interpretation of the landforms to explain landscape evolution associated with the glaciation. In Yorkshire, this was led by the classic paper on the meltwater channels of the Cleveland Hills (Kendall, 1902), which interpreted their origins as a result of glacial lake overflow. Meltwater channel systems in the eastern Dales were subsequently also described as overflow systems from multiple lakes (Kendall and Wroot, 1924). This model was applied to many areas within Britain and beyond, until reassessment led to their interpretation as being formed within subglacial and marginal glacier environments (Sissons, 1960, 1961; Johnson, 1985).

Within the Yorkshire Dales, Kendall's model of overflow channels was developed and amended by his former research student, Arthur Raistrick, whose unpublished doctoral thesis (in 1925) included the first detailed geomorphological mapping of the glacial landforms in the Dales. Whereas the initial work related to Swaledale and Wensleydale, it was later expanded to cover much of the Askrigg Block (Raistrick, 13 papers from 1926 to 1954c), as well as elsewhere in northern England (Raistrick, 1931c). This research also included the first pollen investigations of upland peats in the Pennines (Raistrick and Blackburn, 1931, 1933). The geomorphological papers concentrated less on striations but more on the drift distribution. Prominent landforms, including drumlins and moraine ridges, were mapped, as well as the pattern of 'overflow channels', while also acknowledging the existence of a further suite of meltwater channels that could be explained by formation at lateral ice margins (Raistrick, 1926). This allowed a better reconstruction of ice flow patterns and first placed emphasis on understanding the recessional sequence during the deglaciation of northern England. Regrettably, because of concept changes with respect to the origin of many of the meltwater channels as lake overflows, much of the glacial pattern and deglacial sequence within the Dales still awaits detailed re-mapping. Only then, can the channels be re-evaluated within current concepts of deglaciation.

Raistrick's field mapping (Fig. 3.23) confirmed the earlier work regarding a local ice centre during the glacial maximum. He proposed that ice flow had radiated from an ice centre over Mallerstang, and had crossed the high fells independently of topography, while the lower flow was constrained within the valleys (Raistrick, 1926, 1930). There was a greater focus on the 'drift' distribution, with a classification into upper, high-altitude gravel that differed

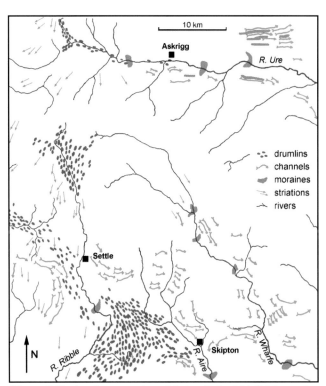

Figure 3.23. *A redrawn version of Arthur Raistrick's field mapping of glacial landforms across the Craven Dales (after Raistrick, 1933).*

from the 'boulder clay' (till) observed in the lower parts of the valleys. These sediments were also differentiated from the materials that formed discrete glacial landforms, notably the drumlin fields that are such a characteristic of many parts of the Dales, as well as fragments of lateral and terminal moraine ridges. This was the first detailed description of the glacial landforms, noting their development in upper Wensleydale and eastwards to Aysgarth as well as identifying drift tails at the different tributary valley confluences (Raistrick, 1926). The drumlins in Ribblesdale and farther south, between Settle and Skipton, (Fig. 3.23) were described later (Raistrick, 1930, 1933), as were the glacial landforms in Wharfedale down to its confluence with Vale of York ice at Wetherby (Raistrick, 1931a). Mapping of drumlins and glacial geology in the Vale of Eden and northern Pennines (Trotter, 1929; Hollingworth, 1931; Trotter and Hollingworth, 1932) was employed to correlate glacial events in the Yorkshire Dales with those in a wider area of northern England and with the complex lithostratigraphy in Holderness (Raistrick, 1931b, 1933, 1934, 1954a).

The thinness of the drift over the high ground, its weathered nature and its local absence were used to define the presence and extent of nunataks (unglaciated areas) that stood above the ice sheet surface, particularly between Wensleydale, Wharfedale and Nidderdale (Raistrick, 1926). However, this interpretation was published before present understanding of the protective role of cold ice; current reconstructions of the Main Late Devensian Ice Sheet indicate that the ice was thicker and covered all the upland surfaces (Mitchell and Hughes, 2012). With respect to present understanding of glacial thermal regimes, the high fells are better explained as preserved surfaces buried by cold-based ice that was capable of only minimal erosion or deposition. Similar passive conditions would also have occurred in the vicinity of ice divides. However, it should be noted that drumlins do occur

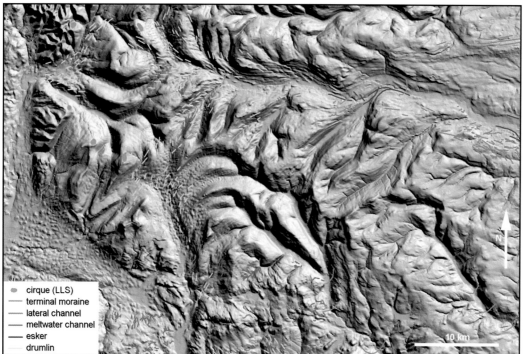

Figure 3.24. Digital Elevation Model with terminal moraines, lateral channels, subglacial and postglacial meltwater channels, drumlins and eskers recorded as layers within the BRITICE GIS database (Clark et al., 2004). Locations of the five niche glaciers, that developed during the Loch Lomond Stadial, are also marked (base DEM from Land-Form Panorama, Ordnance Survey; Edina Digimaps/ JISC).

at high elevations on interfluves, indicating that such areas were also subject to bed deformation at some time during the glaciation (Mitchell, 1994). The thicker ice within the dales was largely temperate in character, with its base at pressure melting point, thereby allowing the production of meltwater that lubricated the bed. This generated faster ice flow, which caused basal ice-sediment deformation to form drumlins where there was sufficient easily eroded bedrock to form subglacial sediment. A broad picture of the glacial patterns and events is presented in the geomorphological maps from the BRITICE project (Clark *et al.,* 2004a; Evans *et al.,* 2005), where landforms have been recorded within a GIS database that includes digital elevation models (Fig. 3.24).

Ice sheet landforms

Drumlins are distinctive features across many parts of the Yorkshire Dales (Mitchell, 1994). They are particularly well-known where extensive drumlin fields form 'basket of eggs' topography in and around upper Wensleydale and upper Ribblesdale (Figs 3.25, 3.26). Current understanding of their genesis suggests formation as glacial bedforms resulting from deformation of the subglacial sediment load, and they form an important indicator of the direction of former ice flow (Boulton, 1987; Clark *et al.,* 2009; Hughes *et al.,* 2010). In the Dales, the most extensive drumlin swarms tend to occur where shales and mudstones of the Yoredale Group, and the Namurian succession, could be easily eroded and entrained into the basal ice, so that subsequent sediment deformation could create these bedforms (Mitchell and Hughes, 2012). It is important to note that drumlins occur not only in the lower dales but also across interfluves; they lie at elevations up to 667m around upper Wensleydale (Mitchell, 1994) and at around 600m at the head of Coverdale (Hughes *et al.,* 2010; Mitchell and Hughes. 2012). This clearly demonstrates that

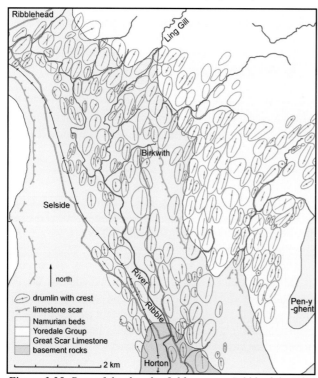

Figure 3.25. Part of the drumlin field in upper Ribblesdale (after Mitchell and Prescott, 2012).

Figure 3.26. The drumlins at Ribblehead aligned on both sides of Chapel-le-Dale, at both ends of the viaduct, with the bare limestone bench of Scar Close extending off the left foreground (WM).

Figure 3.27. The streamlined interfluve with multiple drumlins between Grisedale and Wensleydale at Garsdale Head (WM).

the Devensian ice sheet was thick enough to cover the high fells, including Widdale Fell and Abbotside Common, and was warm-based for at least part of the Late Devensian stage when ice was flowing independently of topography (Mitchell, 1991a, 1994; Mitchell and Hughes, 2012).

In the Yorkshire Dales, drumlins commonly occur in association with drumlinoid drift tails (Fig. 3.27) that formed at valley confluences between main-valley and tributary ice (Raistrick, 1926, Embleton and King, 1975; King, 1976; Mitchell, 1994). These tend to form multiple streamlined ridges that reflect bedrock preservation beneath a thin sediment cover due to differential glacial erosion between the main valley and the tributaries. In upper Wensleydale, they are particularly well-developed and have diverted tributary streams along both sides of the dale (Dakyns *et al.,* 1891; King, 1976). The mouth of Cotterdale has five drumlinoid ridges that extend eastwards from the bedrock interfluve of Cotter End (Figs. 3.28). These mostly have indistinct up-glacier edges, become more streamlined eastwards, and have smaller discrete drumlins on their crest. A further complex of drift tails marks the interfluve between Wensleydale and its southern tributary of Widdale. As with individual drumlins, these indicate former ice flow direction and are part of the wider convergence pattern that characterises

Figure 3.30. The wide limestone pavements above Southerscales, that were eroded by ice flowing down Chapel-le-Dale, away from the camera and right of Ingleborough's summit mass (TW).

upper Wensleydale (Fig. 3.31) (Mitchell, 1994; Mitchell and Hughes, 2012). Such long ridges, separated by series of meltwater channels, are numerous in the Dales where valley confluences are diverted down-ice. Drift tails can also be discerned along the southern edge of the Craven Uplands, but have not been mapped in detail.

It is no coincidence that extensive drumlin fields are generally absent in the southern Craven Uplands where the bedrock is predominantly limestone. Reduced sediment load, away from the mudstones, as well as changes in bedrock permeability, trapped water at the ice/bedrock surface, leading to faster, unconfined ice flow; this changed the dominant subglacial process to erosion, with quarrying of individual limestone beds aided by bedrock fractures (Iverson, 2012). From outcrops newly exposed from beneath sediments, it can be shown that these surfaces were originally striated by glacial abrasion, prior to striae removal by dissolution. These now-bare outcrops subsequently evolved into the extensive pavements of the glaciokarst, notably around the Three Peaks and above Malham (see Chapter 4). This spatial pattern is clearest in upper Ribblesdale and Chapel-le-Dale, where the drumlins that characterise the watershed region of upper Dentdale, Widdale and Ribblehead (Fig. 3.23) are replaced southwards by the wide limestone pavements of White Scars (Fig. 3.30) and Moughton on either side of Ingleborough (Waltham, 1990).

Drumlins again become dominant landforms in the Craven Lowlands, south of the Craven Fault Zone, where they are numerous between Kirkby Lonsdale and Skipton (Fig. 3.31); these demonstrate flow convergence between

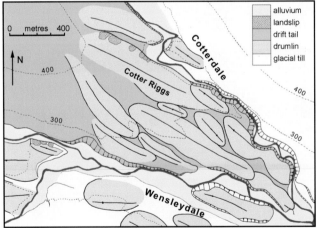

Figure 3.28. Geomorphology of the Cotter End drift tail where Cotterdale converges on Wensleydale; the tail is composed of a number of individual drumlins.

Figure 3.29. The streamlined ridge of the Cotter End drift tail, seen from the east (TW).

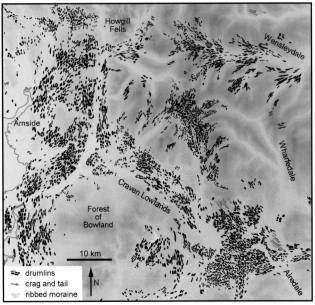

Figure 3.31. *Extract from the map of subglacial bedforms of the Last British Ice Sheet, showing former flow patterns within and around the Yorkshire Dales (Hughes et al., 2010). The southward flow of ice from the eastern Lake District had diffluent flow around the Forest of Bowland, forcing ice eastwards along the Craven Lowlands towards Airedale.*

local ice from the Pennine ice centre and ice flow from the Lake District (Raistrick, 1933; Clark *et al.*, 2004a; Mitchell and Hughes, 2012). Detailed field mapping of the drumlins in upper Wensleydale (Mitchell, 1991a, 1994), the southern Vale of Eden (Letzer, 1987) and at Ribblehead (Mitchell, 2008) has been supported by regional syntheses of former ice sheet activity in the Dales and Vale of Eden (Clark *et al.*, 2004a; Evans *et al.*, 2005; Mitchell and Riley, 2006) and more recently by the use of high resolution DEM to map the bedforms for the last British–Irish Ice Sheet (Livingstone *et al.*, 2008; Hughes *et al.*, 2010; Clark *et al.*, 2012). Consequently, the drumlins can be used to reconstruct specific features of the ice sheet with respect to flow direction, ice stream and divide delimitation and thermal regimes.

From studies of drumlins in the Vale of Eden, Rose and Letzer (1977) were the first to establish that complex drumlin morphology could be explained by superimposition of flow

events on the bedforms, thereby reflecting flow-switching during a glaciation. Similar cross-cutting relationships occur in parts of Grisedale (Fig 3.32), upper Wensleydale and around the confluence of Dentdale and Garsdale. All these indicate switching of flow direction as different outlet glaciers and ice streams ebbed and flowed, reflecting changes in the relative importance of source areas and migration of the Dales Ice Centre divides (Mitchell, 1994; Mitchell and Hughes, 2012). Superimposed drumlins also occur at Ribblehead, reflecting limited flow-switching between Ribblesdale and Chapel-le-Dale (Mitchell, 2008; Mitchell and Prescott, 2012). Spatial drumlin patterns are clearly time-transgressive, and reflect ice-sheet growth and retreat phases, but are dominated by the landforms formed during the later part of the glacial cycle (Clark *et al.*, 2012; Livingstone *et al.*, 2012).

Drumlin distribution can be used to constrain the former location of ice divides. Drumlins develop as a result of subglacial deformation, so they can only form where bed sliding and deformation are initiated by a threshold value of driving stress or basal ice velocity (Boulton, 1987; Mitchell, 1994). Ice divides are defined by low basal stresses and minimal ice velocity, which suppress subglacial deformation until a critical distance from the divide, where stress and velocity cross a deformation threshold to allow drumlin formation (Mitchell, 1994, 2007). In the Yorkshire Dales, the drumlin distribution confirms the earlier concepts of an ice centre over the high fells at the upper end of Wensleydale (Fig. 3.33). However, rather than being small and purely local, this ice divide can be traced westwards across the Howgill Fells (Fig. 3.34) and beyond to the Lake District, as a major linear feature in northern England (Mitchell, 1994; Mitchell and Clark, 1994; Mitchell and Riley, 2006; Mitchell and Hughes, 2012).

Figure 3.33. *Drumlins on the summit of Abbotside Common, at an altitude of over 600m, high above the head of Wensleydale (WM).*

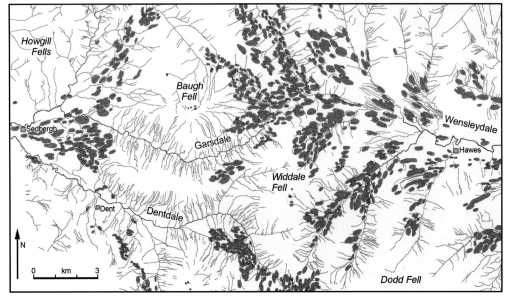

Figure 3.32. *Distribution of drumlins across upper Wensleydale and adjacent fells that underlay the Dales Ice Centre (after Mitchell and Riley, 2006).*

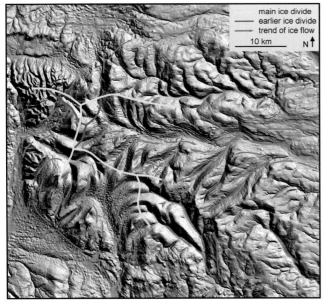

Figure 3.34. Reconstruction of the location and character of the ice divide of the Dales Ice Centre during the Devensian glaciation, with major lines of ice flow, the final position of the ice divide and an earlier position during the glaciation. This is deduced from the superimposed drumlins, and indicates ice divide migration due to piracy by the Wensleydale Ice Stream (after Mitchell and Hughes, 2012) (base DEM from Land-Form Panorama, Ordnance Survey; Edina Digimaps/JISC).

Superimposed drumlins, particularly in Grisedale on the eastern side of Baugh Fell, demonstrate that the ice divide was capable of migration during glaciation, with an initial radial ice flow off Baugh Fell towards Mallerstang. Migration of the ice divide further west and north allowed a later flow-switching down Grisedale. The ice stream piracy generated an expansion of Wensleydale ice at the expense of Mallerstang ice (Mitchell, 1991a, 1994; Mitchell and Hughes, 2012). This established Wensleydale as an ice stream that was 70 km long and 10 km wide (Fig. 3.33) and dominated easterly flow from the Dales Ice Centre. It gained contributions from adjacent tributary valleys, before joining the Vale of York ice stream (Mitchell, 1994; Mitchell *et al.,* 2008, Mitchell and Bridgland, 2011; Boulton, 2010).

Drumlin distribution in Widdale and other southern tributaries of Wensleydale, as well as over the interfluves to Ribblesdale and Dentdale, again shows that the ice sheet was flowing independently of topography, northeastwards up Garsdale (Mitchell, 1994; Mitchell and Hughes, 2012). Former ice flow is also recorded by the drumlins in upper Dentdale, which indicate flow up the valley towards the southeast across Blea Moor. There it coalesced with ice moving southwest down upper Ribblesdale. This was complemented

by ice flow further west in Dentdale where drumlins at Little Combe indicate former ice flow up Deepdale, across White Shaw Moss into Kingsdale, suggesting that a former ice divide was situated across Dentdale between Rise Hill and Crag Hill (Fig. 3.34). Superimposed drumlins across Frostrow Fells at the western end of Garsdale also show cross-cutting ice flow relationships around Sedbergh, where flow from western Baugh Fell down the Rawthey Valley was able to constrain Dentdale ice and force it southwest into the diffluent valley of Barbondale along the Dent Fault, eventually to a convergence with Lune Valley ice moving south (Fig. 3.32). These contrasting flow directions at the upper and lower ends of the major valleys of Dentdale and Garsdale require the reconstruction of an ice divide across the central parts of both dales. This may seem contrary to expectation, but again demonstrates that at its maximum, the Dales Ice Centre was glaciologically independent of the submerged topography.

The Craven Uplands

The Craven uplands are eroded across the main outcrops of the Great Scar Limestone that contain the most extensive karst and caves. From Kingsdale to Wharfedale, each dale is a deep glaciated trough cut into the limestone. Upper Ribblesdale and the surrounding high ground, as well as the low ground of Oughtershaw Moss and Langstrothdale Chase at the head of Wharfedale, were originally thought to have formed a separate smaller ice centre extending over the interfluve area from Dodd Fell to Fountains Fell (Raistrick, 1931a). However, there is no real evidence for separation of an ice centre over Langstrothdale Chase from that on Baugh Fell and Wild Boar Fell. The idea that ice had flowed up Widdale and Snaizeholme, from Wensleydale into Ribblesdale, was based on erratics (Raistrick, 1926), but is in conflict with the drumlins that confirm ice flow down Widdale (Mitchell, 1994). It seems from the drumlin distribution across the wider dales area that there was a single extensive ice divide forming the Dales Ice Centre (Fig. 3.34).

No fieldwork-based research has been reported for the eastern Dales; in fact, the early researchers did not even consider these dales, apart from in the most general of terms. Observations and mapping of subglacial bedforms on currently available digital elevation models (DEM) (Hughes *et al.*, 2010; Mitchell and Hughes, 2012) (Fig. 3.31) indicate that a topographically independent ice divide lay across upper Wharfedale over Oughtershaw Moss and Langstrothdale, east of the present watershed, during the last glaciation. The ice divide extended south from Dodd Fell, where it can be

Figure 3.35. The drumlin field stretching from Cam Fell down into Ribblesdale. The Ribblesdale ice extended over the limestone benches in the distance, both over the slight rise of Moughton and across the low saddle of Sulber to its right and thence into Crummack Dale (WM).

Figure 3.36. The glacial erratics of greywacke blocks spread across the limestone shoulder of Norber, on the southeastern flank of Ingleborough (TW).

continued westwards towards the main ice centre over the interfluve between Widdale and upper Ribblesdale to cross the middle part of Dentdale to Baugh Fell (Mitchell, 1994). South from Dodd Fell, an ice divide can be reconstructed across Langstrothdale towards Eller Carr Moss and then across upper Littondale to Darnbrook Fell and Fountains Fell. Southwest-directed drumlins southeast of Plover Hill appear to converge with further drumlins on the northern side of Darnbrook Fell to indicate former ice flow up Pen-y-ghent Gill to converge with drumlins on Fawcett Moor (Fig. 3.34) (Mitchell and Hughes, 2012). Pen-y-ghent lay west of the ice divide, with ice flowing on both sides and into Ribblesdale. However, the orientation of the breaches, relative to the reconstructed ice divide is difficult to explain as the troughs appear to have been eroded by ice lying to the east over the high ground, a pattern of flow not experienced during the last glaciation.

Ice on the eastern side of this ice divide formed an upper accumulation area centred over Langstrothdale Chase, and supplied ice down the impressive glacial troughs of

Wharfedale and Littondale. Buckden Pike, which forms part of the high fells on the eastern side of Wharfedale, caused the ice to split, with one flow moving northeastwards to erode the major diffluent trough of Bishopdale. This transferred ice into Wensleydale, and was sufficiently erosive to over-deepen the tributary valley relative to the main valley. In contrast, the adjacent eastern valley of Walden Beck was protected by Buckden Pike and has not been modified by glacial erosion (King, 1976); drumlins were formed across its confluence with Bishopdale (Hughes *et al.*, 2010). Clear evidence of glacial streamlining from a topographically independent ice divide can also be seen on the high ground between Buckden Pike and Great Whernside indicating eastwards flow from Wharfedale into Coverdale. However, the main ice flow was into Wharfedale, flowing southeastwards towards Grassington as part of a wider topographically independent ice flow across the Malham High Country from Fountains Fell and Darnbrook Fell (Mitchell and Hughes, 2012).

Drumlins in Ribblesdale and Chapel-le-Dale indicate that ice flowing southwestwards in upper Ribblesdale diverged around Park Fell on the northeastern spur of Ingleborough, the summit of which would have been submerged beneath cold-based ice. The ice spread over the limestone benches east of Ingleborough (Fig. 3.35). One element of this flow is marked by the train of angular erratic boulders of Silurian greywacke at Norber (Figs 3.36, 4.16). These were plucked from scars on the valley side and carried south to rest on a shoulder of limestone (Fig. 3.37), but with minimal uphill transport (Waltham, 1990; Wilson *et al.*, 2012a). The limited extent of the boulder train may reflect a localised 'pulse' of erosion that occurred towards the end of a glaciation (Sugden *et al.*, 1992), rather than a limited re-advance (Vincent *et al.*, 2010). The ice in Crummack Dale formed part of the wider Ribblesdale ice that flowed south off the Askrigg Block, to converge with ice that was flowing southeast in the Craven Lowlands. The complex pattern of ice flow is reflected in the drumlins between Kirkby Lonsdale and Skipton, showing flow deflection around the northern side of the Forest of Bowland and eastwards towards lower Ribblesdale (Raistrick, 1930, 1933; Johnson, 1985).

The Craven Lowlands were partly occupied by local Dales ice that had flowed directly south off the Askrigg Block. However, another part of the Dales ice flowed westwards and then south into the Lune Valley. There it joined Lake District ice, and the combined flow was deflected by the more powerful Irish Sea Ice Stream so that it headed eastwards around the northern side of the Forest of Bowland

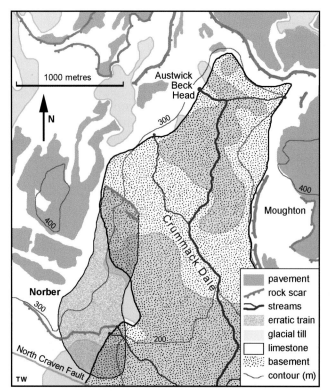

1000 metres

Austwick Beck Head

N

300

400

Moughton

Crummack Dale

400

400

Norber

300

200

North Craven Fault

TW

	pavement
⌒	rock scar
⌇	streams
⣿	erratic train
▨	glacial till
☐	limestone
⣿	basement
⌇	contour (m)

Figure 3.37. The train of erratic blocks over Norber, traced from their source in the crags on the western slope of Crummack Dale (after Waltham, 1990).

and along the Craven Lowlands (Clark *et al.*, 2004a; Hughes *et al.*, 2010). The contribution of Pennine ice to the Irish Sea Ice Stream was limited to its extreme eastern side because it was compressed along the western flank of the Pennines, as a result of a greater ice flux from Scotland, the Lake District and eastern Ireland that occupied the Irish Sea basin (Fig. 3.20) (Johnson, 1985; Evans *et al.*, 2005). There was also divergence of ice flow near Skipton with flow both southwards towards Manchester, along the western edge of the Peak District and into Cheshire (Johnson, 1985; Chiverrell and Thomas, 2010), as well as through a number of cols across the Pennine watershed into upper Airedale and the Yorkshire Calder valley (Aitkenhead *et al.*, 2002). Recent mapping has shown that this area is more complex than previously thought (Raistrick, 1933) with a number of drumlins, reinterpreted as ribbed moraine ridges with superimposed drumlins (Hughes *et al.*, 2010; Mitchell and Hughes, 2012). Ribbed (Rogen) moraines are an enigmatic landform whose formation is poorly understood; their occurrence in northern England has only just been reported and they are conspicuously developed along the edge of the Askrigg Block where ice was deflected eastwards by the upland block of the Forest of Bowland. It is generally agreed that ribbed moraines are of subglacial origin and form transverse to ice flow (Benn and Evans, 2010), but may relate to both extension and compression within the ice sheet (Finlayson and Bradwell, 2008).

Terminal moraines at Apperley Bridge in Airedale, Arthington in Wharfedale and in the upper reaches of Calderdale have been interpreted as the maximum Devensian limit within this part of the Pennines (Penny, 1974: Aitkenhead *et al.*, 2002; Chiverrell and Thomas, 2010), although an alternative more extensive ice limit is thought to extend eastwards and southwards across the former extent of Glacial Lake Humber (Cooper and Gibson, 2003).

As the importance of the various ice centres altered during the glaciation, there was major reorganisation of the ice sheet flow directions (Evans *et al.*, 2009; Livingstone *et al.*, 2008, 2010; Clark *et al.*, 2012). A decline in the Southern Uplands ice centre allowed Dales ice to become part of a major northwards ice flow into the Vale of Eden after the Stainmore ice stream shut down as a major glacial artery (Mitchell and Riley, 2006; Livingstone *et al.*, 2012). Migration and expansion of the Dales Ice Centre may have occurred at the same time with headward capture and expansion of the upper source area of the Wensleydale ice stream indicated by the superimposed drumlins in Grisedale (Mitchell, 1994; Mitchell and Hughes, 2012). This increased activity and migration of the ice divide over Baugh Fell may have caused a readvance of the Wensleydale glacier into an ice-free Vale of York. Evidence for this can be seen at the valleys' confluence where the Leeming terminal moraine and the northern lateral moraines that extend from Bellerby to Tunstall cross-cut, and were therefore later than, the north–south drumlins formed by the Vale of York ice (Fig. 3.38). This has been termed the Wensleydale Readvance (Mitchell and Bridgland 2011) and can be traced southwest towards Masham, where exposures in Marfield Quarry have revealed detailed sedimentological evidence for an oscillating ice margin in the form of ice-thrust till and deformed lake sediments in a series of ice-pushed moraine ridges (Mitchell *et al.*, 2008).

Meltwater channels

The former extent of ice sheets and glaciers may also be deduced from the distribution of meltwater channels. Water was primarily derived from ablation at the ice surface, and then flowed towards the glacier bed and along ice margins, particularly during deglaciation when meltwater discharge was maximised (Fig. 3.24) (Clark *et al.*, 2004b; Evans *et al.*, 2005; Greenwood *et al.*, 2007). Meltwater availability also influences development of ice streams through its complex pattern of melting and freezing in the subglacial environment (Winsborrow *et al.*, 2010). Meltwater channels are formed under a range of distinctive environments controlled by seasonal high discharges of meltwater produced during ablation events. Key features that distinguish meltwater channels include undulating long profiles, abrupt commencement and termination, and independence from topographic slope (Greenwood *et al.*, 2007). Many channels are also 'dry' and no longer part of the present drainage system (Waltham, 2007; Benn and Evans, 2010). Given that they are erosional forms, some channels may also be related to earlier glaciations, and were re-occupied during later events. Further complications arise on the limestone outcrop of the southern Dales where dry valleys and disappearing streams are normal characteristics of the karst landscapes (see Chapter 4).

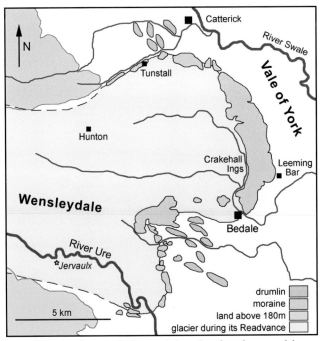

Figure 3.38*. Geomorphology of the abandoned part of lower Wensleydale around Bedale; the lateral and terminal moraines that define the limit of the Wensleydale Readvance cross-cut the drumlins left by the southerly ice flow in the Vale of York (after Mitchell and Bridgland, 2011); the moraines and marginal features left by the glacier have not been mapped in detail further up Wensleydale.*

Whether a meltwater channel was formed in a subglacial location directed by ice sheet hydrology, or in a lateral position relative to former ice margins, is important in constraining reconstructions of the pattern of deglaciation. Although the presence of such landforms has long been established in the literature, they were initially explained, incorrectly, as overflow channels from glacier impounded lakes (Kendall,

Figure 3.39. The meltwater channel containing the Huker and Thornton Mires where it passes south of Addlebrough on the southern flank of Wensleydale (WM).

Figure 3.40. The Trow Gill meltwater channel off Ingleborough before it enters Clapdale (TW).

1902; Kendall and Wroot, 1924). More recently, meltwater channels have been used within reconstructions that emphasise a subglacial origin for these landforms (Sissons, 1958, 1960, 1961; Johnson, 1985) and demonstrate intense fluvial erosion beneath temperate ice. However, mapping in many areas has led to the growing appreciation that many channel sequences occur in juxtaposition with lateral moraines and that they are marginal forms, recording retreat of active ice, possibly as cold-based outlet glaciers from plateau icefields (Kleman *et al.,* 1997; Benn and Evans, 1998; Rea and Evans, 2003). Conversely, it is now appreciated that some channels may relate to drainage of former ice-dammed lakes in suitable upland locations (Russell, 1995). Channels that formed in proglacial situations are poorly reported in the literature (Greenwood *et al.,* 2007) because they are now occupied by the present river network.

Complex channel systems are well developed across many parts of the Yorkshire Dales (Clark *et al.,* 2004a), but many of these still await reappraisal within new ice sheet reconstructions. Along the southern flank of Wensleydale, Raistrick (1926) described a channel system extending from Carpley Green, south of Addlebrough, towards Aysgarth, with the peat bogs of Huker Mire and Thornton Mire on its floor (Fig. 3.39). This was then interpreted as the lake overflow of a much-extended Semer Water with an overflow about 140m above the present lake level. Recent mapping shows that there is no continuous channel, but a series of smaller channels cut through drumlins and a drift tail extends east of Addlebrough with a former lake at Thornton Mire. These channels may relate to an internal thermal boundary between warm-based and cold-based ice along the lateral margin of the Wensleydale ice stream.

Numerous dry valleys on the limestone outcrop of the Craven Uplands have meltwater origins and links to the cave systems without any direct connection to former ice margins. Trow Gill gorge is one a series of channels eroded into the limestone in the lee of Ingleborough and Simon Fell (Figs 3.40, 4.45) (Glover, 1974; Waltham, 1990). Former surface flow in these channels can be explained by an early phase of subglacial meltwater with subsequent modification during deglaciation by surface flow in the continued presence of permafrost that made the limestone impermeable, thereby preventing drainage into the cave systems. Access to Gaping

Gill and the other potholes was re-established, and the surface channels were abandoned, after melting of the permafrost (Waltham, 2007). Alternatively, these dry channels and gorges may originate from catastrophic draining of ice-dammed lakes, causing high magnitude floods (jökulhlaups) during deglaciation (Faulkner, 2006, 2012).

Further channels have been mapped along the southern flank of the Craven Uplands from Settle to Skipton and beyond (Fig. 3.23) (Raistrick, 1930, 1933; Huddart, 2002). The Black Hill channel is a well-known feature that was eroded through the Ribble–Aire watershed west of Malham Tarn (Clark, 1967). However, the most impressive channels at Watlowes (Fig. 4.53), above Malham Cove, and Gordale (Fig. 3.41) are not discussed in the early glacial literature. This may reflect the then-accepted origin for Gordale as a collapsed cave and some outmoded understanding that Malham Cove was somehow associated with spring erosion along joints and cavern collapse (Kendall and Wroot, 1924; Clayton, 1966) or glacial erosion (Clayton, 1981). Current ideas on these landforms explain Malham Cove (Fig. 3.42) as a former waterfall, possibly associated with major jökulhlaup events that carved the Watlowes channel (Pitty *et al.,* 1986). Alternatively, glacial excavation may have been a

Figure 3.41. The deeply incised meltwater channel of Gordale, upstream of Gordale Scar (TW).

Figure 3.42. The site of a former waterfall at Malham Cove, where meltwater flowed down the Watlowes channel and across the Middle Craven Fault (TW).

contributory factor in the formation of the Cove (see Chapter 4). Landscape features around Malham Tarn indicate that Gordale is part of a subglacial meltwater channel system (Fig. 3.43) associated with glacial streamlining that was directed roughly north–south from the Malham High Country that stretches eastwards from Fountains Fell (Clark, 1967). Other features, particularly associated with Malham Cove, are more suggestive of proglacial fluvial processes during deglaciation, when meltwater erosion and channel formation on the surface was facilitated by the presence of permafrost that prevented sinking underground (see Chapter 4). The presence of glaciofluvial sediments in many cave systems does however indicate that meltwater was able to enter and occupy the cave systems (Ford, 2001). A possible problem with development by jökulhlaups is the lack of any deposits associated with such high-energy events downstream within the upper Aire valley. However, both Malham Cove and Gordale clearly reflect the influence of meltwater on the present landscape.

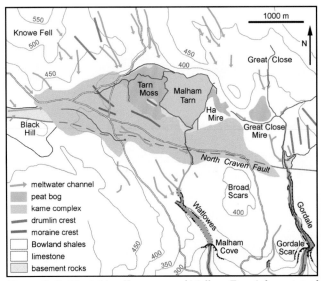

Figure 3.43. Glacial landforms around Malham Tarn (after original mapping by Clark, 1967), re-interpreted within more modern ideas on meltwater channels and proposing some of the 'glaciofluvial' ridges as moraines

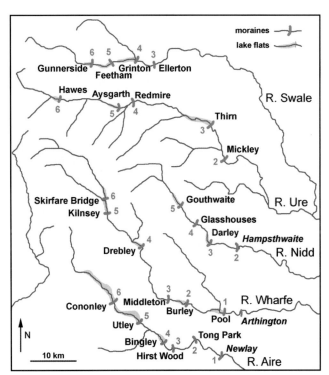

Figure 3.44. Recessional stages of Dales glaciers identified by moraine ridges at a number of locations within each dale. These are the features mapped, named and numbered by Arthur Raistrick (1927), relocated onto modern mapping of the rivers; only the lake flats recorded by Raistrick are shown. Raistrick did not name the Hampsthwaite moraine, as his published map confuses sites and names along the River Nidd. He did not refer to the conspicuous Arthington moraine on the River Wharfe, and he described and numbered, but did not name, the Newlay moraine on the River Aire.

Moraines and glacial retreat

A number of moraine ridges, with distinctive flat areas that have been interpreted as the location of former moraine-impounded lakes, have been identified in the dales from Airedale north to Swaledale (Fig. 3.44). They have been interpreted as recessional moraines that define former limits of a series of increasingly topographically-defined outlet glaciers, with the number of stages identified in each dale declining northwards, reflecting their later separation and retreat from Vale of York ice (Raistrick, 1927, 1934). However, the identified limits are compromised by association with the then-prevalent interpretation of meltwater channels relating to ice-dammed lake overflows, though many of the lateral channels were recognised as relating to former ice margins and were used as such in the reconstruction of retreat stages (Raistrick, 1927, 1933, 1934). Little subsequent research has been directed towards ascertaining their validity.

While widespread stagnation may have occurred in surrounding lowlands, the presence of recessional moraines shows that ice remained active in many mountain areas. In the western Lake District, moraine ridges in a number of valleys indicate a more complex glacial history than previously envisaged, with the possibility of ice marginal fluctuations and readvances during ice sheet deglaciation (Merritt and Auton, 2000; Wilson, 2004). Similarly in northwest Scotland, a number of moraine ridges have been identified to indicate active retreat of the ice sheet as a series of outlet glaciers from mountain icefields of decreasing size (Stoker et al., 2009). Unlike in the Lake District where

Figure 3.45. The Skirfare Bridge terminal moraine lies across Wharfedale just above its confluence with Littondale, in front of the eastern slopes that lie in morning shadow; thick till from Littondale ice forms the uneven terrain of High Wind Bank, which lies in the left centre of this view from the top of the truncated spur of Kilnsey Crag (TW).

there are few dates to constrain these limits, a number of cosmogenic dates indicate that glaciers may well have continued in existence into the Lateglacial (Windermere) Interstadial (Bradwell *et al.*, 2008b). However this is a matter of on-going debate, given that analytical uncertainties associated with cosmogenic production rates, can make the dates too young; more recent recalibration suggests that the ice had retreated into the mountains prior to the end of the Dimlington Stadial (Ballantyne and Stone, 2011).

The presence of recessional moraines clearly indicates that the Dales Ice Centre remained active during deglaciation, feeding topographically constrained valley glaciers within individual dales. The Skirfare Bridge feature (Fig. 3.45) is a well-known moraine at the confluence of Littondale and Wharfedale (Raistrick, 1931a; Howard *et al.*, 1998). The Bear Park moraine (Fig. 3.46) at Aysgarth, in Wensleydale (Raistrick, 1926) is also well known, but may not relate to Wensleydale ice as it could have been formed by a lobe of ice extending out of Bishopdale. A notable sequence of moraines has been mapped for 16 km along the northern side of the original Wensleydale from Bellerby Moor eastwards to Tunstall (Raistrick, 1926). Although shown to be composed of till, they have been interpreted as associated with ice stagnation (Cullingford and Gregory, 1978); this is incorrect and they are clearly lateral moraines associated with the northern margin of a glacier in Wensleydale. These moraines can be correlated with the large terminal moraine at Leeming that marks the eastern extent of the Wensleydale Readvance, as well as the push moraines near Masham (Mitchell and Bridgland, 2011) and clearly pre-date the recessional limits further up-valley (Raistrick, 1926, 1927). It is now accepted that the pattern of ice retreat following the Last Glacial Maximum involved active ice at sequences of marginal

positions that were each distinctive to its own mountain source area (Evans *et al.*, 2005). Patterns of ice retreat in the eastern Dales await re-evaluation with cosmogenic and other dating techniques to establish the age of these moraines.

Recessional moraines are not documented in the Craven Uplands and the western Dales. Channels along the upland margin, from Settle eastwards to Skipton, were associated with converging ice flows from the upper Ribble and upper Aire valleys, and retreat features in the lower Ribble valley may correlate with recessional stages better known in the eastern Dales (Raistrick, 1931, 1934). There are no records of recessional moraines in Ribblesdale upstream of Settle. However, there are moraines in Kingsdale where two limits have been identified at Raven Ray and Brown Hills (Figs 3.47, 3.48); lateral moraines can also be traced up-valley from Wackenburgh Hill to Brown Hills (Waltham, *et al.*, 2010; Waltham, 2012). This cannot have been a simple valley glacier because there is no accumulation area where Kingsdale is linked to Deepdale across a col at White Shaw Moss; rather, it was a southern outlet glacier from the topographically independent Dales Ice Centre when an ice divide existed across Dentdale forcing ice up Deepdale and into Kingsdale (Mitchell, 1991a, 1994).

Fragments of lateral moraine ridges also lie along the southern flank of the Craven Uplands, from Masongill westwards towards Leck (Fig. 3.49). These were formed along the margin of a retreating ice sheet associated with Lake District ice, as well as ice from Barbondale and the Lune Valley which had been deflected eastwards by the Irish Sea ice. Within the western dales, there is little further evidence, except for a lateral moraine that blocks lower Dentdale, associated with more dynamic Rawthey ice that was able to cross Dentdale. The distribution of the moraines

Figure 3.46. The Bear Park terminal moraine at Aysgarth that may mark a recessional stage of the Wensleydale glacier (WM).

Figure 3.47. The Raven Ray recessional moraine across the mouth of Kingsdale, cut into by the meltwater channel now occupied by the River Twiss. The possible lateral moraine of Wackenburgh Hill, as well as the evidence of streamlining, may indicate that the moraine has been overridden by the ice sheet (TW).

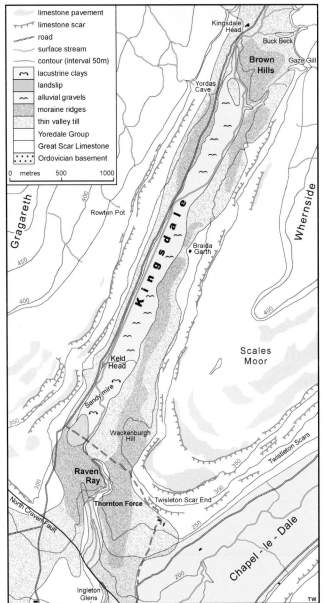

Figure 3.48. Glacial features of Kingsdale, with its recessional moraines at Raven Ray and Brown Hills (after Waltham et al., 2010).

The remaining ice became topographically constrained leading to the collapse of cross-valley ice divides and the re-establishment of outlet glaciers flowing from residual icefields on the high fells. Although a regional synthesis is still awaited, this sequence can be deduced from the pattern of solifluction lobes on the northern slopes of Dentdale; here the altitude reached by the lobes rises eastwards suggesting a former ice margin of a valley glacier in Dentdale from North Lord's Land towards Cowgill and the high ground of Widdale Fell (Mitchell, 1991a). In the eastern-flowing dales, this period of topographically constrained icefields is probably associated with the recessional moraines left by active but diminishing ice masses.

The absence of further moraines up-valley from Aysgarth in Wensleydale, and from equivalent positions in the other dales, suggests that the climate no longer supported the continued existence of valley glaciers. It seems that initial deglaciation and ice recession were initiated under cold, but notably dry, conditions that starved the glaciers (Hubberten *et al.*, 2004). As the ice withdrew, the ground was first dominated by periglacial conditions driven by the continued cold climate. These were followed by more temperate conditions during the early part of the Last Glacial-Interglacial Transition (see below), when geomorphic systems of fluvial and aeolian activity became prominent as the landscape began to adapt to its changed environmental conditions. Many of the present river systems in northern England reflect their meltwater heritage and record changes made as they re-established themselves across new landscapes dominated by glacial sediments and landforms (Chiverrell *et al.*, 2009; Mitchell *et al.*, 2010; Bridgland *et al.*, 2011). Relative sea level within

Figure 3.49. Lateral moraine seen from just above Masongill with the trees at Marble Steps Pot on the skyline. This was associated with retreat of ice that flowed southeast along the Craven Lowlands, along the southern flank of the Askrigg Block (WM).

would seem to offer evidence of an important glaciological signal within these western dales. In contrast, the higher eastern dales remained active, with shrinking valley glaciers that retreated towards mountain icefields.

As the ice sheet retreated into the western part of the Askrigg Block, there was a reversal of ice flow direction within upper Dentdale and possibly upper Garsdale.

the Irish Sea basin was initially high, as indicated by raised shorelines in the Solway Firth. However, deglaciation in the Irish Sea basin was marked by a period of falling sea level as glacio-isostatic uplift exceeded eustatic changes meaning that for most of the period, from 19 to 10 ka, areas of the basin were dry land. This was occupied by sandür (outwash plains) formed by large meltwater discharges from the wasting ice sheet (Chiverrell *et al.*, 2004; Stone *et al.*, 2010). Large quantities of the fine-grained sediments exposed on the sandür were then deflated and entrained by wind, to be re-deposited across the Yorkshire Dales and the rest of northern England as loess (Vincent and Lee, 1981; Jones and Keen, 1993; Bateman and Buckland, 2001; Wilson *et al.*, 2008, 2012b; Telfer *et al.*, 2009). Much of this loess was subsequently eroded and re-deposited by fluvial processes.

A chronology for the last glaciation

In addition to the established chronology determined by multiple uranium–thorium dates from caves within the Dales (see Chapter 10), there are growing numbers of dates from surface deposits, obtained by radiocarbon, optically stimulated luminescence (OSL) and cosmogenic techniques. These help to constrain the geomorphological evidence and greatly improve understanding of the advance and demise of the Late Main Devensian ice sheet (Hughes *et al.*, 2010; Clark *et al.*, 2012). Given the erosive nature of ice sheets and their inherent ability to destroy previous deposits, evidence for the early part of the last glacial event is only known from a limited number of terrestrial sites in Britain; in comparison, there are more sites recording the timing of the deglaciation and its transgressive nature. This record can be correlated with dated offshore sequences to show that the last ice sheet had advanced offshore and reached the shelf edge by c.27 ka (Clark *et al.*, 2012). It is also apparent that ice margin behaviour was asynchronous for different sectors of the ice sheet, with evidence for an earlier advance in the north but with significantly later advances to the southern limits of the ice sheet. Adjacent to the Yorkshire Dales, the Irish Sea Ice Stream advanced to the Scilly Isles after 24.2 ka (O'Cofaigh and Evans, 2007; Scourse *et al.*, 2009) yet the Vale of York Ice Stream reached its maximum extent only after 23.3 ka (Bateman *et al.*, 2008) All of this demonstrates a complex history of ice sheet behaviour in northern England (Mitchell and Bridgland, 2011; Livingstone *et al.*, 2012).

In the Yorkshire Dales, although most speleothem dates record a growth hiatus from either 36 to 13 ka (Gascoyne *et al.*, 1983a) or 26 to 15 ka (Atkinson *et al.*, 1986), the starting dates may reflect not the development of glaciers but the beginning of sufficiently cold temperatures to allow permafrost expansion on the high ground during late MIS 3. Further dates of 29.0 ±2 ka from Stump Cross Caverns

(Sutcliffe *et al.*, 1985), 29.4 ±2.2 ka from Ibbeth Peril Cave (Gascoyne and Ford, 1984), 27.3 ±5.6 ka from Malham Cove Rising (Murphy and Latham, 2001) and 25.5 ±3.6 ka from Victoria Cave (Gascoyne and Ford, 1984), all appear to suggest a later date for cessation of speleothem growth; even allowing for the large standard deviations, this was some time after c.30 ka. Loess, protected from subsequent glacier erosion in the floor of the Dowkabottom doline (Fig. 3.50), above Littondale, has yielded an OSL date of 27.2 ±2.6 ka indicating that the area was ice-free at that time (Telfer *et al.*, 2009). This just pre-dates the start of the Last Glacial Maximum, and provides a maximum age for the advance of the ice sheet across the limestone benches of the Dales. It conforms to the speleothem dates, which suggest that late MIS 3 was a time of periglacial climate and loess deposition before the growth of the Dales Ice Centre; and it also correlates with the terrestrial and marine evidence for the later advance of the ice sheet southern sectors (Clark *et al.*, 2012).

As with the asynchronous behaviour of ice advance out of the different source areas, deglaciation was also highly variable in time. It was marked not only by lateral recession of the ice margins, but also by vertical thinning of the ice sheet, partly by ablation and partly associated with ice stream activity drawing mass out of the centres. Cosmogenic dates from periglacial trimlines in the central Lake District indicate ice-free conditions of some mountain tops by 17.3±1.1 ka (Ballantyne *et al.*, 2009); however, the presence of striations at higher elevations on Bow Fell (Evans, 2003) suggest that the trimline is a feature of vertical thinning and the appearance of nunataks at an early stage of deglaciation. Within the Dales, the higher peaks, such as Ingleborough and Whernside, may have become nunataks some distance behind the ice margin while the high fells of the Dales Ice Centre, centred on the extensive plateau of Baugh Fell, continued to be ice-covered and support active glaciers within the dales.

The first cosmogenic chlorine-36 dates from the Yorkshire Dales have been determined from the Norber erratics where three samples give an age range of 17.1 ±2 ka to 18.8 ±1.4 ka with a mean value of 18.0 ±1.6 ka (Vincent *et al.*, 2010). This suggests that the southern parts of the Craven Uplands were ice-free by this time, which may be regarded as an early date for deglaciation. The exposure dates from these erratics relate to marginal retreat of Ribblesdale ice back towards the high fells as the lowlands became deglaciated; this is supported by the OSL date of 19.3 ±2.6 ka from Warton Crag, near Morecambe Bay (Telfer *et al.*, 2009). Extrapolation of the flow trajectories associated with the Norber erratics suggests that the Ribblesdale ice made a minor contribution to the Irish Sea ice stream. Dales ice was clearly confined to the Pennine fringe and ultimately became part of the Cheshire lobe (Johnson, 1985), so required less distance to retreat in

Figure 3.50. The lower part of the Dowkabottom doline, with its floor of loessic soil that pre-dates the Devensian ice cover; this large doline is set into the wide limestone upland nearly 200m above the floor of Littondale, which lies beyond the col near the right margin (TW).

Figure 3.51. Loessic soils covering glacial bedforms in and around New Pasture, above Gordale; the loess is dated to 16.5 ka, which was after retreat of the main Devensian ice from the Malham High Country (TW).

comparison to the Irish Sea ice that reached to near the Scilly Isles (Scourse *et al.,* 2009; Clark *et al.,* 2012). Cosmogenic beryllium-10 dates from near the summit of Holyhead Mountain, Anglesey, of 18.1 ±1.8 ka to 19.2 ±2.3 ka suggest that the Irish Sea ice stream had thinned substantially and was in rapid retreat by that time (McCarroll *et al.,* 2010). Although the timing of deglaciation in the Irish Sea Basin is one of the least constrained parts of the British–Irish Ice Sheet reconstruction (Clark *et al.,* 2012), these cosmogenic dates suggest that the Irish Sea ice stream had been reduced to a lobe with a terminus in the present Liverpool Bay. It had also separated from ice in the Welsh mountains and Irish ice, and had unzipped from ice on its eastern flanks, where the ice margin had retreated back towards the Pennine uplands by this time.

A further constraint on the timing of deglaciation within the Dales is provided by an OSL date on loess at New Close (Fig. 3.51), above Gordale Scar, that is dated 16.5 ±1.7 ka (Telfer *et al.,* 2009). This compares with the dated loess at Warton Crag, which suggests deglaciation by 19.3 ±2.6 ka of the low ground around Morecambe Bay (Telfer *et al.,* 2009). A radiocarbon date of 17.7 ±1.0 ka for the earliest organic material in sediment cores from Windermere (Coope and Pennington, 1977; Hughes *et al.,* 2011) may be too old, and needs revision. There is no evidence of climatic warming at this time in western Europe (Hubberten *et al.,* 2004), and the retreat of the ice sheet is thought to reflect precipitation starvation and marine calving resulting in loss of ice mass. Later radiocarbon dates from Victoria Cave (14.7–12.9 ka) and Kinsey Cave (14.7–13.3 ka) can be correlated with many lowland sites where basal radiocarbon dates from organic sediments indicate the establishment of warmer conditions that led to disappearance of the permafrost. This warming is dated to 14.7 ka and marks the end of the Main Late Devensian (MIS 2) glaciation and the beginning of the Lateglacial period in northern England (Lowe and Walker, 1997; Innes, 2002; Hughes *et al.,* 2011), with its rapid climatic changes before the beginning of the Holocene (see Chapter 12).

The high-resolution ice-core chronostratigraphy from Greenland (Rasmussen *et al.,* 2006) has provided a means of correlating these time-transgressive records within the detailed event stratigraphy of a series of Greenland Stadials (GS) and Greenland Interstadials (GI) for the North Atlantic region (Fig. 3.2) (Björck, *et al.,* 1998; Lowe *et al.,* 2008; Blockley *et al.,* 2012). Although computer simulations of the Late Devensian ice sheet demonstrate that it was highly responsive to climatic drivers in the North Atlantic, establishing a chronology that fits with the geomorphic record of the BIIS is still a challenge; there are too few dates

to constrain large parts of the ice sheet within the binge-purge model, particularly in association with Heinrich events that added an additional trigger to British–Irish Ice Sheet responses. The computer models suggest that the build-up of the last ice sheet across the British Isles was in response to a series of precursor events; these established a series of cold-based mountain icecaps that were eventually able to extend across lowland areas and shallow offshore waters by the end of GI-3 (Hubbard *et al.,* 2009). However, this is challenged in the Craven Dales by the OSL date of 27.2 ±2.6 ka indicating that the limestone upland was ice-free until the end of this period (Telfer *et al.,* 2009).

A prolonged period of cold conditions in GS-3 (Fig. 3.3) allowed development of the British-Irish Ice Sheet as a large ice mass with wet-based fast flow across lowland and marine sectors (Hubbard, *et al.,* 2009). In the model, this advance is modified by the short climatic warming of GI-2; however, by then the ice sheet has sufficient volume to maintain its advance southwards in the Irish Sea, although evidence suggests recession both along the Atlantic seaboard and in the North Sea (Clark *et al.,* 2012). This demonstrates the dynamism of the ice sheet and its complex response to both external climate controls and internal feedback loops. In northern England, the presence of outwash and lake sediments suggests the formation of ice-free enclaves in the lowlands surrounding the Lake District and Pennines, although there are no dates to constrain this period of ice recession (Livingstone *et al.,* 2012). The presence of superimposed tills in many parts of lowland northern England indicate that the ice sheet was able to re-advance during the period of the Blackhall Wood Re-advance (Gosforth Oscillation), which is thought to have occurred between c.21 and 19.5 ka (Livingstone *et al.,* 2012). This was during GS-2, when the ice sheet models and geological evidence indicate that the ice sheet reached its maximum volume (Hubbard *et al.,* 2009; Clark *et al.,* 2012), during which time the Yorkshire Dales area would have been completely buried under the ice.

Deglaciation is thought to have commenced at about 19 ka (Clark *et al.,* 2012). Modelling shows substantial ice mass loss within two thousand years (Hubbard *et al.,* 2009), reflected in rapid collapse of marine margins with the formation of calving bays as well as stagnation over lowland areas. As with the timing of the Last Glacial Maximum, the only dates from northern England for this time period are the cosmogenic dates of 17.3 ±1.1 ka that indicate initial thinning (Ballantyne *et al.,* 2009). However, these say nothing about the dynamics of the ice sheet, which appears to have remained active with a fluctuating ice margin and regional readvances. During this time, a major Heinrich event (H1) in the North

Atlantic caused a re-advance of the ice margin from Northern Ireland across the northern Irish Sea to southern Scotland during GS-2a (Merritt and Auton, 2000; Livingstone *et al.*, 2012). This has been termed the Scottish Readvance and interpreted as occurring during the Killard Point Stadial (McCabe, *et al.*, 2007; J Clark *et al.*, 2012), which has been dated to 17.2–16.6 ka. This suggests that a large ice mass still existed over Scotland at the time, in contrast to the model (Hubbard *et al.*, 2009). This is also later than the cosmogenic dates from Norber, which suggest that much of the lower land in the Yorkshire Dales was ice-free by about 18 ka. The proposal that the Wensleydale Readvance can be ascribed to the H1 Heinrich event (Mitchell and Bridgland, 2011; Mitchell and Hughes, 2012), and may be correlated with Raistrick's earlier recessional limits, suggests that there was still an extensive active icefield with outlet glaciers across the higher western Pennines at this time. However, no dates have been determined for these moraines, and the development of a more secure chronological sequence has still to be established. Furthermore, there is no evidence in the Yorkshire Dales for down-wasting as a process during deglaciation, at least in the style of 'ice stagnation' (Clark *et al.*, 2012). The ice sheet continued to be a dynamic feature during deglaciation. It thinned vertically, and many of the high fells were exposed between active outlet glaciers with low surface profiles, especially towards the ice margin.

Last Glacial–Interglacial Transition

The period of dramatic climatic fluctuations between the end of the Main Late Devensian glaciation and the start of the Holocene is now referred to as the Last Glacial–Interglacial Transition, occurring between 14.7 ka and 11.7 ka (Lowe *et al.*, 1994, 2008; Björck, *et al.*, 1998; Hoek, 2008; Hoek *et al.*, 2008). Pollen investigations of a number of peat and lake sites indicate that this was a time of remarkable climate changes, marked by rapid temperature changes, associated with both climatic amelioration (interstadials) and deterioration (stadials) across the North Atlantic region. In Britain, the early part of this period is marked by warm climatic conditions that have been termed the Lateglacial or Windermere Interstadial; this was followed by a dramatic climatic reversal to the severe cold climate of the Loch Lomond or Younger Dryas Stadial (Innes, 2002; Bell and Walker, 2005).

Shorter climatic reversals within this period have also been identified at a number of British sites, and can be correlated to similar short-lived events on mainland northwest Europe. There the chronostratigraphy is better constrained, and shows evidence for an earlier short period of cold conditions (Older Dryas Stadial), separating an earlier Bølling Interstadial from a later Allerød Interstadial, before the start of the cold Younger Dryas Stadial (Hoek, 2008). The beginning of the Last Glacial–Interglacial Transition is defined by the boundary between the Dimlington Stadial (GS-2) and GI-1 (Greenland Interstadial 1). The climatic changes recorded from the various records in Europe can be correlated with changes in the ice core signal (Fig. 3.52), allowing GI-1 to be subdivided into five events (GI-1e to GI-1a) before a return to the arctic conditions of the Loch Lomond Stadial (Younger Dryas, GS-1).

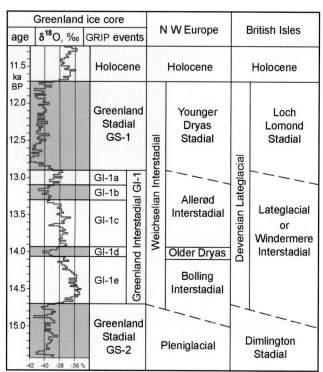

Figure 3.52. *Chronology of the Last Glacial Interglacial Transition (LGIT), with the time-transitional boundaries of the Windermere Interstadial in Britain (from Bell and Walker, 2005); the time scale is GICC05 derived from Greenland ice core, adjusted to the Holocene start that was defined subsequently (Walker et al., 2009).*

Several Lateglacial pollen sites are recorded from the Yorkshire Dales (Innes, 2002; Bridgland *et al.*, 2011). The basal sediments record the time-transgressive nature of deglaciation, but are mostly characterised by un-datable inorganic deposits; these reflect cold climatic conditions as the ice melted and the land surface slowly stabilised, prior to rapid warming at about 14.7 ka (Lowe *et al.*, 2008). Pollen records show that the sparse sedge-tundra cover was rapidly replaced by a shrub-woodland dominated by birch in the lowlands, while the uplands maintained a more open herb cover (Innes, 2002). This can be seen from the Lateglacial pollen record from Malham Tarn Moss, where birch trees may have been absent even during the warmest part of the Windermere Interstadial, and the environment of the limestone upland was dominated by juniper scrub (Pigott and Pigott, 1963). It was, nevertheless, a period of increasing plant cover, soil development and slope stability. This is reflected in a growing number of U–Th age determinations that indicate re-commencement of speleothem growth in various cave systems (Fig. 3.53; see Chapter 10). A series of dates span the last glaciation but have such large error bars that they cannot be used to constrain the chronology, especially with many samples being contaminated by detrital thorium. Similarly, there are few reliable dates for the Last Glacial–Interglacial Transition, even allowing for the higher temperatures during the interstadial, with only evidence from one flowstone, in Old East Passage of Gaping Gill, that demonstrates growth during much of GI-1 (Fig. 3.52). Other dates that correlate with the Transition have large error bars, but indicate that growth appears to have been delayed until the end of the period, possibly reflecting a lag response of the cave system to climate change. Furthermore, a number of dated speleothems record growth during the following

Figure 3.53. Growth periods and dates for Lateglacial and Holocene speleothems from a number of caves in the Yorkshire Dales; error bars are ±1σ and shown as horizontal lines. For speleothem locations and data sources, see Figure 10.15.

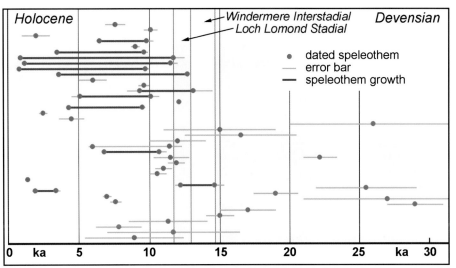

GS-1 (Loch Lomond Stadial), indicating that groundwater flow was maintained during this period of cold periglacial conditions, and suggesting that permafrost may have only developed to a limited extent during this short time period. However, the majority of dates clearly demonstrate that abundant speleothem growth did not commence until the early Holocene with the rapid temperature rise after 11.7 ka.

Geomorphological activity during the Last Glacial–Interglacial Transition period may be described as 'paraglacial', in that the fluvial and slope sediment systems were having to adjust to the removal of glacial and periglacial influence (Church and Ryder, 1972; Ballantyne, 2002). In mountain regions, these responses include numerous landslides within the glacial troughs, largely developed due to valley-side stress-relief and the loss of ice support as well as the changing hydrological conditions on the disappearance of permafrost (Jarman, 2006; Wilson and Smith, 2006). Throughout the Pennines, the Carboniferous rocks above the massive limestone provide optimum situations for deep-seated rotational failures where hillsides are formed in thick sequences of weak mudstones and shales overlain by strong caprocks of sandstone (Cooper, 2007). The mudrocks were also weakened under the intense periglacial conditions that pertained during deglaciation, and flowed as solifluction lobes or debris flows in shallow failures on many slopes (Mitchell, 1991a).

Mallerstang has spectacular and extensive landslide complexes on both sides of its glacial trough. These complex landforms in Mallerstang have previously been interpreted as cirques with terminal and lateral moraines of former glaciers (Rowell and Turner, 1952), or as nivation landforms (King, 1976), but they are more readily explained as the result of complex mass movements (Mitchell, 1991b, 1996). On the eastern slopes of Wild Boar Fell (Mitchell, 1991d), deep-seated rotational failures occur alongside large debris flows that extend along the hillside for over 3 km from Ais Gill to White Walls (Fig. 3.54). Landslides also occur on the west-facing slopes, between Hangingstone Scar and Low Loven Scar, where a number of large mudslides show clear flow structures (Mitchell, 1991e). Further, deep-seated, rotational failures exist elsewhere in the Dales, notably on the upper slopes of the Yoredale and Namurian outliers of Whernside and Ingleborough (Mitchell, 1996, 2012b; Waltham, 2007). Also on the mixed rock sequences of the Yoredale Group, there are large and complex landslides on the slopes of Penhill in Wensleydale (Mitchell, 1991a), in Swaledale (Rose, 1980) and above Halton Gill in Littondale. A large, shallow landslide on Kirkby Fell, west of Malham, has formed in mudstones and sandstones of Namurian age (Wilson, 2007).

Figure 3.54. Aerial view of Wild Boar Fell and the complex landslides occupying its eastern slopes (WM).

Figure 3.55. The terminal moraine from the Loch Lomond Stadial niche glacier on Whernside, forming an arc in the middle distance, overlain by Holocene landslide debris in the foreground (WM).

There are no direct dates for these landslides. On Swarth Fell, moraines from a small cirque glacier of Loch Lomond Stadial age (see below) lie on top of landslide debris, indicating that landslide activity was initiated during deglaciation, probably associated with permafrost degradation, continuing into the Lateglacial period (Mitchell, 1991b, 1991c, 1996). However, most of the large landslides in the Pennines are thought to have occurred in the early Holocene, as indicated by pollen analysis and carbon dates from the Derbyshire Peak District (Johnson, 1987; Waltham and Dixon, 2000). The presence of landslide debris overlying the Loch Lomond Stadial moraine on Whernside (Fig. 3.55) (Mitchell, 2012b) and an early Holocene pollen record from between the debris banks in Mallerstang (Rowell and Turner, 1952) appears to indicate similar Holocene slope conditions in the Yorkshire Dales. The Great Scar Limestone of the Yorkshire Dales is not prone to deep-seated failure. Under the periglacial conditions associated with deglaciation, the limestones scars succumbed to frost shattering, with the formation of extensive talus (scree) slopes below most scars and cliffs (Fig. 3.56). These are notably extensive below the Twisleton Scars in Chapel-le-Dale, are largely covered by trees below Giggleswick Scar, and have in the past blocked the entrance to Victoria Cave.

The later part of the Last Glacial–Interglacial Transition period is marked by the return to cold, glacial conditions across the British mountains during Greenland Stadial 1 (Loch Lomond Stadial) (Gray and Coxon, 1991; Golledge, 2010). Plateau icefields and individual glaciers developed in the Lake District (McDougall, 2001), but only five small niche glaciers in cirques have been identified in the Yorkshire Dales. These former glaciers have been recorded at Cautley Crag in the Rawthey valley, Combe Scar and Great Combe in Dentdale, and on high ground of Swarth Fell and Whernside (Figs. 3.24, 3.57) (Mitchell, 1991b, 1996, 2012b). A claim by Manley (1959) for a 'persistent snow patch' on the north-

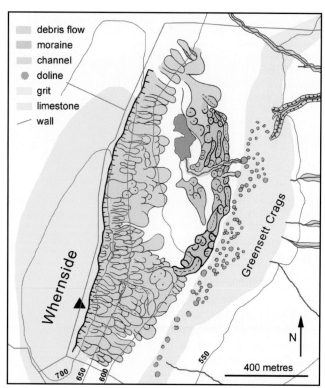

Figure 3.57. Geomorphology of the site of the niche glacier that formed high on Whernside during the Loch Lomond Stadial; only the summit outlier of the Upper Howgate Edge Grit, and the outcrop of the Main Limestone are shown within the cyclic sequence of the Yoredale Group (after Mitchell, 1996).

western side of Ingleborough, during the Loch Lomond Stadial has been reviewed by recent mapping (Fig. 3.58), showing that this part of the mountain scarp is dominated by a large, discrete, deep-seated, rotational landslide and numerous debris flow lobes (Fig. 3.59) (Mitchell, 2012b). Such instability is on-going and may have resulted in back-wasting of the plateau edge throughout the Holocene, as demonstrated by the cosmogenic dates from the plateau rim (Wilson *et al.*, 2012a, 2013).

The limited size of these cirque glaciers indicate that snow-blow, from extensive plateaus lying down-wind of the glaciers, was responsible for generating sufficient

Figure 3.56. Ramps of inactive and active scree at the foot of the limestone scars along the Scales Moor flank of Chapel-le-Dale (TW).

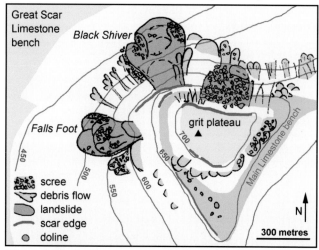

Figure 3.58. The deep-seated landslides and shallow debris flows on the summit slopes of Ingleborough; between the summit grit cap and the wide bench on top of the Great Scar Limestone, the main slopes are formed largely of shales of the Yoredale Group, within which lies the Main Limestone, marked by its dolines.

accumulation to allow their existence in an area that was clearly marginal to glaciation (Manley, 1959; Mitchell, 1996). The moraine ridges associated with the cirque glaciers allow reconstructions of the former glacier extents and thicknesses, and the calculation of former equilibrium line altitudes. The latter range from 311m for the western sites to 608m for the higher eastern glaciers, with the lower values reflecting local conditions associated with snow-blow generated by the prevailing southwesterly winds rather than regional climate (Mitchell, 1996).

Elsewhere in the Dales, the severe climate of the Loch Lomond Stadial encouraged the limited expansion of permafrost and an increase in the intensity of periglacial processes on upland slopes. The most conspicuous landscape responses were reactivation of the talus slopes and solifluction lobes that had been initiated during ice-sheet deglaciation at the end of the Last Glacial Maximum. However, the continued formation of speleothems during this stadial suggests that groundwater percolation persisted, at least through the summers. Climatic conditions were not

severe enough to shut down all flow of water through the cave systems, and the permafrost was probably shallow and discontinuous. However, plant cover was reduced and soil development disrupted, leading to increased sediment flux into the stream and river systems (Bridgland *et al.*, 2011).

Aeolian deflation generally triggers loess deposition in periglacial conditions. Such was probably the case in the Yorkshire Dales during the Loch Lomond Stadial, with loess being derived from exposed glacial and glaciofluvial sediments and then deposited down-wind across the uplands. However, loessic soils in the Dales have yielded dates not from the stadial, but from the early Holocene (Wilson *et al.*, 2008, 2012b). This suggests substantial reworking of the primary loess at the later time, as the landscape stabilised under the new climate conditions (see Chapter 12). Multiple geomorphic processes had been responsible for creating the major landforms of the Yorkshire Dales, largely through the climatic fluctuations of the Pleistocene, but landscape evolution continued into the Holocene, and remained active both above and below ground within the limestone karst.

Deglaciation of the Dales

Cyclical growth of Quaternary ice sheets was primarily the result of astronomical forcing that controlled incoming solar radiation and therefore influenced both temperature and precipitation. As climate cooled, ice was able to develop on favourable upland areas and subsequently expand into surrounding lowlands. This was a relatively slow process taking many millennia; in comparison, deglaciation occurred much more quickly. Furthermore, ice recession in the latter part of a glacial cycle was not smooth, but was punctuated by asynchronous readvances of particular sectors of the ice sheet; this was in response to mass flux variations of the different ice centres, partly in response to complex interactions between ice sheets and the ocean.

Ice sheets are three-dimensional ice masses, so that changes in volume are reflected in both spatial extent and ice thickness. Deglaciation proceeds by volumetric shrinkage of the ice, when summer melting exceeds winter accumulation. This causes retreat of the ice margins and thinning of the ice sheet, exposing the upper slopes of buried topography while ice still covered many lower valley

slopes. The process requires the ice to remain dynamic, in that it continues to flow from source areas, even while experiencing mass loss. This may be due to temperature increase that leads to increased ablation, or alternatively may be the result of reduced precipitation. Across many lowland areas, ice can also become detached from its source areas, resulting in stagnation. In coastal regions, mass loss can also be by iceberg calving.

At the Last Glacial Maximum, the Yorkshire Dales was entirely submerged by the ice sheet. There is limited evidence for the pattern of deglaciation across the Dales, but there is no evidence of ice stagnation in the uplands. Instead, the region appears to have been gradually exposed by active shrinkage of the ice sheet, with margins retreating towards the source area of the Dales Ice Centre on and around Baugh Fell. Deglaciation was asynchronous across the Dales, with the ice sheet transformed first into a topographically independent icecap centred over the Western Pennines.

As the ice became confined to the uplands, its thinning caused peripheral summits, away from the ice centre, to become the first exposed areas, probably around 19,000 years ago. Thus the higher ground of the Craven Uplands and individual fells that were furthest from the source area, such as Ingleborough and Whernside, became nunataks surrounded by individual outlet glaciers that continued to occupy the intervening dales. This ice remained dynamically active, and the recessional moraines in a number of dales, notably Wharfedale and Wensleydale, indicate temporary still-stands during the overall ice retreat. The lack of similar moraines in Ribblesdale suggests that ice retreat continued there without even small stops to allow moraine construction, while incrementally exposing the limestone benches along the Ingleborough flank.

As deglaciation of the Yorkshire Dales entered its final phase, ice cover became increasingly constrained by the landscape. Eventually, the ice was restricted to an isolated icefield, or to a series of small remnant icefields, before finally melting away, probably around 15,000 years ago, as the climate warmed towards the Last Glacial-Interglacial Transition.

Glaciers in western Greenland that currently mimic the conditions in the Yorkshire Dales during their deglaciation (TW).

Figure 3.59. The western flank of Ingleborough, with the wide and shallow Black Shiver landslide on the left and the smaller but deeper Falls Foot landslide on the right (TW).

References

Aitkenhead, N, W J Barclay, A Brandon, R A Chadwick, J I Chisholm, A H Cooper and E W Johnson, 2002. *British Regional Geology: the Pennines and adjacent areas.* British Geological Survey: Nottingham, 206pp.

Atkinson, T C, R S Harmon, P L Smart and A C Waltham, 1978. Palaeoclimatic and geomorphic implications of ^{230}Th/^{234}U Dates on speleothems from Britain. *Nature*, 272, 24-28.

Atkinson, T C, T J Lawson, P L Smart, R S Harmon and J W Hess, 1986. New data on speleothem deposition and palaeoclimate in Britain over the last forty thousand years. *J. Quat. Sci.*, 1, 67-72.

Aveline, W T and T McK Hughes, 1888. *The geology of the country around Kendal, Sedbergh, Bowness and Tebay.* Memoir of the Geological Survey.

Aveline, W T, T McK Hughes and R H Tiddeman, 1872. *The geology of the neighbourhood around Kirkby Lonsdale and Kendal.* Memoir of the Geological Survey.

Baker, A, P L Smart and R L Edwards, 1995. Paleoclimate implications of mass spectrometric dating of a British flowstone. *Geology*, 23, 309-312.

Baker, A, P L Smart and D C Ford, 1993. Northwest European palaeoclimate as indicated by growth frequency variations of secondary calcite deposits. *Palaeogeography, Palaeoclimatology, Palaeoecology*, 100, 291-301.

Ballantyne, C K, 2002. Paraglacial geomorphology. *Quat. Sci. Rev.*, 21, 1935-2017.

Ballantyne, C K, 2010. Extent and glacial chronology of the last British-Irish Ice Sheet: implications of exposure dating using cosmogenic isotopes. *J. Quat. Sci.*, 25, 515-534.

Ballantyne, C K and C Harris, 1994. *The Periglaciation of Great Britain.* Cambridge University Press, 330pp.

Ballantyne, C K and J O Stone, 2011. Did large ice-caps persist on low ground in north-west Scotland during the Lateglacial Interstadial? *J. Quat. Sci.*, 27, 297-306.

Ballantyne, C K, D McCarroll, A Nesje, S O Dahl and J O Stone,. 1998. The last ice sheet in north-west Scotland: reconstruction and implications. *Quat. Sci. Rev.*, 17, 1149-1184.

Ballantyne, C K, D McCarroll and J O Stone, 2006. Vertical dimensions and age of the Wicklow Mountains ice dome, eastern Ireland, and implications for the extent of the last Irish ice sheet. *Quat. Sci. Rev.*, 25, 2048-2058.

Ballantyne, C K, J O Stone and L K Fifield, 2009. Glaciation and deglaciation of the SW Lake District, England: implications of cosmogenic 36Cl exposure dating. *Proc. Geol. Assoc.*, 120, 139-144.

Ballantyne, C K, J O Stone and D McCarroll, 2008. Dimensions and chronology of the last ice sheet in western Ireland. *Quat. Sci. Rev.*, 27, 185-200.

Bateman, M D and P C Buckland, 2001. Late Quaternary record from beyond the ice sheets. 13-20 in M D Bateman, P C Buckland, C D Frederick and N J Whitehouse (eds.), *The Quaternary of East Yorkshire and North Lincolnshire*, Quaternary Research Association: London.

Bateman, M D, P C Buckland, B Chase, C D Frederick and G D Gaunt, 2008. The Late-Devensian pro-glacial Lake Humber: new evidence from littoral deposits at Ferrybridge, Yorkshire, England. *Boreas*, 37, 195-210.

Belbin, S, 1985. Long-term landform development in north-west England: the application of the planation concept. 37-59 in R H Johnson (ed), *The geomorphology of North-west England.* Manchester University Press.

Bell, M and M J C Walker, 2005. *Late Quaternary Environmental Change.* Pearsons: London, 348pp.

Benn D and D J A Evans, 2010. *Glaciers and Glaciation.* Arnold: London, 734pp.

Bennett, M, 2003. Ice streams as the arteries of an ice sheet: their mechanics, stability and significance. *Earth Sci. Rev.*, 61, 309-339.

Björck, S and 7 others, 1998. An event stratigraphy for the Last Termination in the North Atlantic region based on the Greenland ice-core record: a proposal by the INTIMATE group. *J. Quat. Sci.*, 13, 283-292.

Blockley, S P E and 9 others, 2012. Synchronisation of palaeo-environmental records over the last 60,000 years, and an extended INTIMATE event stratigraphy to 48,000 b2k. *Quat. Sci. Rev.*, 36, 2-10.

Blundell, D J and D A Waltham, 2009. A possible glacially-forced tectonic mechanism for the late Neogene surface uplift and subsidence around the North Atlantic. *Proc. Geol. Assoc.*, 120, 98-107.

Bos, J A A, J H Dickson, G R Coope and W G Jardine, 2004. Flora, fauna and climate in Scotland during the Weichselian Middle Pleniglacial – palynological, macrofossil and coleopteran investigations. *Palaeogeography, Palaeoclimatology, Palaeoecology*, 204, 65-100.

Böse, M, C Lüthgens, J R Lee and J Rose, 2012. Quaternary glaciations of northern Europe. *Quat. Sci. Rev.*, 44, 1-25.

Boulton, G S, 1987. A theory of drumlin formation by subglacial sediment deformation. 25-80 in J Menzies and J Rose (eds.), *Drumlin Symposium.* Balkema: Rotterdam.

Boulton, G S, 2010. Drainage pathways beneath ice sheets and their implications for ice sheet form and flow: the example of the British Ice Sheet during the Last Glacial Maximum. *J. Quat. Sci.*, 25, 483-500.

Boulton, G S and M Hagdorn, 2006. Glaciology of the British Isles during the last glacial cycle: forms, flow, streams and lobes. *Quat. Sci. Rev.*, 25, 3359-3390.

Boulton, G S, A S Jones, K M Clayton and M J Kenning, 1977. A British ice-sheet model and patterns of glacial erosion and deposition in Britain. 231-246 in F W Shotton (ed.), *British Quaternary Studies: Recent Advances.* Clarendon Press: Oxford.

Boulton, G S, G D Smith, A S Jones and J Newsome, 1985. Glacial geology and glaciology of the last mid-latitude ice sheets. *J. Geol. Soc.*, 142, 447-474.

Bowen, D Q (ed.), 1999. A Revised Correlation of Quaternary Deposits in the British Isles. *Geological Society Special Report*, 23, 174pp.

Bowen, D Q, F M Phillips, A M McCabe, P C Knutz and G A Sykes, 2002. New data for the last glacial maximum in Great Britain and Ireland. *Quat. Sci. Rev.*, 21, 89-101.

Bradwell, T and 11 others, 2008a. The northern sector of the last British Ice Sheet: maximum extent and demise. *Earth Sci. Rev.*, 88, 207-226.

Bradwell, T, D Fabel, M Stoker, H Mathers, L McHargue and J Howe, 2008b. Icecaps existed throughout the Lateglacial Interstadial in northern Scotland. *J. Quat. Sci.*, 23, 401-407.

Bridgland, D, J Innes, A J Long and W A Mitchell, 2011. *Late Quaternary Landscape Evolution of the Swale-Ure Washlands, North Yorkshire.* Oxbow: Oxford, 336pp.

Briner, J P, G H Miller, R Finkel and D P Hess, 2008. Glacial erosion at the fjord onset zone and implications for the organization of ice flow on Baffin Island, Arctic Canada. *Geomorphology*, 97, 126-134.

Brocklehurst, S and K X Whipple, 2002. Assessing the relative efficiency of fluvial and glacial erosion through simulation of fluvial landscapes. *Geomorphology*, 75, 283-299.

Brook, M S, M P Kirkbride and B W Brock, 2008. Temporal constraints on glacial valley cross-profile evolution: Two Thumb Range, central Southern Alps, New Zealand. *Geomorphology*, 97, 24-34.

Brown, E J, J Rose, G R Coope and J J Lowe, 2006. An MIS 3 age organic deposit from Balglass Burn, central Scotland: palaeoenvironmental significance and implications for the timing of the LGM ice sheet in the vicinity of the British Isles. *J. Quat. Sci.*, 22, 235-250.

Burbank, D W and R S Anderson, 2001. *Tectonic Geomorphology.* Blackwell Science: Oxford, 274pp.

Burek, C, 1991. Quaternary history and glacial deposits of the Peak District. 193-201 in Ehlers *et al., op. cit.*.

Carr, S. J, 2004. The North Sea Basin. 261-270 in J Ehlers and P L Gibbard (eds.), *Quaternary Glaciations: Extent and Chronology: Part I: Europe* (Developments in Quaternary Science, 2), Elsevier: Amsterdam.

Carvill Lewis, 1894. *Papers and Notes on the glacial geology of Great Britain and Ireland.* Longman: London.

Catt, J A, 2007. The Pleistocene glaciations of eastern Yorkshire: a review. *Proc. Yorks. Geol. Soc.,* **56**, 177-207.

Catt, J A, P L Gibbard, J J Lowe, D McCarroll, J D Scourse, M J C Walker and J J Wymer, 2006. Quaternary: ice sheets and their legacy. 429-467 in P J Brenchley and P F Rawson (eds.), *The Geology of England and Wales,* Geological Society: London.

Chiverrell, R C and G S P Thomas, 2010. Extent and timing of the Last Glacial Maximum (LGM) in Britain and Ireland: a review. *J. Quat. Sci.,* **25**, 535-549.

Chiverrell, R C, G C Foster, G S P Thomas, P Marshall and D Hamilton, 2009. Robust chronologies for landform development. *Earth Surface Processes Landforms,* **34**, 319-328.

Chiverrell, R, J Innes, R Middleton, A Plater and G S P Thomas, 2004. Quaternary landscape evolution of the Isle of Man, Lancashire and Southeast Cumbria. 5-38 in R C Chiverrell *et al.* (eds.), *The Quaternary of the Isle of Man and Northwest England; Field Guide.* Quaternary Research Association: London.

Church, M and J Ryder, 1972. Paraglacial sedimentation: a consideration of fluvial processes conditioned by glaciation. *Bull. Geol. Soc. Am.,* **83**, 3059-3071.

Clark, C D and 7 others, 2004a, Map and GIS database of glacial landforms and features related to the last British Ice Sheet. *Boreas,* **33**, 359-375.

Clark, C D, P L Gibbard and J Rose, 2004b. Pleistocene glacial limits in England, Scotland and Wales. 47-82 in J Ehlers and P L Gibbard (eds.), *Quaternary Glaciations: Extent and Chronology: Part I: Europe* (Developments in Quaternary Science, 2), Elsevier: Amsterdam.

Clark, C D, A L C Hughes, S L Greenwood, M Spagnolo and F S L Ng, 2009. Size and shape characteristics of drumlins derived from a large sample and associated scaling laws. *Quat. Sci. Rev.,* **28**, 677-692.

Clark, J, A M McCabe, D Q Bowen and P U Clark, 2012. Response of the Irish ice sheet to abrupt climate change during the last deglaciation. *Quat. Sci. Rev.,* **35**, 100-115.

Clark, P U and 8 others, 2009. The Last Glacial Maximum. *Science,* **325**, 710-714.

Clark, R, 1967. A contribution to glacial studies of the Malham Tarn area. *Field Studies,* **2**, 479-91.

Clayton, K M, 1966. The origin of the landforms of the Malham area. *Field Studies,* **2**, 359-384.

Clayton, K M, 1981. Explanatory description of the landforms of the Malham area. *Field Studies,* **5**, 389-423.

Coope, G R and W Pennington, 1977. The Windermere Interstadial of the Late Devensian. *Phil. Trans. Roy. Soc.,* **B244**, 379-421.

Cooper, A H and A Gibson, 2003. Geology of the Leeds district. *Sheet Explanation British Geological Survey,* Sheet 70.

Cooper, R G, 2007. *Mass Movements in Great Britain.* Geological Conservation Review Series, 33, Joint Nature Conservancy Committee: Peterborough, 348pp.

Cullingford, R and K J Gregory, 1978. Till ridges in Wensleydale, Yorkshire. *Proc. Geol. Assoc.,* **89**, 67-79.

Dakyns, J H, R H Tiddeman, W Gunn and A Strahan, 1890. *The geology of the country around Ingleborough, with parts of Wensleydale and Wharfedale.* Memoir Geological Survey.

Dakyns, J H, R H Tiddeman, R Russell, C Clough and A Strahan, 1891. *The geology of the country around Mallerstang, with parts of Wensleydale, Swaledale and Arkendale.* Memoir Geological Survey.

Davies, B J and 7 others, 2011. Timing and depositional environments of a Middle Pleistocene glaciation of northeast England: new evidence from Warren House Gill, County Durham. *Quat. Sci. Rev.,* **44**, 180-212.

Davis, W M, 1895. The development of certain English rivers. *Geog. J.,* **5**, 127-146.

De Boer, G, 1974. Physiographic evolution. 271-292 in D H Rayner and J E Hemingway (eds.), *The Geology and Mineral Resources of Yorkshire,* Yorkshire Geological Society: Leeds.

Denton, G H, R F Anderson, J R Toggweiler, R L Edwards, J M Schaefer and A E Putnam, 2010. The Last Glacial Termination. *Science,* **328**, 1652-1656.

Dobinski, W, 2011. Permafrost. *Earth Sci. Rev.,* **108**, 158-169.

Duhnforth, M, R S Anderson, D Ward and G M Stock, 2010. Bedrock fracture control of glacial erosion processes and rates. *Geology,* **38**, 423-426.

Ehlers, J, P L Gibbard and J Rose, 1991. *Glacial Deposits in Great Britain and Ireland.* Balkema: Rotterdam.

Embleton, C and C A M King, 1975. *Glacial Geomorphology.* Arnold: London, 583pp.

Etzelmüller, B and J O Hagen, 2005. Glacier-permafrost interactions in Arctic and alpine mountain environments with examples from southern Norway and Svalbard. Geol. Soc. Spec. Pub., 242, 11-27.

Evans, D J A, C D Clark and W A Mitchell, 2005. The last British Ice Sheet: a review of the evidence utilised in the compilation of the Glacial Map of Britain. *Earth Sci. Rev.,* **70**, 253-312.

Evans, D J A, S J Livingstone, A Vieli and C O'Cofaigh, 2009. The palaeoglaciology of the central sector of the British and Irish ice sheet: reconciling glacial geomorphology and preliminary ice sheet modelling. *Quat. Sci. Rev.,* **28**, 739-757.

Fabel, D, A P Stroeven, J Harbor, J Kleman, D Elmore and D Fink, 2002. Landscape preservation under Fennoscandian ice sheets determined from in situ produced 10Be and 26Al. *Earth Planetary Science Letters,* **201**, 397-406.

Fairchild, I J and 7 others, 2006. Modification and preservation of environmental signals in speleothems. *Earth Sci. Rev.,* **75**, 105-153.

Faulkner, T, 2006. The impact of the deglaciation of central Scandinavia on karst caves and the implications for Craven's limestone landscape. *Proc. North Craven Historical Research Group Workshop: Re-thinking Craven's Limestone Landscape,* 4-9.

Faulkner, T, 2012. The Devensian deglaciation and a discussion of the Raistrick evidence. 46-54 in O'Regan *et al., op. cit..*

Finlayson, A G and T Bradwell, 2008. Morphological characteristics, formation and glaciological significance of Rogen moraine in northern Scotland. *Geomorphology,* **101**, 607-617.

Finlayson, A, J W Merritt, M Browne, J Merritt, A McMillan and K Whitbread, 2010. Ice sheet advance, dynamics, and decay configurations: evidence from west central Scotland, *Quat. Sci. Rev.,* **29**, 969-988.

Ford, D C, 1987. Effects of glaciations and permafrost upon the development of karst in Canada. *Earth Surface Processes Landforms,* **12**, 507-521.

Ford, D C, 1993. Karst in cold environments. 199-222 in H M French and O Slaymaker (eds.), *Canada's Cold Environments,* McGill University Press: Montreal.

Ford, T D, 2001. *Sediments in Caves.* Brit. Cave Res. Assoc. Cave Studies Series, 9, 30pp.

Gascoyne, M, 1981. A climate record of the Yorkshire Dales for the last 300,000 years. *Proc. 8th Int. Cong. Speleology* (Bowling Green KY), 96-98.

Gascoyne, M and D C Ford, 1984. Uranium series dating of speleothems: part II, results from the Yorkshire Dales and implications for cave development and Quaternary climates. *Trans. Brit. Cave Res. Assoc.,* **11**, 65-85.

Gascoyne, M, A P Currant and T C Lord, 1981. Ipswichian fauna of Victoria Cave and the marine palaeoclimate record. *Nature,* **294**, 652-654.

Gascoyne, M, D C Ford and H P Schwarz, 1983a. Uranium-series ages of speleothem from north-west England: correlation with Quaternary climate. *Phil. Trans. Roy. Soc.,* **B301**, 143-164.

Gascoyne, M, D C Ford and H P Schwarz, 1983b. Rates of cave and landform development in the Yorkshire Dales from speleothem age data. *Earth Surface Processes Landforms,* **8**, 557-568.

Glasser, N F and M C Ghiglione, 2009. Structural, tectonic and glaciological controls on the evolution of fjord landscapes. *Geomorphology,* **105**, 291-302.

Glover, R R, 1974. Cave development in the Gaping Gill system. 343-384 in Waltham *op. cit..*

Goldie, H, 2012. North west karst: evidence for pre-Devensian development. 6-10 in O'Regan *et al., op. cit..*

Goldie, H S and M E Marker, 2001. Pre-Devensian dolines above Crummackdale, northwest Yorkshire, UK. *Cave Karst Science,* **28**, 53-58.

Golledge, N R, 2010. Glaciation of Scotland during the Younger Dryas stadial: a review. *J. Quat. Sci.,* **25**, 550-566.

Goodchild, J G, 1875. The glacial phenomena of the Eden valley and the western part of the Yorkshire-Dale District. *Q. J. Geol. Soc.,* **31**, 55-99.

Goodchild, J G, 1887. Ice work in Edenside and some of the adjoining parts of North West England. *Trans. Cumberland Westmorland Assoc.,* **14**, 73-90.

Goodfellow, B W, 2007. Relic non-glaciated surfaces in formerly glaciated landscapes. *Earth Sci. Rev.,* **80**, 47-73.

Gordon, J E, 2010. Scottish landform examples 41: the geological formation and landscape evolution of Scotland. *Scot. Geog. J.,* **126**, 41-62.

Gordon, J E and D Sutherland (eds.), 1993. *Quaternary of Scotland.* Geological Conservation Review Series, 6, Chapman and Hall: London, 695pp.

Gray, J M and P Coxon, 1991. The Loch Lomond Stadial glaciation in Britain and Ireland. 89-105 in Ehlers *et al., op. cit..*

Green, P F, R Westaway, D A C Manning and P L Younger, 2012. Cenozoic cooling and denudation in the North Pennines (northern England, UK) constrained by apatite fission-track analysis of cuttings from the Eastgate borehole. *Proc. Geol. Assoc,* **123**, 450-463.

Greenwood, S I, C D Clark and A L C Hughes, 2007. Formalising an inversion methodology for reconstructing ice-sheet retreat patterns from meltwater channels: applications to the British Ice Sheet. *J. Quat. Sci.,* **22**, 637-645.

Gunn, J, 1985. Pennine karst areas and their Quaternary history. 263-291 in R H Johnson (ed.), *The Geomorphology of North-west England,* Manchester University Press.

Hall, A and P Bishop, 2002. Scotland's denudational history: an integrated view of erosion and sedimentation at an uplifted passive margin. 271-290 in A G Dore *et al.* (eds.), Exhumation of the North Atlantic margin: timing, mechanisms and implications for petroleum exploration. *Geol. Soc. Spec. Publ.*, 196, 271-290.

Hall, A and W M Phillips, 2006. Glacial modification of granitic tors in the Cairngorms, Scotland. *J. Quat. Sci.*, 21, 811-830.

Hall, A and D E Sugden, 1987. Limited modification of granite tors in the Cairngorm Mountains, Scotland. *Earth Surface Processes Landforms*, 12, 531-542.

Harris, C and J B Murton (eds.), 2005. Cryospheric systems: glaciers and permafrost. *Geol. Soc. Spec. Pub.*, 242. 161pp.

Hemming, S R, 2004. Heinrich Events: massive Late Pleistocene detritus layers of the North Atlantic and their global climatic imprint. *Review Geophysics*, 42, 1-43.

Hibbert, F D, W E N Austin, M J Leng and R W Gatliff,2010. British Ice Sheet dynamics inferred from North Atlantic ice-rafted debris records spanning the last 175,000 years. *J. Quat. Sci.*, 25, 461-482.

Hiemstra, J F, D J A Evans, J D Scourse, D McCarroll, M F A Furze and E Rhodes, 2006. New evidence for a grounded Irish Sea glaciation of the Scilly Isles, UK. *Quat. Sci. Rev.*, 25, 299-309.

Hoek, W Z, 2008. The Last Glacial-Interglacial Transition. *Episodes*, 31, 226-229.

Hoek, W Z, Yu Z C and J J Lowe, 2008. Integration of ice-core, marine, and terrestrial records (INTIMATE): refining the record of the Last Glacial-Interglacial Transition. *Quat. Sci. Rev.*, 27, 1-5.

Hollingworth, S E, 1931. Glaciation of western Edenside and adjoining areas and the drumlins of the Edenside and Solway Basin. *Q. J Geol. Soc.*, 87, 281-359.

Howard, A J, M G Macklin, S Black and K Hudson-Edwards, 1998. Late Pleistocene and Holocene alluvial history of upper Wharfedale, between Kettlewell and Grassington. 19-29 in A J Howard and M G Macklin, *The Quaternary of the Eastern Yorkshire Dales: Field Guide.* Quaternary Research Association: London.

Hubbard, A and 7 others, 2009. Dynamic cycles, ice streams and their impact on the extent, chronology and deglaciation of the British-Irish ice sheet. *Quat. Sci. Rev.,* 28, 758-776.

Hubberten, H W and 20 others, 2004. The periglacial climate and environment in northern Eurasia during the Last Glaciation. *Quat. Sci. Rev.,* 23, 1333-1357.

Huddart, D, 2002. Giggleswick Scar. 203-208 in Huddart and Glasser, *op. cit.*.

Huddart, D and N F Glasser (eds.), 2002. *Quaternary of Northern England.* Geological Conservation Review Series, 25, Chapman and Hall: London, 745pp.

Hudson, R G S, 1933. The scenery and geology of Yorkshire. *Proc. Geol. Assoc.*, 44, 228-255.

Hughes, A L C, C D Clark and C J Jordan, 2010. Subglacial bedforms of the last British Ice Sheet. *J. Maps*, 2010, 543-563.

Hughes, A L C, S L Greenwood and C D Clark, 2011. Dating constraints on the last British-Irish Ice Sheet: a map and database. *J. Maps*, 2011, 156-184.

Hughes, T, 2011. A simple holistic hypothesis for the self-destruction of ice sheets. *Quat. Sci. Rev.,* 30, 1829-1845.

Imbrie, J and K P Imbrie, 1979. *Ice Ages: Solving the Mystery.* McMillan: London, 224pp.

Innes, J, 2002. The Lateglacial record of northern England. 211-220 in Huddart and Glasser, *op. cit.*.

Iverson, N R, 2012. A theory of glacial quarrying for landscape evolution models. *Geology*, 40, 679-682.

Jansson, K N and N F Glasser, 2005. Palaeoglaciology of the Welsh sector of the British-Irish Ice Sheet. *J. Geol. Soc.*, 162, 25-37.

Japsen, P, J M Bonow, P F Green, J A Chalmers and K Lidmar-Bergström, 2009. Formation, uplift and dissection of planation surfaces at passive continental margins – a new approach. *Earth Surface Processes Landforms*, 34, 683-699.

Japsen, P, J A Chalmers, P F Green and J M Bonow, 2011. Elevated passive continental margins: not rift shoulders, but expressions of episodic, post-rift burial and exhumation. *Global Planetary Change*, 90, 73-86.

Jarman, D, 2006. Large rock slope failures in the Highlands of Scotland: characterisation, causes and spatial distribution. *Engineerig Geology*, 83, 161-182.

Jarman, D. 2010. Issues in the landscape evolution of NW Sutherland. 13-27 in S Lukas and T Bradwell (eds.), *The Quaternary of Western Sutherland and adjacent area: Field Guide.* Quaternary Research Association: London.

Johnson, R H, 1985. The imprint of glaciation on the West Pennine uplands. 237-262 in R H Johnson (ed.), *The geomorphology of North-west England.* Manchester University Press.

Johnson, R H, 1987. Dating of ancient, deep-seated landslides in temperate regions. 561-600 in M G Anderson and K S Richards (eds.), *Slope Stability*. Wiley.

Jones, R L and D H Keen, 1993. *Pleistocene environments in the British Isles.* Chapman and Hall: London, 346pp.

Jouzel, J and V Masson-Delmotte, 2010. Deep ice cores: the need to go back in time. *Quat. Sci. Rev.,* 29, 3683-3689.

Kendall, P F, 1902. A system of glacier lakes in the Cleveland Hills. *Q. J. Geol. Soc.*, 58, 471-571.

Kendall, P F and H E Wroot, 1924. *The Geology of Yorkshire.* Private publication, 660pp..

Kent, P, 1974. Structural history. 13-28 in D H Rayner and J E Hemingway (eds.), *The Geology and Mineral Resources of Yorkshire,* Yorkshire Geological Society: Leeds.

King, W B R, 1924. River capture in the Lunds, Yorkshire. *The Naturalist,* 41-44 and 81-83.

King, C A M, 1976. *Northern England. Geomorphology of the British Isles.* Methuen: London, 213pp.

Kleman, J. 1994. Preservation of landforms under ice sheets and ice caps. *Geomorphology,* 9, 19-32.

Kleman, J and N F Glasser. 2007. The subglacial thermal organisation (STO) of ice sheets. *Quat. Sci. Rev.,* 26, 585-597.

Kleman, J and A P Stroevan, 1997. Preglacial surface remnants and Quaternary glacial regimes in northwestern Sweden. *Geomorphology,* 19, 35-54.

Kleman, J, C Hättestrand, L Borgström and A Stroeven, 1997. Fennoscandian palaeoglaciology reconstructed using a glacial geological inversion model. *J. Glaciology,* 43, 283-299.

Lang, N and E W Wolff, 2011. Interglacial and glacial variability from the last 800 ka in marine, ice and terrestrial records. *Climate Past,* 7, 361-380.

Lee, J R, 2011. Cool Britannia: from Milankovitch wobbles to Ice Ages. *Mercian Geologist,* 17, 274-279.

Lee, J R, F S Busschers and H P Sejrup, 2012. Pre-Weichselian Quaternary glaciations of the British Isles, the Netherlands, Norway and adjacent marine areas south of 68°N: implications for long-term ice sheet development in northern Europe. *Quat. Sci. Rev.,* 44, 213-228.

Lee, J R, J Rose, R J O Hamblin and B P Moorlock, 2004. Dating of the earliest lowland glaciation of eastern England: a pre-MIS 12 early Middle Pleistocene Happisburgh Glaciation. *Quat. Sci. Rev.,* 23, 1551-1566.

Lee, J R, J Rose, J B Riding, R J O Hamblin and B S P Moorlock, 2002. Testing the case for a Middle Pleistocene Scandinavian glaciation in Eastern England: evidence for a Scottish ice source for tills within the Corton formation of East Anglia, UK. *Boreas,* 31, 345-355.

Letzer, J M, 1987. Drumlins of the southern Vale of Eden. 323-334 in J Menzies and J Rose (eds.), *Drumlin Symposium,* Balkema: Rotterdam.

Linton, D L, 1951. Watershed breaching by ice in Scotland. *Trans. Inst. Brit. Geog.,* 15, 1-15.

Lisiecki, L E, 2010. Links between eccentricity forcing and the 100,000-year glacial cycle. *Nature Geoscience,* 3, 349-352.

Lisiecki, L E and M E Raymo, 2007. Plio-Pleistocene climate evolution: trends and transitions in glacial cycle dynamics. *Quat. Sci. Rev.,* 26, 56-69.

Livingstone, S J and 8 others, 2012. Glaciodynamics of the central sector of the last British-Irish Ice Sheet in northern England. *Earth Sci. Rev.,* 111, 25-55.

Livingstone, S J, C O'Cofaigh and D J A Evans, 2008. Glacial geomorphology of the central sector of the last British-Irish Ice Sheet. *J. Maps*, 2008, 358-377.

Livingstone, S J, C O'Cofaigh and D J A Evans, 2010. A major ice drainage pathway of the last British-Irish Ice Sheet: the Tyne Gap, northern England. *J. Quat. Sci.,* 25, 354-370.

Lord, T, J Lundberg and P Murphy, 2012. A guide to work at Victoria Cave, from the 19th to 21st centuries. 84-97 in O'Regan *et al., op. cit.*.

Lowe, J J and M J C Walker, 1997. *Reconstructing Quaternary Environments.* Longman: London, 446pp.

Lowe, J J and 9 others, 1994. Climate changes in areas adjacent to the North Atlantic during the last glacial-interglacial transition (14-9 ka BP): a contribution to IGCP-253. *J. Quat. Sci.,* 9, 185-198.

Lowe, J J and 8 others, 2008. Synchronisation of palaeo-environmental events in the North Atlantic region during the Last Termination: a revised protocol recommended by the INTIMATE group. *Quat. Sci. Rev.,* 27, 6-17.

Lundberg, J, T C Lord and P M Murphy, 2010. Thermal ionization mass spectrometer U-Th dates on Pleistocene speleothems from Victoria Cave, North Yorkshire, UK: implications for palaeo-environment and stratigraphy over multiple glacial cycles. *Geosphere,* 6, 379-395.

Manley, G, 1959. The late-glacial climate of north-west England. *Liverpool Manchester Geol. J.,* 2, 188-215.

Marker, M E and H Goldie, 2007. Large karst depressions on the Yorkshire Dales limestone: interim results and discussion: an early indication of a new paradigm. *Cave Karst Science,* 34, 117-127.

McCabe, A M, P U Clark, J Clark and P Dunlop, 2007. Radiocarbon constraints on readvances of the British-Irish Ice Sheet in the northern Irish Sea basin during the last deglaciation. *Quat. Sci. Rev.,* 26, 1204-1211.

McCarroll, D and 6 others, 2010. Exposure age constraints on the extent, timing and rate of retreat of the last Irish Sea ice stream. *Quat. Sci. Rev.,* **29**, 1844-1852.

McDermott, F, T C Atkinson, I J Fairchild, L M Baldini and D P Mattey, 2011. A first evaluation of the spatial gradients in δ¹⁸O recorded by European Holocene speleothems. *Global Planetary Change, 79*, 275-287.

McDougall, D A, 2001. The geomorphological impact of Loch Lomond (Younger Dryas) Stadial plateau icefields in the central Lake District, northwest England. *J. Quat. Sci.,* **16**, 531-543.

Merritt, J W and C A Auton, 2000. An outline of the lithostratigraphy and depositional history of Quaternary deposits in the Sellafield district, west Cumbria. *Proc. Yorks. Geol. Soc.,* **53**, 129-154.

Merritt, J W, C A Auton, E R Connell, A M Hall and J D Peacock, 2003. Cainozoic geology and landscape evolution of north-east Scotland. *Memoir British Geological Survey,* Sheets 66E, 67, 76E, 77, 86E, 87W, 87E, 95, 96W, 96E and 97 (Scotland), 178pp.

Mitchell, W A (ed.), 1991. *Western Pennines: Field Guide.* Quaternary Research Association: London. 124pp.

Mitchell, W A, 1991a. Dimlington Stadial ice sheet in the Western Pennines. 25-42 in Mitchell, op. cit..

Mitchell, W A, 1991b. Loch Lomond Stadial landforms and palaeo-glaciological reconstruction. 43-53 in Mitchell, op. cit..

Mitchell W A, 1991c. Swarth Fell. 66-70 in Mitchell, op. cit..

Mitchell W A, 1991d. Wild Boar Fell. 71-77 in Mitchell, op. cit..

Mitchell, W A, 1991e. Loven Scars and Hangingstone Scar. 82-90 in Mitchell, op. cit..

Mitchell, W A, 1994. Drumlins in ice sheet reconstructions, with reference to the western Pennines, northern England. *Sedimentary Geology,* **91**, 313-331.

Mitchell, W A, 1996. Significance of snowblow in the generation of Loch Lomond Stadial (Younger Dryas) glaciers in the western Pennines. *J Quat. Sci.,* **11**, 233-248.

Mitchell, W A, 2007. Reconstructions of the Late Devensian (Dimlington Stadial) British-Irish Ice Sheet: the role of the upper Tees drumlin field, northern Pennines, England. *Proc. Yorks. Geol. Soc.,* **56**, 221-234.

Mitchell, W A, 2008. The Ribblehead drumlins. *Geog. Rev.,* **21**, 24-28.

Mitchell, W A, 2012a. Long term climatic change in the Yorkshire Dales. 25-33 in O'Regan *et al., op. cit..*

Mitchell, W A, 2012b. Whernside. 25-33 in O'Regan *et al., op. cit..*

Mitchell, W A and D R Bridgland, 2011. Geomorphology and regional stratigraphy. 26-87 in D R Bridgland et al. (eds.), *Late Quaternary Landscape Evolution of the Swale-Ure Washlands, North Yorkshire.* Oxbow: Oxford..

Mitchell, W A and C D Clark, 1994. The last ice sheet in Cumbria. 4-14 in J Boardman and J Walden (eds.), *Cumbria: Field Guide.* Quaternary Research Association: London.

Mitchell, W A and A L C Hughes, 2012. The Late Devensian glaciation in the Yorkshire Dales. 34-45 in O'Regan *et al., op. cit..*

Mitchell, W A and P W Prescott, 2012. Ribblehead drumlins. 72-78 in O'Regan *et al., op. cit..*

Mitchell, W A and J Riley, 2006. Drumlin map of the Western Pennines and southern Vale of Eden, Northern England. *J. Maps,* 2006, 10-16.

Mitchell, W A, D R Bridgland and J Innes, 2010. Late Quaternary evolution of the Tees-Swale interfluve east of the Pennines: the role of glaciation in the development of river systems in northern England. *Proc. Geol. Assoc.,* **121**, 410-422.

Mitchell, W A, J B Innes, D Bridgland, A J Long, M M Rutherford and S Warwick, 2008. Landscape evolution of the Swale-Ure Washlands. 77-87 in M Atherden and T Milsom (eds.), *Yorkshire Landscapes Past and Future,* PLACE: York St John University.

Mudelsee, M and M Schultz, 1997. The Mid-Pleistocene climatic transition: onset of the 100-ka cycle lags ice volume by 280 ka. *Earth Planetary Science Letters,* **151**, 117-123.

Murphy, P and A G Latham, 2001. A uranium series date from Malham Cove, North Yorkshire, UK. *Cave Karst Science,* **28**, 135-136.

Murphy, P J and T Lord, 2003. Victoria Cave, Yorkshire: new thoughts on an old site. *Cave Karst Science,* **30**, 83-88.

Murphy, P, R Smallshire and C Midgley, 2001. The sediments of Illusion Pot, Kingsdale, UK: evidence for subglacial utilisation of a karst conduit in the Yorkshire Dales. *Cave Karst Science, 28*, 29-34.

Murphy, P, A R Westerman, R Clark, A Booth and A Parr, 2008. Enhancing understanding of breakdown and collapse in the Yorkshire Dales using ground penetrating radar on cave sediments. *Engineering Geology, 99*, 160-168.

Naafs, B D A, J Hefter, P Ferretti, R Stein and G H Haug,. 2011. Sea surface temperatures did not control the first occurrence of Hudson Bay Heinrich Events during MIS 16. *Paleoceanography,* **26**, PA4201. 10pp.

O'Cofaigh, C and D J A Evans, 2007. Radiocarbon constraints on the age of the maximum advance of the British-Irish Ice Sheet in the Celtic Sea. *Quat. Sci. Rev.,* **26**, 1197-1203.

O'Connor, J, D S F Williams and G M Davies, 1974. Karst features of Malham and the Craven Fault system. 395-408 in Waltham *op. cit.*.

O'Regan, H J, T Faulkner and I R Smith (eds.), 2012. *Cave Archaeology and Karst Geomorphology in North West England: Field Guide.* Quaternary Research Association: London, 186pp..

Palmer, J. 1967. Landforms. 16-29 in M W Beresford and G R J Jones (eds.), *Leeds and its Region,* Arnold: London.

Peck, V L, I R Hall, R Zahn, F Grousset, S R Hemming and J D Scourse, 2007. The relationship of Heinrich events and their European precursors over the last 60 ka BP: a multi-proxy ice-rafted debris provenance study in the North East Atlantic. *Quat. Sci. Rev.,* **26**, 862-875.

Penny, L F, 1974. Quaternary. 245-264 in D H Rayner and E Hemingway (eds.), *The Geology and Mineral Resources of Yorkshire.* Yorkshire Geological Society: Leeds.

Phillips, W M, A M Hall, R Mottram, L K Fifield and D E Sugden, 2006. Cosmogenic 10Be and 26 Al exposure ages of tors and erratics, Cairngorm Mountains, Scotland: timescales for the development of a classic landscape of selective linear glacial erosion. *Geomorphology,* **73**, 222-245.

Pigott, M E and C D Pigott, 1963. Late-glacial and post-glacial deposits at Malham, Yorkshire. *New Phytologist,* **62**, 317-34.

Pitty, A F, J L Ternan, R A Halliwell and J Crowther, 1986. Karst water temperatures and the shaping of Malham Cove, Yorkshire. 281-291 in K Paterson and M M Sweeting (eds.), *New Directions in Karst.* Geo Books: Norwich.

Raistrick, A, 1926. The glaciation of Wensleydale, Swaledale and adjoining parts of the Pennines. *Proc. Yorks. Geol. Soc.,* **20**, 366-410.

Raistrick, A, 1927. Periodicity in the glacial retreat in West Yorkshire. *Proc. Yorks. Geol. Soc.,* **21**, 24-28.

Raistrick, A, 1929a. Some Yorkshire glacial lakes. *The Naturalist,* 208-212.

Raistrick, A, 1929b. Glaciation of the Hellifield district. *Yorkshire Naturalist Union Circular,* 346, 3.

Raistrick, A, 1930. Some glacial features of the Settle district. *Proc. Univ. Durham Phil. Soc.,* **8**, 239-251.

Raistrick, A, 1931a. The glaciation of Wharfedale. *Proc. Yorks. Geol. Soc.,* **22**, 9-30.

Raistrick, A, 1931b. The late-glacial and post-glacial periods in the north Pennines: I, the glacial maximum and retreat. *Trans. Northern Naturalists Union,* **1**, 16-28.

Raistrick, A, 1931c. The glaciation of Northumberland and Durham. *Proc. Geol. Assoc.,* **42**, 281-291.

Raistrick, A, 1933. Glacial and post-glacial periods in West Yorkshire. *Proc. Geol. Assoc.,* **44**, 263-269.

Raistrick, A, 1934. The correlation of glacial retreat stages across the Pennines. *Proc. Yorks. Geol. Soc.,* **22**, 199-214.

Raistrick, A, 1938. Linton Mires, Wharfedale. *Proc. Univ. Durham Phil. Soc.,* **10**, 24-31.

Raistrick, A, 1954a. The Ice Age in Yorkshire: I. *Dalesman,* **16**, 329-333.

Raistrick, A, 1954b. The Ice Age in Yorkshire: II, a Dales Lake District. *Dalesman,* **16**, 397-401.

Raistrick, A, 1954c. The Ice Age in Yorkshire: III. *Dalesman,* **16**, 458-462.

Raistrick, A and K B Blackburn, 1931. Pollen analysis of the peat on Heathery Burn Moor, Northumberland. *Proc. Univ. Durham Phil. Soc.,* **8**, 351-358.

Raistrick, A and K B Blackburn, 1933. The late-glacial and post-glacial periods of the North Pennines: III, the post-glacial peats. *Trans. Northern Naturalists Union,* **1**, 79-103.

Rasmussen, S O and 15 others, 2006. A new Greenland ice core chronology for the last termination. *J Geophysical Research,* **111**, D06102, 16pp.

Rasmussen, S O, I K Seierstad, K K Andersen, M Bigler, D Dahl-Jensen and S J Johnsen, 2008. Synchronization of the NGRIP, GRIP and GISP2 ice cores across MIS2 and palaeoclimatic implications. *Quat. Sci. Rev.,* **27**, 6-17.

Rea, B R and D J A Evans, 2003. Plateau icefield landsystems. 407-431 in D J A Evans (ed.), *Glacial Landsystems,* Arnold: London.

Rose, J, 1980. Landform development around Kisdon, upper Swaledale, Yorkshire. *Proc. Yorks. Geol. Soc.,* **43**, 201-219.

Rose, J, 1985. The Dimlington Stadial/ Dimlington Chronozone: a proposal for naming the main glacial episode of the Late Devensian in Britain. *Boreas,* **14**, 225-230.

Rose, J, 2009. Early and Middle Pleistocene landscapes of eastern England. *Proc. Geol. Assoc.,* **120**, 3-33.

Rose J and J M Letzer, 1977. Superimposed drumlins. *J. Glaciology,* **18**, 471-480.

Rose, J, B S P Moorcock and R J O Hamblin, 2001. Pre-Anglian fluvial and coastal deposits in Eastern England: lithostratigraphy and palaeo-environments. *Quaternary International,* **79**, 5-22.

Rowell, A J and J S Turner, 1952. Corrie glaciation in the upper Eden valley. *Liverpool Manchester Geol. J.,* **1**, 200-207.

Russell, A J, 1995. Late Devensian meltwater movement and storage within the Ochil Hills, central Scotland. *Scot. J. Geol.,* **31**, 65-78.

Scheib, A J, J R Lee, N Breward and J B Riding, 2011. Reconstructing flow paths of the Middle Pleistocene British Ice Sheet in central-eastern England: the application of regional soil geochemical data. *Proc. Geol. Assoc.,* **122**, 432-444.

Scourse, J D (ed.), 2006. *The Isles of Scilly. Field Guide.* Quaternary Research Association: London.

Scourse, J D and 7 others, 2009. Growth, dynamics and deglaciation of the last British–Irish ice sheet: the deep-sea ice-rafted detritus record. *Quat. Sci. Rev.,* **28**, 3066-3084.

Sejrup, H P and 8 others, 2005. Pleistocene glacial history of the NW European continental margin. *Marine Petroleum Geology,* **22**, 1111-1129.

Sejrup, H P, A Nygård, A M Hall and H Haflidason, 2009. Middle and Late Weichselian (Devensian) glaciation history of south-west Norway, North Sea and eastern UK. *Quat. Sci. Rev.,* **28**, 370-380.

Siegert, M J, 2001. *Ice sheets and Late Quaternary Environmental Change.* Wiley: London, 231pp..

Sissons, J B, 1958. Subglacial erosion in southern Northumberland. *Scot. Geog. Mag.,* **74**, 163-174.

Sissons, J B, 1960. Some aspect of glacial drainage channels in Britain, Part 1. *Scot. Geog. Mag.,* **76**, 15-36.

Sissons, J B, 1961. Some aspect of glacial drainage channels in Britain, Part 2. *Scot. Geog. Mag.,* **77**, 15-36.

Staiger, J K W and 7 others, 2005. Quaternary relief generation by polythermal glacier ice. *Earth Surface Processes Landforms,* **30**, 1145-1159.

Stanford, J D, E J Rohling, S Bacon, A P Roberts, F E Grousset and M Bolshaw, 2011. A new concept for the palaeoceanographic evolution of Heinrich event 1 in the North Atlantic. *Quat. Sci. Rev.,* **30**, 1047-1066.

Stoker, M S, T Bradwell, J A Howe, I P Wilkinson and K McIntyre, 2009. Lateglacial ice-cap dynamics in NW Scotland: evidence from the fjords of the Summer Isles region. *Quat. Sci. Rev.,* **28**, 3161-3184.

Stoker, M S, S P Holford, R R Hills, P F Green and I R Duddy, 2010. Cenozoic post-rift sedimentation off northwest Britain: recording the detritus of episodic uplift on a passive continental margin. *Geology,* **38**, 595-598.

Stoker, M S and 8 others, 1994. A record of late Cenozoic stratigraphy, sedimentation and climate change from the Hebridean slope, NE Atlantic Ocean. *J. Geol. Soc.,* **151**, 235-249.

Stokes C R and C D Clark, 1999. Geomorphological criteria for identifying Pleistocene ice streams. *Annals Glaciology,* **28**, 67-74.

Stokes, C R and C D Clark, 2002. Palaeo-ice streams. *Quat. Sci. Rev.,* **20**, 1437-1457.

Stone, P and 6 others, 2010. *British Regional Geology: Northern England.* British Geological Survey: Nottingham. 294pp.

Straw, A, 1983. Pre-Devensian glaciation of Lincolnshire and adjacent areas. *Quat. Sci. Rev.,* **2**, 239-260.

Straw, A, 1991. Glacial deposits in Lincolnshire and adjoining areas. 213-221 in Ehlers *et al., op cit.*.

Sugden, D E, N Glasser and C M Clapperton, 1992. Evolution of large roches moutonnées. *Geografiska Annaler,* **74A**, 253-264.

Sugden, D E, 1968. The selectivity of glacial erosion in the Cairngorm Mountains. *Trans. Inst. Brit. Geog.,* **45**, 79-92.

Sutcliffe, A J, T C Lord, R S Harmon, M Ivanovitch, A Rae and T N Hess, 1985. Wolverine in Northern England at about 83,000 yrs BP: faunal evidence for climatic change during Isotope Stage 5. *Quat. Res.,* **24**, 73-86.

Sweeting, M M, 1950. Erosion cycles and limestone caverns in the Ingleborough District. *Geog. J.,* **115**, 63-78.

Sweeting, M M, 1972. *Karst Landforms.* Macmillan: London, 362pp.

Sweeting, M M, 1974. Karst geomorphology in north-west England. 46-105 in Waltham *op. cit.*.

Telfer, M W, P Wilson, T C Lord and P J Vincent, P J, 2009. New constraints on the age of the last ice sheet glaciation in NW England using optically stimulated luminescence dating. *J. Quat. Sci.,* **24**, 906-915.

Thierens, M and 11 others, 2011. Ice-rafting from the British-Irish ice sheet since the earliest Pleistocene (2.6 million years ago): implications for long-term mid-latitudinal ice-sheet growth in the North Atlantic region. *Quat. Sci. Rev.,* **44**, 229-240.

Thomson, S N, M T Brandon, J H Tomkin, P W Reiners, C Vásquez and N J Wilson, 2010. Glaciation as a destructive and constructive control on mountain building. *Nature,* **467**, 313-317.

Thornalley, D J R, I N McCave and H Elderfield, 2010. Freshwater input and abrupt deglacial climate change in the North Atlantic. *Paleoceanography,* **25**, PA1201,16pp.

Tiddeman, R H, 1872. On the evidence for the ice sheet in North Lancashire and adjacent parts of Yorkshire and Westmorland. *Q. J. Geol. Soc.,* **28**, 114-123.

Toucanne, S and 9 others, 2010. The first estimation of Fleuve Manche palaeoriver discharge during the last deglaciation: evidence for Fennoscandian ice sheet meltwater flow in the English Channel ca. 20-18 ka ago. *Earth Planetary Science Letters,* **290**, 459-473.

Trotter, F M, 1929. Glaciation of the eastern Edenside, the Alston Block and the Carlisle Plain. *Q. J. Geol. Soc.,* **88**, 549-607.

Trotter, F M and S E Hollingworth, 1932. The glacial sequence in the north of England. *Geol. Mag.,* **69**, 374-380.

Valla, P G, D L Shuster and P A van der Beek, 2011. Significant increase in relief of the European Alps during mid-Pleistocene glaciations. *Nature Geoscience,* **4**, 688-692.

Versey, H C, 1948. The Skipton earthquake of 1944. *Trans. Leeds Geol. Assoc.,* **6**, 95-97.

Vincent, P J and M P Lee, 1981. Some observations on the loess around Morecambe Bay, north-west England. *Proc. Yorks. Geol. Soc.,* **43**, 281-294.

Vincent, P J, P Wilson, T C Lord, C Schnabel and K M Wilcken, 2010. Cosmogenic isotope (36Cl) surface exposure dating of the Norber erratics, Yorkshire Dales: further constraints on the timing of the LGM glaciation in Britain. *Proc. Geol. Assoc.,* **121**, 24-31.

Vincent, P J, 1996. Palaeokarst, pits and problems. *Proc. Cumberland Geol. Soc,* **6**, 134-136.

Walker, M and 16 others, 2009. Formal definition and dating of the GSSP (Global Stratotype Section and Point) for the base of the Holocene using the Greenland NGRIP ice core and selected auxiliary records. *J. Quat. Sci.,* **24**, 3-17.

Waltham, A C (ed.), 1974. *Limestones and Caves of North-west England.* David & Charles (for British Cave Research Association): Newton Abbot, 477pp.

Waltham, A C, 1990. Geomorphic evolution of the Ingleborough karst. *Cave Karst Science,* **17**, 9-18.

Waltham, T, 2007. *The Yorkshire Dales: Landscape and Geology.* Crowood: Marlborough, 224pp.

Waltham, T, 2012. The Yorkshire Dales karst. 1-5 in O'Regan *et al., op cit.*.

Waltham, A C and N Dixon, 2000. Movement of the Mam Tor landslide, Derbyshire, UK. *Q. J. Eng. Geol. Hydrogeol.,* **33**, 105-123.

Waltham, T and Long, H, 2011. Limestone plateaus of the Yorkshire Dales glaciokarst. *Cave Karst Science,* **38**, 65-70.

Waltham, T, P Murphy and A Batty, 2010. Kingsdale: the evolution of a Yorkshire dale. *Proc. Yorks. Geol. Soc.,* **58**, 95-105.

Waltham, A C, M J Simms, A R Farrant and H S Goldie, 1997. *Karst and Caves of Great Britain.* Chapman & Hall (for Joint Nature Conservation Committee): London, 358pp.

Westaway, R, 2009. Quaternary uplift of northern England. *Global Planetary Change,* **68**, 357-382.

Westaway, R, D Maddy and D R Bridgland, 2002. Flow in the lower continental crust as a mechanism for the Quaternary uplift of south-east England: constraints from the Thames terrace record. *Quat. Sci. Rev.,* **21**, 559-603.

White, T S, D R Bridgland, R Westaway, A J Howard and M J White, 2010. Evidence from the Trent terrace archive, Lincolnshire, UK, for lowland glaciation of Britain during the Middle and Late Pleistocene. *Proc. Geol. Assoc.,* **121**, 141-153.

Whiteman, C A and J Rose, 1992. Thames river sediments of the British Early and Middle Pleistocene. *Quat. Sci. Rev.,* **11**, 363-375.

Widdowson, M, 1997. The geomorphological and geological importance of palaeosurfaces. *Geol. Soc. Spec. Pub.,* **120**, 1-12.

Wilson, P, 2004. Description and implications of valley moraines in upper Eskdale, Lake District. *Proc. Geol. Assoc.,* **115**, 55-61.

Wilson, P, 2007. The Kirkby Fell rock-slope failure, Malham, Yorkshire Dales, *Northwest Geography,* **7**, 1-9.

Wilson, P and J Smith, 2006. Geomorphological characteristics and significance of Late Quaternary paraglacial rock-slope failures on Skiddaw Group terrain, Lake District, NW England. *Geografiska Annaler,* **88A**, 237-252.

Wilson, P, T C Lord, T T Barrows and P J Vincent, 2012a. Cosmogenic isotope analysis and surface exposure dating in the Yorkshire Dales. 117-135 in O'Regan *et al., op. cit.*.

Wilson, P, T C Lord, M W Telfer, T T Barrows and P J Vincent, 2013. Dating in the Craven Dales. *Geology Today,* **29**, 16-23.

Wilson, P, M W Telfer, T C Lord and P J Vincent, 2012b. Loessic sediments in Northwest England. 143-150 in O'Regan *et al., op. cit.*.

Wilson, P, P J Vincent, M W Telfer and T C Lord, 2008. Optically stimulated luminescence (OSL) dating of loessic sediments in northwest England. *The Holocene,* **18**, 1101-1112.

Winsborrow, M C M, C D Clark and C R Stokes, C R, 2010. What controls the location of ice streams? *Earth Sci. Rev.,* **103**, 45-59.

Worsley, P. 1991. Possible early Devensian glacial deposits in the British Isles. 47-51 in Ehlers *et al., op. cit.*.

CHAPTER 4
Karst geomorphology
Tony Waltham

The limestone terrains of the Yorkshire Dales provide spectacular examples of well developed glaciokarst. The broader landscapes and many of the individual landforms owe their origins to processes of both karstic dissolution and glacial erosion. Glaciokarst is defined as a karst that is actively being, or has recently been, glaciated (Fig. 4.1). In this context, 'recent' extends back into the Pleistocene, when the Yorkshire Dales region was glaciated during several of the cold stages and karst was developed on the limestone during the intervening warm stages. There is huge variation among the landforms of glaciokarst, depending largely on the altitude and aspect, on any inheritance of earlier features, and on the thickness, flow and erosional power of either warm-based or cold-based ice within each glaciation.

In a global perspective, the youngest glaciokarsts have been exposed for only a few hundred years since the Neoglacial retreat, and have extensive bare rock, small and immature sinks, and minimal dissolutional rounding of landforms (Fig. 4.2). Older glaciokarsts, which have been exposed for 10,000 to 15,000 years since retreat of the Devensian ice, retain the bare outcrops, though with dissolutional modification, and have a proportion of larger and more mature sinks. The Yorkshire Dales glaciokarst is of the latter type. Limestone pavements are diagnostic of glaciokarst, though their morphological details vary with the antiquity of the glaciation, as well as with lithology, joint densities and aspect. The pavements on the great limestone benches between the dales of Yorkshire are justifiably famous, and are the most conspicuous feature of the glaciokarst. They evolved from surfaces that were eroded and scoured by ice sheets, largely during the Devensian. Many or most pre-existing karst features are destroyed by a glaciation, but some relics can survive, and the landforms of the Dales karst still include some large dolines and open caves that have survived from before the Devensian glaciation.

The limestones of some alpine glaciokarsts have, or had, high-altitude glaciers feeding meltwater into them and resurging far below in valleys without glaciers. This was generally not the case in the Yorkshire Dales, where the ice cover was total during the Pleistocene glacial maxima, analogous to the ice cover now in Greenland. Valley glaciers existed in the Dales only during the phases of advance and retreat, and the prolonged retreat phase of the Devensian glaciation was largely responsible for trimming the distinctive U-shapes of the main dales (see Chapter 3). There is still debate about the extent and capability of underground drainage beneath the ice cover (see Chapter 7).

Surface karst geomorphology, by Tony Waltham,
Nottingham; tony@geophotos.co.uk
Chapter 4, pages 65–92 in **Caves and Karst of the Yorkshire Dales**,
edited by Tony Waltham and David Lowe.
Published 2013 by the British Cave Research Association,
978-0-900265-46-4 and at www.bcra.org.uk

Periglacial activity (in cold conditions but without ice cover) during those same marginal phases of ice advance and retreat further complicates detail in some of the sub-aerial and sub-surface landforms.

The terrain of the Yorkshire Dales is essentially one that has been greatly modified by ice action. Karst features are merely superimposed on the large-scale glaciated topography, though this does not imply that they are all later than the Devensian glaciation. The great glaciated troughs of the dales, which give their name to this part of Yorkshire, are the dominant landforms (Fig. 4.3). The karst largely fits around these, mainly in the form of the cave systems that lie beneath the flanks, and in some cases beneath the floors, of the dales and their ancestral valleys. Though the dales were modified and deepened by flows of ice directed along them, ice also swept over the limestone benches and over even the highest summits during each glacial maximum (see Chapter 3). Where this ice was moving enough to maintain some erosional power it left behind expanses of bare limestone pavement, but wasting of the ice, particularly where it slowed or stagnated in the lee of hills, left sheets of till that were later pocked by subsidence dolines. The landforms of the high benches combine with those along the glaciated troughs to produce an impressive glaciokarst within the Dales.

The limestone benches

A major element of the Yorkshire Dales landscape is the series of broad plateaus and benches formed roughly on the top of the strong, sub-horizontal Great Scar Limestone and standing 100–150m above the floors of the intervening dales. In the Craven Dales, they are all overlooked by residual masses of Yoredale rocks that form the main summits, including the Three Peaks, so are best described as benches, though they are also commonly referred to as plateaus. The best of these, notably around most of Ingleborough and along both flanks

Figure 4.1. Bare limestone, open pavements and rock scars are the elements of glaciokarst at Comb Scar above Malham (TW).

Figure 4.2. An ice-scoured rock pavement of limestone in a young glaciokarst, only exposed for a few hundred years since Neoglacial ice retreat in the Canadian Rockies; much of the Dales pavement looked like this prior to evolution by post-glacial dissolution (TW).

Figure 4.4. The expanse of limestone pavement, a characteristic karst landform of the Yorkshire Dales, on the eastern bench of Ingleborough; Pen-y-ghent rises in the distance (TW).

of Chapel-le-Dale, are great rock platforms surfaced with extensive limestone pavements (Fig. 4.4). At other locations, notably along the sides of Wharfedale and Ease Gill, the top of the Great Scar Limestone is marked by little more than gently rounded shoulders, with thin strips of pavements and limestone crags almost masked by blankets of glacial till.

Stratimorphs are topographical surfaces formed by individual beds of strong rock, where weaker cover material has been stripped away by erosion. It is clear that most of the great limestone plateau surfaces within the Dales karst are stratimorphs (Waltham and Long, 2012). They are developed on the top surfaces of just a few beds of strong limestone in the uppermost part of the Great Scar Limestone succession (Fig. 4.5). These are the same beds that now form the largest of the limestone pavements with the particularly extensive unbroken clints. The stratimorphs were developed by progressive stripping of overlying beds of weaker rock, largely by ice-quarrying (or plucking as it used to be known) from their down-glacier margins (Fig. 4.6).

The stratigraphical control of these surfaces is most evident where they are inclined to follow the local dips. This is particularly conspicuous on the western flank of Chapel-le-Dale, where the great pavements of Scales Moor slope northwards from their horizontal expanse on the wide bench above Twisleton Scars, and descend more than 50m to where they are partially obscured by till between Weathercote and Bruntscar. Gently sloping pavements also follow the various gentle folds on Moughton Scar, above Crummack Dale. There, the large-scale feature that is the plateau surface is best described as a number of stratimorphic surfaces on a series of closely-spaced bedding planes.

The expanses of limestone pavement on the main benches are perhaps the highlight of the Dales glaciokarst (see Chapter 5). They are less jagged than most pavements

Figure 4.3. The glaciated trough of Wharfedale, with the steeper parts of its flanks exposing almost the entire thickness of the Great Scar Limestone (TW).

Figure 4.5. The extents of the wide benches and pavements on the limestone plateaus west of Ribblesdale; the main bench is a stratimorph on the highest beds of the Great Scar Limestone, whereas the lower bench is less well-defined on beds at lower stratigraphical levels. The younger rocks on Ingleborough are largely the Yoredale Group with a summit cap of Millstone Grit, whereas those in the southwest are mainly Upper Carboniferous Coal Measures; the basement rocks are Lower Palaeozoic slates and greywackes; contours are in metres.

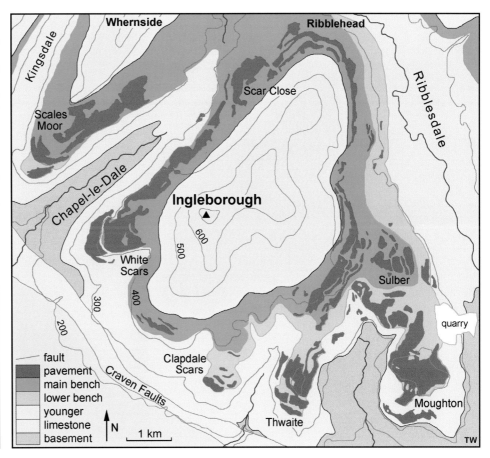

Great Scar Limestone

Within this chapter the term 'Great Scar Limestone' is used informally to describe the main limestone unit within which the major karst landforms and caves are developed; it includes the Great Scar Limestone Group and also any of the limestones within the Yoredale Group that are locally continuous with it.

in the high alpine chains of Europe, as they are dominated by rundkarren and benefit hugely from being developed on the cleanly-defined bedding surfaces. Whether these are extensive horizontal expanses as along Chapel-le-Dale, steeply inclined slabs as at Hutton Roof, or across sequences of steps as on The Clouds, they are all stratimorphs. Pavements over ice-rounded hills, as in the Malham High Country (the high ground around Parson's Pulpit and High Mark, northeast of Malham Tarn), are broken into strips that roughly follow the contours and so lack clints more than a few metres across.

The outer edge of each pavement terrace is at the crest of a long and low limestone scar, many of which overlook another pavement on the bench below. Scar height is limited

Figure 4.6. Erosion of the overlying beds and glacial stripping of the stratimorphic surface at Shining Stones on Great Asby Scar, Cumbria. Devensian ice moved towards the camera, and quarried the edge of the higher bed as it stepped down to the next strong bed. Most blocks from the upper bed were entrained within the ice and completely removed, but some were left close to their source. The net result was retreat of the scar on the upper bed, and evolution of the ground surface by the glacial stripping (photo: Simon Webb).

by the thickness of the bed that supports the pavement above it, except where higher crags are cut through multiple beds. A bank of scree stands on the back of the bench below each scar, and commonly masks the bedding plane or shale bed that defined the level of that bench and its pavement (Fig. 4.7). At many sites, a strip of till or Holocene soil is preserved in the most sheltered position along the lower edge of the scree. The nature and extent of these screes are also influenced by the fracture patterns within the limestone scar (Sweeting, 1966), but the rates of scree formation are clearly lower than they were immediately after deglaciation of the Dales, as many are now stable enough to be masked, partly or wholly, by soil.

The margins of the limestone benches and their pavements are mostly defined by the broad topography of the valley sides, though in detail the local features are aligned on joints. Faults do influence the topography, notably in the hills east of Settle, but most limestone scars are eroded well back from any formative faults. The exception is Giggleswick Scar, a major feature on the South Craven Fault immediately west of Ribblesdale. This is a fault-line scarp where the topographical step is due to differential erosion, and is not just due to the fault displacement as in a true fault scarp. Over a length of more than 2 km, the limestone crags rise nearly 100m above the eroded Bowland Shales; known caves within the Scar are all short, and are most notable for their archaeological materials.

Though the rundkarren and grike fissures are dissolutional and therefore karstic, the main pavement surfaces clearly originated by glacial erosion. The wide pavements both west and east of Ingleborough lie where the limestone was swept clean beneath the margins of more powerful ice flows down Chapel-le-Dale and Ribblesdale, with that from the latter

Figure 4.7. Limestone scars and screes above Thieves Moss, on Ingleborough's eastern plateau; Simon Fell forms the skyline (TW).

also over-riding the low plateau of Moughton. In contrast, the slopes of Newby Moss are almost devoid of pavement and lie shrouded in till deposited in the lee of Ingleborough's summit mass (Fig. 4.8). As further evidence of erosion by ice moving southwards, glacial striations survive beneath till close to Long Kin East Pot on Ingleborough's Allotment (Fig. 4.9). So the pavements are glaciokarst. They have elements of biokarst, as their rundkarren formed largely beneath a soil or plant cover that was rich in biogenic carbon dioxide and through much of post-glacial time was more extensive than it is at present. Much of the soil is loessic, and was largely blown onto the limestone benches soon after retreat of the Devensian ice, though much of it was re-worked during the cold interlude at 8.2 ka BP (Wilson *et al.*, 2012c). The pavements also have elements of 'anthropokarst', because they are now largely maintained as bare rock by the grazing activity of the sheep that were introduced by humans since

Neolithic times; some were picked clean more recently by extractors of rockery stone. There is considerable variety within the morphologies of the Dales pavements (see Chapter 5), and they clearly have complex origins, including elements from pre-Devensian stages of development.

Most of the Dales limestone benches lie at altitudes very close to 400m. Consequently, they were described as the remnants of a peneplain, which was widely known by its historical name as the 1300-foot erosion surface (Sweeting, 1950, 1974). Its named altitude was an approximation and the mapped plateaus, benches and shoulders lie between 15m below and 25m above the 1300-foot (396m) level. Much of this mapped feature coincided with the main benches on top of the limestone around and west of Ingleborough, which were subsequently described as stratimorphs that are related to geological structure (Waltham, 1970).

The reality of such upland erosion surfaces has long been regarded with some scepticism (Clayton, 1981). Many parts of the 1300-foot surface were mapped across the outcrops of

Figure 4.9. Glacial striations on limestone pavement immediately after clearance of the till blanket, near Long Kin East on eastern Ingleborough; the striae had survived because the till cover has a low permeability and probably a high content of limestone debris, both factors that would restrict dissolution of the buried limestone surface by percolation water (TW).

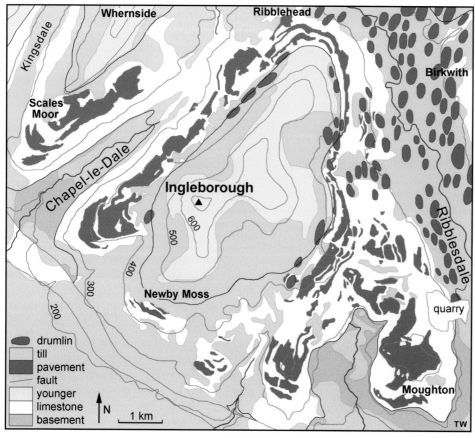

drumlin
till
pavement
fault
younger
limestone
basement

N   1 km

Figure 4.8. Distribution of limestone pavements and glacial deposits around Ingleborough; the patterns of the till sheets and the drumlins reflect ice flow from the north with the Newby Moss shoulder in the lee of the summit (compiled from field mapping by Angus Tillotson and Tony Waltham and from various sources).

Yoredale rocks (Sweeting, 1950), but a correlation of these with the recognisable breaks of slope at altitudes close to 396m reveals that many are at the transition from the shale-dominated Yoredale sequences downwards to the Great Scar Limestone (including any Yoredale limestones that are locally continuous with it). Though these hillside shoulders have not been stripped down to form stratimorphs, they appear to be features of the geology and are not purely the products of erosional processes (Waltham and Long, 2011). It is also significant that the surface was not mapped across the area of steeper dip around Bruntscar between Whernside and Chapel-le-Dale. A 1300-foot "erosion surface" across the Yorkshire Dales cannot now be regarded as tenable. There is no place for it within a credible model for the incision of the dales and the evolution of the limestone benches (see below). Similarly, any concept of an earlier and partly deformed erosion surface at about 600m, with the Three Peaks among the residuals that rose above it (King, 1969; Clayton, 1981), must be regarded with considerable caution.

One location with evidence of an erosion surface is between Malham and Malham Tarn (Fig. 4.51), where a platform cuts across both the limestone and the basement rocks on either side of the North Craven Fault (Sweeting, 1950). The northern half of this, north of the North Craven Fault and around Malham Tarn, is cut into both limestone and basement rocks, whereas the southern half rises gently as a slightly eroded stratimorph on the top of the Great Scar Limestone. There appears to have been erosional planation of the Malham Tarn basin, but this is purely a local feature, and it does not imply any wider occurrence of an erosion surface (Waltham and Long, 2011).

Incision of the dales

There has long been debate over the ages of the large-scale landforms of the Yorkshire Dales, but early estimates of late Tertiary origins, and a rather vague "pre-glacial" age for the perceived 1300-foot erosion surface, lacked any constraint from an absolute chronology. Radiometric dating has now provided some constraints, especially with pre-Devensian dates from analyses of cave stalagmites. These data have been used to indicate rates of valley incision (Atkinson *et al.*, 1978; Gascoyne *et al.*, 1983; Waltham, 1986; Waltham *et al.*, 1997). As stalagmites can be deposited only in air-filled caves, their existence indicates that they were above the contemporary local water level. At most sites, this was at, or not far above, the resurgence level in the adjacent valley, and therefore indicates a maximum altitude for the contemporary floor of that particular valley, or dale. Any sections of perched phreas, forming sumps along the main cave conduits, would preclude local stalagmite deposition, and could be interpreted incorrectly as indicating a higher contemporary valley floor. Details are also slightly complicated because the positions of the earlier resurgences along the sloping dale floors are generally not known. However, most dale floors have only low gradients, and the first generations of resurgences are assumed to have been located close to the North Craven Fault where they were at the lowest local outlets from the karst aquifer. These were at high stratigraphical levels within the Great Scar Limestone, as the basement was still far below the contemporary valley floors.

Within these limitations, graphical correlation of ages and altitudes of stalagmites then produces very approximate time profiles of the dale floors (Fig. 4.10). Mean values for dale-floor incision, derived from the stalagmite data, have been estimated as <0.2 m/ka (Gascoyne *et al.*, 1983) and 0.12 m/ka (Waltham, 1986), and overviewed as 0.2 m/ka (Waltham *et al.*, 1997). A best estimate based on current data (Fig. 4.10) is probably closer to 0.15 m/ka, but this is still based on a very small data set where the critical few stalagmites are those of greatest age and lowest altitude.

Valley floor time profiles, for the valleys west of Ingleborough, are merely drawn around the clouds of points on a graph (Fig. 4.10). Any new stalagmite analysis that plots below or left of any clouds deflects its profile and indicates a lower incision rate. The rate of 0.15 m/ka for Chapel-le-Dale is probably most representative for incision of the major glaciated dales, though its rate may be as high as 0.22 m/ka if a single less reliable date of >350 ka is ignored. The rate of 0.09 m/ka for Ease Gill reflects the minimal ice action in its sheltered location. The comparably low rate for Kingsdale is clouded by large uncertainties in its older dates and by concealment of the dale's rock floor beneath sediment, but may also reflect the low power of its ice flow that lacked a major catchment. All these figures are mean rates that encompass both glacial and interglacial erosion; in reality they should probably be stepped to indicate increased rates of incision by ice erosion. Furthermore, most of the available data only reach back about 350 ka, so do not cover the erosional impact of the largest glaciation, the Anglian. This was in Marine Isotope Stage (MIS) 12, at around 450 ka, though there may have been a comparable or larger glaciation in MIS 16 at around 640 ka (see Chapter 3). There are no data on the activity of earlier glaciations that may well have impacted the Dales area (Lee, 2011; Lee *et al.*, 2012).

Along the southern margin of the Askrigg Block, Kingsdale, Chapel-le-Dale and Wharfedale are each entrenched about 200m below the main limestone benches. The calculated incision rates therefore imply periods of

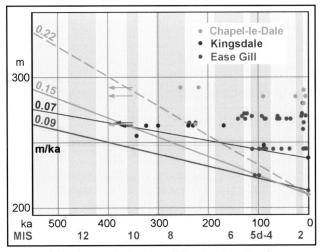

Figure 4.10*. Ages and altitudes of dated stalagmites from caves beside the western valleys of Ease Gill, Kingsdale and Chapel-le-Dale, with mean incision rates interpreted for each valley (see text); the cold Marine Isotope Stages are shaded, but within these time intervals the glacial cover was not continuous in the Yorkshire Dales, as is apparent from some of the stalagmite deposition; arrows indicate ages determined only as >350 ka.*

around 1.3 Ma for their excavation. Ribblesdale is wider than the three neighbouring dales, and traverses a structural high on the edge of the Askrigg Block (Arthurton et al., 1988). The top of the Great Scar limestone is exposed at an altitude of around 550m on Dick Close, high on the shoulder of Fountains Fell, and 370m above the floor of Ribblesdale at Stainforth. This might imply a first exposure of the limestone at about 2.5 Ma, though this concept figure could be reduced slightly if incision of Ribblesdale was more rapid under erosion by the most powerful sector of the southbound Pleistocene ice flow. Stalagmites from Victoria Cave date at least as far back as MIS 13, with finite age determinations of about 480 and 523 ka, and also estimated ages of >600 ka (Lundberg et al., 2010). However, these are from a truncated cave fragment at such high altitude that it is likely to have been drained long before those times, when the floor of Ribblesdale was already much lower by any estimate of its incision rate. Furthermore, Victoria Cave may not have been among the first generation of caves, as these may equally well have developed in the structurally higher limestone north of the North Craven Fault prior to their complete removal by subsequent surface lowering.

The limited available evidence suggests that an early exposure of the Great Scar Limestone in the Yorkshire Dales area took the form of an inlier surrounded by Yoredale outcrops in the floor of a proto-Ribblesdale more than two million years ago. Outcrops in the floors of the dales to the west probably followed at around 1.3 Ma. Valley incision through the weak Yoredale sequences created outcrops of the underlying limestone that initially were quite small on the floors of narrow valleys that were the proto-dales. The wide outcrops on the top of the Great Scar Limestone then developed by shale retreat as the weak Yoredale cover was eroded back more rapidly than the dales were entrenched, and widened, within the limestone (Fig. 4.11). These were

subsequently left to become the main benches and plateaus, on each side of upper Ribblesdale and the other neighbouring dales. The oldest benches, adjacent to the lower reaches of Ribblesdale and Wharfedale, were not so well developed in the disturbed limestone of the Craven Fault Zone, and have been largely lost to subsequent slope retreat.

The plateau surfaces developed as the valleys widened more rapidly above the limestone. Retreat of the shale margin at the inner edges of the limestone benches is recognised by the occurrence of isolated large potholes that appear to be pre-Devensian and now lie well away from the shale catchments that fed streams into them. Features along the western and eastern flanks of Ingleborough suggest that the shale margin has retreated by a few hundred metres since just before the Anglian glaciation (Sweeting, 1974; Waltham, 1990), though there has been less retreat on the southern flank that was sheltered from strong ice action. By extrapolation, the shale margin might be expected to have retreated by about 600m since 1.3 Ma, thereby increasing the extent of the stratimorphic surfaces on top of the Great Scar Limestone.

It is important to recognise that the 1.3 Ma figure for initial exposure of the limestone in the western dales is approximate and is also only a minimum. Any new analyses that reveal greater ages of stalagmites at lower altitudes would reduce the interpreted valley incision rates and thereby extend the timescales of the limestone landscapes to well before 1.3 Ma. Any former existence of perched water levels could have a similar effect. The figure also assumes roughly steady denudation rates over time, but the mean rate may have been lower prior to the mid-Pleistocene climatic transition at 1.0–0.8 Ma that prompted accelerated glacial valley incision (Hauselmann et al., 2007). Extending the timescale to 2 Ma would allow for perhaps a kilometre of shale retreat, a figure that is more compatible with the widths of the main benches around the Three Peaks.

Through this period of 1.3 Ma or more, the dales were entrenched into the limestone to depths of around 200m (Fig. 4.12). Fluvial lowering of the dale floors across the limestone outcrop would have been seriously compromised by the development of underground drainage. An estimate of 46 mm/ka for dissolutional lowering beneath a soil cover (Parry, 2007) would produce significantly less than 50m of surface lowering in 1.3 Ma, after again discounting intervals of reduced activity during cold stages and also accepting that soil cover would not have been permanent through the warm stages. This would account for only a small fraction of the depth of the main dales, which confirms that a significant proportion of their excavation was by glaciers. The rounded, U-shaped valley profiles indicate that, even if they were not largely excavated by ice, the dales were significantly modified by glacial erosion. This may or may not have been entirely within 1.3 Ma, but that period does appear to have included the major glaciations in the Yorkshire Dales, notably after the mid-Pleistocene increase in the scale of glacial activity at around 0.8 Ma. Sound evidence relating to the evolution of the Dales region prior to 1.3 Ma is lacking, and will remain so unless and until appropriate clastic cave sediments are dated by their contents of cosmogenic aluminium-26 and beryllium-10 (see Chapter 10).

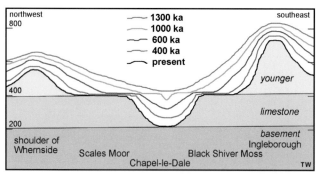

Figure 4.11. *Concept sketch profiles across Chapel-le-Dale and Ingleborough, with an interpreted sequence of stages in the denudation of the area; profiles are drawn relative to the geology, and absolute altitudes increased over time with isostatic response to the erosional loss; the main bench surfaces are all on the top of the limestone, and are only separated for clarity; vertical scale is exaggerated by about 3. The drawn stages are: 1300 ka ago, when the Great Scar Limestone was only exposed further down the valley; 1000 ka ago, with a trench cut into the limestone while Yoredale rocks were stripped from adjacent benches; 600 ka ago, with limestone benches above a valley profile that may have been more rounded from previous glaciations; 400 ka ago, after the Anglian glaciation, with a rounded dale profile between wide benches; and at present, after the Devensian glaciation, with a deeper dale profile between benches that have retreated by erosion of the Yoredale rocks.*

Figure 4.12. The broad U-shaped glaciated trough that is Chapel-le-Dale, entrenched nearly 200m below the level of the limestone benches on each side (TW).

A nation-wide survey of long-term uplift rates suggested a mean value of about 0.2 m/ka for the Askrigg Block (Westaway, 2009). However, many of the local data were derived from interpretations of cave stalagmite ages (largely from Waltham *et al.*, 1997), and uplift rates are not the same as the denudation rates inferred from the stalagmite records. Models of crustal viscosity and deformation suggest that isostatic rebound in response to denudation generates uplift that is about 85% of the mean value of surface lowering by erosion (Burbank and Anderson, 2001). Fission track analysis of apatite crystals within Lake District rocks has indicated rock removal of about 700m from the summits and 1500m from glaciated valleys by surface erosion through the Cenozoic (Green, 2002). Application of that ratio to the Yorkshire Dales would imply that while the dale floors were eroded by about 200m, over a period of about 1.3 Ma, the surfaces of the summits and high ground between the dales were lowered by about 100m. This is, however, a tenuous line of evidence, and interfluve lowering could be less than half the valley incision. A value of about 150m for the mean denudation would then imply around 130m of uplift over the same period. A mean uplift rate of about 100m per million years places the top of the main limestone mass (now at altitudes of 400m to 500m across the heart of the karst) at sea level at around four to five million years ago. Such a time-scale is broadly compatible with that for the southern Pennines, where Neogene sediments of the Brassington Formation are preserved in collapse dolines and were uplifted from near sea level during and since Pliocene times (Walsh *et al.*, 1999). Whatever the history of the region prior to about 2.5 Ma, the Great Scar Limestone was nowhere exposed through most of it.

A question remains as to the destination of all the rock material that has been eroded from the Dales region. On the Askrigg Block and within the Lune and Ribble catchments (which include the Dales' main karst), clastic material removed from the Yoredale sequences and from the overlying grits below the main summit levels amounted to about 60 km³ (estimated from the modern geology and topography); this was within the last few million years. Initially this contributed to the alluvial flats towards Morecambe Bay and to the mantle of till across large areas to the south.

Ultimately much of it was reworked into glacial outwash that now floors the Irish Sea and extends to and beyond the edge of the continental shelf, where it forms huge fans of sand and mud deep under the Bay of Biscay (Zaragosi *et al.*, 2000). Largely within the last million years or so, since the limestone was widely exposed at outcrop, roughly another 15 km³ of limestone was removed. While some of this was entrained in till after the glaciers deepened the dales and scoured the limestone stratimorphs, most was carried away in solution, and it ended up as part of the carbonate solute load of oceanic waters.

Initiation of the Dales karst

It is likely that the first exposures of the Great Scar Limestone were just north of the North Craven Fault, and probably in Ribblesdale, where its proto-valley crossed the structurally highest part of the Great Scar Limestone. An interpretation of the extent of the early karst landscapes can be created by correlating the structure and altitudes of the top of the limestone with estimated altitudes of the palaeo-topography based on inferred rates of surface lowering (Fig. 4.13). This reconstruction is only an approximation and an interpretation that is based on a series of assumptions, but it conforms to the fragments of evidence that are currently available. It is dated to around 1.3 Ma solely on the basis of the valley floor erosion rate determined for the dales west of Ingleborough. Altitudes relate to the present position of the limestone, with no account of uplift, and both the geology and the topography are likely to have been about 130m lower 1.3 M years ago.

An initial Ribblesdale inlier would have expanded towards the high ground north of Malham. It may also have extended eastwards beyond Malham, but with rather poorer karst development on the thinly bedded Yoredale limestones (which are locally almost continuous with the Great Scar). Palaeo-surface levels can only be estimated, but there may have been limestone outcrops in Wharfedale and Littondale and perhaps also in a proto-Darnbrook (Fig. 4.13) The main unit of limestone was probably also exposed in three small inliers between the North and Middle Craven Faults. It is difficult to correlate the earliest karst landscapes on the Malham High Country with those in lower Ribblesdale. The early limestone outcrop may have been broken by shale cover

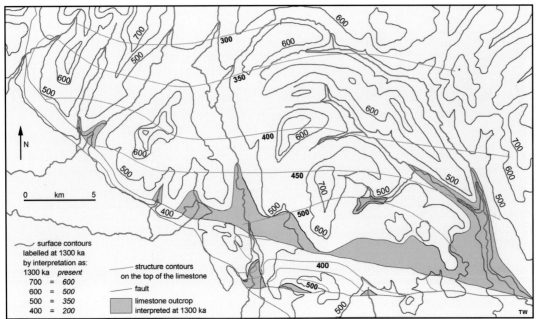

Figure 4.13. An interpretation of the extent of karst on the southern Askrigg Block around 1.3 million years ago, soon after the limestone was first exposed by erosion of the younger rocks. Structure contours are drawn for the top of the integral karst unit; this is not definable by stratigraphy, as it extends only to the top of the Hawes Limestone in the west but includes the Gayle and Hardraw Scar limestones in the east. Structure contours north of the North Craven Fault are based on altitudes of stream sinks into the main limestone mass (thereby excluding sinks in the higher Yoredale limestones). Between the North and Middle Craven Faults structure contours are
largely interpolated from those drawn on the base of the Gordale Limestone (Arthurton et al., 1988) and measured thicknesses of that limestone and the Yoredale Group (Dunham and Wilson, 1985). An approximation to the old topography is indicated by contours that are the present contours re-labelled as tabulated in the key; these are 200m higher than those at present along the dale floors, 100m higher over the interfluves and proportioned in between (see text). The old outcrops are interpreted from the structure contours and the re-valued topographical contours. Rivers are drawn in their present positions, and are only included to make the map easier to follow.

south of Fountains Fell, but underground drainage from the Malham Tarn area to Ribblesdale could have been among the earliest to reach maturity within the Dales. Little is known of the geological structure and the extent of the early karst in a possibly similar situation between the Malham high ground and lower Wharfedale. Both dales were subsequently deepened and widened, thereby destroying any early suite of karst features on and beneath their flanks.

Karst also developed on smaller inliers of limestone where the other dales cross the upturned southern edge of the Askrigg Block (Fig. 4.13). The presence of an inlier in Chapel-le-Dale is inferred from the stalagmite chronology of the dale (Fig. 4.10). An early limestone outcrop in lower Ease Gill cannot be identified from this interpretation (Fig. 4.13), but probably did exist within the zone of folding against the Dent Fault at or very soon after this early stage. The early inlier in Clapdale may not have existed if the valley is a younger feature. There was a second inlier in Ribblesdale, in the more folded limestone against the Middle Craven Fault. This would have extended to the area of Attermire Scar, and would at some stage have overlain enlargement of the cave passage of which a remnant survives as Victoria Cave. This small inlier had no hydrological continuity across the North Craven Fault to the main area of karst at that time (Fig. 4.13) because the throw on the fault is greater than the limestone thickness, but it may have had an underground link with a small inlier just below the site where Malham Cove subsequently developed.

These early inliers developed as karst on benches and platforms of the limestone where and when the cover of weaker Yoredale shales was stripped away. It is likely that

ice swept over these outcrops during pre-Anglian cold stages, and limestone pavements comparable to those on the modern benches existed at some subsequent times. All traces of these early karst landscapes were destroyed as the dales were widened and deepened, though some features survived on the high ground north of Malham. Alongside the main dales, the limestone benches retreated towards the high ridges. As they progressively shifted towards their present positions, many of them also became much wider, as the weak Yoredale cover rocks were stripped away from their inner edges more rapidly than their outer edges receded in the strong limestone. The main process of denudation on the limestone benches was probably a series of events of glacial quarrying of individual beds, alternating with dissolutional lowering during the interglacial and postglacial stages, and ultimately creating the stratimorphs within the modern landscape of the Dales.

On the main limestone benches, overall surface lowering, solely by dissolution, may be taken broadly to match estimated mean Holocene rates of 3–13 mm/ka (Goldie, 2005; see below). Discounting intervals of reduction or loss of dissolutional activity during cold stages, this could account for about 5–15m of limestone denudation since initial exposure at about 1.3 Ma. Dissolution rates may have been higher during periods of soil cover (Parry, 2007), but probably pertained only through limited intervals. However, these total figures were nowhere achieved, as the initial karst landscapes have since been removed by incision of the dales and by the denudation that has caused migration of the karst areas across the newly exposed limestone outcrops and towards the interfluves.

Figure 4.14. Broad shallow dolines and limestone scars that are typical of the very old karst on the Malham High Country (TW).

The karst north of Malham was initially developed over the area of the Tarn and eastwards across the Mastiles bench, and karst has only existed on High Mark and Parson's Pulpit for somewhat less than 1.3 Ma. Nevertheless, the oldest surviving karst landforms in the Yorkshire Dales are probably the large dolines within the polygonal karst on this area (Fig. 4.14). Some of the rounded karst features on the Malham High Country have been variously described as tors, towers or pinnacles, though they are essentially isolated clints and blocks that survive from a pavement that has since been largely eroded away. They have long been interpreted as very old (Goldie, 2006a, 2007), but suggestions that they are pre-Quaternary cannot be substantiated. Their location high on the interfluve between Ribblesdale and Wharfedale makes them difficult to date. Preservation of this polygonal karst does indicates how minimal was glacial erosion at its interfluve site, during at least the Devensian glaciation, in contrast to the rather more conspicuous ice quarrying and abrasion on the pavements that were over-run by more-active ice adjacent to the faster flows both east and west of Ingleborough.

Limestone dissolution

As in almost any karst, stream waters and percolation waters carry dissolved carbonate, both within the Dales caves and on the fells above (Table 4.1). Most percolation waters are enriched with biogenic carbon dioxide from their passage through the soil and plant cover. The concentration of carbon dioxide in the water is then a key factor, along with flow rates and temperature, in the dissolutional removal of limestone (Palmer, 1991; Dreybrodt, 2004; Faulkner, 2009). Concentrations of dissolved carbonate are merely a consequence of the dissolution kinetics, but, combined with records of rainfall or stream flows, can be useful indicators of the mean rates of removal of limestone where more detailed chemical data have not been recorded (Gabrovšek, 2009).

Typically in the Dales karst, percolation waters carry between 150 and 250 mg/L of solute (expressed as calcium carbonate, but generally including a small proportion of magnesium carbonate). Values show considerable variation between sites and over time, relating to the nature and extent of flow paths down through the limestone (Pitty, 1974).

Standing pools on bare rock gain carbon dioxide from their lichens and mosses, and then dissolve the limestone; their solute concentrations increase further with evaporation losses, and may lead to re-precipitation, whereas they decrease after recharge from rainfall events that make the water aggressive again (Sweeting, 1966).

The aggressiveness of soil waters, and their potential capacity for limestone weathering, can be assessed by the weight losses of prepared limestone tablets placed within the soils. Significant chemical contrasts have been found in different soil types in the Malham area (Trudgill, 1985). Calcareous soils in slopes above Cowside Beck have developed over talus and soliflucted head, both composed of limestone debris, and showed minimal weight losses of tablet samples, except in a thin zone immediately below the surface. In contrast, acid soils in slopes above Darnbrook Beck have formed on till that mantles the limestone and is derived largely from the shales and sandstones of the Yoredale and Millstone Grit sequences. Large tablet losses throughout the thickness of the Darnbrook soils showed the capability of limestone weathering by percolation water in and beneath these acid soils that have developed on the glacial deposits.

Within the Dales karst, conduit flows through the limestone, in stream caves and at resurgences, typically carry between 100 and 200 mg/L of calcium and magnesium carbonates (Table 4.1). Allogenic streams that flow onto the Great Scar Limestone typically have carbonate solute levels of 30–50 mg/L, which are derived largely from the Yoredale limestones higher up their courses. The increases in solute concentrations as the streams flow through the limestone caves are almost entirely due to increments from fissures and tiny inlets of percolation waters that have gained high carbonate concentrations after their initial passage through the cover of soil and peat. Increments of 20 mg/L of solute per 800m length of flow-path have been recorded in streams on the limestone surface (Sweeting, 1966), but solute increases were immeasurably small along the 500m of the Long Churn streamway (Fig. 4.15) that lacks any significant inlets of peat water along its course to Alum Pot (Richardson, 1974). Solute concentrations at all resurgences show marked decreases at high stage due to dilution by flood

$CaCO_3$	locations	source
	autogenic waters	
156 – 227	seepages in Ingleborough Cave	Pitty, 1974
130 – 250	seepages in Alum Pot area	Richardson, 1974
175 – 275	percolation springs around Malham	Trudgill, 1985
78 – 342	pools on bare limestone	Sweeting, 1966
	allogenic streams	
36 – 64	Alum Pot Beck, at high and low stage	Richardson, 1974
48	Fell Beck	Pitty, 1974
30 – 36	typical sinking streams	Sweeting, 1966
	resurgent waters	
82	Clapham Beck Head	Pitty, 1974
137 – 200	Malham Cove and Aire Head	Trudgill, 1985
	Darnbrook Fell, 5 risings –	Ternan, 1974
111 – 174	mean values	
88 – 113	minima in flood	
148 – 217	maxima at low stage	
140	typical risings	Clayton, 1981
90 – 120	typical risings, at high and low stage	Sweeting, 1966

Table 4.1. Representative solute loads, in mg/L of calcium carbonate, carried in streams and from springs within the karst of the Yorkshire Dales.

pulses with short flow-through times (Table 4.1). However, the high flood flows account for greater total carbonate loads, and therefore cause the maximum rates of both chemical and mechanical erosion.

Karst denudation rates

Rates of dissolutional denudation, or mean surface lowering on the limestone, can be assessed by various methods: 1) from data on solute loads in stream waters, 2) by direct measurements on rock surfaces, 3) by weight losses of prepared limestone tablets, and 4) by inference from rock pedestal heights beneath boulders. Though each method measures a different component of the overall denudation, correlation of the data sets provides a broad picture of the total denudation process (Table 4.2). Dissolution is however only a part of the total denudation process in the Yorkshire Dales, which includes major glacial erosion, especially along the dale floors where surface lowering rates are significantly higher than on the main limestone benches.

Estimates of dissolutional denudation can be made by application of the Corbel formula (Trudgill, 2008). This indicates that D = 4ET/10,000, where D = denudation rate in mm/ka, E = annual precipitation less evapotranspiration in mm, T = mean solute concentration in mg/L, with the approximation that limestone density is 2.5 t/m^3. The main limitation with these estimates relates to the origins of the solute, which is derived from three distinct sources: dissolution on the ground surface or at rockhead beneath a cover of soil or drift, dissolution within fissures in the epikarst, and dissolution in cave passages deep within the karst.

Dissolution at the surface, or at the sub-soil rockhead, generally accounts for only about 30% of the total carbonate in karst waters (Gabrovšek, 2009); consequently denudation rates calculated in this way are generally higher than direct measurements unless sub-surface erosion is estimated and accounted for. Dissolution of rock within the few metres closest to the surface, in the zone known as epikarst, contributes to long-term denudation when voids in the fissure system coalesce to allow surface lowering. Calculated rates are only long-term means (on scales of at least 10 ka), and then involve inaccuracies through glacial removal of partially eroded epikarst. The dissolution in deep caves does not contribute to surface denudation, except in the very long term. Deductions from measured stream solute concentrations allow for solutes derived from allogenic input.

Despite these limitations, the Corbel formula does provide very rough estimates of mean dissolutional denudation on the limestone outcrops (Ford and Williams, 2007). An estimate of 41 mm/ka for the rate of surface lowering in the Dales excludes an almost equal contribution from underground dissolution (Sweeting, 1966), but it is unclear how much of the latter is in fissures and cave passages and how much is at rockhead beneath a soil cover. Comparable rates can be deduced from data on specific resurgences (Table 4.2), but also without distinction between surface lowering and underground losses.

Direct measurements of surface lowering on bare limestone pavements indicate only one component of denudation in a karst with any degree of soil cover. Rates of 12–74 mm/ka have been determined with a micro-erosion meter (Trudgill et al., 1981) on the Highfolds pavement above Malham Tarn. Maximum rates of cave stream entrenchment, deduced from dated stalagmites close to the floors of canyon passages in Lost John's, White Scar and Ingleborough Caves are 20–50 mm/ka (Gascoyne et al., 1983). These cave floor measurements are means over periods of 100 ka, which include cold stages of reduced flow and perhaps even phases of sediment accumulation, but cannot be related to external limestone surface lowering as the sites are all perched above local base-levels.

Erosion rates that are orders of magnitude higher have been deduced (only approximately) where acidic peat water has drained onto freshly exposed limestone pavement (Sweeting, 1966). Part of the glacially striated pavement on the Ingleborough Allotment was lowered by 30 mm or more between 1947 and 1960, after its clay-rich till was removed from a small area. When peat was cleared from a small area of pavement on Scales Moor, water draining from the adjacent remaining peat was reported to have carved runnels 70–150 mm deep, also within 13 years (Sweeting, 1966), but this is an extraordinarily high rate of channel incision that cannot be regarded as representative. Similar runnels, up to 30 mm wide and 90 mm deep, score a fresh limestone exposure in Meal Bank Quarry, Ingleton, having formed probably within about a hundred years since closure of the quarry in 1911. These originate at seepage from a shale bed and the associated deposition of yellow jarosite (hydrated iron sulphate) indicates the local role of strong acids derived from pyrite (iron sulphide) within the shale. All these high rates are created by concentrated flows of acidic water, and do

mm/ka	method	location	source
83	solutes	Dales average (total denudation)	Sweeting, 1966
41	solutes	Dales average (surface dissolution)	Sweeting, 1966
62 – 97	solutes	Darnbrook Fell	this chapter
65	solutes	Malham	this chapter
12 – 74	direct (MEM)	Malham (pavement)	Trudgill et al., 1981
< 20 – 50	(stalagmite)	cave streamways (over >100 ka)	Gascoyne et al., 1983
2300	direct	Ingleborough (runnels in peat water)	Sweeting, 1966
20 – 40	tablets	Cowside (in calcareous soil)	Trudgill, 1985
100 – 600	tablets	Darnbrook (in acid soil)	Trudgill, 1985
26 – 33	pedestals	Norber (over 15 ka)	Sweeting, 1966
3 – 13	pedestals	Norber and Scar Close (over 15 ka)	Goldie, 2005
46	pedestals	Norber (sub-soil, over 10 ka)	Parry, 2007
10	pedestals	Scales Moor (sub-aerial, over 15 ka)	Parry, 2007
150	(dale incision)	(total erosion, for comparison)	this chapter

Figure 4.15. The streamway of Upper Long Churn Cave feeding to Alum Pot (TW).

Table 4.2. *Estimates of limestone denudation rates at sites within the Yorkshire Dales karst.*

Figure 4.16. Glacial erratic of strong grit standing on a high steep-sided limestone pedestal at Norber, on Ingleborough's flank; this erratic, the most photographed and iconic of the Norber boulders, toppled off its pedestal 2009; its demise was probably due to a shear failure that allowed the thin upper bed to detach, slide sideways and unbalance the main block before both fell to the grass surround (TW).

not represent overall denudation rates. Rates of surface loss, calculated from weight losses, of buried limestone tablets are indicative of denudation rates beneath different soils (Table 4.2), and these results also show the importance of acid soil waters in dissolutional denudation (Trudgill, 1985).

Denudation rates estimated from pedestal heights

Limestone pedestals sheltered beneath large erratic boulders have long been used to infer denudation rates on the unprotected limestone; among the finest are those beneath large blocks of strong grit at Norber, on the southeastern flank of Ingleborough (Fig. 4.16). Numerous estimates of pedestal heights, and deductions of denudation rates (see listings in Goldie, 2005, and in Parry, 2007) remain questionable because they did not take full account of bedding-related steps in the limestone profiles. Many pedestal heights are unclear or debatable, and further doubts over deduced denudation rates are raised by the degree of real protection that the boulders provide.

Early estimates of the heights of the Norber pedestals centred around 400–500 mm, implying denudation rates of 26–33 mm/ka since retreat of the Devensian ice. Subsequently, re-assessment, particularly with regard to stepping of the limestone surface, has indicated heights of only 50–200 mm, and rates of only 3–13 mm/ka (Goldie, 2005, 2012). This contrasts with the claim for a mean height of 460 mm for steep-sided pedestals interpreted as developing due to sub-soil dissolution at Norber (Parry, 2007). These measurements were taken to imply a mean denudation rate of 46 mm/ka, subsequent to soil developing only with climatic amelioration at about 10 ka, whereas pedestals with sloping walls that averaged 150 mm high, on Scales Moor and elsewhere, were interpreted as forming under sub-aerial conditions with a denudation rate of 10 mm/ka (Fig. 4.17).

Figure 4.17. A glacial erratic on a low pedestal with sloping sides, on Scales Moor (photo: Brian Parry).

All these pedestal-deduced rates (Table 4.2) would decline slightly if re-calculated from an ice retreat that may have been as early as 16.5 ka (Telfer *et al.*, 2009), or possibly even earlier at Norber (Vincent *et al.*, 2010; Wilson *et al.*, 2012b.). They are all only approximations as they span climatic variations through the Holocene; it is also unclear when processes stabilized following the main ice retreat (see Chapter 3) and whether dissolution was briefly interrupted by periglacial conditions during the Loch Lomond Stadial (Faulkner, 2009). An added complication is provided by the possibility of pedestal development being influenced by nivation processes localised within hollows in wind-blown snow that developed around the erratics in periglacial conditions (Wilson *et al*, 2012a). Some pedestal heights may also be a factor of bed thickness, and others may have been increased by artificial removal of limestone blocks. Denudation rates inferred from pedestal heights can only be simplifications regarding complex processes, and must be assessed with due caution.

Progress in karst geomorphology

Studies of the surface landforms of limestone karst evolved over the centuries in different parts of the world, but were commonly regarded as a mere variant within wider studies of geomorphology and surface processes. A breakthrough was the research by Jovan Cvijić on the Dinaric karst of his home country, which generated his two landmark publications (1893, 1918).

Since the initial work by Cvijić, karst science has evolved into a wide understanding of geomorphological processes backed up by the physics of hydrogeology and the chemistry of dissolution. The standard text on the subject is the comprehensive discourse by Derek Ford and Paul Williams (2007), while the most readable overview of karst landforms is still that by Joe Jennings (1985), a Yorkshireman who emigrated to the Australian karst.

Karst studies in the Yorkshire Dales were similarly relegated to incidental diversions from either geomorphology or geology, with the exception of works that focussed on the caves. Notable among the latter was the research by Marjorie Sweeting, who worked for many years on the Dales limestone country. Her papers are cited in this chapter, and her textbook (1972) on karst geomorphology includes numerous references to the Yorkshire Dales.

(1)	sink altitude	rising altitude	underground flow			time in flood (2)	surface flow (3)		
			distance	drop	gradient		distance	drop	gradient
Dentdale	220	148	3200	72	2.2	10%	4000 (4)	24	0.6
Ease Gill	349	213	2300	136	5.9	1%	---	---	---
Kingsdale	290	253	3100	37	1.2	20%	1200	33	2.7
Chapel-le-Dale	292	224	3300	68	2.1	<1% (5)	---	---	---
Ribblesdale	297	277	500	20	4.0	1%	2500	40	1.6
Malhamdale	366	188	3500	178	5.1	0	---	---	---
Littondale	268	230	3500	38	1.1	50%	11500 (6)	65	0.6
Wharfedale	---	---	---	---	---	---	22500 (7)	200	0.9
Nidderdale	222	160	3200	62	1.9	<1% (8)	---	---	---

Table 4.3. *Underground flows of the trunk rivers along the main dales.*
Footnotes
1. Altitudes and distances are all in metres, and distances are straight-line; gradients are percentages.
2. Time in flood is a rough percentage of the total time that a parallel surface flood overflow channel is occupied.
3. Surface flow data apply to river lengths where flow is always above ground.
4. Surface flow in Dentdale is only that downstream of Popples.
5. Chapel-le-Dale has its top sinks near Ivescar, but flood time is only for the stretch downstream of Haws Gill Wheel.
6. Surface flow in Littondale is only that downstream of Litton, but includes the distance that flow is confluent with that of the Wharfe as far as Grassington.
7. Wharfedale has some stretches with partial underground flow, in Langstrothdale, which are not included.
8. Flood time in Nidderdale is only that for the channel downstream of Goyden Pot.

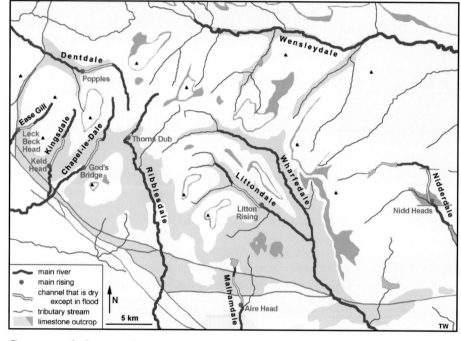

Figure 4.18. *The surface courses of the main rivers, and their sections that are normally dry across the Great Scar Limestone in the southern Yorkshire Dales; the channel above Aire Head always carries a small flow from the Malham Cove Rising.*

Stream sinks, potholes and risings

The shale-dominated Yoredale sequence that overlies the Great Scar Limestone provides numerous sources of allogenic water that sink into the top of the limestone and resurge near its base, having travelled through the extensive cave systems that are a key component of the Dales karst. The sinks can be distinguished in two groups, those on the streams and rivers that flow along the main dale floors, and those on the smaller streams that flow from the high Yoredale outliers onto the main limestone benches. A third important component of water within the karst is the direct rainfall onto the limestone or onto its cover of soil or permeable drift. This enters either by percolation through the soil, by very small flows into individual fissures on the exposed karst, or by point recharge in doline floors (see Chapter 9).

The main river courses

Of the nine trunk rivers and streams along the floors of the dales through the main karst, all but two have long lengths with underground flow, where the stream courses are dry except in times of flood (Fig. 4.18 and Table 4.3).

Dentdale: The River Dee loses water into various sinks from Cassa Dub downstream, and its rocky channel is normally dry as far as the resurgence at The Popples, beyond which the river flows entirely in daylight except for two short sections with some parallel underground flow. Downstream of the underground section, the river flows on alluvium and till.

Ease Gill: This is the only main valley that is not a glaciated trough, though Pleistocene ice left extensive till and traces of a recessional moraine. The valley is in the lee of Great Coum, and was therefore sheltered from powerful glacial erosion. Its stream sinks at the shale margin, at Top Sink, and resurges at Leck Beck Head, with much of its underground course under the north bank known through the Ease Gill Cave System. The gill carries floodwater only after storm events. The resurgence is close to the Dent Fault, and Leck Beck shortly crosses onto impermeable basement rocks.

Kingsdale: The headwater stream normally disappears into choked sinks just downstream of Kingsdale Head, and flows through the West Kingsdale Cave System to the resurgence at Keld Head. Flows exceed the sink capacity for about 20% of the time, when the artificially straightened channel over the alluvium becomes active. The resurgence is from a truncated cave passage about 40m above the base of the limestone. Downstream, the River Twiss flows over alluvium and then descends over thinly bedded basal limestones to reach the basement at Thornton Force (Waltham *et al.*, 2010).

Chapel-le-Dale: Winterscales Beck, the main headwater stream, is lost into choked sinks near Ivescar in dry weather, and flows as far as the Haws Gill Wheel sink in flood (Fig. 9.3). Only in major flood events is there any surface flow further downstream, where the underground course is known through flooded caves behind the God's Bridge resurgence, which is close to the base of the limestone.

Ribblesdale: The River Ribble flows above ground in a wide dale with a complete floor of till and alluvium, to and beyond the concealed base of the limestone just upstream of Horton. The main headwater, Gayle Beck, flows underground for just a short distance through the Katnot and Thorns Gill caves, but floodwaters also occupy a parallel surface ravine. Further downstream, an enlarged River Ribble flows for 4 km over limestone between its crossings of the North and South Craven Faults. This section has a gradient of 1.2%, but is largely on thinly bedded limestone that is covered with drift sediments; underflow leakage may exist, but no sinks or risings have been identified.

Malhamdale: The geology at Malham differs from the other dales, as its allogenic stream from Malham Tarn flows from the basement and across the North Craven Fault onto the limestone, before disappearing into choked sinks and resurging from the choked Aire Head risings and from the submerged cave at the foot of Malham Cove. Surface flow down the Watlowes valley and over the Cove has not occurred since the early 1800s (Howson, 1850; Halliwell, 1979.).

Littondale: The River Skirfare has surface flow largely over till and alluvium, as far as its underground section past Litton village where the rocky surface channel is occupied only for about half the time (Fig. 4.19). Below the main Litton risings, the river is on the surface, flowing over alluvium, to its junction with the Wharfe.

Wharfedale: The River Wharfe maintains surface flow across the entire limestone outcrop, though there are sections with

Figure 4.19. The rocky bed of the River Skirfare close to Litton village in Littondale, when all flow is underground and when the channel becomes active in mild flood conditions.

Figure 4.20. Kingsdale Beck flowing over thinly bedded limestones in its final descent towards the head of Thornton Force (TW).

components of underground flow beneath Langstrothdale upstream of Yockenthwaite. Downstream of that section, the dale is floored entirely by alluvium, and this may conceal a small inlier of basement rock near Kilnsey.

Nidderdale: The underground flow of the River Nidd is through caves that are largely within the Yoredale Middle and Three Yard limestones, from sinks near Manchester Hole to Nidd Heads. Beyond the choked sinks, surface flow is frequent as far as Goyden Pot, but is only rare beyond there, except for tributary streams that drain off the grit and create flows along sections of the main channel before sinking.

Wensleydale and its tributary dales, along with Swaledale, have no sections of underground flow along their trunk rivers, as outcrops of Great Scar Limestone are absent or minimal along their floors. In Wensleydale, the River Ure cascades over the low steps of Aysgarth Falls carved into the top of the Great Scar Limestone, but the water does not sink, and it flows off the valley-floor inlier not far below the falls. The smaller southern valleys of Crummack Dale and Clapdale were glaciated and do carry modern streams, but they are effectively elements of the drainage off the high benches, as described below.

Most of the data on the drainage along the main dales (Table 4.3) could be taken to imply that underground flow is achieved (except in flood conditions) where the hydraulic gradients across the limestone outcrop are steeper than about 1%, while surface flow is maintained over lower gradients. This may then be seen as an indication of the maturity of the karst, though its picture is simplified as the development of complete underground drainage is greatly dependent on the size of the allogenic flow, the scale of glacial or alluvial sediments masking the limestone and also on local details of the limestone stratigraphy and structure.

The two exceptions in the drainage regimes can be explained. In Kingsdale, the underground flow emerges onto the surface where its cave was truncated by Pleistocene glaciation. The conduit is now back-flooded by about 7m, partly by post-glacial sediments, and emerges in the pool at Keld Head. The surface stream's steep descent to the lip of Thornton Force is then over thinly bedded basal limestones (Fig. 4.20), where bedding planes effectively return to the surface any developing loops of underground flow; there is some leakage into fissures just behind the waterfall, feeding to a tiny resurgence cave near the base of the limestone half way down and just beside the waterfall. Along the great proportion of Ribblesdale, surface flow is maintained over a steeper gradient by a locally thick and extensive blanket of almost impermeable till, to the extent that the conduit from Alum Pot to Turn Dub passes beneath the surface channel without any hydrological link.

Some smaller streams do maintain surface flows across the limestone outcrops, mostly on valley floors of alluvium or till; these include many streams in upper Ribblesdale that emerge from caves at high level and continue in daylight down to the valley floor. Cowside Beck, a tributary to the Skirfare, has the longest surface course over limestone that is not in a glaciated dale. It is partly over thin alluvium, but owes much of its existence to its very low overall gradient and a lack of fissures that can swallow the stream, even though part of it has the cave carrying water from Darnbrook Fell at just a few metres depth and almost directly beneath it. Gordale Beck also maintains continuous surface flow, except in very dry conditions when all the water can sink into an immature route beneath the valley to springs downstream of the Scar. The Beck water is saturated with respect to calcite, so fractures and fissures along most of its bed are not opened by dissolution; instead, they are choked by deposition of travertine (see Chapter 6), and probably by clastic sediment derived from the till.

Sinks and risings of the limestone benches

Around the inside margins of the limestone benches, small streams arrive off higher slopes that are dominated by shales and mudstones within the Yoredale sequence. These sink into hundreds of caves and potholes; there are more than a hundred around Ingleborough alone (Carter and Dwerryhouse, 1904). The caves are described in Chapter 7, but their sinks are conspicuous features of the karst. One of the characteristic landforms of the Dales is the open pothole, where an allogenic stream falls anything from 5m to 50m

Figure 4.22. The shaft of Jingling Pot, in Kingsdale, rounded and fluted by spray corrosion and widened along its initial fracture (photo: Jerry Wooldridge).

into the depths. Most potholes are enlarged from vertical joints, though some are on minor faults. Many remain as elongate fissures (Fig. 4.21), others have developed into rounded shafts, commonly elliptical along a fracture (Fig. 4.22), and others have expanded by wall collapse on multiple joints (Fig. 4.23).

Alongside the pothole sinks, many allogenic streams flow into open cave entrances. Many of these are into quite low passages, with roofs along bedding planes that are only a bed or two down from the top of the limestone. The initial sink was down a joint through the top one or two beds, but this has been cut back into a short canyon that now ends at the cave.

Figure 4.21. Hunt Pot, on the west side of Pen-y-ghent, a classic stream sink into a deep fissure (TW).

Figure 4.23. The quarry-like sink of Hull Pot, on the west side of Pen-y-ghent, which was enlarged by multiple wall failures along parallel fractures and takes a large stream in flood conditions (TW).

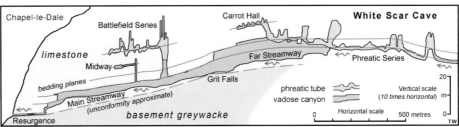

Figure 4.24. Extended profile through the outer part of White Scar Cave with its stream flowing for only a short distance on the base of the limestone out to the resurgence on the unconformity; basement rock is seen only at Grit Falls and at the resurgence; major bedding planes are only shown where recognised in the cave; minor faults are not shown.

Some streams continue in daylight beyond the shale margin, either by flowing over till that covers the limestone, or by flowing over bare limestone until they reach a vertical feature that can swallow their flow. But they too eventually sink, many at sites that are partially choked by coarse debris. Some older potholes have been left dry by retreat of the shale margin, though Alum and Rowten Pots are among those with younger stream caves opening into them at depth. Around Ingleborough, a former position of the shale margin may be indicated by the line of large old potholes (Fig. 7.42); originally considered only as "pre-glacial" (Sweeting, 1974), a pre-Anglian age may be inferred from the extent of the shale retreat (Waltham, 1990).

The large number of stream sinks on the Dales limestone benches drain through to a much smaller number of resurgences. Most underground streams converge with others in extensive, dendritic cave systems. Many caves descend 150–200m through almost the whole limestone thickness, and resurgences are commonly towards the base of the limestone. White Scar Cave is one of the very few that resurge in textbook fashion right on the base of the limestone. The lowest few metres in the Great Scar are commonly impure limestones, thinly bedded, with many shale beds and interrupted by rises in the local relief of the unconformable base of the limestone; all these are features of the patchy and uneven drowning of the pre-Carboniferous land surface. Consequently many of the low-level cave passages were initiated at inception horizons within the overlying, cleaner limestones, and feed resurgences that are above the basal unconformity. White Scar Cave would also do that if Pleistocene glaciers had cut Chapel-le-Dale a little wider, as its stream flows at a higher level for most of its length, and only descends to the base of the limestone in its last 160m out to daylight (Fig. 4.24).

White Scar Cave is one of the majority of Dales resurgences that pour water from cave passages initiated on bedding planes, though some do rise on joints. Many of the resurgence caves have been truncated by valley deepening (see Chapter 7). These include a significant number of smaller resurgences that lie at high stratigraphical levels within the Great Scar, notably Birkwith, Browgill and other caves in upper Ribblesdale (Fig. 4.25). These cave passages have

developed on bedding planes, shale beds or other inception horizons high in the limestone sequence, and have then been truncated by valley incision to leave the resurgences perched well above the valley floors. Another reason that these caves and their drainage have not descended to the base of the limestone may relate to the relative scarcity of deep, open joints far from the Craven Faults (see Chapter 7). The deep shafts of Alum and Diccan Pots are on a single, major, north–south joint (which is probably a small fault); much of the passage in Red Moss Pot is also along a single joint, but is nearly horizontal as it stays at one bedding horizon.

Besides the sinks and risings in the Great Scar Limestone, the Yorkshire Dales also have large numbers of both in the various thin limestones of the Yoredale sequence. Across Wensleydale and the northern dales, and also on the higher slopes of the southern dales, the topography of the Yoredale outcrops is characterised by rock benches formed on each limestone and sandstone, separated by gentler slopes on the interbedded shales. It is not a karst landscape, except that each limestone bench creates a narrow strip of karst, with broken limestone scars, patches of pavement and short caves connecting sinks and risings respectively atop and beneath their own bench. Many sinks are choked with debris, and few of the open potholes are more than about 10m deep because they are limited by the limestone thickness. The Buttertubs, in Swaledale, are a group of beautifully fluted and unusually well-developed potholes about 15m deep in

Figure 4.26. The fluted potholes of the Buttertubs, high on the southern flank of Swaledale (TW).

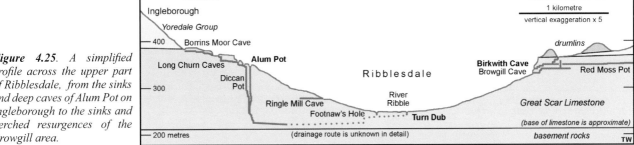

Figure 4.25. A simplified profile across the upper part of Ribblesdale, from the sinks and deep caves of Alum Pot on Ingleborough to the sinks and perched resurgences of the Browgill area.

the Main Limestone (Fig. 4.26). Many of the resurgences within the Yoredale succession are from small caves with sandstone floors at the base of the limestone units.

In the main karst of the southern Dales, the Lower Hawes Limestone (at the base of the Yoredale Group) is effectively continuous with the Great Scar Limestone, and consequently forms just a part of the Great Scar karst. The Middle Limestone is among those that thicken to the southeast, where it contains the caves and underground drainage of Nidderdale. Beneath and around Great Whernside, it is separated from the Great Scar Limestone by only a reduced thickness of non-carbonates, and the major stream sink at Mossdale Scar is also into the Middle Limestone, but has its resurgence at Black Keld low down in the Great Scar Limestone.

The third component of the Dales karst groundwater is the percolation flow supplied by dispersed recharge (see Chapter 9). A proportion of this emerges from small risings that are independent of flows from sinking streams. Many of these percolation risings are seepages with high solute loads, and they therefore precipitate carbonate when they reach open air, creating the localized travertine deposits that are yet another component of the Dales karst (see Chapter 6).

Dolines and shakeholes

The periodic glacial incursions of the Pleistocene ensured that the limestone terrain of the Yorkshire Dales never evolved into a fully mature karst, but remained as a glaciokarst. And whereas dolines are widely recognised as the diagnostic landforms of karst, they are little more than details in most of the overall landscape of the Dales.

Dolines include all types of closed depressions in karst (excluding poljes, which are much larger features and are not present in the Dales karst). Their common feature is underground drainage that prevents them filling with rainwater to create ponds; they can also be known

Figure 4.29. A small and deeply fluted solution doline in strong and massive limestone on Scales Moor, above Chapel-le-Dale (TW).

as sinkholes (particularly in America and by engineering geologists). Within the Dales, the dolines fall into three groups (Fig. 4.28). Those in bedrock can be separated into solution dolines and collapse dolines, whereas those in the cover of soil or drift are described as subsidence dolines (Waltham et al., 2005); the latter are widely known within the Yorkshire Dales as shakeholes.

Caprock dolines are formed in non-karstic outcrops by collapse into underlying limestone. Within the Dales, these are only significant on some of the gritstone outcrops east of Wharfedale. Three caprock dolines up to 60m across and 10m deep, along with some smaller features, lie within the Grassington Grit high on Barden Fell, south of Stump Cross (Fig. 4.27). These may have developed through as much as 50m of the gritstone, but the structure of the underlying limestone is unknown, and a buried reef mass could be capped by a smaller thickness of non-carbonates. Above Black Edge, on Grassington Moor, another group of three caprock dolines, each up to 70m across, are formed entirely in the Grassington Grit where it lies above Yoredale limestones. These are floored by collapsed blocks of the gritstone, and have no known connections to passages in Mossdale Caverns, which lie obliquely beneath within the Middle Limestone.

Dolines in bedrock

Solution dolines develop by dissolution of rock on the surface, beneath the soil and within the epikarst, collectively lowering the surface around the central drainage outlet (Williams, 1983). In contrast, collapse dolines form largely or wholly by collapse into cave chambers or passages. In the Dales and elsewhere, most dolines in bedrock involve both processes, and therefore constitute a spectrum of morphologies that range from solution to collapse.

Figure 4.27. One of the caprock dolines on Barden Fell, formed where Grassington Grit has collapsed into underlying limestone (TW).

Figure 4.28. Cross sections of the three main types of doline that occur in the Yorkshire Dales.

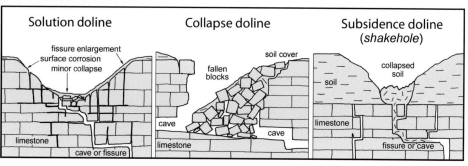

Solution doline	Collapse doline	Subsidence doline (shakehole)
fissure enlargement, surface corrosion, minor collapse, limestone, cave or fissure	soil cover, fallen blocks, cave, limestone, cave	collapsed soil, soil, limestone, fissure or cave

Figure 4.30. Bar Pot, on Ingleborough, a collapse doline with steep walls and fallen blocks of limestone (TW).

Profiles of solution dolines vary from shallow bowls to vertical, cylindrical shafts. Whether the many open potholes that characterise the Dales karst are referred to or subdivided as dolines, shafts, stream sinks or potholes is a detail of terminology, as they cover a spectrum of morphologies. The smallest are just a metre or so across, and include some beautifully fluted conical depressions in clean rock (Fig. 4.29). Dissolution is a slow process, so solution dolines tens of metres across cannot have formed in the Dales karst since the Devensian ice cover. All the larger dolines have been over-run by ice. While some potholes have survived unscathed, all the wider and shallower dolines have been eroded or partially filled by glacial processes (see below).

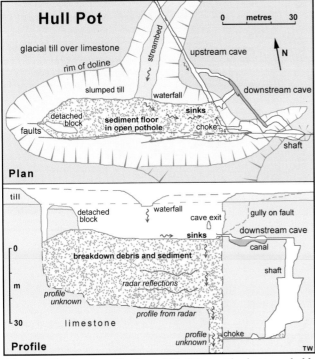

Figure 4.31. Sketch profile through Hull Pot, with what is probably the lower part of a massive boulder pile reached through the adjacent shaft on the fault; the stream and waterfall are only active in flood conditions, and there is now leakage from the streambed into the upstream cave where it crosses beneath; the radar reflections are probably breaks on layering within the breakdown pile (after surveys by Arthur Gemmel and Phil Pappard, with ground radar data from Murphy et al., 2008).

Rock collapse is largely a process that is only secondary to dissolutional cave development in karst terrains, and collapse features constitute only a minority of the dolines in the Yorkshire Dales. The Jingling Caves above Kingsdale, and many other stream caves that follow the highest bedding planes at shallow depths in the Great Scar Limestone, have their thin roof rocks penetrated by daylight windows. Some of these windows are just single fissures opened by dissolution on individual cross-joints, whereas others are longer stretches of open stream channel. Of these, some were cleanly unroofed by ice action, but some still contain the fallen blocks from roof collapse. The latter qualify as collapse dolines, but their sizes are limited to the few metres of the cave widths. There are a few larger collapse dolines, with Hull Pot (Fig. 4.23) and Bar Pot (Fig. 4.30) providing well known examples. Tempting though it is to ascribe these to "cavern collapse" there is scant evidence that there has ever been wholesale failure of roofs across wide cave chambers. It is just as likely that their first appearances as surface features were as single open fissures along joints, and these were then widened largely by wall collapse with progressive failure of adjacent joint-bound blocks of rock and subsequent dissolutional removal of the fallen blocks. There is ongoing wall failure at Hull Pot, but evidence of its early stages of collapse are now obscured by the breakdown blocks and stream debris that may be 60m deep (Fig. 4.31).

Large dolines cut into the bedrock of any karst involve both dissolution and collapse. Dissolution may well be the dominant process in most cases, but it works alongside the undercutting of joint-defined blocks of individual beds. These blocks are inevitable features along the internal slopes of large dolines, and their subsequent displacement, landsliding or collapse contributes to development of the doline, besides exposing further surfaces to sub-aerial or sub-soil dissolution. Morphologies of all the large bedrock dolines in the Dales karst have been complicated by the Pleistocene ice that intermittently covered them, partially filled most of them with till and perhaps modified their rock profiles.

An exhaustive survey identified 473 large karst depressions on the limestone outcrops of the southern Askrigg Block between Leck Fell and Grassington Moor (Marker and Goldie, 2007). Of these, 140 are on the Malham High Country, and another 82 lie on the southeastern benches of Ingleborough. Not included in that total are 32 large depressions on the wide bench of the Yoredale Main

Figure 4.32. The largest of the ancient solution dolines on the Malham High Country (TW).

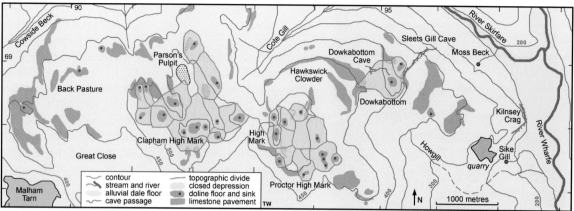

Figure 4.33. *Major karst features on the Malham High Country; clusters of very large dolines combine to form the areas of polygonal karst; the top of Parson's Pulpit is an outlier of Yoredale sandstone.*

Limestone above and west of Bishopdale. The largest of the depressions is that lying between Parson's Pulpit and Clapham High Mark (Fig. 4.32); it is nearly 800m in diameter, with an area of about 38 ha, and with most of its rim about 50m above its floor, though one saddle is only 20m above floor level (Fig. 4.33). Another 21 of the depressions each exceed 30 ha in area, and mean dimensions of the smallest 100 in the survey are 47m long and 27m wide; only 30 of the 473 are more than 7m deep. Nearly all of these depressions are true dolines, in that they have been created largely by dissolution of the limestone, with variable (but generally small) contributions from collapse processes during wall

retreat. A few wide and shallow depressions on the north end of the Moughton plateau of Ingleborough are stratimorphic, as their floors largely follow the bedding across very gentle synclinal folds (Fig. 4.34). These could have been excavated solely by glacial stripping of the upper bed, but their profiles distinguish them even from the dolines with the widest and shallowest profiles.

The larger dolines on the Malham High Country combine to form limited areas of polygonal karst (Fig. 4.33), where the entire surface is formed by the dolines between nets of interdoline watershed ridges (Waltham *et al.*, 1997). These may be regarded as a holokarst, and the only true karst, as opposed to glaciokarst, in the Yorkshire Dales. They are clearly the most mature karst features in the Dales, and are too large to have formed in post-Devensian time. They lie within

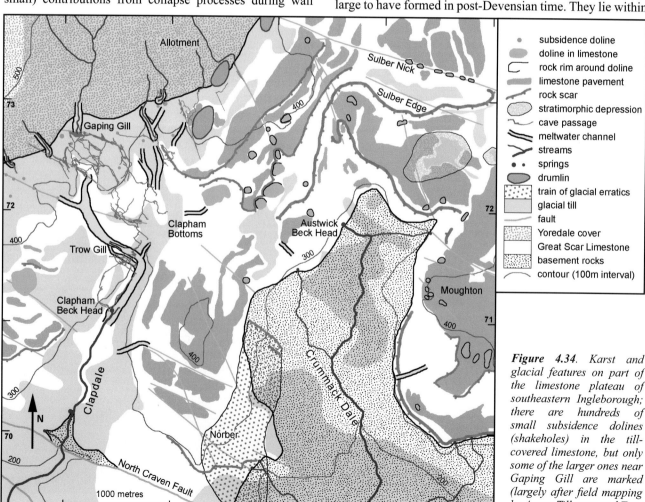

Figure 4.34. *Karst and glacial features on part of the limestone plateau of southeastern Ingleborough; there are hundreds of small subsidence dolines (shakeholes) in the till-covered limestone, but only some of the larger ones near Gaping Gill are marked (largely after field mapping by Angus Tillotson and Tony Waltham).*

Figure 4.35. One of the large old dolines with well-defined rock rims along the fault trace of Sulber Nick, eastern Ingleborough (TW).

an area distinguished by many boulders, clints, pavements and pinnacles of limestone all of which are so rounded that they are interpreted as being significantly older than much of the Dales karst (Goldie, 2006b). The Malham High Country appears to have spent long intervals beneath an ice cover, which was probably almost static, cold-based ice with little or no erosive power. This ice sat on the high ground along the upturned southern edge of the Askrigg Block, between a faster flow of ice down Wharfedale and a zone that moved a little more rapidly across the basin of Malham Tarn.

No evidence has been found of glacial erosion in the polygonal karst, but details within the dolines are largely obscured by extensive drift deposits. Parts of these have been mapped as till (Arthurton *et al.*, 1988), though it may be that they are entirely loessic (Marker and Goldie, 2007). In the largest doline, augering has revealed a metre of clayey sand, and geophysical surveys indicate about 5m of underlying clays above well-fissured bedrock (Gullen, 1999). Deepening of the dolines may have been aided by sub-soil dissolution beneath the drift during interglacial stages (Clayton, 1981). Smaller shakeholes pock the drift floors within the dolines, but are irrelevant to the long-term doline genesis. That the large dolines and their polygonal karst above Malham are formed largely on the Gayle and Hawes limestones is incidental, as these are locally continuous with the Great Scar.

Large dolines on southeastern Ingleborough, around the head of Crummack Dale (Fig. 4.34), are very different from those at Malham, as they were over-run and modified by significant Pleistocene ice flows across the wide bench adjacent to Ribblesdale (Waltham, 1990; Goldie and Marker, 2001). Most of these dolines are 10–50m in diameter, and are characterised by low, well-defined, bedrock scars around their perimeters, with floors of grass-covered drift no more than a few metres below rim level. Their scar edges suggest glacial quarrying, or perhaps a greater component of collapse during their pre-glacial development, but many are notably close to circular in plan, indicating their evolution into mature dolines. Those along Sulber Nick are elongated parallel to the fault line that defines the feature, but are neverthless rounded in plan (Fig. 4.35). Coring of their soil floors has revealed loessic silts and clays (Goldie and Marker, 2001), which could include sediment from deglaciation lakes. Only two profiles came from dolines with the well-defined rock rims; one on the main upper bench revealed at least 2m of sediment fill, while one on the lower bench above Clapham

Bottoms met bedrock, or a large boulder, beneath only 0.5m of sediment (Fig. 4.34). Geophysical surveys of the large doline, without a rock rim, at the head of Clapham Bottoms found sediments continuing to 4m deep (Gullen, 1999); between that unconsolidated fill and a bedrock floor, the same geophysics indicated about 13m of "altered" limestone, distinguished by its low seismic velocity, which could be interpreted as a pile of collapse blocks, or as heavily fissured bedrock, or conceivably as a block-rich till. Some of these Ingleborough dolines appear to have been deep and steep-walled features more like potholes than the wide and shallow depressions of Malham; they were formed at some time prior to the Devensian, or possibly by subglacial or proglacial meltwater, before being largely filled with clastic sediment.

A comparable feature on the opposite side of Ingleborough is Braithwaite Wife Hole, a conical doline 60m in diameter and 25m deep. Its southeastern side is broken by small scars and limestone outcrops, and once had an entrance into the cave chambers now only accessible from Sunset Hole. The other sides are ramps of till, mostly covered in grass. How much wider and deeper this doline might be remains unknown, but it is set into the limestone bench above Chapel-le-Dale so no more than a few metres can have been removed from its limestone rim by either dissolution or ice erosion. It stands as a fine example of a large and very old doline over-ridden by ice and partially filled by glacial debris.

Shakeholes within the soil cover

Subsidence dolines, or shakeholes, are those formed entirely within the soil profiles. In this context, the soil is any type of unconsolidated sediment that is alluvial or glacial, together with surface materials with an organic component, which are known as top-soil for their biological properties. Within the

Figure 4.36. Numerous small shakeholes in the remains of a thin sheet of till that covers part of the limestone pavements on Fell Close, on northern Ingleborough (TW).

Figure 4.37. A typical Dales shakehole, in Ribblesdale, in glacial till with sloping sides of grass-covered till and with bedrock limestone hidden beneath the slumped debris (TW).

Dales karst these materials include the glacial till and valley alluvium that may also be known as drift, as well as loess, lake sediments and hill peat, and soil is simply a convenient lithological term that includes all these loose materials that may overlie the limestone. These dolines have formed where the soil has been washed down into voids in the underlying limestone, in a process known as suffosion or ravelling, and can be separated into two broad types. Dropout dolines form rapidly by collapse of cohesive soils in arches over voids where soil had been washed out from beneath, whereas suffosion dolines form slowly as less cohesive soil slumps downwards as it is washed into the void beneath. These are only end-members of a series of landforms, and most of the dolines in the soils in the Dales have formed through a combination of slumping and collapse. They are therefore best described collectively as subsidence dolines, but locally they are generally known as shakeholes. There are thousands

of shakeholes in the drift blanket of till and loess that lies across much of the Great Scar and Yoredale limestones (Fig. 4.36); about 3500 are recorded on Ingleborough alone (Waltham and Tillotson, 1989).

The simplest form of a Dales shakehole is a conical depression with sides of grass-covered soil converging downwards to a narrow limestone fissure, through which the soil has been lost over time (Fig. 4.37). Any cohesion within a clay-rich soil allows voids to develop initially at the base of the soil profile and over the bedrock fissure, until the soil arches over them collapse; this can create new shakeholes with steep sides in the bare soil (Fig. 4.38), until they slump and degrade. Shakehole profiles therefore show considerable variation, which are further complicated by any choking of the outlet, whereupon a pond and its sediments may accumulate on the shakehole floor. Only some shakeholes have bedrock exposed on their floors. A typical shakehole has internal slopes of 10–40°, so its diameter is about two or three times its depth, and, if fully developed to expose bedrock on its floor, is up to about three times the soil thickness. Most Dales shakeholes are 2–10m across because they are limited by the 1–5m depth that is typical for the cover of till and loess.

Clusters of much larger shakeholes occur in areas of thicker till, notably in the lee of the hills that deflected southward-moving Pleistocene ice. The southwestern flank of Gragareth is notable for having more than a dozen shakeholes that are 20–40m across. Many of these are well choked with rock and soil debris, and one frequently contains a temporary lake (Fig. 4.39). Ashtree Hole is a large shakehole less than 10m deep, but the soil debris of its floor is exposed in the side of a cave passage (in Gavel Pot) 35m below (Fig. 4.40); this is clearly within a bedrock shaft, the width of which is unknown. Other shakeholes have open shafts on their floors, and many of the larger shafts were formed prior to the till being deposited over the limestone and locally slumping into the open voids. Death's Head Hole has slopes of slumped till that fall 5m to a rock lip, above a nearly cylindrical shaft 7m wide and 60m deep. Some shakeholes also have discrete streams draining into them, and are elongated where their small valleys have entrenched into the drift blanket. A depression 40m wide and 80m long, with a small stream entering at one end in wet weather, has the entrance to Ireby Fell Cavern in its floor, surrounded by soil slopes more than 10 m high. Whether this is described as a large shakehole or a small blind valley, or as a conspicuous stream sink, is immaterial, as all lie within a continuum of karst landforms created where water finds its way underground.

Figure 4.38. A newly formed shakehole on Newby Moss, Ingleborough, with sides of glacial till that have not yet slumped to a stable profile (TW).

Figure 4.39. The very large shakehole that commonly contains a small lake near Notts Pot, on the southern flank of Gragareth (TW).

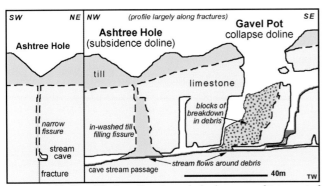

Figure 4.40. Simplified profiles through the known and interpreted (broken lines) features of the large dolines of Ashtree Hole and Gavel Pot, on Leck Fell, related to the stream cave passage that lies beneath; the main fracture is probably a minor fault; the debris in Gavel Pot is a mix of limestone breakdown and glacial till.

Because the mechanism behind shakehole enlargement is seepage water washing the finer components of the soil cover down into limestone voids, new shakeholes tend to appear, or old ones become larger, after rainstorm events or when a tiny surface stream happens to take a new course across the drift cover. In the winter of 1946, the floor dropped out of a shakehole originally less than 10m deep on Leck Fell; the event was unseen, but it revealed the entrance to Notts Pot. Also unseen, on Ingleborough during the winter of 1980, a whole side of the deep shakehole of Marble Pot sloughed into the chamber beneath (Fig. 4.41). Changes in stream courses have created new shakeholes on Newby Moss, and enlarged the existing shakehole now known as the entrance

to Boxhead Pot on Leck Fell. Shakeholes are essentially post-glacial features, as they are set into Devensian drift, but they owe their existence to dissolutional widening of their underlying fissures in the limestone. At many, if not most, sites, that process started in pre-Devensian times, and only the soil loss is strictly post-glacial.

Patterns within the distribution of shakeholes are not generally recognisable, because a shakehole can develop over any of the myriad fissures that lie hidden in the limestone beneath the drift cover. Some larger joints, or faults, create lines of shakeholes, but there is normally no correlation between distributions of shakeholes, rock fractures and cave passages (Fig. 4.42). The exception is that there is commonly some concentration of shakeholes along the line of a shale margin buried beneath the drift, where seepage water within the drift flows downhill until it reaches the buried limestone. Similarly there is a better chance of enterable cave lying beneath the largest shakeholes. Conspicuous lines of shakeholes do lie over some narrow and buried outcrops of Yoredale limestones (Clayton, 1981), but locations of fractures and caves beneath cannot be inferred from distributions along the lines.

Valleys and gorges

Fluvial landforms within the Dales karst include a variety of valleys and gorges that all owe at least elements of their morphology to erosion by meltwater from the Pleistocene ice cover. There are dry valleys and gorges that are typical of karst landscapes, but there are also features that still carry surface water with significant flows that are either permanent or ephemeral.

Within the current karst environment of the Yorkshire Dales, most drainage across the limestone outcrop is underground, other than at flood stage when numerous flood

Figure 4.41. The deep shakehole at Marble Pot, on eastern Ingleborough, with a small stream flowing into it, and the scar left after 1980 by the massive slump in its sloping wall of till (TW).

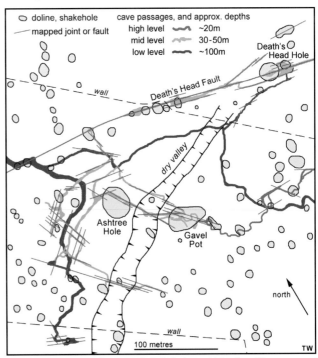

Figure 4.42. Distribution of shakeholes within the till on part of Leck Fell, correlated with known cave passages and major bedrock fractures mapped within the caves; there are fewer shakeholes in the area of thick till around Gavel Pot and Ashtree Hole.

channels become temporarily active. The notable exceptions are the larger allogenic rivers that flow through the glaciated dales with very low gradients and therefore have significant lengths of their flows above ground (Table 4.3). The flood channels themselves include some spectacular little canyons and gorges that are dry for most of the time. Short sections of Ease Gill are entrenched into clean and polished limestone, and the middle section of the Dee through Dentdale is along a small, rock-walled box canyon. Potts Beck and Crystal Beck both descend narrow valleys cut into the steep northern slope of upper Littondale, with flood channels that descend first over the Yoredale outcrop and then over the Great Scar Limestone. Both have their channels alternating between steep and narrow sections cut into thick beds of coarse sparry limestones and more open sections over more thinly bedded, fine-grained micritic limestones (Sweeting and Sweeting, 1969). In the northern dales, some of the larger streams flowing across narrow outcrops of Yoredale limestone have cut surface canyons faster than they can find underground routes. This down-cutting has been aided by steep descents over the terrace edges that characterise such sites, whereas many parallel and smaller streams cross the outcrops underground. Hell Gill (Fig. 4.43), at the top end of Mallerstang, has a narrow twisting gorge 500m long (Waltham *et al.*, 1997), and the rather more accessible How Stean Gorge in Nidderdale is only slightly shorter.

Blind valleys develop where streams sink underground at fixed points for long enough to entrench their surface courses, but those in the Dales karst are limited to short features cut into areas of thicker till. The stream approaches to Gaping Gill Hole and Hurnel Moss Pot are two of the larger blind valleys on Ingleborough. Similarly, pocket

valleys (or headless valleys) occur downstream of some resurgences in the Dales karst, but again are of very limited size. In Ribblesdale, Douk Gill Head is cut back into the basal limestone beds, and lies at the top end of one of the larger headless valleys, though this has an extension above and behind the scar as the dry valley reaching down from Hull Pot. Malham Cove is much larger, but has complex origins (see below).

The largest dry valleys and gorges in the Yorkshire Dales karst are those that were formed by meltwater from Pleistocene ice over largely frozen ground and have been left dry since climatic amelioration allowed drainage to return underground. Gordale and Watlowes are among the largest features, above Gordale Scar and Malham Cove respectively (see below). Trow Gill is a 300m-long, deeply entrenched section of a dry valley that descends from the Ingleborough bench into Clapdale (Waltham *et al*, 1997). Its steep and narrow upper part, just 70m long, has vertical walls indented by the remnants of breached moulins, and its lower part widens into a deep fluvial valley (Figs 4.44, 4.45). Though often referred to as a collapsed cave in the far past, later descriptions included or debated cavern collapse as just a part of its development, and it was subsequently described as a purely fluvial landform (Glover, 1974). The wide flare of Trow Gill below its upper fluvial slot, and the cave in its right wall that may extend beneath the debris slope, could indicate a role of headward erosion at a large old resurgence (Murphy, 1997). Two comparable meltwater features are Dib Scar and Conistone Dib, both of which are entrenched into the limestone slopes of Wharfedale below Conistone Old Pasture (Waltham *et al.*, 1997). Dib Scar is a tapering gorge formed by waterfall retreat into a resistant, thick bed

Figure 4.43. Hell Gill cut into the Yoredale Main Limestone at the top end of Mallerstang (photo: Mark Shinwell).

Figure 4.44. The narrow upper end of the Trow Gill meltwater gorge on Ingleborough (photo: John Cordingley).

Figure 4.45. The Trow Gill meltwater gorge on Ingleborough, together with the adjacent Foxholes valley and an approximate outline, in blue, of the underlying cave passages (modified from Waltham, 1990).

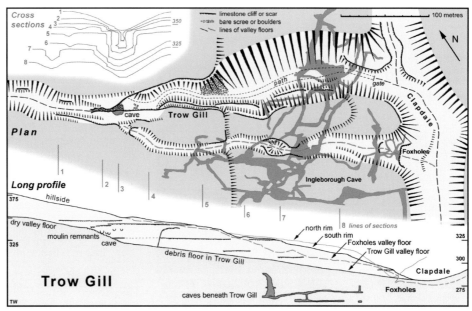

of limestone, and strongly resembles the wider part of Trow Gill. Most of Conistone Dib is a broad dry valley, but its lower end closes in to a short narrow canyon that is very similar to the fluvial slot in Trow Gill.

Though cavern collapse has long been recognised as an untenable hypothesis for the formation of most gorges in karst, caves do play a role within the overall fluvial excavation of valleys and gorges, in the Yorkshire Dales karst and elsewhere. Beneath an active riverbed, underground loops develop wherever gradients and geological structure provide opportunity. The loops evolve into small caves, and are then unroofed by down-cutting, but thereby contribute to total erosional process. Such caves in the Dales include the various sites known as God's Bridge, of which the finest is that on the River Greta in Stainmore (Fig. 4.46), and the wide area of collapse on the bedding plane caves at Giant's Grave (Fig. 4.47), at the top end of Pen-y-ghent Gill (both in Waltham *et al*, 1997). The active Hell Gill gorge has both a remnant rock arch and a short abandoned loop in its wall.

While these dry valleys and gorges can be ascribed largely to excavation by Pleistocene meltwater, none can be dated to any particular glacial stage, except to note that the fresher features must have been created or re-occupied during

the Devensian ice retreat for their clean rock walls to have survived until the present. Furthermore, there is variation within the environments of the meltwater streams. Proglacial erosion was restricted as glacier snouts were largely on the dale floors, below the limestone benches, and even those were short-lived during retreat phases. It has been suggested that Trow Gill could have been rapidly entrenched just below a tongue of ice that survived for some time on the Ingleborough benches (Sweeting, 1974), but the patterns of ice retreat are not known in detail. Subglacial meltwater was widespread and numerous channels have been mapped on the limestone uplands around Malham (Clayton, 1981; Arthurton *et al*, 1988); these include the channels that cross watersheds both north and west of Malham Tarn with reverse gradients that indicate flow under pressure beneath the ice. This water was derived from seasonal surface melt that descended through crevasses and moulins within the ice sheets. There may also have been a significant component from ice-dammed marginal lakes that could have been widespread around the Yoredale nunataks during stages of ice retreat (Faulkner, 2006); these temporary lakes would have fed water onto the limestone, but beneath the ice, in patterns broadly similar to those of today's hillside drainage.

Figure 4.46. God's Bridge in Stainmore, where the River Greta has a very short underground section in its path across the Namurian Great Limestone (known as the Main Limestone further south) (TW).

Figure 4.47. Collapsed ground at the head of Pen-y-ghent Gill with thick beds of limestone that have dropped just a few metres where they were undercut by the wide bedding plane passages of the Giant's Grave Caves (TW).

Figure 4.48. The meltwater channel of Cowside Beck between Darnbrook Fell and the Malham High Country (TW).

Cowside Beck (Fig. 4.48) and Pcn-y-ghent Gill are both conspicuously large V-shaped valleys that drain into the south side of Littondale. Their morphologies are those of fluviokarst, with many similarities to dry valleys in the Derbyshire Peak District that were modified and enlarged under periglacial conditions. The same applies to some other dry valleys in the Dales, notably the wide section of Conistone Dib (Fig. 4.49). The Yorkshire Dales did not have the long period of Devensian periglacial conditions that distinguished the Derbyshire Peak, but these fluvial landforms may indicate similar conditions during any of the cold stages of the 'Wolstonian' (MIS 10, 8 and 6), or parts of them, when there was no ice cover on the high interfluves of the karst between the dales. They survived the Devensian and earlier glaciations because their orientation meant that ice moved across them, instead of along them. Also, the ice on the limestone high ground was slow-moving, with much of it cold-based so that it was frozen to the bedrock and therefore had minimal erosive power. This was in marked contrast to the main ice flows that were directed along, and thereby enlarged, the Littondale trough. Subglacial meltwater would have continued their excavation.

Both Cowside Beck and Pen-y-ghent Gill lack the steep cross-profiles of purely subglacial channels such as Gordale and Watlowes, and their relative contributions of periglacial and subglacial erosion remain open to debate. They are old features that were elements of the dendritic drainage pattern imprinted on the Yorkshire Pennines, of which most elements have since been glacially modified into the U-shape dales. Both are also distinctive in that they normally maintain surface flows along most of their lengths over the limestone outcrop, largely due to their low gradients. Ease Gill is a largely fluvial valley; it was occupied by Pleistocene ice, but this lacked erosive power in the lee of Great Coum. Subglacial meltwater is likely to have excavated much of the modern ravine that is entrenched through the till and into the limestone (Fig. 4.50), and also any ancestral valley features now obscured beneath the till.

Subglacial meltwater is a feature of warm-based ice, and its widespread influence on the landforms of the Dales' limestone uplands conflicts with the evidence for cold-based ice indicated by the preservation of the pavements on the high ground. It is likely that conditions varied beneath the Pleistocene ice on the Dales limestone benches, with both warm-based and cold-based ice existing in different areas at the same time, in addition to variations over time as conditions changed at any one place through a glacial phase; such a complex pattern has been recognised under other ice sheets (Faulkner, 2010). Clast-rich sediments in Dale Barn Cave, below Kingsdale, are interpreted as sliding bedload within a pipe-full, glacier tunnel (Murphy *et al.*, 2001), but there is considerable variation in the environments and roles of old and contemporary cave passages beneath the Pleistocene ice (see Chapter 7). The lack of glacial erosion across many of the high-level limestone benches may be due in part just to the reduced speed of the ice. The slow-moving, thinner ice sheets had less erosive power than the faster flows of ice that followed the lines of existing valleys and contributed to deepening the glacial troughs of the major dales.

Figure 4.49. The dry valley of Conistone Dib, cut by a meltwater stream that descended the steep eastern flank of the Wharfedale glaciated trough (TW).

Figure 4.50. The dry channel of Ease Gill entrenched about 15m into the floor of the wider valley (TW).

Malham and Gordale

Above the village of Malham, Gordale Scar and Malham Cove are among the most spectacular landforms within the Yorkshire Dales. Each is a large step within the profile of its own drainage channel off the limestone high ground, and each has retreated about 600m from the bench margin along the Middle Craven Fault, which juxtaposes the limestone against weaker Bowland Shales to the south (Fig. 4.51).

The white limestone cliff of Malham Cove is 70m high and about 200m wide (Fig. 4.52). It lies at the lower end of Watlowes (Fig. 4.53), a dry valley entrenched 30m into the

Figure 4.53. The Watlowes dry valley, extending downstream from the cliffs of Comb Scar (TW).

limestone surface for 850m downstream of its dry waterfall at Comb Scar. Upstream of the Scar, a shallower valley is dry as far as the Water Sinks that swallow the outflow from Malham Tarn. The hydrology between those sinks, the rising below the Cove and the Aire Head rising is complex (see Chapter 9). At the foot of the Cove a stream emerges from a cave that has been followed, entirely underwater, for 700m, following the bedding in a passage up to 9m wide and 3m high (Monico, 1995).

Gordale Scar has an amphitheatre, also about 200m wide. Its scale is comparable to that of Malham Cove, except that it is more deeply recessed, has taller and more broken cliffs (reaching to 100m high) and has its rear wall breached by a deep gorge (Fig 4.54). Within the gorge, the stream pours through the Hole in the Wall, which was formed in 1730 when the water broke through a thin blade of rock between two deep fault-guided gullies. Prior to that, the eastern gully had been choked with sediment and the stream dropped into the head of the western gully where a large bank of travertine still marks the site of the former waterfall (Fig. 4.55).

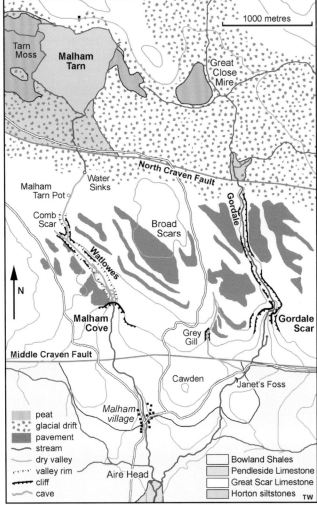

Figure 4.51. Outline geology and the main karst features of Malham and Gordale; numerous small faults, mainly aligned NW–SE, are omitted for clarity, and both limestones include units of the reef facies that are not distinguished; only the main area of glacial drift around Malham Tarn is marked, and a thin mantle of till is extensive on the lowlands south of the South Craven Fault (geology mainly after Arthurton et al., 1988).

Figure 4.52. The limestone cliff of Malham Cove (TW).

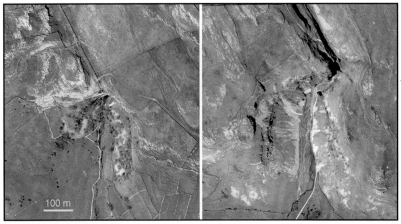

Figure 4.54. The equally wide erosional amphitheatres in front of Malham Cove (on the left) and Gordale Scar (on the right), with Gordale more deeply recessed and also scarred by the fluvial canyon incised into its back wall (satellite imagery from Infoterra).

Figure 4.56. The deeply entrenched meltwater channel of Gordale upstream of the Scar (TW).

Above the Scar's gorge, the rocky valley of Gordale is comparable to Watlowes, except that it is 1200m long and still carries an underfit stream for its entire length (Fig. 4.56). The water drains from the basin containing Great Close Mire, and is responsible for the various travertine deposits along and downstream of Gordale (see Chapter 6). Deposition of the travertine may be partially responsible for blocking bedrock fissures and preventing underground capture of Gordale Beck (Moisley, 1955); springs downstream of the Scar are fed by percolation water direct from the high ground.

Both Watlowes and Gordale are impressive meltwater channels. They were cut largely or entirely by subglacial streams, though components of their origins may lie in earlier fluvial or periglacial erosion, or in deepening by short-lived proglacial drainage from remnants of Devensian ice on the Malham High Country. The deeper of the two is Gordale, both in its upstream valley and its Scar gorge, where incision was more rapid on the weaknesses created by small faults.

The main debate concerns the origins of Malham Cove. Historically it was broadly accepted as a "dry waterfall" (Clayton, 1966), though early papers on the Dales karst avoided specific mention of the Cove (Sweeting, 1950; Moisley, 1955). Genesis of the Cove has to rely on some combination of four processes, all of which could have contributed to some extent.

Figure 4.55. Inside Gordale Scar, the beck pours through the Hole in the Wall, and the pre-1730 travertine lies to its left (TW).

Fluvial erosion. A simple history as a dry waterfall is supported by the dry fluvial valley of the Watlowes feeding to the head of the Cove. The problem arises in the 200m width of the Cove, which far exceeds the width of the Watlowes floor at less than 50m, as Niagara-style waterfall retreat typically forms a cliff little wider than the river channel.

Glaciofluvial erosion. Any consideration of fluvial erosion at the Cove has to rely heavily on Pleistocene flows of meltwater, from or beneath ice sheets, especially during their retreat phases. Surface flow over the limestone then occurred when cave flows were restricted or eliminated by permafrost, or when meltwater flows temporarily exceeded the capacity of the contemporary sinks. A variation on the meltwater origin of the Cove is waterfall retreat during periodic massive subglacial floods, known as jökulhlaups after their occurrences in Iceland. Such floods are indicated by consideration of sub-ice water temperatures in the Malham Tarn basin that would have acted as their source, and their estimated flows of 25–50 m^3/sec could account for the large width of the Watlowes and perhaps that of the Cove (Pitty *et al.*, 1986).

Figure 4.57. Profiles along the meltwater channels of Watlowes and Gordale and their wider sections downstream of Malham Cove and Gordale Scar.

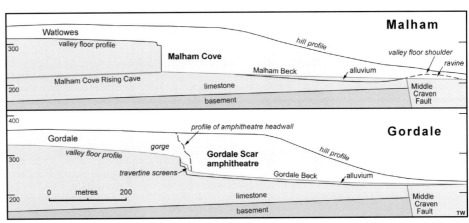

Figure 4.58. Gordale Scar, with the deep and narrow gorge in the shadow that breaks the wall of the main amphitheatre of limestone cliffs (TW).

Ice action. The site of Malham Cove lay beneath the ice during each of the Pleistocene glaciations. Limestone pavements above the Cove indicate a level of ice erosion, but there is no specific evidence of ice action on the Cove itself. Support for the role of ice erosion comes from the Cove's width of about 200m being so much greater than that of the Watlowes valley feeding to its head (Clayton, 1981; Waltham *et al.*, 1997). Much of the Cove's morphology could derive from origins as a subglacial step, excavated by glacial quarrying and wall retreat beneath a southward flow of ice that was channelled along a proto-valley roughly on the line of Watlowes and over the fault scarp. The basin below the Cove has been glacially over-deepened, with a post-glacial trench through bedrock at its outlet rim (Fig. 4.57).

Karstic processes. The Cove has been described as a pocket valley, created by a combination of spring sapping, cavern collapse and river erosion (Sweeting, 1972). Water emerging from the cave behind the rising would contribute to shaping of the Cove by dissolutional erosion, removal of rock debris and some undercutting of the cliff. However, the cave passage is less than 5m wide, and its impact can only be minor, even if it was once a vauclusian rising with an ascending passage where the face of the Cove now lies.

It is likely that all four processes have contributed to the distinctive and unusual morphology of Malham Cove, but it is far from certain as to which processes were dominant. Subglacial meltwater, with or without jökulhlaup floods, must have contributed to shaping the Cove at critical stages through the glaciation cycles. Karstic processes cannot have played a major role. And it is difficult to explain the width of the Cove without some element of ice action. The age of the Cove and the scale of its pre-Devensian ancestor are both unknown. Stalagmite from inside the Cove Rising is dated to at least 27 ka, and suggests that the valley in front of the Cove had been eroded to close to its present profile prior to the main Devensian glaciation (Murphy and Latham, 2001).

The rock-walled amphitheatre that is the lower, outer part of Gordale Scar is a landform similar in size to Malham Cove, except that is more deeply recessed into the limestone high ground (Fig. 4.58). Its origins are probably comparable to those of Malham Cove, and are likewise unknown in detail, though it is clear that the narrow gorge that forms the inner section of Gordale Scar was cut largely by meltwater.

Though the Yorkshire Dales karst is actually a glaciokarst, these two of its best known landmarks are fluvial features. Yet these apparent anomalies are perhaps appropriate, as they indicate the complexities of multiple processes that have combined to create the landscapes of the Dales karst.

References

Arthurton, R S, E W Johnson and D J C Mundy, 1988. Geology of the country around Settle. *Mem. Brit. Geol. Surv.*, Sheet 60, 148pp.

Atkinson, T C, R S Harmon, P L Smart and A C Waltham, 1978. Palaeoclimatic and geomorphic implications of ^{230}Th/^{234}U Dates on speleothems from Britain. *Nature*, **272**, 24-28.

Burbank, D W and R S Anderson, 2001. *Tectonic Geomorphology*. Blackwell Science: Oxford, 274pp.

Carter, W L and A R Dwerryhouse, 1904. The underground waters of north-west Yorkshire: part II, Ingleborough. *Proc. Yorks. Geol. Soc.*, **15**, 248-292.

Clayton, K M, 1966. The origin of the landforms of the Malham area. *Field Studies*, **2**, 359-384.

Clayton, K M, 1981. Explanatory description of the landforms of the Malham area. *Field Studies*, **5**, 389-423.

Cvijić, J, 1893. Das Karstphänomen. *Geographische Abhandlungen von A Penck*, **5**, 218-329.

Cvijić, J, 1918. Hydrographie souterraine et évolution morphologique du karst. *Recueil Travaux Institute Géographie Alpine*, **4**, 375-426.

Dreybrodt, W, 2004. Erosion rates: theoretical models. 323-325 in J Gunn (ed.), *Encyclopedia of Caves and Karst Science*, Fitzroy Dearborn: New York.

Dunham, K C and A A Wilson, 1985. Geology of the Northern Pennine Orefield: 2, Stainmore and Craven. *Econ. Mem. Brit. Geol. Surv.*, 247pp.

Faulkner, T, 2006. The impact of the deglaciation of central Scandinavia on karst caves and the implications for Craven's limestone landscape. *Proc. North Craven Historical Research Group Workshop*, 4-9.

Faulkner, T, 2009. Limestone pavement erosion rates and rainfall. *Cave Karst Science*, **36**, 94-95.

Faulkner, T, 2010. An external model of speleogenesis during Quaternary glacial cycles in the marbles of central Scandinavia. *Cave Karst Science*, **37**, 79-92.

Ford, D and P Williams, 2007. *Karst Hydrogeology and Geomorphology*. Wiley: Chichester, 562pp.

Gale, S J, 2000. *Classic Landforms of Morecambe Bay*. Geologists' Association: London, 48pp.

Gabrovšek, F, 2009. On concepts and methods for the estimation of dissolutional denudation rates in karst areas. *Geomorphology*, **106**, 9-14.

Gascoyne, M, D C Ford and H P Schwarcz, 1983. Rates of cave and landform development in the Yorkshire Dales from speleothem age data. *Earth Surface Processes Landforms*, **8**, 557-568.

Glover, R R, 1974. Cave development in the Gaping Gill System. 343-384 in Waltham, *op. cit.*

Goldie, H S, 2005. Erratic judgements: re-evaluating solutional erosion rates of limestone using erratic-pedestal sites, including Norber, Yorkshire. *Area*, **37**, 433-442.

Goldie, H S, 2006a. Re-thinking the glaciation-karst relationship in NW England (abstract). *Cave Karst Science*, **33**, 90-91.

Goldie, H S, 2006b. Mature intermediate-scale surface karst landforms in NW England and their relations to glacial erosion. *Acta Geographica Szegediensis*, 225-238. (www.sci.u-szeged.hu/eghajlattan/baba/Goldie.pdf)

Goldie, H, 2007. Relationships between karst and glaciation in the Yorkshire Dales and Northwest England. *Proc. Fifth Malham Tarn Research Seminar* (Field Studies Council), 38-39.

Goldie, H, 2012. Pedestal studies at Norber, Ingleborough, Yorkshire. 136-142 in O'Regan *et al., op. cit.*

Goldie, H S and M E Marker, 2001. Pre-Devensian dolines above Crummackdale, northwest Yorkshire, UK. *Cave Karst Science*, **28**, 53-58.

Green, P F, 2002. Early Tertiary paleo-thermal effects in northern England; reconciling results from apatite fission track analysis with geological evidence. *Tectonophysics*, **349**, 131–144.

Gullen, T, 1999. Non-invasive investigation of polygonal karst features: Yorkshire Dales National Park (abstract). *Cave Karst Science*, **26**, 96.

Hauselmann, P, D E Granger, P-Y Jeannin and S-E Lauritzen, 2007. Abrupt glacial valley incision at 0.8 Ma dated from cave deposits in Switzerland. *Geology*, **35**, 143-146.

Halliwell, R A, 1979. Gradual changes in the hydrology of the Yorkshire Dales demonstrated by tourist descriptions. *Trans. Brit. Cave Res. Assoc.*, **6**, 36-40.

Howson, W, 1850. *An Illustrated Guide to the Curiosities of Craven*. Whittaker: Settle, 134pp.

Jennings, J N, 1985. *Karst Geomorphology*. Blackwell: Oxford, 294pp.

King, C A M, 1969. Trend surface analysis of Central Pennine erosion surfaces. *Trans. Inst. Brit. Geog.*, **47**, 47-69.

Lee, J R, 2011. Cool Britannia: from Milankovich wobbles to Ice Ages. *Mercian Geologist*, **17**, 274-279.

Lee, J R, F S Busschers and H P Sejrup, 2012. Pre-Weichselian Quaternary glaciations of the British Isles, the Netherlands, Norway and adjacent marine areas south of 68°N: implications for long-term ice sheet development in northern Europe. *Quat. Sci. Rev.*, **44**, 213-228.

Lundberg, J, T C Lord and P J Murphy, 2010. Thermal ionization mass spectrometer U-Th dates on Pleistocene speleothems from Victoria Cave, North Yorkshire, UK: implications for palaeoenvironment and stratigraphy over multiple glacial cycles. *Geosphere*, **6**, 379-395.

Marker, M E and H Goldie, 2007. Large karst depressions on the Yorkshire Dales limestone: interim results and discussion: an early indication of a new paradigm. *Cave Karst Science*, **34**, 117-127.

Moisley, H A, 1955. Some karstic features in the Malham Tarn district. *Council for Promotion of Field Studies Annual Report*, 1953-4, 33-42.

Monico, P (compiler), 1995. *Northern Sump Index*. Cave Diving Group: Swindon, 286pp.

Murphy, P, 1997. Trow Gill gorge, Ingleborough, North Yorkshire: its origins reconsidered. *Cave Karst Science*, **24**, 137-139.

Murphy, P J and A G Latham, 2001. A uranium series date from Malham Cove Rising, North Yorkshire, UK. *Cave Karst Science*, **28**, 135-136.

Murphy, P J, R Smallshire and C Midgley, 2001. The sediments of Illusion Pot, Kingsdale, UK: evidence for sub-glacial utilisation of a karst conduit in the Yorkshire Dales? *Cave Karst Science*, **28**, 29-34.

Murphy, P, A R Westerman, R Clark, A Booth and A Parr, 2008. Enhancing understanding of breakdown and collapse in the Yorkshire Dales using ground penetrating radar on cave sediments. *Eng. Geol.*, **99**, 160-168.

O'Regan, H J, T Faulkner and I R Smith (eds.), 2012. *Cave Archaeology and Karst Geomorphology in North West England: Field Guide*. Quaternary Research Association: London, 186pp.

Palmer, A N, 1991. Origin and morphology of limestone caves. *Geol. Soc. Amer. Bull.*, **103**, 1-21.

Parry, B, 2007. Pedestal formation and surface lowering in the Carboniferous Limestone of Norber and Scales Moor, Yorkshire, UK. *Cave Karst Science*, **34**, 61-68.

Paterson, K and M M Sweeting (eds.), 1986. *New Directions in Karst*. Geo Books: Norwich, 613pp.

Pitty, A F, 1974. Karst water studies in and around Ingleborough Cavern. 127-139 in Waltham, *op. cit.*.

Pitty, A F, J L Ternan, R A Halliwell and J Crowther, 1986. Karst water temperatures and the shaping of Malham Cove, Yorkshire. 281-291 in Paterson and Sweeting, *op.cit.*.

Richardson, D T, 1974. Karst waters of the Alum Pot area. 140-148 in Waltham, *op. cit.*.

Sweeting, M M, 1950. Erosion cycles and limestone caverns in the Ingleborough district. *Geog. J.*, **115**, 63-78.

Sweeting, M M, 1966. The weathering of limestones. 177-210 in G H Dury (ed.), *Essays in Geomorphology*, Heinemann: London.

Sweeting, M M, 1972. *Karst Landforms*. Macmillan: London, 362pp.

Sweeting, M M, 1974. Karst geomorphology in north-west England. 46-78 in Waltham, *op.cit.*.

Sweeting, M M and G S Sweeting, 1969. Some aspects of the Carboniferous Limestone in relation to its landforms. *Méditerranée*, **7**, 201-209.

Telfer, M W, P Wilson, T C Lord and P J Vincent, 2009. New constraints on the age of the last ice sheet glaciation in NW England using optically stimulated luminescence dating. *J. Quat. Sci.*, **24**, 906-915.

Ternan, J L, 1974. Some chemical and physical characteristics of five resurgences on Darnbrook Fell. 115-126 in Waltham, *op. cit.*.

Trudgill, S T, 1985. Field observations of limestone weathering and erosion in the Malham district, North Yorkshire. *Field Studies*, **6**, 201-236.

Trudgill, S T, 2008. Classics revisited: Corbel, J, 1959: Erosion en terrain calcaire (intense d'érosion et morphologie). *Progress Phys. Geog.*, **32**, 684-690.

Trudgill, S T, C J High and F K Hannah, 1981. Improvements to the micro-erosion meter. *Brit. Geomorph. Res. Gp. Tech. Bull.*, 29, 3-17.

Vincent, P J, P Wilson, T C Lord, C Schnabel and K M Wilcken, 2010. Cosmogenic isotope (^{36}Cl) surface exposure dating of the Norber erratics, Yorkshire Dales: further constraints on the timing of the LGM glaciation in Britain. *Proc. Geol. Assoc.*, **121**, 24-31.

Walsh, P T, M Boulter and I Morawiecka, 1999. Chattian and Miocene elements in the modern landscape of western Britain and Ireland. *Geol. Soc. Spec. Publ.*, **162**, 45-63.

Waltham, A C, 1970. Cave development in the limestone of the Ingleborough district. *Geog. J.*, **136**, 574-585.

Waltham, A C (ed.), 1974. *Limestones and Caves of North-west England*. David and Charles (for British Cave Research Association): Newton Abbot, 477pp.

Waltham, A C, 1986. Valley excavation in the Yorkshire Dales karst. 541-550 in Paterson and Sweeting, *op. cit.*

Waltham, A C, 1990. Geomorphic evolution of the Ingleborough karst. *Cave Karst Science*, **17**, 9-18.

Waltham, T, 2007. *The Yorkshire Dales: Landscape and Geology*. Crowood: Marlborough, 224pp.

Waltham, T, Bell, F and Culshaw, M, 2005. *Sinkholes and Subsidence*. Springer: Berlin, 382pp.

Waltham, T and H Long, 2011. Limestone plateaus of the Yorkshire Dales glaciokarst. *Cave Karst Science*, **38**, 65-70.

Waltham, T, P Murphy and A Batty, 2010. Kingsdale: the evolution of a Yorkshire dale. *Proc. Yorks. Geol. Soc.*, **58**, 95-105.

Waltham, A C, M J Simms, A R Farrant and H S Goldie, 1997. *Karst and Caves of Great Britain*. Chapman & Hall (for Joint Nature Conservation Committee): London, 358pp.

Waltham, A C and A C Tillotson, 1989. *The Geomorphology of Ingleborough*. Nature Conservancy Council, Peterborough, **1**, 159pp.

Westaway, R, 2009. Quaternary uplift of northern England. *Global Planetary Change*, **68**, 357-382.

Williams, P W, 1983. The role of the subcutaneous zone in karst hydrology. *J. Hydrology*, **61**, 45-67.

Wilson, P, T C Lord and P J Vincent, 2012a Origin of the limestone pedestals at Norber Brow, North Yorkshire: a re-assessment and discussion. *Cave Karst Science*, **39**, 5-11.

Wilson, P, T C Lord, T T Barrows and P J Vincent, 2012b. Cosmogenic isotope analysis and surface exposure dating in the Yorkshire Dales. 117-135 in O'Regan *et al., op. cit.*

Wilson, P, M W Telfer, T C Lord and P J Vincent, 2012c. Loessic sediments in Northwest England. 143-150 in O'Regan *et al., op. cit.*.

Zaragosi, S, G A Auffret, J C Faugères, T Garlan, C Pujol and E Cortijo, 2000. Physiography and recent sediment distribution of the Celtic deep-sea fan, Bay of Biscay. *Marine Geology*, **169**, 207–237.

CHAPTER 5

Limestone pavements

Simon Webb

Bare grey expanses of limestone pavement, criss-crossed by deep fissures, are the most striking landscape feature of the Yorkshire Dales. They are the surface expression of the limestone dissolution processes that form caves, and are landforms that have taken thousands of years to evolve.

The regularity of the blocks and cracks, the clints and grikes, belies a surprising variety in surface patterning. Meandering channels, rounded basins, cracks and clefts, fluted and fretted stone are all part of the intricacy of the pavements (Fig. 5.1). Understanding their origins goes a long way towards explaining the changes in the Yorkshire Dales over about 16,000 years since the ice sheets progressively withdrew from the limestone plateaus at the end of the Devensian glaciation. Recent studies point to greater ages of some pavement features that are clearly of pre-Devensian origin.

Limestone pavements are relatively rare, covering only 2600 ha in Britain, with the majority of this (2228 ha) being in northern England (Webb, 1995), More than a third of British pavement (1050 ha) lies within the Yorkshire Dales. The main pavement areas in the Dales are on the limestone benches surrounding Whernside, Ingleborough and Pen-y-ghent, and over the Malham High Country between Malham and Arncliffe, with smaller areas in Upper Wharfedale and immediately east and west of Settle (Fig. 5.2). Just outside the Dales, there are further extensive limestone pavements in the ring of Carboniferous limestone surrounding the Lake District in Cumbria, round the northern margins of Morecambe Bay and into the peninsula with Arnside and Silverdale that extends into northern Lancashire. Britain's only other pavements are small, and are scattered across the Carboniferous limestones in north and south Wales and on the Lower Palaeozoic limestones in northwest Scotland

In addition to its undoubted geological value, limestone pavement supports unusual and diverse plant communities, which include eighteen rare or scarce species. Each crack or crevice is exploited by flowers and ferns, their colourful fronds and blooms splendid against the grey backdrop of the limestone (Fig. 5.3). Limestone pavement is not only a record of glacial and post-glacial history, but is also one of the most distinctive and beautiful landscape features of the Yorkshire Dales National Park.

Pavement formation is the result of a number of different processes acting over various timescales upon limestone bedrock. The two key processes are the action of glacial scouring during the Pleistocene and the subsequent sub-soil and sub-aerial dissolution of the surface limestone. Erosion

by Pleistocene ice sheets produced the uniform, level or gently sloping surfaces that are so characteristic of the Dales pavements. The surface patterning of the pavement, with the clints and grikes, runnels, pits and pans, is derived from the slow dissolution of limestone, generally considered to have developed largely within about 16,000 years since the end of the Devensian glaciation. Pavement formation is consequentially described as polygenetic (Vincent, 2004; Ford and Williams, 2007).

Limestone pavement as glaciokarst

The Yorkshire Dales landscape contains erosional and depositional features from Devensian and earlier glaciations, and the pavements are clearly part of a glaciated karst landscape or glaciokarst. The erosive action generated by the ice was a powerful agent in moulding the landscape. At its maximum, Devensian ice covered the whole area and most of the valleys – the dales – are deep, glaciated troughs flanked by ice-plucked limestone scars.

Carboniferous Limestone is a rock well-known for its strength but also for its regular planes of weakness – the joints, bedding planes and interbedded shale beds. Moving south across the Dales, glacial ice plucked the limestone blocks that were defined by these weaknesses. Above Chapel-le-Dale and Ribblesdale, ice removed the overlying weaker

Figure 5.1. The wide ice-scoured benches of Scales Moor expose the top of the Great Scar Limestone; the level pavements are crossed by deep grike fissures that divide the surface into regular clint blocks; these pavements are devoid of tree cover and are scattered with glacial erratics of grit; Ingleborough rises in the distance (TW).

Limestone pavements, by Simon Webb,
Natural England, Kendal; simon.webb@naturalengland.org.uk
Chapter 5, pages 93–110 in **Caves and Karst of the Yorkshire Dales**,
edited by Tony Waltham and David Lowe.
Published 2013 by the British Cave Research Association,
978-0-900265-46-4 and at www.bcra.org.uk

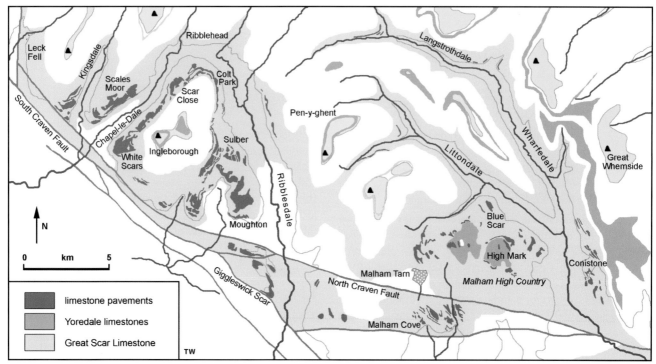

Figure 5.2. *Distribution of the larger areas of limestone pavement across the Great Scar Limestone outcrops within the southern Yorkshire Dales; small strips of pavement on some of the Yoredale limestones are not shown except on the Malham High Country.*

Figure 5.3. *Bloody Crane's-bill growing in the shelter of a grike in the Scar Close pavement on Ingleborough (SW).*

materials and left the top of the strong limestone exposed, to form the wide expanses of pavement that are now so conspicuous (Waltham and Long, 2011). The extent and distribution of pavement is therefore limited to the suitable expanses of limestone on the mainly sub-horizontal, ice-scoured benches (Williams, 1966; Goldie and Cox, 2000).

In contrast, pavement development is limited where glacial erosion was restricted in the lee of sheltering topography. The limestone outcrops of Leck Fell and Casterton Fell were protected from the erosive impact of the main ice flows by Great Coum and Crag Hill (Waltham, 1990). This both reduced the extent of ice-scoured limestone and also left a thicker mantle of glacial till. It is likely that proto-pavements lie beneath the till cover, but limestone is now exposed only in the steeper slopes above Ease Gill and in windows through the overlying till.

Smaller-scale topographical variation influences the distribution of pavements around Feizor, northwest of Settle, so that they occur only where the slope of the terrain is similar to the dip of the limestone. Thus pavements form on the tops of knolls, on the north-facing slopes and on the few level terraces. There are abundant and complex transitions from pavements to screes, low scars and bed-end outcrops.

The nature of the ice-scoured benches has been related to hardened bedding surfaces that originate from sub-aerial exposure of the limestone in Carboniferous times (Vincent, 1995, 2004; Burgess and Mitchell, 1994). The pavements were therefore described by these authors as palaeokarst, with glacial scour re-exposing these lithological features; descriptions also included lumpy and pitted limestone features unrelated to modern processes. Although this helps to explain the origin and distribution of the glaciated limestone platforms, the term palaeokarst is unhelpful with respect to the pavements themselves. The processes that produced the clint and grike patterns seen today are predominantly recent ones, and the dissolution features on pavements are largely un-related to older irregularities of sediments exposed in the Carboniferous. However, palaeokarst features may act as the locus for modern karren development, and there is a degree of relationship between the denudation process of glacial erosion and the stratigraphical variations in the parent limestone (Vincent, 2004). Palaeokarstic kamenitza and grikes are exposed in the old Trowbarrow Quarry, near Morecambe Bay (see below).

Where the landscape shows the classic stepped sequence of scar and bench, the pavements do likewise. The stepped terraces (schichttreppen karst) of Twisleton Scar End and Kingsdale form staircases of pavement descending from the top of the main bench for 150m down towards the valley floor (Sweeting, 1966). Scars that are 2–15m high have at their bases aprons of scree that grade into till cover on the backs of the next benches down. Each bench is fronted by a narrow band of pavement with deep grikes that extend to

Figure 5.4. Well-developed pavements on the tops of two of the successive strong beds within the Great Scar Limestone on the eastern bench of Ingleborough (TW).

the top of the next scar. There are also very fine examples of schichttreppen at Borrins Moor Rocks, near Alum Pot, where pavement has developed on three different beds (Fig. 5.4).

At its Devensian maximum, ice fully over-rode even the highest summits of Ingleborough and Whernside. Limestone pavements in the Yorkshire Dales can therefore be found at altitudes of 500– 620m, well above the main expanses of pavement that are close to the 400m level. The rocks at these altitudes are the shales, limestones and sandstones of the Yoredale Group, and the pavements are less massive and more platy, reflecting the thinner beds of many of the Yoredale limestones (Fig. 5.5). There are few deep grikes, and most are broad and grassy, so that these pavements are of limited floristic interest and there are almost no tree or shrub species (Ward and Evans, 1975). Some of the Yoredale pavements are reasonably extensive, and they cover 16 ha in total, but most grade into turf-covered areas where the structure of the rock is discernable beneath the turf. The main Yoredale pavements occur in a group on the watershed between Hawes and Ribblehead, and also high on the summit slopes of Ingleborough and Whernside. Some of the pavements on the higher parts of the Malham High Country are also on Yoredale limestones.

There is increasing debate over the degree to which the Yorkshire Dales pavements are entirely a product of the last glaciation, and to what extent pre-Devensian features survive. A series of features in pavements across northwest England are considered to have been either sheltered from glacial erosion, so that glacial scour removed some material and left the truncated older features (Goldie, 2009a, 2009b). These include pinnacles or tors of 2–3m height on parts of the Malham High Country, where they are mainly on the edges of the large depressions (see below), and there are also rounded scar edges and deep, wide grikes with flared tops. Similar tor-like features also occur at The Clouds on the Lake District fringe. These features have some altitudinal grouping, with more of them on the higher ground that probably experienced reduced glacial erosion beneath the cold-based ice sheets. Two ages of grikes might be demonstrated by the bi-modal distribution of grike dimensions in the Morecambe Bay pavements and at Little Asby Scar on the Orton Fells, with the narrower mode representing younger grikes that had formed since the Devensian glaciation (Rose and Vincent, 1986, Waltham *et al.*, 1997).

Glacial origins of the pavements and ice-eroded benches are also indicated by the presence of erratics that are ice-transported boulders. The classic localities within the Dales are the Norber boulders of dark basement rock that lie on the western side of Crummack Dale, and the gritstone boulders that litter the pavements on Scales Moor (Fig. 5.6). Most Dales pavements have glacial erratics, though many of the larger and more conspicuous boulders are of limestone, such as the Cheese Press above Kingsdale. The pavements of Feizor carry an impressive array of erratics from overlying Brigantian sandstones, from the Great Scar Limestone and from Silurian greywackes of the basement inliers. Some of the latter are more than a metre across and stand on limestone pedestals, comparable with those of Norber.

Figure 5.5. Pavement on the Middle Limestone at Greensett Crags high on Whernside is typical of those on the thinly bedded limestones of the Yoredale Group, with its platy clints and wide, shallow, grassy grikes that have limited botanical interest (SW).

Figure 5.6. Glacial erratics are scattered across the pavement on Scales Moor, with some standing on low limestone pedestals (SW).

The heights of the limestone pedestals on which the erratics stand has classically been used to calculate the likely rate of post-glacial surface lowering. However, critical re-evaluations indicate that the old pedestal height data are redundant (Goldie, 2005; Parry, 2007), and this has prompted new consideration of the age of many of the larger pavement features. A distinction is also made between pedestals with vertical sides, formed beneath a soil cover, and those with sloping sidewalls, formed sub-aerially (Parry, 2007). New rates of surface lowering in sub-soil and sub-aerial environments have been proposed (see Chapter 4), but difficulties are acknowledged in applying a single rate of lowering to the whole Carboniferous Limestone surface.

Role of soils in pavement development

The characteristic surface feature of limestone pavement, both in the Dales and elsewhere, is its division into blocks known as clints (flachkarren) that are bounded by deep linear fissures known as grikes (kluftkarren). This clint-and-grike structure developed beneath a soil cover where dissolution picked out the linear weaknesses in the limestone. Most grikes were formed on joints, but some are on minor faults.

The ice-eroded platforms acquired most of their surface patterning and evolved into limestone pavements in about 16,000 years following the Devensian de-glaciation, though it is difficult to re-construct the exact history of pavement formation through this period. Evidence from the morphology of pavement features and from current patterns of soil loss shows that the limestone benches have previously had a more extensive cover of soil and vegetation than now exists (Waltham, 1990, Vincent, 2009). The clints and grikes that are characteristic of limestone pavements have formed mainly beneath this cover and have been exposed relatively recently by erosion and soil loss (Fig. 5.7).

Figure 5.7. The gently sloping pavement on Holmepark Fell has rounded rundkarren that was developed beneath a soil cover (SW).

Figure 5.8. A well-formed pavement with deep grikes that was exposed from beneath a thick soil cover by engineering works for widening the trunk road over Stainmore (SW).

In view of the high purity of the Great Scar limestones, this soil cover cannot have been derived solely as a residuum from weathering of limestone. Till, left behind as the glaciers retreated, covered the ice-scoured platforms to varying degrees. Windblown silt was deposited as loess when immediately post-glacial periglacial environments prevailed, and much was re-worked later in the Holocene (see Chapter 12). It is likely that the loess was much more extensive than was the till, and appears to have played a major role in the formation of the Dales pavements.

Enhanced rates of sub-soil dissolution are a result of both biogenic carbon dioxide and organic acids associated with the plant and soil cover. Plant and soil cover also retain moisture, which subjects bedrock to prolonged dissolution compared to sub-aerial limestone where contact is shorter. However, evidence from the limestone pavements show that the scale of subsoil processes varies with the type of soil cover (Jones, 1965; Trudgill, 1985; Zseni *et al.*, 2003; Zseni, 2009). A cover of impermeable or highly calcareous soil inhibits limestone dissolution, so that grikes do not develop to create a dissected pavement morphology. A small limestone outcrop near Long Kin East Cave, on the Ingleborough Allotment, has glacial striae preserved on its surface beneath a clay soil (Fig. 4.9), indicating that not all surface detail left by glacial ice has been destroyed by karstic processes (Sweeting, 1966). In contrast, the dissolution rate may be much higher under a permeable acidic soil or a peat cover, and a silt-rich loess forms a more permeable soil, beneath which pavement formation is favoured.

Pavements and karren

The German term *karren* is used widely in the literature to describe the different small-scale dissolution forms that make up a limestone pavement, which may also be known as a karrenfield. Their primary description was by Bögli (1960, 1980). He illustrated and analysed the individual features systematically and introduced a genetic classification of the main karren forms, linking the dissolution of the limestone and the conditions of drainage with the small-scale landforms seen in the field. Critically, Bögli recognized that different karren developed under varying degrees of soil cover.

The most up-to-date classifications of karren forms are provided by Gines (2004, 2009) and Ford and Williams (2007). These differ in detail, but both cover the large-scale karren assemblages and karrenfields, and also the small-scale karren features that occur within them. Both retain the terminology used by Bögli, but constitute classifications that are both morphological and genetic.

With the passage of time the cover of soil and till has been eroded away, much of it being washed into the developing grikes. Pavements have therefore emerged from beneath their mantle. This emergence was greatly accelerated in historic times, by woodland clearance and grazing sheep, both of which accelerated soil loss (Drew, 1983). The soil cover may have been washed through fissure systems and deep into caves, leaving grikes open to a metre or more depth. Thus dissolution processes associated with any particular pavement have changed as the soil and vegetation evolved and disappeared.

The loss of soil cover generally halts or slows the formation of the larger dissolutional runnels and grikes. The widespread occurrence of 'proto-grikes' demonstrate this; once they have been exposed, these narrow and discontinuous fractures in the limestone do not develop into full-size grikes. The initial stage of grike formation is as a series of vertical tubes (splitkarren) forming along the line of a tight fracture (Jones, 1965). Exposure to sub-aerial weathering can modify the morphology of clints and grikes by sharpening and fretting the rounded features that had previously developed beneath the soil (see below), but this process is slow, only occurs when there is surface run-off and does not change the basic form (Zseni, 2009).

Across the Dales, there are numerous sites where limestone pavements have not yet been exposed, but their patterns of clints and grikes are clearly visible beneath the turf. These may be the bare pavements of the future if the current pattern of soil loss continues. The evolution of clints and grikes beneath a soil cover is also demonstrated by artificial exposure of buried limestone surfaces (Fig. 5.8). Excavations for the widening of the A66 road through the Stainmore Gap, north of the Dales, revealed a pavement complete with clint and grike morphology beneath half a

Figure 5.10. Pavements developed at The Crumbles on Leck Fell are close to the Dent Fault zone, where a locally high joint density defines pavement with narrow clints resembling knife-blades (SW).

metre of soil (Webb and Glading, 1998). This was consistent with other sites exposed purely for purposes of research (Sweeting, 1966; Trudgill, 1985). Excavations on Scales Moor revealed highly dissected sub-soil features, including hollows more than 800 mm across containing erratic boulders up to 600 mm in diameter, along with grikes and furrows choked with boulders, clay and sand derived from the drift (Sweeting, 1966). At that time, these provided critical evidence to confirm the sub-soil formation of pavements.

Clints, grikes and runnels

The clint-and-grike structure has only developed where dissolution picked out the linear weaknesses in the limestone. These vertical planes of weakness have widened and opened over thousands of years to create the grikes. In the Dales pavements, grike widths are typically 50–500 mm. Larger forms are likely to be either of pre-Devensian origin, or are associated with mechanical opening due to rock relaxation close to scar edges (Goldie, 2009a). De-glaciation unloading and stress relief may also play some role in opening joints at the surface.

The pattern of joints, faults and veins within the limestone therefore has a profound influence on the form and appearance of pavements (Fig. 5.9). The clear relationship between density of joints and proximity to the Craven and Dent fault zones accounts for much of the variation in clint sizes across the various Dales pavements. The Crumbles and Scar Close illustrate the opposite ends of this spectrum.

The Crumbles lie just above the Ease Gill valley, on the Leck Fell side. They form a regular staircase of benches and low scars dropping about 20m down towards the Ease

Figure 5.9. Two sets of joints at right-angles define the grikes and the square clints on part of the pavement on Great Asby Scar (SW).

Figure 5.11. Massive smooth-topped clints can reach to 10m across with little dissection by runnels at Scar Close, Ingleborough (SW).

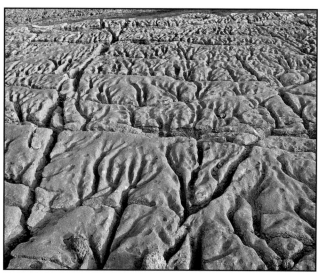

Figure 5.12. Branching runnel systems, on the gently dipping pavement of Great Asby Scar (SW).

In stark contrast, the pavements of Scar Close and those above Sulber Gate (on the northwestern and eastern slopes of Ingleborough respectively) are farther from the fault zones. At these locations, the limestone has only widely spaced joints, and the resultant clints are large. Clints on Scar Close reach to more than 10m across, and many are remarkably smooth with little or no dissection by runnels (Fig. 5.11).

The surfaces of most clints are patterned by small-scale dissolution features. Many of these were also formed beneath a soil cover, but most have been modified by sub-aerial weathering subsequent to loss of the soil. The most common of these features are runnels, the shallow, gutter-like channels that drain the clint surfaces into the grikes. Typically, these are 100–400 mm wide and deep, and only rarely reach greater depths in the Dales pavements.

Gill beck. The local density of joints is very high because the site is less than half a kilometre from the Dent Fault (though not all the limestone between the site and the fault is so closely fractured). The assemblage of narrow clints and grikes constitutes a spitzkarren that is barely recognizable as a limestone pavement. Grikes follow the joints, and the resultant clints are tiny, in some places less than 50 mm wide. The outcrop looks like a series of vertical blades stacked alongside each other, creating a highly dissected pavement with very few other solution features (Fig. 5.10). This is the best English example of this type of pavement, which is comparable to the Welsh pavements at Foel Fawr and Castell-y-geifr (Thomas, 1970). These examples stretch the classic description of limestone pavements, and are perhaps better described as karrenfields or lapies.

Terminology of karren (from the German language)

Felsenmeer: a 'stone sea' of frost-shattered rock fragments.
Flachkarren: clints; limestone blocks between grikes.
Hohlkarren: undercut runnels, wider at the bottom than top.
Kamenitza: circular or rounded shallow pan on clint surface.
Karrenfeld: bare rock expanse with small solution features.
Kluftkarren: grikes; deep fissures on joints between clints.
Rillenkarren: small runnels between sharp crests.
Rinnenkarren: long, rounded runnels with sharp rims.
Rundkarren: large rounded runnels between rounded crests.
Schichttreppen: pavement stepped across rock terraces.
Spitzkarren: narrow clints that are pinnacles or blades.
Splitkarren: open vertical fissures along a joint.
Trittkarren: shallow, heel-shaped pans on sloping clint.

Figure 5.13. Centripetal runnels draining the end of a large, almost level clint on Scar Close, Ingleborough (SW).

Figure 5.14. Dissolutional pits in the bare pavement at Underlaid Wood, on the edge of Morecambe Bay, formed beneath a soil cover, and their regular alignment demonstrates their origins on fractures that were planes of weakness in the limestone (SW).

Figure 5.15. Many dissolution pans, or kamenitzas, on the pavements at Gait Barrows have fissures along their floors, but others have intact, flat floors and often hold water (SW).

Across the Dales, the most abundant runnels are the rundkarren with their rounded cross-sections between smooth and rounded interfluve ridges. Less common are the rinnenkarren with sharper crests between the channels (Veress, 2009). The rundkarren develop where soil cover is deep enough to ensure that dissolution occurs over the runnel interfluves to produce rounded profiles. Shallower soil leaves the crests exposed and modification towards rinnenkarren occurs. The size of these features is related to the scale of biochemical processes within the soil, and also increases with time spent beneath the soil cover (Zseni, 2009).

The slope of the pavement surface is a strong influence on the morphology of the runnels. Those that form on steeply sloping surfaces are generally parallel and closely spaced. This type is rare in the Dales, but is well developed on a small pavement dipping at 15° in ash woodland in Brazen Gate Wood near Threshfield, Wharfedale. The dipping bedding plane slopes have diamond-shaped clints scored by parallel and sub-parallel runnels. Among the largest parallel runnels are those on the sloping pavements of Hutton Roof,

west of Kirkby Lonsdale. Here, an area of pavement known as The Rakes supports parallel runnels with sharp crests (rinnenkarren) that extend for 5–10m down clint surfaces sloping at 25–30° (Fig. 5.32). On all pavements the runnel length is limited by the grikes that formed on cross-joints into which the runnels drain.

Where the pavements slope only gently, the runnels are typically branched or dendritic. This pattern is common on the pavements of Orton and Asby, on the Lake District fringe, where gently dipping limestones support extensive pavements with a variety of runnel forms (Fig. 5.12). Within the Dales, branching runnels are numerous on the extensive pavements of Ingleborough and around Malham. Centripetal runnels that converge at a central drainage point occur on beds that are effectively horizontal, notably on Scar Close, around Sulber Gate and on the broad and level pavements of Scales Moor (Fig. 5.13).

At some sites beneath a cover of acidic soil, rundkarren can become broader and deeper with undercut sides, reaching 0.6–1.0m deep and 0.5m wide (Zseni, 2009). These are known as hohlkarren, and are as much as 2m deep on the pavements between Southerscales and White Scar, above Chapel-le-Dale; they become almost tube-like under a peaty cover at Harry Hallam's Moss (Sweeting, 1972).

Pits and pans can also form on flat clint tops. These are superficially similar, but pits are deeper and are generally freely drained (Fig. 5.14), whereas pans (also known as kamenitzas: Cucchi, 2009) have high width:depth ratios and commonly hold water over an impervious base (Fig. 5.15). Both features originate beneath a soil cover, but the pans are commonly modified by sub-aerial weathering following exposure. Features holding water may have a decantation runnel as an overflow channel, and this accounts for the tadpole-shape of some pans. Good examples occur at Southerscales, above Chapel-le-Dale, and at Gait Barrows, near Morecambe Bay. Pits in the Dales pavements are mostly fissure controlled (splitkarren), and related to proto-grikes. Where there is no obvious alignment they are best described as sub-soil-tubes that have become exposed (Gines, 2009). There is considerable overlap in the morphology and origin of these two pit types.

Figure 5.16. Rillenkarren formed by aggressive water draining down a sloping limestone face on Scales Moor (TW).

Rillenkarren are small, parallel runnels, typically 10–20 mm wide, with sharp intervening crests that diminish and may die out downslope. They develop sub-aerially with rapid dissolution occurring at the point of raindrop impact. Down-slope they are extinguished where there is a critical change in the thickness of the water film flowing over the surface, thereby reducing the impact of the rainwater dissolution (Lundberg and Gines, 2009). They are rare on British pavements, but have been described on some sites around Morecambe Bay (Vincent, 1996) and occur at places on Scales Moor (Fig. 5.16).

Most rock surfaces have a thin layer of covering micro-organisms, known as the biofilm (Viles, 2004, 2009). On limestone pavements, lichens dominate, with fungi and cyanobacteria playing a subordinate role. Other plants, mosses or algae can form a slimy biofilm surface. The pale grey surface that characterizes limestone pavements in the Dales is not the colour of the limestone, which varies between a paler, creamy white and a darker grey, but is largely the colour of the lichen mosaic veneer (Fig. 5.17). The biofilm can have a dual role in both biochemical and biomechanical weathering of the limestone and also in protecting the surface from dissolutional corrosion, but there is some uncertainty over how much biofilm processes contribute to karren formation. A lichen cover does have a role in kamenitza development, where cycles of wetting and drying produce mechanical weathering as the contraction of the lichen thallus plucks tiny fragments of limestone from the rock surface (Moses and Smith, 1993). This recognition

Figure 5.17. A mosaic of lichens forming a thin biofilm that covers the limestone surface of a pavement at Ribblehead (TW).

that dissolutional features develop by a combination of biophysical and biochemical processes has implications for the development of many features of limestone pavements. Pavement surfaces can quickly become colonized by biofilms after retreat of any soil cover (Viles, 2009). Where the rate of vegetation retreat exceeds the rate of biofilm colonization, pale lichen-free zones can occur, and these characterize English pavements, including those with no grazing impact (Webb and Glading, 1998). This pattern of soil loss is repeated in the Burren in western Ireland, though there it is complicated by an expansion of hazel scrub due to reduced levels of grazing (Feeser and O'Connell, 2009; Moles and Breen, 1991; Drew, 1983).

Major pavements of the Yorkshire Dales

Limestone pavements occur over large areas within the Dales (Fig. 5.2), and are matched by extensive and excellent pavements on limestone outcrops west of the Dales, close to Morecambe Bay (Fig. 5.26) and round the Lake District fringe (Fig. 5.33). Morphologies of this impressive suite of pavements vary widely, from the huge flat slabs on parts of Ingleborough and at Gait Barrows, to the mature and degraded forms on the Malham High Country, to the deeply fretted pavements of The Clouds. Every pavement demonstrates a regular or uniform surface which is level or gently dipping, together with a pattern of clints and grikes. The range of variation reflects the geology of the limestones, the nature of the glacial erosion and deposition and the post-glacial dissolution. Pavements thus show both striking variability and broad similarity in their nature (Goldie and Cox, 2000). Only the most important areas of pavement can be described in a review of their more significant characteristics.

Figure 5.18. Well-developed pavement at Fell Close on the eastern bench of Ingleborough (TW).

Pavements of Ingleborough

These lie on the wide benches on the top of the sub-horizontal Great Scar Limestone and almost surround the summit pyramid of Yoredale and Millstone Grit rocks. This is the largest area of limestone pavement in Britain, covering more than 570 ha (Ward and Evans, 1976). It is without doubt the most spectacular example of this type of landform in the country (Waltham *et al.*, 1997), and is amongst the richest botanically (Ward and Evans, 1975). The broad bench of pavements, which almost surrounds Ingleborough at altitudes close to 400m, presents a wonderfully varied suite of geological and botanical features.

The variety in pavement morphology on Ingleborough is largely due to a combination of factors introduced by the post-glacial landscape, by the lithology of the limestone and by the post-glacial cover of soil and vegetation. Distance from the Craven Fault zone broadly influences the density of bedrock joints and therefore the size, regularity and shape of the clints. The thickness of the beds and the lithology of the limestone produce contrasts between the massive and solid pavements of Scar Close and the platy and degraded forms on Moughton. Clint tops are dominantly patterned with rounded runnels because the broad bench of pavement was entirely covered by soil in the past (Fig. 5.18).

Eastern Ingleborough

South from Ribblehead, Colt Park Wood stands on a narrow band of pavement that is characterized by its mature, semi-natural woodland cover. This is a remnant of the more extensive ash woodland that previously covered much of the Craven Pennines (Ratcliffe, 1977). The dissolution features are very large, dominated by grikes that are both wide and deep, but much of the detail is hidden beneath a thick cover of mosses, ferns and colourful herbs (Fig. 12.16). It is likely that the grikes were partially widened by stress relief along the scar edge, and not entirely by prolonged biogenic dissolution. The site's position in the direct line of ice erosion from the north makes it unlikely that there is any substantial inheritance of pre-Devensian features.

Above Horton in Ribblesdale, the extensive pavements of Sulber include areas that are notably massive, with large un-dissected clints. Branching, rounded runnels drain into enlarged dissolution hollows, and are centripetal on the more level pavements. South of a long line of scars, and capped by bedding planes that are stratigraphically lower, the gently sloping Moughton plateau wraps around the head of

Figure 5.19. Broken pavement on the thinly bedded limestones that crop out on Moughton, south-east of Ingleborough (TW).

Figure 5.20. Some of the larger clints on the expanse of pavement above the Southerscales Scars on Ingleborough (TW).

Crummack Dale. Scattered juniper bushes lie across a mosaic of pavements, scree and grassland. Some of the pavements have long and narrow clints, reflecting their proximity to the North Craven Fault, and there are also numerous kamenitzas. Many of the Moughton pavements have decayed naturally to platy fragments and rubble on the more thinly bedded limestones, and locally to a felsenmeer of frost-shattered shillow fragments (Fig. 5.19). Further destruction of the pavements has been by the removal of clints for sale as rockery stone. A number of large depressions, up to 40m across, are scattered among the pavements, and are most likely of pre-Devensian origin. These are set within a mosaic of younger pavement with features that give little hint of such an age (Goldie and Marker, 2001). Between Crummack Dale and Clapdale, there are extensive pavements above Thwaite Scars, but the limestone outcrops of Norber have only very broken pavement that is better known for its spread of perched erratics (see Chapter 4).

The southern flank of Ingleborough, between Gaping Gill and Crina Bottom, does not have extensive areas of pavement. It was sheltered from the main impact of glacial erosion from the north, and the limestone is overlain by a thick mantle of drift in the lee of Ingleborough's summit mass. Small areas of pavement on Clapdale Scars and Gray Scars are highly dissected as they lie close to the North Craven Fault.

Western Ingleborough

Above Chapel-le-Dale, a broad bench of exposed pavements dominates the north-western flank of Ingleborough. The pavements lie on limestones dipping at 0–5°, above a series of conspicuous scars that were plucked by the glacial ice. From White Scars to Raven Scar and onwards to Southerscales and Scar Close, the pavements become increasingly massive.

These pavements are particularly free of till, soil and plant cover, thereby exposing well the patterns of morphological features. Transects across the benches reveal large clints that are smoothly rounded by rundkarren on the inner bench margins, where glacial cover and limestone are still interacting. The central sections have deeper runnels with sharper edges (rinnenkarren), whereas the pavements on the outer parts of the benches are well dissected with clints too small to retain systems of deep runnels. This differs from the classic sequence at the top of Malham Cove (Fig. 5.22); the reason for the contrast is unclear but appears to relate to the lithology, thickness and duration of the soil cover at each site.

Some of the finest of Ingleborough's pavements lie above Southerscales Scars with splendid examples of runnelling on almost horizontal and gently inclined pavements (Fig. 5.20). Runnels are dominated by rundkarren that meander across the clints and converge onto the larger grikes. Kamenitzas are well represented and many are tadpole-shaped where they are drained by decantation runnels.

Above the Old Hill Inn, a scar just 3m high marks the front of a strong bed of limestone that supports the pavement within the Scar Close National Nature Reserve. Clints reach up to more than 10m across and are generally un-dissected. Large areas of the bedding and the main pavement surface are close to horizontal, so suites of centripetal runnels are numerous. The inner edge of the pavement demonstrates runnel features relating to acidic drainage from the cover and from peat islands (Goldie, 2009b).

Clint-top islands of peat are characteristic of Scar Close and have a heather-rich plant cover (Gosden, 1968). They appear to sit directly on the pavement surfaces, but it is possible that they were formed originally when a cover of till and loess was more extensive (Jones, 1965). Small amounts of residual till and erratic boulders are scattered across the site. The margins of these peat islands, and of the patches of till, are sites of active karren formation. Varying surface levels can be related to vegetation loss, and even though the site has been ungrazed for more than 40 years the cover seems to be retreating. This was described half a century ago (Jones, 1965) and is still the case, with characteristic lichen-free zones particularly abundant towards the back of the bench where till cover is greater. Progressive loss of till and post-glacial loess is therefore continuing, but woodland

clearance by early humans and the introduction of livestock grazing significantly accelerated the soil loss in the past. Scar Close shows that removal of grazing impact is not sufficient to halt or reverse the trend of soil losses within the time frame of fifty years that it has been fenced off. However, Scar Close is botanically the richest single pavement in the Dales, with its lush plant cover spilling onto the clint tops and including globeflower, alpine cinquefoil, baneberry and bloody crane's-bill among many other species.

Scar Close is probably a fair indicator of how the Dales karst landscapes would develop in a totally natural environment that did not have grazing sheep. A subsequent stage would be the development of woodland and scrub comparable with that at Colt Park Wood. Seed source and a lack of deep soil are additional limiting factors that would shape the distribution and composition of any future woodland development on the pavements.

Pavements of Scales Moor and Twisleton

Scales Moor appears as an expanse of bare white limestone, completely devoid of any tree cover and littered with dark gritstone boulders. The pavements cover more than 100 ha, and form the largest continuous area of pavement in the Dales (Fig. 5.21). They cap the main bench of Great Scar Limestone extending south from Whernside above the Twisleton Scars and across to the mouth of Kingsdale. These thickly bedded and resistant limestones are almost horizontal, except north of the Ullet Gill Fault, where they dip at up to 10° on the slope down to Weathercote. The wide benches and pavements almost mirror those on the Ingleborough side of Chapel-le-Dale. These sites have a historical significance as they were the focus of early morphometric analysis and research that led to identification of the key processes behind the origins and nature of limestone pavement (Sweeting, 1966, 1972; Goldie, 1973).

Clint sizes relate to the proximity of the North Craven Fault, with huge un-dissected clints both north and south of Ullet Gill, and typically smaller clints above Twisleton Scar End. There is clearly lithological variation superimposed on this pattern (Sweeting, 1966; Goldie, 1973). The Ewes Top pavements, at the southern end, are flaky and lamellar with

Figure 5.21. The barren expanse of limestone pavement on the wide bench of Scales Moor, between Kingsdale and Chapel-le-Dale (TW).

Figure 5.22. The classic pavement at the top of Malham Cove, with its wide variety of dissolution features and a textbook demonstration of pavement morphology emerging from beneath a soil cover (TW).

honeycomb weathering on their exposed aspects, but lie on a bed just beneath the very strong limestone unit that forms the more massive pavements to their north-east.

There are also variations in the small-scale dissolution features along the same bed that supports the main pavement. Clints in the north are relatively un-dissected and have few runnels. Farther south, the pavements are more mature with grikes as deep as 3m, large well-rounded runnels and numerous centripetal runnel systems. This contrast again appears to be derived from variations in the age and nature of the drift cover. Despite detailed mapping (Sweeting, 1966), the pattern of features across the Scales Moor pavements is yet to be fully explained.

Pavements of Malham and High Mark

Limestone pavements at Malham are best known for the classic sites above Malham Cove and over the high ground south of the Tarn between and around Comb Scar and Gordale. However, pavements are also scattered across the limestone upland of the Malham High Country, extending over High Mark towards Littondale. Together these areas have more than 250 ha of pavement, and that figure omits some smaller outcrops that are not fully documented. The pavements have formed both on the Great Scar Limestone and on the Hawes, Gayle and Hardraw Scar limestones within the Yoredale sequence.

The pavements immediately above Malham Cove are justifiably well-known as a teaching site, as they have good examples of the classic dissolution features (Fig. 5.22). The clints are square, or almost so, and the pattern of intersecting joints is readily identifiable along the grikes. Rundkarren dominate, in both dendritic and centripetal systems. The role of the soil cover is perfectly demonstrated by the change from the smooth un-dissected clints along the front of the bench, on the lip of the Cove, to the clints that are increasingly densely runnelled towards the back of the bench where they emerge from beneath the adjacent soil cover. The runnels have formed beneath the soil. Where soil cover was thinner and perhaps discontinuous, out towards the Cove edge, rounded dissolution features are not as well developed as they had insufficient time to develop before the soil cover was lost. By analogy with excavations of the soil cover elsewhere, rundkarren of slightly larger dimensions than those currently exposed can be expected to continue beneath the soil cover between ribs of highly-dissected limestone (Sweeting, 1966). The classic rundkarren adjacent to the pavement-cover margin has rounded runnels so closely packed that no clint surfaces remain between some of the grikes. Significant visitor pressure at the site probably accounts for an accelerated loss of cover by erosion, as shown by the narrow lichen-free fringe on the bare pavement adjacent to the edge of the soil and vegetation. Visitor numbers have also led to polishing of the clint tops by footfall.

Figure 5.23. A mature ash tree rooted in a grike between elongated clints on the pavement south of Malham Tarn (SW).

Figure 5.24. A patch of old, degraded pavement on the edge of a large pre-Devensian dolines on the Malham High Country (TW).

South of the Tarn, the gently dipping Great Scar Limestone has extensive sheets of pavement that are bare except for a few scattered ash and hawthorn trees (Fig. 5.23). A wide sheet of open pavement at Broad Scars has numerous rounded runnels and solution basins, but clint sizes are too small for complex systems of runnels to develop. Many of these clints, and those on the adjacent New Close, are linear between grikes on the dominant NE–SW joint alignment. Broad Scars also demonstrate the influence of lithology where a stratigraphically lower bed of more massive limestone around the southern margin has pavement with notably deeper grikes and more mature runnel systems.

The Malham pavements are also important because they occur over a wide altitudinal range, between 300m and 500m, and on both the Great Scar and Yoredale limestones, which locally form an almost continuous carbonate succession. North and east of the Tarn, pavements are set within a confusing landscape of large dolines, scars and dry valleys across the Malham High Country. This is a mature karst landscape that may have inherited most of its major forms from pre-Devensian times. The pavements are scattered through it, seemingly independent of relief through the pattern of wide depressions, but mostly on scar tops and nowhere in extensive

Figure 5.25. One of the small patches of well-developed limestone pavement on Conistone Old Pasture, above Wharfedale (TW).

sheets (Fig. 5.24). Mature landforms include pinnacles and tors 2–3m tall, generally associated with the edges of large depressions (Goldie, 2009b). Pavements commonly form scar-top rims to the depressions with steeper profiles, and are also present on limestone exposures in the floors of some smaller depressions, notably on Blue Scar, above Arncliffe. The pavements at higher altitudes on the Yoredale limestones have recognizable differences in their morphology from those on the top beds of the Great Scar Limestone. Their grikes are broad, shallow and grassy, and clint sides show distinctive lamellar weathering. Clints are commonly platy with a rubbly surface that is easily displaced. They also have a scatter of sandstone erratics, which are not present on the lower pavements around the Tarn.

Pavements of Wharfedale

Limestone pavements are scattered along the eastern flank of Wharfedale from Grassington in the south to Cray in the north. Many of them lie in enclosed fields and allotments amid the remarkable pattern of ancient human settlement in this area. These pavements total about 40 ha in extent.

The finest of the Wharfedale pavements are those on Conistone Old Pasture (Fig. 5.25). At Hill Castles Scar, two terraces of almost level pavement are separated by the meltwater valley of Conistone Dib. These pavements are particularly massive, with abundant deep grikes, rounded runnels and a wide variety of morphological detail in kamenitzas, small-scale rippling and dissolutional pitting (Waltham et al., 1997). Nearby, the massive pavements just north of Dib Scar dip at about 15°, so have longer solution runnels orientated down their slopes. On the same pavements, some large-scale dissolution holes are more than a metre across, and are filled with grass-covered sediment.

Similar large-scale dissolution hollows occur around Beckermonds at the head of Langstrothdale, where pavements occur on straggling terraces fronted by low scars close to valley-floor level. Many of these rounded hollows are more than 2m across; it is not clear whether these are of pre-Devensian origin, or have formed in the Holocene by locally enhanced dissolution associated with the root-balls of trees. Other pavements nearby, at Cray and above Hubberholme, have classic sequences across benches with narrow and deep grikes on scar edges, large regular clints in the bench centres and deep, rounded runnels at the cover margins.

There is some debate about the extent of past disturbance of the Wharfedale pavements. They have been described as remarkably intact (Ward and Evans, 1975). However, between Kettlewell and Grassington, where the Celtic settlement patterns are particularly dense, there is localized damage to the pavements and the whole surface layer of clints has been removed from some areas.

Pavements of the Morecambe Bay area

The limestones of the Yorkshire Dales extend westwards into Cumbria and Lancashire, and around the margins of Morecambe Bay there are limestone pavements that contrast in character and appearance with those in the Dales (Fig. 5.26). These lowland pavements cover some 771 ha at altitudes between 30m and 275m. Their most conspicuous feature is their woodland cover, dominated by ash and hazel

Figure 5.26. Locations of the main limestone pavements and other karst features across the Arnside-Silverdale lowland adjacent to Morecambe Bay and on the high ground of Farleton Knott and Hutton Roof further to the east.

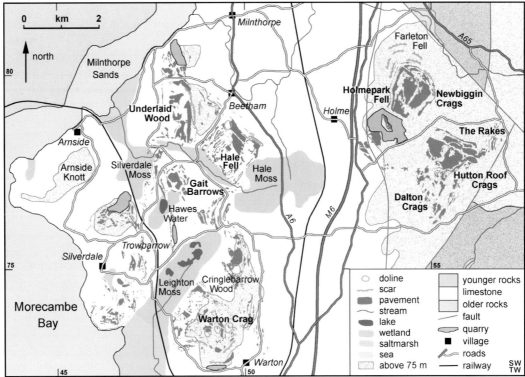

with scattered stands of yew or juniper. Pavement clearings and woodland-edge habitats support a rich and diverse flora. Whereas the patterns of clints and grikes are clear, many of the wooded pavements have a mossy cover on their clints, obscuring some of the smaller surface dissolution features.

The pavements on the eastern side of Morecambe Bay lie within the Arnside and Silverdale Area of Outstanding Natural Beauty. The most important site is Gait Barrows, with open pavements of huge smooth-surfaced clints that are visually spectacular (Fig. 5.27); botanically, this is the richest single pavement site in the British Isles (Ward and Evans, 1975, 1976). The two main pavements at Gait Barrows are dominated by clints that are 25–30m across and virtually undissected by runnels (Fig. 5.28). The widely spaced grikes

follow en-echelon joint zones. Thin mineral veins are aligned with the joint pattern, and many stand proud of the weathered pavement surfaces. The veins influence the distribution of the numerous kamenitzas (Rose and Vincent, 1986). These are wider than they are deep, commonly contain algal crusts or clastic sediments, and have active dissolutional corrosion on their sharp and pinnacled margins. Kamenitzas are up to half a metre across, and some feed decantation runnels that can be 100 mm wide.

Many of the grike walls at Gait Barrows are scored with fine, sharp-edged rillenkarren, but these are so small that they are only easily identified in low-angle sunlight (Vincent, 1996). They have developed sub-aerially and occur in areas free of plant or soil cover. They are rare in Britain, and are

Figure 5.27. In a clearing within the woodland, one of the main areas of pavement at Gait Barrows is dominated by smooth clints that can be more than 20m across (SW).

Figure 5.28. The pavements of Gait Barrows have straight grikes formed along joints and also meandering runnels that are etched into the clint surfaces (SW).

Figure 5.29. The deepest of the pavement undulations on Hale Fell, which appear to have been formed by subglacial erosion (SW).

only described at Gait Barrows, at a nearby site on the coast at Arnside and at a number of coastal localities in Wales and Ireland (Vincent, 1996).

Away from the central zone at Gait Barrows, the clints are smaller and more intensively runnelled, with much of the clint surfaces masked by a dense moss cover. Some of the outer pavements were damaged by abstraction of rockery stone during the 1970s, and clints are locally disrupted and piled up. This does not detract from the quality of what remains, and the site is slowly recovering to a more natural state. The grikes and dissolution pits drain to a series of peripheral springs and into Hawes Water and Little Hawes Water, both marl lakes with active carbonate deposition.

The Gait Barrows pavements show some gentle undulations, but these are significantly more pronounced on the nearby Hale Fell, close to Marble Quarry. Pavement removal has damaged them to some degree, but clint surfaces undulate by a metre or more on parts of the pavement (Fig. 5.29). The undulations appear to be a result of uneven subglacial erosion rather than folding of bedrock, though profiles within the grikes show tapering and variable bed thicknesses. The nearby 'Marble Quarry' is actually a deep, flat-floored doline that was in-filled with rubbish in the 1970s so that a steep headwall is all that remains. Another large doline survives among the sloping pavements in Cringlebarrow Wood; it is more than 50m across and is floored by impermeable sediment.

An open pavement at the northern end of Underlaid Wood has large, gently-inclined clints similar to those of the main pavements at Gait Barrows. Numerous dissolution pits are mostly 100 mm in diameter, circular and deep; they drain freely, and are of sub-soil origin. Glacial erratics of limestone, sandstone and older Lake District volcanic rock are scattered across many of the pavements around Morecambe Bay. Numerous smaller erratics lie within the grikes, and their morphology suggests that they were emplaced by glacier ice, into open pre-glacial grikes, and were not carried into younger grikes by post-glacial re-distribution (Standing, 2011). Large erratics of limestone occur beneath the wooded canopy in Underlaid Wood, and stand on low pedestals whose sloping sides indicate that they were formed by sub-aerial lowering of the adjacent surface (Parry, 2007).

Trowbarrow Quarry lies one kilometre south of Gait Barrows; it is disused and now forms a nature reserve. The western side of the quarry, in an area known as Red Wall, has exposed vertical limestone beds with kamentizas and grikes eroded into their bedding planes, all now rotated through 90° by the folding. The orientation of the dissolutional features means that they cannot be related to Quaternary processes, and they appear to have originated from a palaeokarst of Carboniferous age (Goldie 2009a).

Further extensive pavements lie on the northern and western margins of Morecambe Bay. Of the two fault-bounded blocks of Whitbarrow and Hampsfield Fell, the former is more prominent with its spectacular cliffs of White Scar and Chapel Head Scar. Their pavements are similar with stepped schichttreppenkarst dipping broadly to the east at 10–12°; parts of the pavements slope at up to 22° due to local folding. The clints have rundkarren runnels forming narrow meandering and branching systems; these can be trough-like, and grade to sharply crested rinnenkarren. On the sloping clints the runnels become increasingly incised down-slope, producing fluted grike edges with rare delicate bridges left as residuals from the original clint surfaces.

An area of Whitbarrow known as Pether Pots is characterized by dissolution runnels draining into potholes about 0.25m in diameter; these are inaccessible, but appear to drain into bedding-guided caves at shallow depths. Dissolution pits in this area are up to 4m depth. Grikes are also locally deep, with one reaching 5m depth and a metre wide, below a surface opening only 200 mm across.

Further west, on the Urswick Limestone of the Furness peninsular, pavements are small and fragmented, with the area around Birkrigg Common, Ulverston, containing the most extensive. Dipping sheets of pavement dominated by parallel runnels are conspicuous around Bardsea Park and Ulverston Golf Course.

Pavements of Hutton Roof and Farleton Fell

Between the wooded lowland pavements of Morecambe Bay and the bare upland pavements of the Dales, two important and spectacular areas of pavement lie on the prominent adjacent hills of Hutton Roof and Farleton Fell (Fig. 5.26). The pavements of Hutton Roof are also of exceptional botanical interest, with their strong populations of rigid

Figure 5.30. One of the shallow dissolution dolines with centripetal drainage runnels on the pavement of Holmepark Fell (SW).

buckler-fern, dark red helleborine, angular Solomon's seal and limestone fern. The hills are formed by a fault-bounded inlier of Holkerian and Asbian limestones that are equivalent to the Great Scar Limestone of the Dales. Some 193 ha of pavements lie at altitudes of 120–275m.

The north side of Farleton Fell bore the full impact of the southbound Devensian ice sheets. Steep scree slopes and low scars characterize the northern slopes of the hill, which has little pavement development. Away from the northern end, the limestone dip coincides with the hill slope so that extensive sheets of open pavement have formed with a range of dissolution features. Across Holmepark Fell the main sheets of pavement are scored by meandering and dendritic systems of runnels that reach to 15m in length. These have classically rounded profiles, but with sharp rim edges at the pavement surface, suggesting development under a discontinuous vegetation cover. Rinnenkarren with sharper crests are dominant on the more steeply dipping pavements that slope into a small syncline near the summit of the hill. Heel-shaped trittkarren have formed on the steeper pavement surfaces that may have remained largely clear of soil and plant cover since de-glaciation (Vincent, 1983).

Scattered across the Holmepark Fell pavements, large limestone erratics were derived from glacial plucking of the local scars and now sit on low pedestals. Smaller erratics are of fine-grained greywacke, derived from the Lake District and pale sandstone probably of Carboniferous age. At the southern end of Holmepark Fell, the pavements have been lost to a large quarry except where they survive on a large 'island' surrounded by the worked faces. The island's pavements are of high quality, with large clints scored by solution runnels that again have sharp rims, and also by many well-developed kamenitzas. They are broken by dolines some 5–8m across and 1–2m deep, with varying amounts of infill but consistently with centripetal drainage in long runnels from their perimeters (Fig. 5.30). Similar dolines occur on the lower parts of Holmepark Fell and high on Newbiggin Fell, but are few in number; their sizes suggest a pre-Devensian origin. At the northern end of Newbiggin Crags, rounded clints and flared grikes occur along the pavement margins only a few metres away from more angular pavement on the same beds. An interpretation of these rounded clints is that some pre-Devensian weathering features survived the intensive scour by the subsequent ice cover (Goldie, 2009b).

Southwest of the quarry, pavements have been damaged by removal of rockery stone, but remaining clints have sharp-crested rinnenkarren. Some are more than 15m long, 400 mm wide and 500 mm deep, and have developed under patchy and acidic cover that has now been lost.

On the eastern side of Farleton Fell, Newbiggin Crags are a series of low scars with narrow terraces of almost level pavement above each. These are characterized by large square clints between grikes on two dominant sets of joints intersecting at right angles. The clints are scored by spectacular, deep rundkarren, so closely spaced that little of the original clint surfaces remain (Fig. 5.31).

East of a wide col, the extensive and varied pavements of Hutton Roof have various degrees of scrub cover dominated by hazel and juniper. The hill is formed by an anticline

of limestone with sheets of pavement dipping both to the southeast and northwest, though locally disrupted within a zone of small faults. The pavements are distinguished by their schichttreppenkarst forming a series of benches and steps; this pattern derived from glacial scour across a sloping hill site and over rock with bedding-plane weaknesses. The pavement of the more level benches is comparable to that of Newbiggin Crags, with intricate rundkarren deeply scoring the clints. Across Lancelot Clark Storth and Dalton Crags, parallel sharp-crested rinnenkarren dominate, reaching 10m in length and locally 400 mm in depth. Several of these inclined sheets are gently undulating. The undulations are symmetrical, and bedding planes exposed in the grike sides appear to be parallel to them, so that they appear to be a feature of small-scale folding of the limestone, and not of uneven ice erosion.

Above the village of Hutton Roof, the eastern limb of the anticline dips at about 30°, creating three parallel escarpments with dip slopes facing east. On the bare rock slopes known as The Rakes, massive diamond-shaped clints lie between two sets of joint-guided grikes orientated symmetrically down the slope, and each clint is deeply grooved by long, parallel rinnenkarren (Fig. 5.32). Their sharply defined runnels start at the top edges of the clints, rapidly increase in depth down the slopes, and drain directly into the grikes below. These are spectacular limestone pavements.

Figure 5.31. *The mature limestone pavement on Newbiggin Crags, with numerous deep rundkarren on the clints bounded by deep rectilinear grikes (TW).*

Figure 5.32. The spectacular Rakes on Hutton Roof Crags, with their very long rinnenkarren down the steeply sloping, diamond-shaped clints (photo: Mel Heath).

Pavements of the Lake District fringe

On the eastern margins of the Lake District and across the Vale of Eden on the northern Pennine Hills lie further extensive pavements (Fig. 5.33). Their main features are only briefly summarized below, as comprehensive descriptions exist elsewhere (Waltham *et al.*, 1997).

The Orton Fells, between Shap and Kirkby Stephen, have the most extensive and spectacular pavements on the dip slopes of a south-facing escarpment of the Great Scar Limestone, much of which is now within the Great Asby Scar National Nature Reserve (Fig. 5.34). The pavements slope at about 10°, and display a wide range of morphologies. Notable are the many, steep-sided dissolution pits, 2–3m across and fretted by centripetal drainage runnels, which may be exhumed features of Carboniferous palaeokarst that formed on emergent calcretes (Vincent, 1995, 2009; Goldie, 2009b). Pavements on the adjacent Little Asby Scar

have a distinctive sub-set of grikes 1–2m wide that may also have a significantly older origin. Cosmogenic dating of erratic boulders on the fess west of the Asby Scars indicate deglaciation by about 17 ka (Wilson, *et al.*, 2013)

Southeast of the Orton Fells, large areas of pavement form the Stennerskeugh Clouds and the Fell End Clouds, both on the slopes of Wild Boar Fell, within a kilometre of the Dent Fault. These pavements are stepped across multiple benches on the upper beds of the Great Scar Limestone, with the highest bench on the Robinson Limestone, the top bed within the Great Scar succession. The main benches dip back into the hillside. Dissolution features are dominated by small clints, which are locally knife-edged between closely spaced grikes, but the site also has some well-developed rundkarren systems. The Clouds pavements were sheltered from the strongest glacial erosion due to their proximity to the Dales ice centre. where they probably lay beneath cold-based ice that was moving only very slowly. Bevelled scar tops and mature rundkarren are considered to be inherited from pre-Devensian dissolution (Goldie, 2009b).

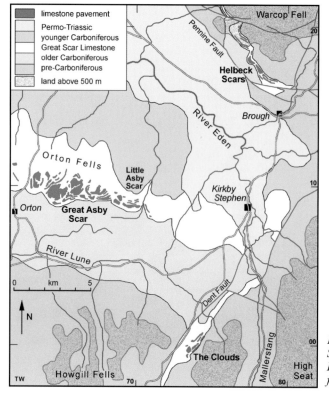

Figure 5.34. Limestone erratics stand out from breakdown blocks derived from the adjacent scar that overlooks a wide dipping pavement with deep runnels on Great Asby Scar (SW).

Figure 5.33. Locations of the main pavements around Kirkby Stephen, close to the faults that form the western edge of the Pennine blocks and on the dip slope of the Orton Fells escarpment fringing the Lake District inlier.

Figure 5.35. The well-developed, sloping pavements of Helbeck Scars, on folded limestone adjacent to the Pennine Fault above the Vale of Eden (photo: Mel Heath).

A third area of important pavement lies high on the North Pennine escarpment above Brough. These pavements form a narrow band that extends for 4 km along the outcrop of the Great Scar Limestone between Helbeck and Long Fell (Fig. 5.35). The regional dip is about 10° to the east, but significant local folding and faulting produce considerable variation in the dip and consequently in the morphology of the pavements. On the pavements of Key Scar, many of the rundkarren runnels appear to have evolved from sequences of linked and overflowing kamenitzas, thereby confusing the issue of sub-soil or sub-aerial development. Helbeck Scars are also notable for their trittkarren (Fig. 5.36).

Conservation of the pavements

The geological value of limestone pavement, as a record of glacial and post-glacial history, is undeniable. However, the conservation interest is largely focussed on its unusual and diverse plant communities, which include eighteen rare or scarce plant species.

The floristic value of limestone pavements is a direct result of their complex dissolutional features, and is a good example of geodiversity underpinning biodiversity. The pavement landforms offer a wide variety of ecological niches and microhabitats that are exploited by distinctive

Figure 5.36. Trittkarren on a sloping limestone clint at Hellbeck Scars; the coin is 20 mm across (SW).

groups of plants (Ward and Evans, 1976; Webb and Glading, 1998). Woodland plants are characteristic, representing relict features of the times when woodland cover was much more extensive. Plants in the shady grikes are those of the woodland floor. Woody species and ferns are also represented, but it is the suite of colourful and attractive species that gives limestone pavement its conservation importance. These include dark-red helleborine, baneberry, bloody crane's-bill, lily-of-the-valley, downy currant, angular Solomon's seal and lesser meadow rue. These plants and microhabitats are also utilized by an important assemblage of invertebrates including fritillary butterflies, *Vertigo* whorl snails and even a rare species of midge that breeds in dissolution cups.

The pavement habitat is of conservation importance in both British and European contexts. About 65% of all limestone pavement lies within SSSIs that have been selected for either their geological features, their biological importance or in most cases both. Limestone pavement is also a priority habitat of the 1992 European Union Habitats and Species Directive (EU92/43). Many Dales pavements carry its designation of Special Areas of Conservation, which offer the highest level of protection to sites and habitats that are the finest of their kind within Europe.

Limestone pavements have long been exploited for the production of agricultural lime, by burning in lime kilns, and for stone for building and walling. However, the main threat to limestone pavements has been their widespread and systematic destruction in order to yield 'decorative' stone for garden rockeries and wall-tops. This so-called 'water-worn' stone first became popular in Victorian times, but the impact was restricted when stone was largely lifted by hand. Then, as heavy machinery became available, and enthusiasm for gardening grew, the scale of damage accelerated hugely; it was at its worst in the 1970s and 1980s.

A mechanical excavator can destroy in a few hours an entire landform that has taken 16,000 years or more to form. As glacial erosion no longer operates as a geomorphological process in the Yorkshire Dales, these landforms are non-renewable. At an extraction site, clints are broken up by a variety of machinery, and are then removed wholesale (Fig. 5.37). The aftermath is shattered rock with grikes in-filled by rubble and mud. Nearly all the dissolutional features are removed, leaving a rough, quarried bedding surface (Goldie, 1986). A damaged pavement has minimal dissolution features, and cannot therefore support the rich and characteristic flora of the natural habitat. The removal of the clints also destroys the geological record that is set within the pavements.

The scale of the damage was so significant that in the early 1970s a nationwide survey of pavements was commissioned by the Nature Conservancy Council. The results revealed a shocking picture of destruction across the north of England (Ward and Evans, 1975, 1976). Of the 537 individual pavements examined, only 16 sites were wholly intact, and 40% of the habitat, by area, had been totally destroyed. The legislative system had failed. The results of the survey were central to securing better protection, and in 1981 the Wildlife and Countryside Act contained a provision to make Limestone Pavement Orders, which make it a criminal offence to damage pavements. By the year 2000 all pavements in England were covered by this protection; there are 32 Orders covering the

Figure 5.37. *Total destruction of a limestone pavement by a mechanical excavator in the course of extracting water-worn stone for ornamental gardens, at a site that has subsequently closed (SW).*

Yorkshire Dales pavements, and a further 66 cover pavements around Morecambe Bay and on the Lake District fringe.

The Limestone Pavement Orders have been highly effective in virtually eliminating pavement extraction in Britain (Webb, 1995), except that they could not overturn existing planning permissions. At the Winskill Stones, near Settle, an existing permission for surface stone removal was eventually purchased by the conservation charity, Plantlife, and was revoked. The remaining stone can no longer be removed, and the rather despoiled area is now a nature reserve and a grim reminder of how fragile this landform can be; little remains of the massive clints that once dominated the site. A similar permission for the removal of rockery stone on Orton Scar was also bought out and revoked by English Nature and Cumbria County Council. All activity there has now ceased.

The landscapes of the limestone pavements are spectacular, especially when sheets of fretted limestone gleam in the sunlight. They are a major component of the karst, they record glacial erosion in the Pleistocene, and they are alive with gardens of lush ferns and colourful herbs. Their future in the Yorkshire Dales now looks more secure, and there is increasing understanding of their beauty and value.

References

Bögli, A, 1960. Kalklosung und Karrenbildung. *Zeitschrift fur Geomorphologie*, Supplbd. 2, 4-21.

Bögli, A, 1980. *Karst Hydrology and Physical Speleology*. Springer: Berlin, 284pp.

Burgess, I C and M Mitchell, 1994. Origin of limestone pavements. *Proc. Cumberland Geol. Soc.*, **5**, 405-12.

Cucchi, F, 2009. Kamenitzas. 139-150 in Gines *et al., op.cit.*.

Drew, D P, 1983. Accelerated soil erosion in karstic terrains: the Burren, Co. Clare, western Ireland. *J. Hydrology*, **61**, 113-24.

Feeser, I and M O'Connell, 2009. Fresh insights into long-term changes in flora, vegetation land use and soil erosion in the karstic environment of the Burren, western Ireland. *J. Ecology*, **97**, 1083-1100.

Ford, D C and P W Williams, 2007. *Karst Hydrogeology and Geomorphology*. Wiley: Hoboken NJ, 562pp.

Gines, A, 2004. Karren. 470-473 in J Gunn (ed.) *Encyclopedia of Caves and Karst Science*. Fitzroy Dearborn: New York.

Gines, A, 2009. Karrenfield landscapes and karren landforms. 13-24 in Gines *et al., op.cit.*.

Gines, A, M Knez, T Slabe, and W Dreybrodt, 2009. *Karst Rock Features: Karren Sculpturing*. Zalozba: Ljubljana, 561pp.

Goldie, H S, 1973. The limestone pavements of Craven. *Trans. Cave Res. Gp.*, **15**, 175-90.

Goldie, H S, 1986. Human influence on landforms: the case of limestone pavements. 515-540 in K Paterson and M M Sweeting (eds.), *New Directions in Karst*. Geobooks: Norwich.

Goldie, H S and N J Cox, 2000. Comparative morphometry of limestone pavements in Switzerland, Britain and Ireland. *Zeitschrift fur Geomorphologie*, Supplbd. 122, 85-112.

Goldie, H S and M E Marker, 2001. Pre-Devensian dolines above Crummackdale northwest Yorkshire, UK. *Cave Karst Science*, **28**, 53-8.

Goldie, H S, 2005. Erratic judgements: re-evaluating solutional erosion rates of limestones using erratic-pedestal sites, including Norber, Yorkshire. *Area*, **37**, 433-42.

Goldie, H S, 2009a. Kluftkarren or grikes as fundamental karstic phenomena. 89-103 in Gines *et al., op.cit.*.

Goldie, H S, 2009b. Case studies of grikes in the British Isles. 275-290 in Gines *et al., op.cit.*.

Gosden, M S, 1968. Peat deposits of Scar Close, Ingleborough, Yorkshire. *J. Ecology*, **53**, 345-53.

Jones, R S, 1965. Aspects of the biological weathering of limestone pavement. *Proc. Geol. Assoc.*, **76**, 421-433.

Lundberg, J and A Gines, 2009. Rillenkarren. 185-210 in Gines *et al., op.cit.*.

Moles, R and J Breen, 1991. Surveillance of recent vegetation change in the Burren, County Clare, Republic of Ireland. *Global Ecology Biogeography*, **1**, 151-156.

Moses, C A and B J Smith, 1993. A note on the role of the lichen *Collema auriforma* in solution basin development on a Carboniferous limestone substrate. *Earth Surface Processes Landforms*, **18**, 363-8.

Parry, B, 2007. Pedestal formation and surface lowering in the Carboniferous Limestone of Norber and Scales Moor, Yorkshire, UK. *Cave Karst Science*, **34**, 61-68.

Ratcliffe, D, 1977. *A Nature Conservation Review*. Cambridge University Press, Volume 2, 320pp.

Rose, L and Vincent P, 1986. The kamenitzas of Gait Barrows National Nature Reserve, north Lancashire, England. 497-514 in K Paterson and M M Sweeting (eds.), *New Directions in Karst*. Geobooks: Norwich.

Standing, P, 2011. The emplacement of erratics in grikes; a study of the limestone pavements of the Arnside and Silverdale AONB (abstract). *Cave Karst Science*, **38**, 102.

Sweeting, M M, 1966. The weathering of limestones. 177-210 in G H Dury (ed.), *Essays in Geomorphology*. Heinemann: London.

Sweeting, M M, 1972. *Karst Landforms*. Macmillan: London, 362pp..

Thomas, T M, 1970. The limestone pavements of the North Crop of the South Wales Coalfield. *Trans. Inst. Brit. Geog.*, **50**, 87-105.

Trudgill, S, 1985. *Limestone Geomorphology*. Longman: Harlow, 196pp.

Veress, M, 2009. Rinnenkarren. 211-222 in Gines *et al., op.cit.*.

Viles, H, 2004. Biokarstification. 147-148 in J Gunn (ed.) *Encyclopedia of Caves and Karst Science*. Fitzroy Dearborn: New York.

Viles, H, 2009. Biokarstic processes associated with karren development. 37-46 in Gines *et al., op.cit.*.

Vincent, P J, 1983. The morphology and morphometry of some arctic trittkarren. *Zeitschrift fur Geomorphologie*, **27**, 205-222.

Vincent, P J, 1995. Limestone pavements in the British Isles: a review. *Geog. J.*, **161**, 265-74.

Vincent, P, 1996. Rillenkarren in the British Isles. *Zeitschrift fur Geomorphologie*, **40**, 487-97.

Vincent, P, 2004. Polygenetic origin of limestone pavements in northern England. *Zeitschrift fur Geomorphologie*, **48**, 481-90.

Vincent, P, 2009. Limestone pavements in the British Isles. 267-274 in Gines *et al., op.cit.*.

Waltham, A C, 1990. Geomorphic evolution of the Ingleborough karst. *Cave Science*, **17**, 9-18.

Waltham, A C, M J Simms, A R Farrant and H S Goldie, 1997. *Karst and Caves of Great Britain*. Geological Conservation Review 12. Chapman and Hall: London, 358pp.

Waltham, T and H Long, 2011. Limestone plateaus of the Yorkshire Dales glaciokarst. *Cave Karst Science*, **38**, 65-70.

Ward, S D and D F Evans, 1976. Conservation assessment of British limestone pavements based on floristic criteria. *Biological Conservation*, **9**, 217-33.

Ward, S D and D F Evans, 1975. *A Botanical Survey and Conservation Assessment of British Limestone Pavements*. Institute of Terrestrial Ecology: Bangor, (10 volumes).

Webb, S, 1995. Conservation of limestone pavement. *Cave Karst Science*, **21**, 97-100.

Webb, S and P Glading, 1998. The ecology and conservation of limestone pavement in Britain. *British Wildlife*, **10**, 103-13.

Williams, P W, 1966. Limestone pavements. *Trans. Inst. Brit. Geog.*, **40**, 155-70.

Wilson, P, T Lord and A Rodés, 2013. Deglaciation of the eastern Cumbria glaciokarst, N W England, as determined by cosmogenid nuclide (^{26}Be) surface exopposure dating. *Cave Karst Science*, **40**(1), in press.

Zseni, A, H Goldie and I Barany-Kevei, 2003. Limestone pavements in Britain and the role of soil cover in their evolution. *Acta Carsologica*, **32**, 57-67.

Zseni, A, 2009. Subsoil shaping. 103-122 in Gines *et al., op.cit.*.

CHAPTER 6

Travertine and tufa

Allan Pentecost

Travertine has been defined as 'all non-marine carbonate precipitates in or near terrestrial springs, rivers, lakes and caves' (Fouke *et al*., 2000), but this is a broad definition that includes a wide range of carbonate precipitates. The definition has been elaborated in terms of process (Pentecost, 2005), and also narrowed so that lake marls and certain calcretes are excluded. Calcareous tufa, a form of travertine, is a brown to cream coloured deposit of calcium carbonate that forms in the springs, streams and rivers of karst terrains (Fig. 6.1). Although differing from the calcite deposits of caves (also a form of travertine, but commonly described as speleothems), calcareous tufa is less crystalline and more porous, though a continuum of forms exists between the two. Its porosity is due to the inclusion of aquatic plants, especially algae and bryophytes, living and dead, together with clay, silt and sand.

The processes by which travertine forms are well known, as the consequence of calcium carbonate precipitation following limestone dissolution by soil-derived water that is a dilute carbonic acid. Karst soils are capable of producing substantial amounts of carbon dioxide through the respiration of the plants and microbes within them. Carbon dioxide levels a hundred times the atmospheric concentration have been recorded. Although much of this gas escapes to the atmosphere by diffusion and other processes, some forms a solution of carbonic acid in rainwater that then percolates below the soil into the limestone. This weak acid dissolves the calcium carbonate of the underlying limestone to produce a solution of calcium and bicarbonate ions, and continues to flow underground until a spring or resurgence is reached. These springs are in contact with the open atmosphere, so that, on emergence, the water loses much of the soil carbon dioxide, most of which is converted into bicarbonate. Rates of loss are especially rapid where springs emerge on steep ground since the water becomes strongly agitated, assisting the loss of the carbon dioxide. As it is lost, the calcium is no longer held in solution by the bicarbonate and becomes re-deposited as travertine (Fig. 6.2).

Soon after travertine formation was explained in the early 1800s, the French chemist Raspail recognised that the back reaction (carbonate precipitation) could also be driven by photosynthesis. During photosynthesis of aquatic plants such as algae, carbon dioxide is withdrawn from water to produce sugars. Clearly both water aeration and photosynthesis are therefore capable of forming travertine. Over the past two centuries the relative importance of carbon dioxide evasion (loss to the atmosphere) and photosynthesis have been discussed in relation to travertine formation, but it is only within the past four decades that experiments have been conducted to measure their relative contributions. Several of these have been conducted in the Yorkshire Dales. All have demonstrated that photosynthesis assists travertine formation, but its significance has always been found to be less than that of evasion (Pentecost, 2005; Pedley and Rogerson, 2010). In cave travertines, photosynthesis has no direct influence, except locally at threshold sites.

Different forms of travertine are associated with lime-burning. Here, lime residues consisting of calcium hydroxide enter groundwater, which upon emergence reacts rapidly with carbon dioxide in the atmosphere to form travertine.

Tufa and travertine

The term *tufa* is widely used in Britain for the soft and porous deposits deposited by karst waters, and the term *travertine* is sometimes used to imply deposition from geothermal waters. Terminology is also confused by the origins in Italy; there, *tufo* was used by the Romans for poorly consolidated volcanic ash that is now termed *tuff*, although other poorly consolidated sediments may also have been included. A geothermal calcite deposit (that was harder and would take a polish) was known as *lapis tiburtinus* (travertine) but in this case there is no doubt as to the meaning of the term. The terms *travertine* and *tufa* are now effectively interchangeable, each being favoured in various parts of the world. The term *travertine* is used in this chapter, but the term *tufa* remains in use as an acceptable alternative.

Travertine and tufa, by Allan Pentecost,
Kings College London; allan.pentecost@kcl.ac.uk
Chapter 6, pages 111–116 in **Caves and Karst of the Yorkshire Dales**,
edited by Tony Waltham and David Lowe.
Published 2013 by the British Cave Research Association,
978-0-900265-46-4 and at www.bcra.org.uk

Figure 6.1. Active deposition of travertine in Waterfall Beck where it descends into the Cowside valley north of Malham (TW).

Travertine sites within the Yorkshire Dales

National grid references are in parentheses; these are within the SD 100 km square unless stated otherwise. Numbered sites within the Craven Dales are located on the map in Figure 6.4.

1. Ingleton Glens (6974). Several small deposits along the River Twiss, including active cascades beside Pecca Falls and relic cascades at Thornton Force, and also cemented boulders along the River Doe in the adjacent glen.

2. Meal Bank Quarry, Ingleton (697735). Invasive mini-dams with calcite flows, below the old limekilns

3. Laithbutts, Clapham (738699). Stream crusts and small mounds.

4. Clapham Beck, Ingleborough (752707). Local paludal deposits with mollusc horizons, and minor stream crusts downstream.

5. Clapdale, Ingleborough (757714). Several active and inactive cron-cascades at and above the entrance to Ingleborough Cave.

6. Nappa Scars, Austwick (766696). Small but impressive cascade deposits below the springs along the base of the limestone.

7. Thieves Moss, Ingleborough (777732). Small paludal seepages below the main scar.

8. Selside, Ribblesdale (783757). Active deposit on a ledge, with a rich flora.

9. Giggleswick Scar (789662). Old remora on the wall of the large rock shelter of Cave Ha.

10. River Ribble, Stainforth (816666). Series of cascades along the river banks, with abundant impressions and encrustations of common bryophytes and alder leaves; most are relics but one area is partially active.

11. Langcliffe Quarry, Ribblesdale (823664). Invasive deposits below the old lime kilns, both beside the railway line and lower down towards the banks of the Ribble.

12. Stainforth Beck, Ribblesdale (827674). Relic and active remora deposits on the south side of the beck.

13. Scaleber Force, Settle (841625). Relic cascade with bryophyte incrustations.

14. Stainforth, Ribblesdale (820652). Series of cascade deposits up to 600 mm thick on the steep bank of the railway cutting, which have permitted long-term estimates of growth rates.

15. Victoria Cave, Settle (838650). Cemented scree and breccia, found during archaeological excavations in the 19th Century, overlain by Romano-British material.

16. Mealy Bank, Settle (826633). Relict cascade deposit on steep hillside, with plant and invertebrate fossils with abundant alder.

17. Catrigg Force, Stainforth (832672). Good pro-grading deposits over seepages below the waterfall.

18. Pikedaw, Malham (889636). Two small relic cascades and a modern stream crust.

19. Malham Tarn (8966). Littoral crusts on the cobbles, notably on the north shore, and encrusted seepages issuing from till near the sluice gate.

20. Great Close Mire (908664). Paludal deposits in open moorland with small mounds associated with a rich flora; the spring waters flow into Gordale Beck.

21. Gordale Beck (9165). The largest system of travertine deposition in the Dales, extending for 3.5 km along the beck, with stream crusts, oncoids, small cascades, paludal deposits, relic dam systems and cascades.

22. Gordale Scar (915641). Three large cascade deposits associated with the lower Gordale Beck waterfalls that descend a total of 30m; only that below the Hole in the Wall waterfall is active, whereas the other two are inactive and eroding, indicating that travertine deposition was more active in the past.

23. Janet's Foss, Malham (911633). Mossy cascade deposit, being eroded by the beck, in wooded ravine below Gordale Bridge.

24. Grey Gill, Malham (908639). Relic cascade deposit, with little calcite still in place.

25. Cow Close Sike, Malham (908622). Crusts and cascade deposits on a stream issuing from calcareous glacial drift that overlies Bowland Shales.

26. Pen-y-ghent Gill (865740). Minor stream crusts reported.

27. Heber Side Barns, Littondale (884756). Active cementation of gravels above glacial drift beside the River Skirfare.

28. Raisgill, Langstrothdale (907784). Stream crusts with well-developed *Rivularia* colonies.

29. Litton (913743). Small relic cascade on Crystal Beck.

30. Scoska Cave, Littondale (916724). Seepages by the cave entrance, and cemented alluvium beside the River Skirfare below.

31. Cowside Waterfall Beck, Arncliffe (908696). Small system including cascades, stream crusts and paludal deposits.

32. Cowside Lower Beck, Arncliffe (913699). A large cascade deposit, with stream crusts, small paludal deposits with mounds, and a relic clastic deposit that contains a rich post-glacial molluscan fauna.

33. Yew Cogar Scar, Arncliffe (917706). Relic remora deposits of dense, columnar travertine on the cliffs.

34. Cote Gill, Littondale (937695). Cascade deposit near Cote Gill Pot, and some old cemented scree further downstream.

35. Sleets Gill, Littondale (963697). Small cascades along the lower course of the gill, and a larger area beside the River Skirfare, including mini-dams below seepages from the drift.

36. Cam Gill Beck, Kettlewell (974736). Small cascades and cron-cascades with some relic cemented scree, with high floristic value.

37. Rainslack Gill, Kettlewell (978726). Two relic cascades on the lower banks.

38. Knipe Scar, Wharfedale (976701). Stream with relic cascades and clastics, with some active deposition.

39. Throstles Nest, Wharfedale (981688). Impressive pro-grading cascade on the easts bank of the River Wharfe, with a rich bryophyte flora and associated relic cascades and cemented gravels.

40. Kilnsey Crag, Wharfedale (974684). Small cascade deposits below the springs at the base of the cliff.

41. Howgill Beck, Kilnsey (973672). Small paludal deposits and clastics, a series of small dams and stream crusts, and a relic cascade, with more in the adjacent Sikes Beck.

42. Grysedale Beck, Threshfield (980636). Cemented scree in the stream bank.

Unnumbered sites are at locations outside the area covered by the map in Figure 6.4.

White Beck, Melmerby, Vale of Eden (NY626393). Small cascades with stream crusts containing abundant oncoids (not mapped).

Tarn Moor, Orton, upper Lonsdale (NY6707). Paludal deposits with small mounds and stream crusts (not mapped).

Boggle Hole Gorge, Whitsun Dale, upper Swaledale (NY866026). Impressive and colourful series of cron-cascade deposits and active wall remora that are rich in flora, over a length of 250m along the cliffs above the beck.

Mud Beck, Arkengarthdale (NY9608). Large active deposits reported below the Robin Dub spring.

White Beck, Grinton, Swaledale (SE0498). Area of relic clastic and active cascade deposits close to the beck.

Thornton Rust Moor, Wensleydale (SD963875). Extensive stream crusts with oncoids containing the blue-green alga *Dichothrix*.

Barbondale (SD6785). Cascade deposits along the eastern side of the upper dale.

Foss Gill, Airton, upper Aire valley (SD911595). Small cascades and dams in a wooded valley.

How Stean Gorge, Nidderdale (SE092735). Several active cascade deposits fed by trickles of water.

Figure 6.2. *Colourful travertine in the Boggle Hole Gorge, in Whitsun Dale, an upper tributary to Swaledale, formed below seepages from fractures that extend between the Crow Limestone and Main Limestone in the upper part of the Yoredale Group succession (TW).*

These are referred to as invasive travertines, since the carbon dioxide enters water directly from the atmosphere to form carbonate (Ford, 1989; Ford and Pedley, 1996; Pentecost, 2005). Within the Dales, small deposits have formed below sites of past lime-burning, notably below the disused Hoffmann kilns in the large quarries at Ingleton and Langcliffe. Some of their indurated stream crusts are highly reflective, owing to the scarcity of algae and bryophytes that are inhibited by the high alkalinity. The crusts locally develop into small rimstone dams forming intricate patterns on the seepage surface.

Figure 6.3. *A large loose block of travertine in Gordale Scar, with its laminations caused by seasonal growth of algae and bryophytes. The scale bar is 100 mm long (AP).*

Travertine distribution in the Dales

Small deposits of epigean travertine are widely distributed in the dales (Fig. 6.4). They occur in several morphologies and locally in complex depositional systems based within particular catchments or stream sections. Within the Dales, travertine locations are dependent upon a range of factors based ultimately upon the underlying geology and particularly upon the occurrence of the Great Scar Limestone. They are normally found directly upon this limestone, although they locally extend onto non-carbonate rocks. A small number develop from waters flowing out of calcareous drift of Pleistocene age. These deposits are however, far from ubiquitous. There are many streams flowing over the Dales limestones where travertine is not found. There are other sites where old deposits exist in association with streams that no longer deposit carbonate.

There is a notable concentration of travertine occurrences around Malham (Pentecost, 1981), and the largest and best known Dales deposits occur along the Gordale valley and down into Gordale Scar (Fig. 6.5); that local abundance is related to both topography and geology. Throughout the Dales, the Great Scar Limestone, up to about 250m thick, crops out extensively on the hill tops, forming steep cliffs and scars at their margins. Infiltrating rainfall comes into contact with thin soils that are moderately productive of biogenic

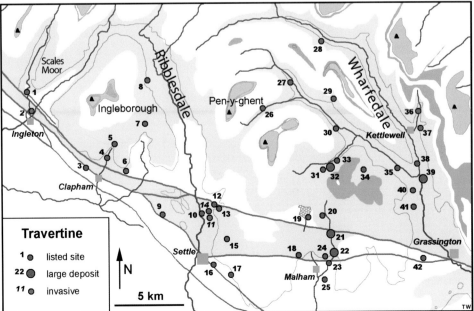

Figure 6.4. *Locations of the main travertine deposits in the southern part of the Yorkshire Dales, with individual sites numbered as in the tabulated list on the opposite page.*

carbon dioxide, before percolating down into the limestone, which it then corrodes. Resulting spring waters consist of an almost pure solution of calcium bicarbonate, from which travertine is deposited (Fig. 6.6). Lake travertines are rare in Britain, and those of Malham Tarn are the best known.

Ingleborough and adjacent hills in the western Dales have caps of Yoredale sandstones and shales above the Great Scar Limestone, and these commonly support thick deposits of peat. The non-carbonate rocks eliminate direct infiltration into the limestone beneath them, and rainwater flows close to the ground surface until it reaches the Great Scar Limestone. There it enters the limestone via potholes and caves, and does not tend to deposit travertine below its resurgent springs. The chemical composition of this water varies widely, and during high rainfall may be occasionally acidic owing to the short flow-through time and the presence of acidic compounds derived from the peat. Whereas travertine may form under low-flow conditions, when the more acidic water becomes neutralised by the limestone through which it slowly passes, complete neutralisation may not be possible under flood conditions, thereby leading to corrosion of any travertine. Humic substances in the water dissolved from the peat may also inhibit the nucleation of calcium carbonate crystals (Otsuki and Wetzel, 1973), but this is not always the case since some cave stalactites are stained with humic compounds derived from peat.

In the northerly parts of the Craven Dales many of the pure limestones are at lower topographical levels with spring water emerging onto flat ground where vigorous aeration does not occur. Evasion of carbon dioxide still takes place, but over a much greater distance, so that the deposits

Figure 6.6. Calcite-encrusted bryophytes (mainly Palustriella commutata*) and nodular growths (on the right) associated with* Schizothrix *cyanobacteria, at a seepage by the River Ribble south of Little Stainforth; the coin is 20 mm in diameter (AP).*

become thinly spread and are then subject to erosion. Most of the travertines in the north thus tend to be small-scale and developed only below perched risings. However, in the northern Pennines, north of Wensleydale, limestones support locally extensive travertines where calcareous springs break out on steep gradients; those at White Beck on Melmerby Fell are fine examples.

Travertine morphologies

Morphological types of travertine differ in their frequency of occurrence across the Dales (Table 6.1). The most common are cascade deposits forming on limestone cliffs and benches.

The largest series of cascades is at Gordale Scar, where the total fall is close to 30m, but only one cascade is actively depositing, immediately beneath the Hole in the Wall (Pentecost, 1981). This entire bank of travertine has formed since 1730, when the stream broke through the thin limestone wall above it, but erosion now keeps pace with deposition, leading to an outline resembling an inverted parabola. The pre-1730 travertine still survives, just to the west of its successor, as the relict bank at the foot of the earlier waterfall (see Chapter 4, Fig. 4.53). The finest relict cascades occur about 50m further downstream, and still within the Gordale Scar gorge; these have been carbon-dated to 4850–1910 BP (Thorpe *et al.*, 1981) and contain several well-marked fossil fabrics including those of algal origin (Pentecost *et al.*, 1990; Pentecost and Zhang, 2008). The lowermost travertine is at Janet's Foss, well known to walkers but difficult of access owing to a deep plunge pool that has developed below it (Fig. 6.7). The abundance of travertine deposition in Gordale appears to be enhanced by its southerly aspect that leads to higher soil temperatures. The Gordale waters contain significantly higher carbonate concentrations than do the north-facing streams on the other side of the same hill. However, several travertine cascades occur on the descents of Waterfall Beck and Lower Beck into the Cowside valley (Fig. 6.8); more than fifty species of aquatic plant, mostly algae, have been recorded from these sites (Pentecost, 1985, 1991). The travertine in Lower Beck has a post-Devensian molluscan horizon (Keen, 1989).

Other forms of cascade are less regular in shape owing to more erosion. These pro-grading cascades occur on grassy hillsides throughout the southern Dales. Many are small boggy

Figure 6.5. The lower bank of travertine in Gordale Scar, a relict cascade dating to the late Holocene and now much eroded; the cobbles and boulders in the foreground are encrusted in calcite that is coloured by mats of diatoms and cyanobacteria (TW).

Figure 6.7. Janet's Foss, on the lower part of Gordale Beck; the moss on the cascade is mostly Rhynchostegium riparioides, *and the deep plunge pool below is popular for recreation in summer (TW).*

Figure 6.8. Travertine on Lower Beck where it descends into the Cowside valley, north of Malham; the upper part of this cascade deposit is covered in bryophytes, mostly Palustriella commutata *and* Rhynchostegium riparioides, *whereas the dark areas below have mats of cyanobacteria where the impact of water is greatest (TW).*

crons that occur below small springs and are rich in plants, but some are much larger, as at Throstle's Nest on a river cliff of the River Wharfe. There, a large protuberant deposit, has built out from the river bank. Water seepages also form cascade-like deposits, known as remora or aussenstalactite, on some limestone cliffs; the best examples are at Boggle Hole Gorge, in Whitsun Dale, a tributary to upper Swaledale, where the seeps are brightly coloured with algae (Fig. 6.9).

The next most widespread morphology is represented by stream crusts. These consist of thin and commonly ephemeral layers of travertine on stream beds, plus mobile forms known as oncoids (see Table 6.1). The oncoids at Mastiles (part of the Gordale system) have been shown to travel about 5m per year and grow by annual increments of about 0.15 mm. Lake crust is similar, and is known only from Malham Tarn, where it probably results from evasion of carbon dioxide from the lake water, although photosynthesis in the extensive *Chara* beds is also likely to assist in the travertine formation. These crusts are superficial and do not contain oncoids. The Malham site is one of very few in England that has lake crusts.

Travertine dam systems are not common in the Dales. The active dams are small-scale features and occur mainly as small en-echelon dams with crest heights of 100–300 mm and as mini-dams with crest heights less than 100 mm. The relict dams of upper Gordale must have been considerably larger, since their back-fills are up to 3m thick. No traces of the original dam crests survive, but a series of clastic travertine-rich sediments form benches on both sides of Gordale Beck upstream of the Scar. Carbon-dating of these sediments has provided an age of 3500–4620 years. Cemented rudites (coarse alluvium and scree) commonly lie along streams in the Dales because they are resistant to erosion and stand out like blocks of concrete in the banks. There is little evidence of their formation today, but much of the cementation may be occurring below the surface and out of view. Judging from their positions in the banks, it appears probable that at

Type	Morphology	Description	Active	Relict
Evasive	Mound	Hummocks <1m high in marshes.	4	-
	Cascade	Deposits forming on waterfalls. Remora is a stalactite-like deposit forming in vertical seepages. Crons are boggy cascades from small springs, rich in plants.	19	13
	Dam	Deposits on a stream obstruction that impounds water. (Mini-dams are smaller, with dam crests <100 mm high.)	3 (1)	1
	Paludal	Deposits forming in marshy ground.	6	2
	Stream crust	Superficial (<20 mm thick) and mobile encrustations of streams. Oncoids are rounded encrustations up to 50 mm in diameter.	12	1
	Lake crust	Superficial (<20 mm thick), mobile encrustations of lake edges.	1	-
	Cemented rudite	Cemented gravels and screes, the cementation of which may be epigean (sub-aerial) or spelean (sub-surface).	1	7
	Clastic	Deposits of travertine that have been eroded and redeposited.	-	4
Invasive	Stream crust	Superficial (<20 mm thick) and mobile encrustations, associated with lime-burning.	2	-

Table 6.1. Summary statistics of travertine and tufa types, active and relict, in the Yorkshire Dales, from the data listed on page 112.

Figure 6.9. Travertine colonised by colourful cyanobacteria in Boggle Hole Gorge, in Whitsun Dale, including uncommon algae such as Cosmarium quadratum *and* Chroothece richterianum *(TW).*

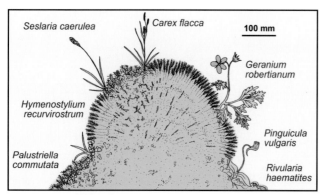

Figure 6.10. Diagrammatic section through a small travertine mound (50 cm high) typical of those in the Yorkshire Dales.

least some of these deposits are several thousand years old, perhaps relating to times when the water tables were higher. Petrological evidence suggests that cemented gravels at West Tanfield, north of Leeds, have been formed in the vadose zone by calcite-supersaturated groundwater passing through soil horizons (Strong *et al.*, 1992). The threshold deposits at Victoria Cave are clearly very old since they were overlain by Romano-British strata (Pentecost and Lord, 1988).

Paludal deposits, in marshy ground, occur locally in the Dales karst. The largest area of actively forming deposits is Great Close Mire, above Gordale Beck, where many springs seep through upland grassland and together form a small area of marshland. Within this wet ground, small travertine mounds up to 500 mm high are thought to develop as a result of capillary rise through cushions of moss such as *Hymenostylium*. As the spring water flows upwards, it is evaporated at the moss surface, and the large surface area permits rapid evasion loss of the carbon dioxide. Photosynthesis must also play some part; the mounds are well known for their rich calcicolous flora (Fig. 6.10).

The chemical composition of travertine-depositing waters has been well studied in the southern Dales. Early work revealed that there is a regular temporal variation of water hardness in Gordale Beck (Pitty, 1971), and this was later shown to be a common phenomenon in the area; the variations are closely related to soil temperature. Most of the travertine-depositing waters have calcium and total carbon dioxide concentrations in the ranges 0.8–2.6 and 1.5–5.0

mmol/L respectively (Pentecost, 1992). The concentrations of dissolved carbon dioxide and calcium are strongly correlated, and differences are attributed to water residence time, soil fertility and aspect.

Travertine growth rates tend to be more rapid than those of speleothem owing to more rapid carbon dioxide evasion and the widespread presence of plants that can make the deposits more porous. Deposition rates increase with mean annual air temperature; maximum rates in Britain do not normally exceed about 10 mm per year (Pentecost, 2005) and are generally lower than that. The laminated travertines in parts of Gordale (Fig. 6.3), which were formed in association with growth of blue-green algae, indicate deposition rates of just 1–3 mm per year (Pentecost and Zhang, 2008). The rate may be locally higher where mosses form an open framework, and this then becomes encrusted with calcite. On the walls of the railway cuttings north of Settle, some large travertine cascades are depositing material at rates ranging from 5 to 16 mm per year (Fig. 6.11).

The Dales travertines are developed only on a small scale owing to their position at 51°N where the mean air temperature is about 9°C. In warmer climates, such as that around the Mediterranean Sea, travertines are developed on a much greater scale. Despite this, they are widely distributed and of diverse form in the Yorkshire Dales. Owing to their fragile nature and rich biota where actively forming, they are prone to damage and erosion by trampling, and they should be examined with due caution.

References

Ford, T D, 1989. Tufa: the whole dam story. *Cave Science*, **16**, 39-49.
Ford, T D and H M Pedley, 1996. A review of tufa and travertine deposits of the world. *Earth Science Reviews*, **41**, 117-175.
Fouke, B W, J D Farmer, D J Des Marais, L Pratt, N C Sturchio, P C Burns and M K Discipulo, 2000. Depositional facies and aqueous-solid geochemistry of travertine-depositing hot springs (Angel Terrace, Mammoth Hot Springs, Yellowstone National Park, USA). *J. Sed. Res.*, **70**, 565-585.
Keen, D H, 1989. The molluscan fauna of a Flandrian tufa at Lower Beck, Malham, North Yorkshire. *J. Conchology*, **33**, 173-178.
Otsuki, A and R G Wetzel, 1973. Interaction of yellow organic acids with calcium carbonate. *Limnology Oceanography*, **18**, 490-493.
Pedley, H M and M Rogerson (eds.), 2010. Tufas and speleothems: unravelling the microbial and physical controls. *Geological Society London Special Publication*, **336**, 355pp.
Pentecost, A, 1981. The tufa deposits of the Malham District, North Yorkshire. *Field Studies*, **5**, 365-387.
Pentecost, A, 1985. *Alnus* leaf impressions from a postglacial tufa in Yorkshire. *Annals Botany*, **56**, 779-782.
Pentecost, A, 1991. Algal and bryophyte flora of a Yorkshire (UK) hill stream: a comparative approach using biovolume estimations. *Archiv für Hydrobiologie*, **121**, 181-201.
Pentecost, A, 1992. Carbonate chemistry of surface waters in a temperate karst region: the southern Yorkshire Dales, UK. *J. Hydrol.*, **139**, 211-232.
Pentecost, A, 2005. *Travertine*. Springer: Heidelberg, 446pp.
Pentecost, A and T C Lord, 1988. Postglacial tufas and travertines from the Craven District of Yorkshire. *Cave Science*, **15**, 15-19.
Pentecost, A, P M Thorpe, D D Harkness, and T C Lord, 1990. Some radiocarbon dates for tufas of the Craven District of Yorkshire. *Radiocarbon*, **32**, 93-97.
Pentecost, A and Zhang Z, 2008. Microfossils and geochemistry of some modern, Holocene and Pleistocene travertines from North Yorkshire and Derbyshire. *Proc. Yorks. Geol. Soc.*, **57**, 79-94.
Pitty, A F, 1971. Observations of tufa deposition. *Area*, **3**, 185-189.
Strong, G E, J R A Giles and V P Wright, 1992. A Holocene calcrete from North Yorkshire, England: implications for interpreting palaeoclimates using calcretes. *Sedimentology*, **39**, 333-347.
Thorpe, P M, D T Holyoak, R C Preece and M J Willing, 1981. Validity of corrected ^{14}C dates from calcareous tufa. *Actes du Colloque, Formations carbonatées externes, tufa et travertins*, Association Gèographes Françaises: Paris, 151-156.

Figure 6.11. The travertine cascade near Stainforth (at site #14), formed since the railway cutting was excavated in about 1873 (TW).

CHAPTER 7
Cave geomorphology
Tony Waltham and Phil Murphy

A key component of the Yorkshire Dales karst is its suite of long and spectacular cave systems (Fig. 7.1). More than 500 kilometres of cave passages have been mapped and documented within the Dales (Table 7.1), and there are certainly many more still to be discovered. A single cave system with more than 88 km of interconnected passages lies beneath Casterton, Leck and Ireby Fells at the western end of the Dales karst. Between its 52 entrances, this cave system crosses the county boundary from Yorkshire into a narrow tongue of Lancashire and then into Cumbria, hence its name as the Three Counties Cave System (Table 7.2). The same cave is the deepest in the Dales, with a vertical range of 253m. While further discoveries will surely lead to even greater lengths of the cave systems, depths are constrained in the Dales by the thickness (and the low angle of dip) of the Great Scar Limestone (Table 7.3).

The earliest stage of cave genesis, known as inception, is perhaps the least understood. The initial dissolutional openings were strongly guided by the geology of the limestone, with groundwater exploiting existing weaknesses in the rock (see Chapter 8). The weaknesses included bedding planes and lithological boundaries from the original sedimentation, and also bedding structures, faults and joints that were developed during tectonic deformation. At that stage, the limestone permeability was very low, groundwater flows were minimal, and dissolution was extremely slow. The inception stage therefore lasted for millions of years, perhaps stretching back to include expulsion of connate water, some component of hydrothermal water and input of groundwater through adjacent aquifers. Inception was largely unrelated to rainwater input through outcrops of the limestone, as it was a feature of early hypogene systems with their deep-seated circulation of fluids, but the sizes reached by any fissures or conduits within these remain unknown.

After inception, most caves in limestone have developed largely through dissolution of the rock by groundwater that originated as rainfall. Allogenic streams drain off outcrops of shale or impermeable till, sink into the limestone at upland sites, flow through the caves, enlarging them on their way, and return to daylight at resurgences that are generally close to the levels of the dale floors. In contrast, much of the meteoric water enters fissures and fractures within the limestone as autogenic recharge; this may percolate through to open caves where it re-deposits calcite and partially blocks the passages.

The various processes of cave inception continue unabated in the limestone, developing new proto-caves and ever greater levels of karstic maturity. But it was only after exposure of the limestone by surface denudation that significant through-flows of water could pass through the limestone, between sinks and risings at disparate altitudes. At that stage, cave development could accelerate hugely to create the extensive systems of accessible passages that now penetrate and drain the karst. In the main part of the Yorkshire Dales karst (in the Great Scar Limestone across the southern dales), the earliest caves were formed beneath the southern fringes, adjacent to the Craven Faults, where the geological structures are highest and the regional topography is lowest. As the ground surface was lowered, and the valleys were entrenched, the limestone was more widely exposed, and caves developed across wider areas, along longer flow paths and to greater depths. Initial geological guides on the patterns of cave development were then partly overcome by hydrological factors. Lines of through-drainage, from the sinks of allogenic streams (derived from adjacent non-karstic outcrops) through to available resurgences, then became the foci of dissolutional (and mechanical) erosion, and hence

Number of cave entrances	>2000
Number of caves >5m long or deep	~1500
Total length of mapped cave passages	>500 km
Cave systems >1 km long	65
Cave systems >100m deep	41

Table 7.1. The extent of known caves within the Yorkshire Dales.

Figure 7.1. Calcite straws of The Haywagon, in Voldermort Pot, part of the Three Counties Cave System (photo: Mark Shinwell).

Cave geomorphology, by Tony Waltham and Phil Murphy,
Tony Waltham: Nottingham; tony@geophotos.co.uk
Phil Murphy: University of Leeds; p.j.murphy@leeds.ac.uk
Chapter 7, pages 117–146 in **Caves and Karst of the Yorkshire Dales**,
edited by Tony Waltham and David Lowe.
Published 2013 by the British Cave Research Association,
978-0-900265-46-4 and at www.bcra.org.uk

Three Counties Cave System	Casterton Fell and Gragareth	88 km
Kingsdale Cave System	Gragareth and Whernside	27
Gaping Gill Cave System	Ingleborough	17
Mossdale Caverns	Grassington Moor	11
Langcliffe Pot	Great Whernside	9.6
Goyden Pot System	Nidderdale	7.1
Gingling Hole	Fountains Fell	6.9
White Scar Cave	Ingleborough	6.5
Stump Cross Caverns	Greenhow Hill	5.8
Penyghent Pot	Pen-y-ghent	5.2
Dale Barn Cave	Whernside	5.0

Table 7.2. Cave systems longer than 5 km in the Yorkshire Dales. These are surveyed lengths. The total length of passage explored in the Three Counties System is nearer to 90 km at the time of publication, and is continually being increased by new discoveries.

enlarged to develop from small conduits into larger cave passages. These drainage lines and their caves were far from straight, as they were still greatly influenced by the geology.

Once they had reached the stage of cave passages with significant through-flows, development and enlargement continued in line with the hydrological and geological influences. All caves were initially phreatic, as they were full of water until they had developed to sizes where the aquifer could freely drain down to a water level at or close to the contemporary outlet resurgence. From then on, caves matured both above and below this water table, to create vadose and phreatic passages respectively. The water table itself became a complex feature, partly controlled by the caves, and partly controlling some of the cave features. Surface lowering, especially during the Pleistocene glacial episodes, caused repeated rejuvenations of the surface and the caves when base levels and water tables fell to lower altitudes. Some, but not all, phreatic caves were drained and subsequently modified by vadose processes, and new cave passages developed at lower levels. At the same time, clastic sedimentation, calcite deposition and rock collapse further modified the cave passages, and some caves were truncated when denudation and surface lowering removed the rock that contained segments of their passages. The end result is a complex system of multi-phase caves. To some extent, this sequence of events is recognizable in most karst terrains. It is certainly true in the Yorkshire Dales, where there are many components to the morphology of the caves and the processes within them.

More examples and further details of all the cave features and sites described in this chapter can be found in the chapters of Volume Two, which describe in words, maps and photographs the main caves within each of the different parts of the Yorkshire Dales.

Three Counties Cave System	Casterton Fell and Gragareth	253 m
Gaping Gill Cave System	Ingleborough	197
Penyghent Pot	Pen-y-ghent	196
Meregill Hole	Ingleborough	181
Gingling Hole	Fountains Fell	177
Long Kin West	Ingleborough	168
Kingsdale Cave System	Gragareth and Whernside	165
Dale Head Pot	Pen-y-ghent	165
Black Shiver Pot	Ingleborough	157
Strangle Pot	Fountains Fell	157
Tatham Wife Hole	Ingleborough	155

Table 7.3. Caves deeper than 150m in the Yorkshire Dales.

Active vadose caves

The archetypal Dales cave is an active streamway that can be followed along canyons and down waterfall shafts. For the visiting caver, it typically ends at a sump. But that pool of water is not the end; it merely marks the transition to a phreatic cave that continues, and is seen only by the cave diver or has to be conceived by the geomorphologist. The descending streamway is the perfect example of a vadose cave, and Swinsto Hole, in Kingsdale, has been suggested as the type example of vadose development in a Dales cave (Waltham *et al.*, 1981).

A vadose cave stream has a free air surface to its water, so is analogous to a surface channel cut into bedrock except that water cannot overflow the channel margins during times of high discharge (though it may be re-routed into other passages). Vadose erosion primarily lowers the canyon floor (Fig. 7.2), and incision thereby advances headwards. The classic Dales stream caves, exemplified by the tributary inlets in the Ease Gill Cave System and the Long Churn passages above Alum Pot, are gently graded with ceilings formed along gently dipping bedding planes or shale beds (Fig. 7.3). The canyon ceilings are almost uneroded, indicating that vadose entrenchment took place from a very early stage; others were rounded by dissolution, some to the point of being well-formed half-tubes, indicating that there was significant phreatic development before the aquifer matured sufficiently to allow drainage to a vadose state. Some canyons have been entrenched in the floors of older, mature phreatic passages, creating the keyhole profile of a multi-phase cave passage.

Figure 7.2. A powerful stream in the clean-washed vadose canyon of Dow Cave, Wharfedale (photo: John Forder).

Figure 7.3. The vadose canyon beneath a bedding plane roof in the Upper Long Churn Cave, Ingleborough, with a thin rib of rock inside a short passage loop (TW).

Figure 7.4. Small scallops in the walls of a vadose streamway in County Pot (photo: Mark Shinwell).

Anastomosing channels, left as branching and braiding half-tubes in the roof bedding planes, are rare, but some passages are notable for immature tributaries, distributaries and loops on the same bedding plane; the Long Churn streamway is unusual in that many of these roof branches are large enough to be accessible. Some stretches of the initial openings are aligned on joints, but others meander considerably, though commonly with an overall down-dip direction. Meanders along the streamway canyons have generally deepened by almost vertical entrenchment, with only modest degrees of migration or exaggeration that create those canyons that lean to one side or other.

Canyon width is largely dependent on mean stream-flow, with most canyons in the Dales caves no more than a metre wide. Larger canyons occur in some of the main drains, and there are also many much narrower canyons. Typically, canyons in the Dales caves are a few metres tall, though some have been entrenched by more than 10m and others form only the smallest of incisions in the floors of low bedding-plane passages. Many have high-level loops and ox-bows. The floors and walls of the vadose canyons are commonly etched into asymmetrical scallops, with the steeper faces on the upstream sides. Scallop sizes are inversely related to stream velocities (Curl, 1974); scallops a few centimetres long are common in the Dales stream caves, formed by water flowing at around a metre per second (Fig. 7.4).

In a typical Dales cave, a vadose streamway descends through the limestone by dropping down joints or faults in

Research in cave geomorphology

Studies of cave origins and their subsequent development could be viewed as maturing through three main phases within the last hundred years, focussing first on the environments of cave genesis, then on the geological influences over cave morphology, and latterly on the evolution of caves.

Davis (1930) proposed that most cave development had been phreatic (beneath the water table), with only minor vadose modification occurring above the water table after rejuvenation and drainage. Bretz followed the same line, and also produced his classic paper (1942) on vadose and phreatic cave morphology. Within the Yorkshire Dales, Simpson (1935) indicated that most caves were largely vadose, following Dwerryhouse (1907) who had suggested the same; earlier ideas have been reviewed by Halliwell (1974). Myers (1948) concurred, but also recognised that many of the phreatic high-level passages were much older. Meanwhile, Swinnerton (1932) proposed that cave development occurred mainly at or just below the water table, thereby accounting for 'levels' of cave passages left behind by rejuvenations. This led the way for Sweeting's description (1950) of levels and rejuvenations in the Dales caves.

Geological factors were emphasized by Waltham (1970), who described Dales caves that are both old and young, and both phreatic and vadose. Research on the geological influences evolved into Lowe's concepts of cave inception, which have specific reference to the Dales (2000). Outside the Dales, geological factors were eventually given due recognition in a wider model by Ford and Ewers (1978), and maze caves (important in the northern Dales) were assessed by Palmer (1975). The understanding of dissolution chemistry in cave waters advanced with Bögli's recognition of mixing corrosion (1964), though its role was subsequently re-assessed (Gabrovsek and Dreybrodt, 2000). Hydrological processes were clarified by Thrailkill (1968) and followed by major researches into dissolution kinetics by Palmer (1981, 1991) and Dreybrodt (1990). Many other landmarks and advances in cave geomorphology were reviewed by Lowe (1992), and more recent research relevant to the Dales is covered within this chapter. Most aspects of cave geomorphology are well summarised by Palmer (2007).

Studies of cave geomorphology in the Dales gained the beginnings of an absolute chronology with the first radiometric age determinations of stalagmites (Waltham and Harmon, 1977; Atkinson et al, 1978), followed by a much larger programme by Gascoyne and colleagues (1983, 1984). Subsequent isotope studies to determine both ages and palaeo-environments are reviewed in Chapter 10. Much of the future of cave research, in the Yorkshire Dales and elsewhere, lies in the information that cave sediments can provide with respect to wider investigations into landscape and climate development.

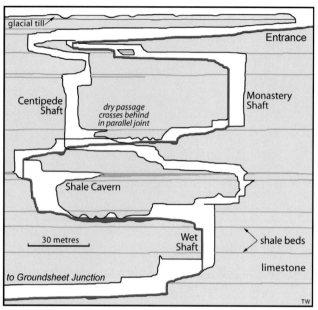

Figure 7.5. Profile of the Old Roof Traverse and Centipede routes through the entrance series of Lost John's Cave, with shafts and rift passages descending on joints and faults between canyons that are largely entrenched beneath bedding planes and shale beds (after surveys by London University Caving Clubs and University of Leeds Speleological Association).

order to step down through a sequence of bedding planes and thin shale beds. The multiple routes down the entrance series in Lost John's Cave all have shafts dropping between shale beds (Fig. 7.5), though passages in the middle levels are primarily developed along the same fractures that determine the positions of the shafts. Many waterfall shafts are wider than their canyon inlets and outlets, because they have been enlarged by spray corrosion, as is apparent from the fluted walls on some (Fig. 7.6). Others have cut back into deep stream notches, and some of these have eliminated the initial shaft to leave steeply descending canyon floors upstream of steps in the roof profile.

While bedrock fractures are recognizable in the origins of nearly all the vertical elements within a vadose stream cave, they also constitute the inception features behind some of the sub-horizontal elements. Rift passages, enlarged along vertical joints, include those that are largely phreatic and others that are almost entirely vadose. Sections of the stream passages in the Lost John's entrance series are clearly aligned along fractures, and include some that were cut by vadose streams and others that are still short, perched, phreatic loops. Almost the whole of Juniper Gulf is formed within a single fissure system on a strike-slip fault, where vadose enlargement has created deep, straight canyons with floors descending in steps to the lip of the deep final shaft (Fig. 7.7). Within the Yoredale limestones, many of the stream caves, mostly with small passage cross sections, have zig-zag patterns as they follow the joints. The streamway in Smeltmill Beck Cave is more than 1500m long, yet it covers a straight-line distance of less than 500m. In many Yoredale caves, much of the passage enlargement was phreatic (as in the more mature mazes in the same limestones), but vadose development has continued. This is most noticeable where the

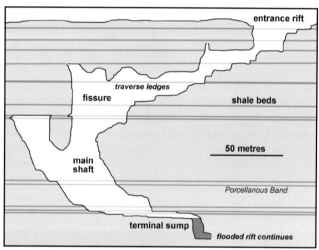

Figure 7.7. Long profile of Juniper Gulf, on Ingleborough, stepping down the shale beds and then back beneath itself all within the single fissure system; the one thick shale bed has been eroded out to create the long high-level traverse in the deep and narrow rift (after survey by University of Leeds Speleological Association).

Figure 7.6. The fluted shaft of Boxhead Pot, on Leck Fell, formed on a vertical joint but enlarged by spray corrosion into an almost cylindrical section (photo: Robbie Shone).

Figure 7.8. The sandstone floor that is continuous through the long and tortuous crawlway passages of the Marathon Series in Mossdale Caverns (photo: Dave Judson).

cave streams have sandstone floors at the base of the limestone, most famously in the Marathon Passages of Mossdale Caverns (Fig. 7.8), where vadose widening at floor level has given many small passages a triangular cross sections.

Many of the Dales stream caves have walls and floors of clean-washed rock because they are active features still in the process of dissolutional erosion and enlargement. Once a cave has been formed, modifications are inevitable, and include rock breakdown, calcite deposition and clastic sedimentation. These are consequences of age, and become increasingly dominant factors in the older cave passages.

Active phreatic caves

The lower ends of the great majority of cave systems in the Yorkshire Dales consist of phreatic passages that loop below the levels of their own resurgences. These active phreatic cave passages are not as well known as their vadose inlets, simply because they are only ever seen by the small numbers of cave divers. They are however equally important components of the Dales cave systems. Keld Head was proposed as the type example (Waltham *et al*, 1981), when only a single passage had been mapped right through to its resurgence. As an example Keld Head is still valid, except that a modern map of the underwater cave shows a much more complex pattern of branching and looping passages that have subsequently been explored (Murphy *et al*, 2008).

Figure 7.9. An active phreatic passage in Boreham Cave, Wharfedale, developed from a bedding plane and almost achieving a circular cross-section (photo: Oliver Statham).

The basic phreatic cave is a tube (Fig. 7.9). In a cave that is permanently full of water and without extensive sediments, dissolution is equal across walls, floor and ceiling. A circular cross section therefore forms, and this is also the most efficient in terms of hydraulic flow (Lauritzen *et al.*, 1985), though it is commonly distorted in response to geological factors. The dominance of bedding planes and shale beds as inception features, on which the caves developed in the Yorkshire Dales, means that the phreatic tubes are commonly widened out to elliptical cross-sections. Long sections of underwater passage behind both Malham Cove Rising and Keld Head are bedding planes up to 10m wide and only around a metre high.

In similar style, vertical joints guide tall rift features within the phreatic conduits, either as segments along the passages with upright elliptical profiles, or as tall cross rifts, some of which rise far enough to create air-bells. Many of these phreatic rifts rise above the main conduits much further than they extend laterally or below the conduit level. They are unlikely to have been initiated by mixing dissolution where water entered through the guiding fractures, as the water is unsaturated in most Dales cave streams. Their upward development appears to be a feature of phreatic water stratification whereby chemically aggressive flood water remains in the roof pockets while less aggressive base-flow water passes beneath (Cordingley, 1991). At some sites, clastic sediment may prevent or reduce dissolution of the floor, but tall roof rifts also occur above uniform floors that are devoid of sediment.

Some phreatic caves, both active and abandoned, within the Dales are single tubular conduits, but many have loops and braids that constitute complex systems without reaching the stage of true maze caves (Fig. 7.10). Phreatic loops in the lower conduits of the main cave systems are generally no more than about 40m deep, and many reach only to shallower depths. This is due largely to the low dips of the limestone and the numerous joints that allowed initial routes to step between the bedding planes, but depths are also limited by the base of the limestone at many sites. The active phreatic

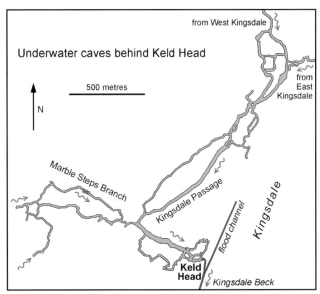

Figure 7.10. Branching and looping passages in both branches of the active phreatic cave system behind the Keld Head resurgence, Kingsdale (after surveys by Cave Diving Group).

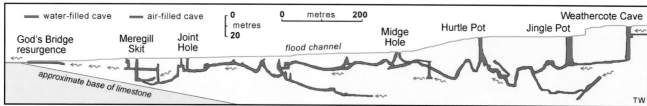

Figure 7.11. Projected profile through the shallow phreatic loops in the main caves behind God's Bridge, Chapel-le-Dale; the vertical scale is exaggerated by 2.5 (after surveys by Cave Diving Group).

Figure 7.12. Scallops on the floor of the underwater passage in Joint Hole, Chapel-le-Dale, with sand and pebbles that are entrained during flood events; the image is 50 cm across (photo: John Cordingley).

caves beneath both Kingsdale and Chapel-le-Dale have saw-tooth profiles where they rise along gently-dipping bedding planes and then descend joints to repeat the pattern on lower bedding planes(Fig. 7.11).

The deepest known active phreatic lift (the downstream, rising end of a downwards phreatic loop) rises more than 60m in Gavel Pot, beneath Leck Fell (Monico, 1995). This lift is up an almost vertical shaft, but steeply inclined ramps also occur, including one that rises nearly 20m just inside Leck Beck Head, further down the same drainage route. Comparably steep descents are also known in the active conduits. Deeper phreatic loops have existed in the past, when resurgence levels were further above the base of the limestone (see below). Despite the abundance of available fractures, many of the phreatic cave passages in the Dales gain or lose much of their depth by following the gently dipping bedding planes. Descending loops are created where passages swing obliquely down the dip and then obliquely back up, at some sites guided by intersecting joints.

Perched phreatic loops create flooded sections part-way along some vadose streamways. Invariably, these are determined by local features of the geology that guided inception away from the down-dip staircase profile that is

dominant in the Dales caves. As they are components of small active streamways, many of these short loops, or sumps, are in passages that are smaller, to the point of being constricted, compared with the large tubes that form the trunk passages with their greater water flows out to the main resurgences.

The walls of the phreatic conduits are commonly indented by scallops, typically much larger than those in the vadose streamways as they are etched by waters moving more slowly within the phreas. Scallops on the roof of the main passage of Boreham Cave, in Littondale, form two generations. Those with wavelengths of about 300 mm formed in water flowing at about 0.1 m/sec; superimposed scallops about 60 mm long were formed by a later phase of flooding by waters moving at about 0.6 m/sec. Some conduits in other caves have scallops that are smaller on the floor than on the roof, and both sets are formed under flood conditions when abrasion by entrained sediment becomes a factor, as in the trunk passage beneath Chapel-le-Dale in Joint Hole (Fig. 7.12) (Murphy *et al.*, 2000). In the same cave, large moulins in the floor of the phreatic tunnel contain rounded boulders up to 600 mm across, which are swirled around in every flood event, leaving snowflake bruises (impact marks, generally of paler rock that has locally been crushed) on the moulin walls. Ramps of cobbles, rising in the downstream direction, are features of many large conduits, and their debris is moved up on each flood before slumping back on the wane. Flood transport of clastic debris is a significant factor in the erosion of the phreatic conduits; clearly these are not purely dissolutional features. Recesses, domes and alcoves may be created by eddies within complex flow patterns through the flooded tunnels, but the morphologies of most of these are determined by geological structures. Multiple loops are a feature of some phreatic caves (Fig. 7.10), with some loops lying almost dormant as very slow-moving backwaters at times of low flow but becoming active in flood conditions. Looping and branching also includes passages at different levels within the phreas (Fig. 7.11).

Figure 7.13. Profile through the cave passages draining beneath the western flank of Kingsdale and out to Keld Head, with water surfaces (and hence local water tables) stepping down between short sections of descending vadose streamway; the passages behind Keld Head are formed mostly on four bedding planes, and vertical curvature is largely due to gentle folding; a fifth bedding plane guides Rowten Passage across a shallow syncline and also guides most of the passage to Valley Entrance (after surveys by University of Leeds Speleological Association and Cave Diving Group).

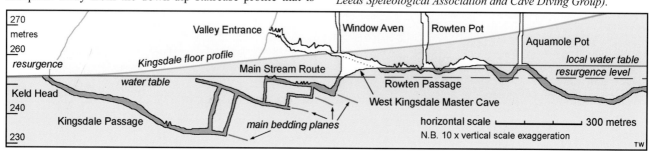

Cave development at the water table

The interface between air and water has long been recognised as a prime site for limestone dissolution, both within surface karst at the edges of alluvial flats and underground at a water table. The nature of the water table is complex in karst, in which its conduit systems do not conform to the normal hydrological rules that dictate features in a diffuse aquifer (see Chapter 9). Individual conduits may change along their lengths between vadose and phreatic conditions, so that a water table related to them is not necessarily related to a water table applicable to percolation flows within the rock's fissure networks. However, the cave conduits contain a large proportion of the groundwater flow, and it is reasonable to conceive a regional karst water table that conforms to the resurgences. This dictates groundwater conditions in that all caves at lower altitudes must be phreatic, but active phreatic passages can also exist above resurgence level where perched loops drain out into vadose streamways. The regional karst water table falls in a series of steps, with vadose streamways descending from one ponded section to the next. In Kingsdale, a phreas has a water table that is horizontal (but for a minute hydraulic gradient) extending for nearly 2 km upstream of Keld Head and beneath the valley floor. Except that, under the western flank, the short canyon streamway of the Kingsdale Master Cave descends about 3m, so that the phreatic caves upstream of the canyon are beneath water surfaces some 3m and 4m higher than Keld Head for at least another 1500m up the valley (Fig. 7.13).

Of more than 20 km of cave passages mapped at low level in Kingsdale, only about 200m are at the water table, where phreatic tubes are half-filled with long canals of slowly moving water. But these canals only exist by chance behind a small local rise in the floor of the half-drained phreatic tube (Fig. 7.13). No true water table caves, actually formed at the water table, have yet been identified in the Yorkshire Dales. Only in the Morecambe Bay karst, west of the Dales, have some of the maze caves formed at least in part at the water table in the low hills adjacent to the poljes (Ashmead, 1974; Waltham *et al*, 1997).

Within the Dales, some cave passages pass through the local water tables, following the geological features (mostly the dipping bedding planes) that guided their initial profiles. Each such passage therefore transits from a vadose canyon into a phreatic tube, though the passage morphology is more complex and variable due to bedding and rift features superimposed on the simple profile. The transition occurs at each downstream sump in the active stream caves, and has also survived in some of the older passages where the original water table has fallen to new levels.

Concepts of 'water table caves' are widely taken to include cave passages formed just below the water table, so that they are also described as 'shallow phreatic caves' (Swinnerton, 1932). Purely in terms of hydraulics, there are advantages to groundwater flow just beneath the water table, which therefore becomes a focus for cave development (Worthington, 2004). These shallow phreatic caves are more widespread than true water table caves that are largely restricted to 'foot caves' around the margins of alluvial flats in tropical karsts. Extensive cave passages formed at altitudes

just below a resurgence constitute a 'level' of development, and successive rejuvenations and water table declines create multiple levels within a cave system or a group of caves. Within the Yorkshire Dales, three levels of cave development have been recognized by the abundance of cave passages within three zones, close to the top of the Great Scar Limestone, near its base and at about mid-level. These have been interpreted as levels at and beneath successive water tables during the Quaternary (Sweeting, 1950). However, cave levels can develop in response to a variety of factors, which are extremely difficult to differentiate without accurate surveys that are specifically designed to identify the relative positions of the passages (Palmer, 1987). Furthermore, cave levels are most difficult to interpret in limestones that lie close to the horizontal. It is now recognized that the 'levels' within the Dales caves are largely features of the geology, notably the very uneven distribution of the shale beds that are so important among the features that guided the initial positions of the caves (Waltham, 1970, 1971a).

Paragenetic canyons develop upwards within the phreas, by dissolutional erosion of the roof over accreting layers of clastic sediment, thereby eliminating the down-loops in a switchback profile of a cave passage as is matures towards a graded profile (Farrant and Smart, 2011). None has been recognised in the Dales caves, and it may be that none exists, as the sub-horizontal limestones do not favour development of the steep phreatic loops that are prime candidates for paragenesis. Commonly associated with paragenesis are notches cut into cave walls at past levels of standing water. A notch is conspicuous in the walls of Rowten Passage in the West Kingsdale System, at a level about 600 mm above the present level of ponded water; it originates from a past water level held behind a knick point over a rock lip that has now been entrenched by the same 600 mm at the Master Junction (Brook, 1969). Wall notches can also be recognised within Broadway, a segment of relict passage that crosses beneath Ease Gill; these probably relate to local ponding of water behind ephemeral clastic fills during the changing environments of the Pleistocene (Fig. 7.14). Comparable notches have also been observed in some active phreatic

Figure 7.14*. A notch, about 150 mm high, in the wall of the Broadway passage directly beneath Ease Gill, appears to have been created by water flowing over a floor of clastic sediment in the past; the notch's fluctuation in level reflects the changing positions of the active sediment surface prior to all being eroded away (TW).*

Figure 7.15. Ledges formed by more resistant bands of limestone, in Far Streamway of White Scar Cave, beneath Ingleborough (TW).

tunnels; it may be possible that these relate to corrosion within contrasting layers of stratified water in the past (Cordingley, 1981), or they could have formed over layers of sediment that were once present.

Elsewhere in the Dales caves, wall notches may not easily be recognised where they are masked by stratigraphical features within the limestone. The entrance canyons of Lost John's Cave and the main streamway in White Scar Cave are both notable for their numerous, thin, rock ledges that are formed by more resistant, and probably less soluble, beds, leaving lithologically guided notches and undercuts between them (Fig. 7.15).

Erosion rates and cave enlargement

There is no simple answer to the old question of how long it takes for a cave to be formed. A concept diagram (Fig. 7.16), has up to 5000 years for the initial stage up to the breakthrough where turbulent flow and accelerated erosion develop once a fissure is more than about 5 mm wide (White, 1988). Its time-scale does not include the even longer period of inception required before laminar flow can develop in fissure networks (Lowe, 2000; and Chapter 8). Conduit diameter at breakthrough can be greater or smaller than the 5 mm depending on the hydraulic ratio (head/length squared) of the flow path (Dreybrodt, 1990; Faulkner, 2006), and the time to breakthrough has similar variation. Subsequently, the rate of wall retreat may be up to about 1 mm per year (Palmer, 1991; Faulkner, 2006), but this is only achieved under ideal environmental conditions. Through glacial stages, in long

spells of periglacial conditions in shorter and less intense stadials, and during cold winters in all but the warmest of interglacials, dissolutional wall retreat in the caves of the Dales was at much lower rates.

From breakthrough time, a cave conduit several metres in diameter can develop within a period of 5000 to 20,000 years, but field evidence (without quantification) suggests that caves may take more like 100,000 years to develop (White, 1988). The chronology of Mammoth Cave, USA, suggests that phreatic tubes with diameters in the range of 1–5m took at least 100,000 years to mature, whereas postglacial caves in upstate New York have developed to about 1m in diameter within 13,000 years (Palmer, 2003), a figure matched broadly for caves in the Bahama Islands (Mylroie and Carew, 1987). Aspects of dissolution kinetics suggest cave passages of that size can form within about 10,000 years (Dreybrodt, 1987). Wall retreat can be much faster, allowing caves to form in shorter time scales (Palmer, 2007). Phreatic caves up to 2m in diameter are considered to have developed within only a few thousand years of flooded conditions beneath ice-dammed marginal lakes in the Scandinavian karst (Faulkner, 2009), and it is reasonable to expect that similar conditions could have pertained in the Dales during Quaternary deglaciation.

The youngest of the Dales caves include many small vadose canyons. Five dated flowstones, growing close to their floors, indicate that maximum rates of incision in them are 22–83 mm/ka (Gascoyne *et al.*, 1983). The only one of these flowstones that was *in situ* came from Lost John's Cave, where the stream is entrenched by about 2.5m below the flowstone dated at 115 ka, at a maximum mean rate of 22 mm/ka. But this is in the cave's low-level, main drain, where water velocities are low except during flood and transient sediment commonly masks the floor (Fig. 7.17); furthermore, stream flows were interrupted during the Devensian glaciation within the time-span of the interpretation. Comparable low incision rates have been recorded in stream canyons in New York caves (Palmer, 2003). However a rate of 1200 mm/ka was recorded (the mean of 91 direct measurements with a micro-erosion meter over a period of 26 months in 1969–1971) in the Lower Hughes Cave in West Virginia (Julian Coward, *pers. comm.*). This was in a clean-washed vadose

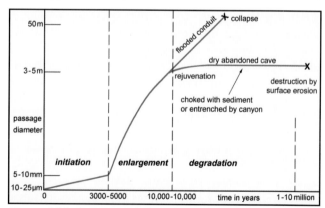

Figure 7.16. A concept of the evolution of a cave passage from initiation (including inception) through enlargement and eventually to decay (after White, 1988). Both the size and time scales are generalizations as they can vary even beyond the ranges quoted; caves in the Dales do not reach the 50m diameter that causes widespread collapse. The enlargement stage is more commonly phreatic, whereas the degradation stage is more commonly vadose.

Figure 7.17. Midway along the low-level trunk streamway that is the Lost John's Master Cave under Leck Fell, with the remains if a pre-Devensian phreatic tube above the younger vadose canyon (TW).

canyon carrying a small stream not far downstream of its entrance sink, in a situation and environment that are very similar to those of typical Dales cave entrance passages. Within the Dales caves, mechanical incision rates may be expected to be higher beneath fast-flowing streams through high-level canyon passages, whereas chemical incision rates are likely to be maintained along the active passages as most stream waters remain unsaturated and aggressive through to the resurgences (see Chapter 9).

The interpreted and theoretical rates of cave expansion indicate that some of the smaller cave passages in the Yorkshire Dales could have developed in the period since retreat of the Devensian ice cover (though this excludes the longer stages of inception before the caves accelerated their growth rates). This is compatible with field evidence in terms of the passage morphology and the cave locations beneath hills and plateaus that were modified by glaciation. Within the Dales, many small stream canyons, entrenched by a metre or so beneath bedding plane roofs, extend downstream of stream sinks at positions that appear to have been exposed only by Devensian glaciation and retreat of the shale margin.

The West Virginia data on streamway incision may well be matched in these Dales caves if ever it was measured, and could support the concept that most of the growth of these cave passages has been post-glacial.

Solute loads in karst waters do not offer evidence of the rates of cave enlargement, because it is the dissolution rate that is important, and because so little of the solute pick-up takes place within the open cave stream routes. Most dissolution takes place on first contact with the limestone. Soil-derived percolation water dissolves large amounts of limestone, principally in the epikarst, and contributes most of the carbonate increase from sinking streams to resurgent streams. Solute measurements along streamways in Swinsto Hole and White Scar Cave confirm that the downstream increases are due almost entirely to additions of inlet water and not to streambed erosion (Halliwell, 1980). Most cave waters in the Dales are chemically aggressive at the sink entrances, and their short traverse times mean that they are still aggressive at the resurgence exits after having continued to enlarge both their vadose and phreatic passages.

Abrasion is a nearly ubiquitous component of cave erosion (Newson, 1971), and clastic sediment is continually in transit through the Dales caves. Abrasion by sand grains is recorded even in phreatic conduits (Murphy and Cordingley, 1999), but amounts of abrasion and sediment transport have not been measured in the Dales caves.

Abandoned cave passages

A feature of all the major cave systems within the Yorkshire Dales is the presence of older, mainly large, high-level passages that are no longer active. Notable among these are the phreatic tunnels that appear to have carried the trunk drainage once the Great Scar Limestone was exposed and the karst was established. Most of these tunnels were only active prior to the main deepening of the dales by subsequent glaciations, when they were abandoned as resurgence levels dropped past them and new cave passages developed beneath them. Many are more than 5m in diameter over lengths of more than a kilometre, though much of their height may be obscured by sediment fills and breakdown (Fig. 7.18). At

Figure 7.18. Monster Cavern, a part of the abandoned high-level passage from Ease Gill through to Lancaster Hole beneath Casterton Fell; parts of a half-tube survives in the roof bed, but the floor is formed by large-scale breakdown (photo: Mark Shinwell).

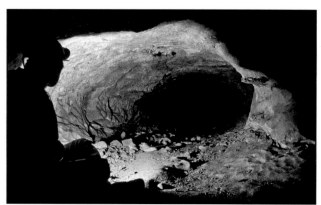

Figure 7.19. Drained phreatic tube that forms part of Southeast Passage in the Gaping Gill Cave System (TW).

most sites, only fragments of these abandoned passages have been discovered and mapped, and their continuations are either obscured beyond boulder chokes or sediment fills, or have been truncated by surface lowering.

Some of these relict passages had developed into mature phreatic tubes (Fig. 7.19), but most have cross profiles distorted to some degree by enlargement along bedding structures or fractures. Flat roofs are commonly defined by bedding (though many in the older caves are features of subsequent breakdown). The extreme example of bedding development is the well-known Hensler's Crawl in the Gaping Gill System (Fig. 7.20); for more than 500m in length this is 2–6m wide and is nowhere more than a metre high. Tall rift passages along joints are also common as distortions from a circular cross section (Fig. 7.21). Cross rifts, also developed on joints, are prominent features that create repeated local enlargements along many of the passages; these may be the only open sections of an old cave passage where mud and sand were deposited by a declining stream until it filled to the roof in the low sections between the cross rifts. While the large relict trunk passages are conspicuous within the cave systems of the Yorkshire Dales, there are also extensive networks of smaller phreatic tributary passages, which are noted for the arduous or unpleasant caving that they offer. Most of these networks appear as 'levels of development', because they are constrained to the zones of clustered bedding planes that were their inception horizons.

The old phreatic caves were the lower ends of drainage routes that largely developed as equally old vadose canyons at their upper levels. The finest example is the main streamway of Short Drop Cave, under Leck Fell, which descended gently to its contemporary water table and continued as the phreatic tube in Gavel Pot (Fig. 7.22); it still carries a stream,

which is now vadose as far as the current resurgence level some 90m below its ancestral position when the passage was largely formed. Many of the older vadose inlets are preserved only as fragments forming high-level ox-bows in canyons that are still active, and commonly are distinguished only by their more extensive calcite deposits. Many more of the earlier vadose caves were lost to surface erosion as the dales were deepened and widened, and there is a disproportionate scarcity of old vadose passages when compared to the extent of their contemporary phreatic caves. This also reflects the situation that when the dales were shallower, and had more limestone beneath their floors, more cave development could have been within the larger volume of a deeper phreas.

The classic two-phase cave is the 'keyhole' passage with a vadose canyon cut into the floor of a phreatic tube. Without diversion of its stream into a newer, lower route, the keyhole passage is the automatic consequence of the decline of regional base level or local water table in an evolving karst. Small keyhole passages developed over short time-scales, with smooth transitions from phreatic to vadose flow taking place as and when their downstream continuations permitted free drainage (Fig. 7.23). The larger keyhole passages in the Dales include the relict trunk caves with much younger canyons sunk into their floors (Fig. 7.24). Many parts of the long, high-level tunnel from the earlier phase of Ease Gill inlets through to Lancaster Hole have the younger canyon entrenched in its floor, though in other sections the canyon

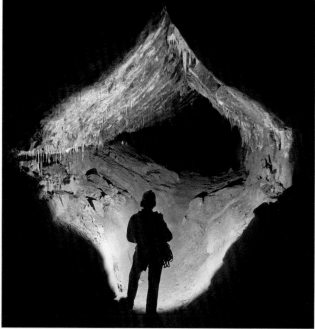

Figure 7.21. One of the Minarets, developed within the phreas on a joint/bedding intersection along a part of the old, high-level trunk route from Ease Gill Caverns to Lancaster Hole (TW).

Figure 7.20. Hensler's Crawl, a long, low and wide passage developed on a bedding plane under phreatic conditions, in the Gaping Gill Cave System (TW).

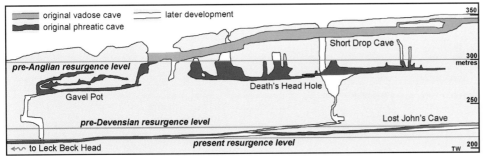

Figure 7.22. Simplified profile of the cave passages under part of Leck Fell, showing passage morphologies related to three successive resurgence levels; the horizontal scale is roughly that of the vertical but some parts are projected and fore-shortened. The pre-Anglian age of the upper resurgence level is interpreted from stalagmites older than 350 ka in related passages of nearby caves; the middle resurgence level is not reliably dated but is likely to be pre-Devensian. Passage continuations in Death's Head Hole and Gavel Pot are blocked by sediment and breakdown. The apparently large passages in Death's Head Hole are mainly tall rifts just a few metres wide.

Figure 7.23. A small keyhole passage with a deep and narrow vadose canyon cut in the floor of an older phreatic tube, in the Avalanche Pot inlet in the Gaping Gill Cave System (TW).

has formed loops separate from the older passage. In some caves, the older phreatic tubes and the younger vadose canyons formed in very different flow regimes, in which cases there may be considerable disparity in size between the two elements of the keyhole.

Most of the large, relict, trunk passages in the Dales caves have very little gradient because they largely follow the sub-horizontal dip of their guiding inception horizons. These levels were not at past water tables, and their depths below the contemporary water level cannot always be recognized. Beneath Leck Fell, the phreatic tube in Gavel Pot appears to have been about 30m below its vadose feeder in Short Drop (Fig. 7.22). Its exact depth is not known, as the passage appears to have descended straight through the contemporary water surface, but the transition from vadose to phreatic morphology at that level is lost behind the collapse features and subsequent vadose modification beneath the Gavel entrance. Phreatic lifts do occur to indicate minimum depths of the earlier phreatic zones. The two great ramps in Sleets Gill Cave, in Littondale, rise from an almost horizontal main tube (Fig. 7.25); the inner ramp was a phreatic lift of at least 70m, but the outer ramp, at the cave's present entrance, was truncated by glacial widening of the dale. Little is known for certain about the depths at which the very old complex of relict phreatic tunnels developed as the main level of the Gaping Gill System, but it is possible that Bar Pot was an outlet above a phreatic lift of about 100m (Glover, 1974). Major phreatic descents are also known in some caves. In the Lost John's Cave under Leck Fell, the high-level passage above Lyle Cavern descended 40m, and this has left a steeply inclined half-tube down one wall of the chamber (Waltham, 1974b), and the main roof tube above the Notts Pot 2 streamway appears to descend about 30m into a sediment floor in the Kleine Scheidegg chamber.

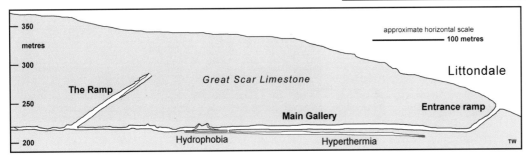

Figure 7.25. Profile of the old passages in Sleets Gill Cave, in Littondale, with the two phreatic ramps rising from the low-level phreatic tube; the small lower streamways are later developments (after survey by University of Leeds Speleological Association).

Geological influences on the cave systems

If a single overall model is to be recognized within the Yorkshire Dales caves, it is that of a sink high on a limestone bench, draining into a down-dip vadose cave (generally northwards), descending in steps, until resurgence level is met, from where a shallow phreatic loop reaches (generally up-dip and southwards) to a resurgence in a dale floor. Clearly this is a generalization, but it is the pattern at a large number of sites, including the Kingsdale system from Swinsto Hole to Keld Head that serves as the type example of a Dales cave (Waltham *et al.*, 1981). The many variations from this model relate either to particular geological features or to hydrological influences that are related largely to the local topography.

Groundwater that did not derive directly from rainfall is also recognized as a factor in developing some caves. Waters rising from hydrocarbon reservoirs can produce sulphuric acid that is extremely corrosive, and this has been shown to be a significant factor in the development of some large caves in other parts of the world (Hill, 1987; Palmer and Hill, 2005). Hydrothermal waters, rising from depth, are also warm and corrosive, and are recognized in forming an important suite of hypogene caves (Klimchouk, 2007). No evidence has yet been found of either of these styles of cave within the Dales, though sulphuric acid, derived from oxidation of pyrite, may have played some role during the earliest stages of cave inception. Hydrothermal mineralisation pre-dates the main phase of cave enlargement by a long interval (see Chapter 2); the zinc minerals in the Pikedaw Calamine Caverns are secondary deposits (Raistrick, 1954, Arthurton *et al.*, 1988). The mineralizing fluids must have impacted on the fissure permeability of the limestone, and very likely left traces that were subsequently exploited by development of some cave passages and shafts; but nothing has yet been recognised in the Dales caves that is comparable to the large vein cavities in the caves of the Peak District (Ford, 2000).

Shale beds and inception horizons

It has long been recognized that large proportions of both the active stream caves and the abandoned phreatic tunnels in the Yorkshire Dales have very low gradients because they are broadly aligned on the sub-horizontal bedding of the limestone. This was ascribed to many of the passages initially developing along the many thin shale beds (Fig. 7.26) within the limestone sequence (Waltham, 1970), but the concept has now been extended to encompass the caves formed initially on inception horizons that are more than just the shales (Lowe, 2000). The inception horizons may be shale beds, but may also be shale-free bedding planes distinguished by lithological contrasts or palaeokarst surfaces (see Chapter 8). Cave development has been found to be broadly favoured in limestones that have smaller dolomite fractions and are lower in clay and other impurities, though the matrix of variations makes cave distributions with respect to lithology very complex (Rauch and White, 1970, 1977). The same research, in America, found more caves in fine-grained micritic limestones, whereas a limited survey in the Yorkshire Dales recorded only more breakdown in the micritic limestones and less in the stronger, coarser, massive, sparry limestones (Sweeting and Sweeting, 1969). A pilot project in the Dales caves, to identify chemical and physical contrasts between pairs of limestone samples, from above and below bedding planes that had cave passages developed on them, was inconclusive (Waltham, 1971b). It may be significant that all this research examined the lithology of the beds, and none was directed towards the exact nature of the bedding planes or the lithologies immediately above and below them (on the millimetre scale). It is the variations away from absolute purity of the limestones that appear to create the chemical opportunities for cave inception, whether these are visible shale beds or much more subtle lithological contrasts within the limestone.

The morphology of the deep caves of Gragareth and Kingsdale reveal more than 15 stratigraphical horizons on which cave inception has been followed by significant passage development (Fig. 7.27). Each of these horizons is either a shale bed some centimetres thick (and locally up to about a metre thick), or a bedding plane that may or may not carry a visible paper-thin parting of shale. One notable inception horizon is the Porcellanous Bed, a thin micritic limestone that may lack any shale on its margins, may form multiple beds, and may be locally absent (see Chapter 2). Altitudes of the horizons around Gragareth vary due to the gentle northerly dip, and this structural influence is indicated on Figure 7.27 by the position of the widely recognisable Porcellanous Bed. Correlation of the other horizons is difficult. Though shales were recorded on the original cave surveys, these were incidental observations and not the primary target of the mapping, so some exposures in the caves may remain unrecorded. Many shale beds are seen to be laterally extensive, but their regional continuity cannot be confirmed from the isolated cave exposures. It is likely that variations of the limestone bed thicknesses account for much of the non-correlation of the horizons that is apparent on Figure 7.27. Though the details remain uncertain, the shale beds and bedding planes have certainly been significant factors in the inception and development of the Dales caves (see also Chapter 8).

Cave inception also takes place on joints and faults within the limestone, and may develop into passages either along or up and down the fractures. Many sub-horizontal caves originated along the intersections between favourable fractures and bedding horizons. All the open potholes that characterize the limestone landscapes in the Dales, and the

***Figure 7.26**. A shale bed about 400 mm thick exposed in the wall of a passage in the Ease Gill Cave System (TW).*

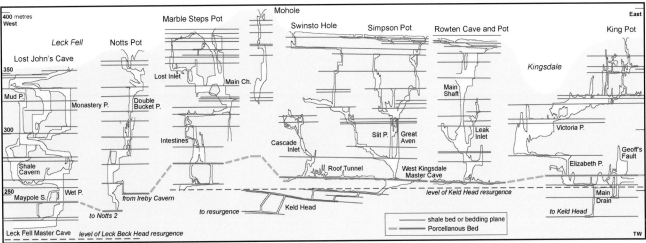

Figure 7.27. The many shale beds and bedding planes that have guided sections of sub-level passage in the cave systems of Gragareth and Kingsdale. Horizontal scales are greatly compressed, as are the distances between the caves. From Lost John's Cave to King Pot is 5.5 km along the line of the profile. Some passages have been omitted for clarity; in Notts Pot, only the Left Hand Route is shown, and the Porcellanous Bed is displaced by a fault. No account is taken of sediments that hide some lower floor profiles. Variations in altitude between bedding features in the different caves are largely due to the gentle, and slightly variable, dip of the limestone, but may also include local variations in bed thickness; contrasts in dip between the Keld Head and Swinsto Hole passages are largely artefacts of the survey projections, but may be distorted by some minor faults. The Kingsdale profile is only symbolic as its floor is close to the level of Keld Head (compiled from surveys by Dave Brook, Tony Waltham, John Thorp and John Cordingley that recorded the shale beds, with some additional survey interpretations).

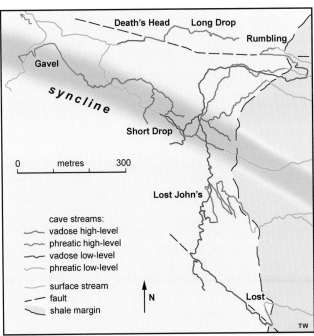

Figure 7.28. Convergence of underground drainage into a gentle synclinal trough across Leck Fell; vadose streamways follow bedding planes, so are broadly aligned down-dip; some passages are influenced by faults and joints, notably the zone of deep joints or strike-slip faults that constrain the streamway in the Lost John's entrance series; the high-level streamway in Short Drop Cave is about 100m above the low-level main drain from Lost John's Cave; part of the low-level passage developed within the phreatic zone and could therefore rise out of the synclinal trough, but was subsequently rejuvenated and now lies above the phreas (survey from Waltham and Hatherley, 1983).

waterfall shafts that create steps within the cave passages below, can be traced to origination on some joint or fault that breaks the limestone and provided the initial pathway through a rock that is essentially impermeable in its unfractured state. Physical opening of joints takes place due to stress relief or unloading following surface denudation that reduces the rock overburden, notably on de-glaciation in mountainous karst (Faulkner, 2010). The impact of unloading by denudation is greatest near the surface, and the process may have been important in opening up bedding planes between the uppermost beds in the Great Scar Limestone to allow initiation of the large number of long and nearly horizontal cave passages that form the entrance crawls of so many Dales cave systems and lie only a few metres below the glacially stripped plateau surfaces. Stress relief by unloading could be significant with respect to permitting the initial entry of water into both the fractures and the bedding planes, but the scale of its role has not been identified in the Dales caves.

With so much cave inception on bedding planes and shale beds, the dip of the limestone beds becomes a guiding factor with respect to gravitational drainage within the vadose zone. Though cave inception takes place prior to any opportunity for vadose drainage, subsequent enlargement of the proto-caves may be in a vadose environment, where the opportunity for faster drainage favours those proto-passages that are broadly aligned down-dip and therefore enlarges them into stream caves. The gentle regional dip therefore accounts for the northerly orientation of so many cave streamways in the Dales, and also for the convergence of vadose caves in the gentle synclines that flex the limestones on the Askrigg Block. Beneath Leck Fell, the high-level and low-level vadose streamways each collect in a single syncline, plunging to the northwest, with Short Drop Cave lying directly above Lost John's Cave (Fig. 7.28). Synclinal influence is also apparent in West Kingsdale (Waltham, 1970), and detailed mapping may reveal it elsewhere. Phreatic flow does not have to be down the geological structures, but it may be influenced by the partial tectonic opening of fractures along fold axes, both synclinal and anticlinal. Passages in Bull Pot of the Witches are aligned in the small (and relatively steep) folds adjacent to the Dent Fault. There may well be other locations where very gentle flexures of the limestone have guided cave development within the bedding, but these may be too gentle to be recognized by any practicable mapping, whereas they may be enough to influence vadose drainage.

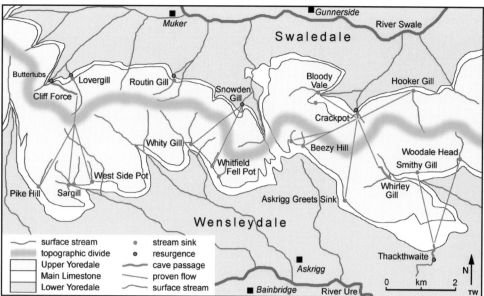

Gravitational flow down-dip can also account for drainage that passes beneath surface interfluves. Many of the sinks into the Yoredale Main Limestone on the northern slopes of Wensleydale drain north beneath the topographic divide to resurgences on the southern slopes of Swaledale (Fig. 7.29). Most of this current vadose drainage appears to be through the joint-guided fissure passages that characterize the caves in the Yoredale limestones (Myers, 1963). Though inception along the joints determined the details of the cave passages, down-dip flow within the thin bed of limestone determined the overall lines of underground drainage.

Figure 7.29. Underground flows in the Yoredale Main Limestone that largely passes beneath the topographic divide between Wensleydale and Swaledale; Thackthwaite Beck Cave is in the underlying Underset Limestone where the local dip is gently to the south (after Ryder, 1975, and work in progress by Tony Harrison).

Figure 7.31. The tall and narrow descending rift in Diccan Pot, formed on the Alum Pot Fault, Ingleborough (TW).

Joints and faults

Minor faults are scattered throughout the limestones in the Dales, and many have some degree of cave development on them. Within the Great Scar Limestone, the deep potholes of the Allotment on Ingleborough, including Juniper Gulf, Rift Pot and Nick Pot, are all developed on faults, though displacements and brecciation are minimal (Fig. 7.30). Fractures are features of most caves, where they have either been picked out by dissolution or determine the locations of shafts on which passages step from one bedding plane to another. The great majority are simple joints that developed in the limestone in order to relieve tectonic stresses. Some of the more extensive fractures have been popularly described as master joints, but are probably small strike-slip faults which have no vertical displacements to indicate movement in the sub-horizontal limestones. Much of Tatham Wife Hole is formed along a fault that does reveal normal displacement with shale beds at levels half a metre apart in opposing walls, and there are many other cave passages that are developed along faults and not just down them (Fig. 7.31).

A notable example of fracture guidance in the Dales caves is the Dowbergill Passage in Wharfedale; this passes beneath a shoulder of Great Whernside, from sinks in the Dowber Gill valley to an inlet in Dow Cave, which resurges in the Caseker Gill valley. Over a length of 1300m, the passage is almost perfectly straight, forming a vertical rift 10–25m

Figure 7.30. The main shaft of Rowten Pot, in Kingsdale, developed on a major fracture that is probably a minor strike-slip fault (photo: John Forder).

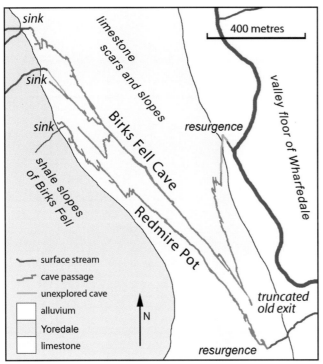

Figure 7.32. The parallel fracture-guided caves of Birks Fell and Birks Wood, in upper Wharfedale; the sinks along the shale margin are about 140m above the dale floor (after surveys by Craven Pothole Club and Cambridge University Caving Club).

high but rarely more than a metre wide. Its guiding fracture appears to be a major joint or a strike-slip fault, as there is no evidence of fault displacement (Halliwell, 1979). The rift passage is largely phreatic in origin, though vadose flow has modified its floor profile.

Also in Wharfedale, fracture control of cave development is conspicuous in Birks Fell Cave (Coe, 1968) and the parallel system of Redmire Pot through to Birks Wood Cave (Fig. 7.32). Most of Birks Fell Cave is developed along a single, vertical, strike-slip fault, whereas inlet passages and Redmire Pot are developed on sub-parallel joints and minor faults. Even though these two caves are formed on major fractures, it is significant that both their profiles are stepped with sections of almost level passages following shale horizons between waterfall shafts along the same fractures (Coe, 1968; Monico, 1995).

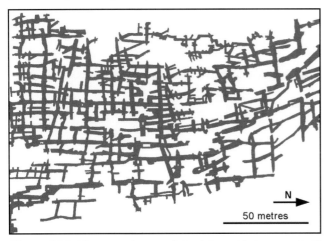

Figure 7.33. The central part of the joint-guided maze of rift passages in Knock Fell Cave, in the Yoredale Great Limestone on the Alston Block (after survey by Gritstone Club).

Caves within the Yoredale limestones

There are some long streamway caves in the Yoredale limestones, including Fairy Holes in the northern Pennines (Jones 1957; Waltham *et al.*, 1997), Cliff Force Cave in Swaledale (Ryder, 1981) and those in the eastern Dales (described below). These mainly linear caves have varying degrees of vadose development superimposed on phreatic origins, and are largely comparable with caves in the Great Scar Limestone except for their constraint within the thin beds of the Yoredale sequences. However, the Yoredale limestones are most distinctive for their maze and network caves that were developed entirely under phreatic conditions when strictly guided by bedrock joint systems (Ryder, 1975).

These maze caves are developed in the Main Limestone on the Askrigg Block, and also in the Great Limestone on the Alston Block (both are now formally described as Great Limestone within the Yoredale succession – see Chapter 2). The caves consist of spectacular mazes of phreatic rifts developed on multiple sets of intersecting joints (Fig. 7.33). Most of the rifts stay within limited stratigraphical zones and their walls are ribbed and fretted to etch out small differences in the limestone lithology (Fig. 7.34). Their morphologies include no flow features, and they were enlarged by slowly moving water when the Yoredale aquifers were confined. The Yoredale limestones are characteristically underlain by porous and fractured sandstones (locally known as

Figure 7.34. A rift passage in the Knock Fell Caverns maze, with wall ledges picked out on lithological variations within the Great Limestone of the northern Pennines (TW).

grits), and the larger phreatic maze caves lie in areas where unconformities also bring similar sandstones to the tops of the limestone. Groundwater input, upwards or downwards, from these permeable sandstones appears to have been a factor in the development of such extensive maze caves, in addition to the very slow lateral flow through the limestones themselves (Ryder, 1975; Palmer, 1975). Hypogene development of maze caves within the Yoredale limestones, with water migrating in from adjacent aquifers and by transverse flow, may be suggested by their maze patterns and by features of their passage morphology (Klimchouk, 2007). Though hypogene caves are increasingly being recognized, dissolution kinetics indicate that hypogene speleogenesis has significant limitations in limestone, and may not be as widespread as it is in gypsum (Palmer, 2011).

Alternatively, the maze caves may have been wholly or partly developed by sub-glacial or deglacial meltwater impounded by warm-based ice. Such an origin has been inferred for many maze caves along the narrow marble outcrops in the stripe karst of Norway (Skoglund and Lauritzen, 2011). In the Pennines, Knock Fell Caverns lie largely beneath the outcrop of the limestone and are reached through a small shaft (Sutcliffe, 1985), whereas the maze caves of Swaledale all lie well back beneath their covers of shale and sandstone and are only reached from old mine levels (Ryder, 1975; Harrison, 2006, 2012a, 2012b). None has yet been found with passages opening onto, or truncated along, a valley-side outcrop, as is normal in the Norwegian caves. This would be surprising if they had formed beneath Devensian ice by meltwater flows into the limestones at their subglacial outcrops; any formed beneath earlier ice sheets would probably have been removed by the Devensian glaciation. Neither the sug-glacial nor the hypogenic processes are compatible with all the features in the Pennine maze caves, and origins and subsequent development of this type of cave remain unresolved (Palmer, 2011).

Figure 7.36. The main stream passage in New Goyden Pot, carrying the River Nidd beneath the grit outcrop (photo: Andy Jackson).

Langcliffe Pot and Mossdale Caverns, the two long cave systems above Wharfedale, are both formed largely in the Middle Limestone of the Yoredale sequence. They both have long stream passages with significant flows through them, but they are also guided by the joints, so that their plan forms are essentially rectilinear, with little or no trace of passage meandering. Unlike the majority of Yoredale caves, which are each restricted to a single limestone within the Yoredale sequence, both Langcliffe and Mossdale drain through to lower limestones, as they both resurge from Black Keld, which lies at floor-level in Wharfedale near the base of the Great Scar Limestone. The escape from the Middle Limestone, stratigraphically downwards, is seen only in Langcliffe Pot (Brook, 1989), where the stream has cut a canyon through undisturbed shale in Boireau Falls Chamber to reach the lip of a shaft that descends through the entire thickness of the Simonstone Limestone (Fig. 7.35). The cave stream then drops into the Hardraw Scar Limestone, but the boulder choke obscures the bedrock structure and the nature of the descent through the intervening Dirt Pot Grit. The extensive collapse suggests that this is located in a strike-slip fault zone, but the lack of continuous exposure prevents confirmation of the geological details. The Hardraw Scar is continuous with the Hawes and the Great Scar Limestones, but the water cannot be followed beyond a choked sump in the Hardraw Scar (beyond the margin of Fig. 7.35).

The main passages of the known caves beneath the floor of Nidderdale appear to be entirely within the Middle Limestone. The Three Yard and Five Yard Limestones are both exposed in the inliers, and the shafts of New Goyden Pot appear to descend through at least part of this overlying sequence. Downstream from the sinks into Manchester Hole and Goyden Pot, the caves are distinguished by large phreatic conduits, where maze development is subsidiary and may have been caused by flooding at high hydraulic gradients (Palmer, 1991). The main passages cross a number of small faults, and parts of them step up or down to follow stratigraphic inception horizons (Davies, 1974). Some of the faults are marked by cross rifts, have segments of passage aligned on them, or have tributaries joining on them, but others are crossed by passages with no lateral development on the fault plane.

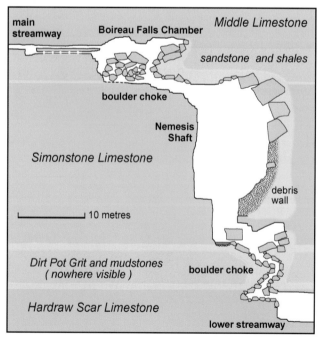

Figure 7.35. Sketch profile of a part of Langcliffe Pot, Wharfedale, where its stream descends through non-carbonate beds between the Yoredale limestones; grey areas are unseen (survey by Dave Brook).

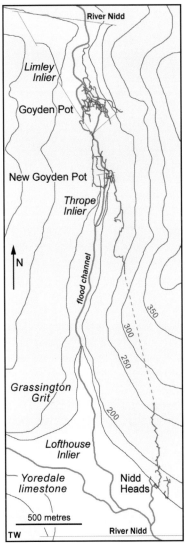

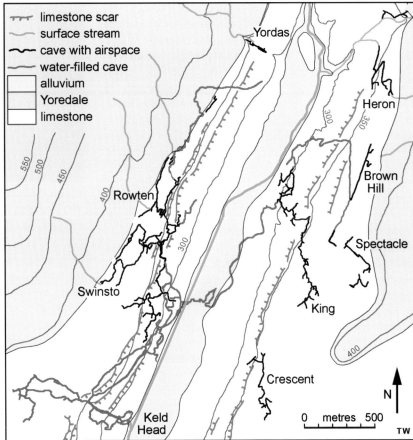

Figure 7.37. *The course of the River Nidd through caves beneath the outcrop of Grassington Grit between the limestone inliers of Limley and Lofthouse (after surveys by Yorkshire Underground Research Team, Cave Diving Group and Black Sheep Diggers).*

Figure 7.38. *The caves of Kingsdale, including the flooded passage that crosses beneath the valley floor from the East Kingsdale sinks to the Keld Head resurgence (after surveys by Cave Diving Group, University of Leeds Speleological Association, Northern Cave Club, and a rough sketch of the southern inlet in Brown Hill Pot).*

A notable feature of the Nidderdale drainage is the route of the main conduit, which lies beneath a cap of Grassington Grit for more than 2 km between New Goyden Pot and Nidd Heads (Figs 7.36, 7.37). The cave passage is underwater for most of its length, but has been largely mapped by divers, and it lies well away from small outcrops of the limestone along the river bed (which is dry except for small streams collected on the caprock). This large and mature cave offers some indication of the scale to which passages can grow beneath a caprock prior to its removal by denudation and consequent expansion of the limestone outcrops; such may be relevant to consideration of some of the earliest stages of cave development within the Dales.

Hydrological features of cave development

The concept of the 'master cave' in the Yorkshire Dales caves became established following discovery of the low-level trunk drain in Lost John's Cave under Leck Fell (Foley, 1930). These were conceived as long passages developed at the 'water table', where they collected numerous tributaries, and may then have been exposed as open vadose passage following a slight fall in resurgence level. The notion of a main drain, or a trunk cave on which numerous tributaries converge, is valid, but there is no direct relationship to a water table (except that such a vadose trunk cave commonly defines the local karst water table within a cavernous

limestone in the same way as a surface stream controls the water table in a diffuse aquifer). The term 'master cave' has been rather over-used. It may be appropriate for the long, low-level stream caves in Lost John's Cave and Ease Gill Caverns, which collect much of the drainage beneath Leck Fell and Casterton Fell respectively. However, the Out Fell Master Cave in Hammer Pot is merely a powerful streamway at high-level beneath Fountains Fell; this continues down a 15m-deep waterfall shaft to a sump that is perched 30m above passages where the water is next seen in downstream caves.

The active main drains, or trunk passages, within the Dales cave systems are both vadose and phreatic. Keld Head is the outlet of a phreatic system with multiple loops and branches converging from disparate sites, including the East Kingsdale Branch that crosses beneath the floor of the surface valley (Fig. 7.38). The West and East Kingsdale master caves are merely short sections of vadose passage within a dominantly phreatic collector system that drains up-dip. In contrast, the trunk caves beneath Casterton, Leck and Fountains fells, each with multiple tributaries, have long stretches of vadose passage where they are aligned obliquely down the local dip of the limestone.

Development of the trunk cave passages commonly involves multiple stages of under-capture as they adjust to resurgence levels that are declining in response to surface denudation (Worthington, 2005). This leaves some distributary passages at only slightly higher levels, where they can then be re-activated as flood outlets. Such a pattern is almost normal among the larger cave systems in the Yorkshire Dales. Leck Beck Head, God's Bridge, White Scar Cave, Clapham Beck Head, Turn Dub, Brants Gill Head, Aire Head and Nidd Heads all have distributary resurgences; Keld Head is the exception in its present state, but its underwater passages have at least three distributary outlets that have been active in the past. Brants Gill Head is perhaps the most complicated of the Dales underground drainage systems (Fig. 7.39), with tributary streams from at least 20 sinks, many feeding through long stretches of known cave (Fig. 7.40). The waters all drain to Brants Gill, except when flood flows go to Douk Gill Head and Dub Cote Cave, both of which can be dry exits in normal conditions. Dub Cote has 4 km of mapped passages beyond flooded sections that never drain clear, and these carry a base flow that drains through another distributary to the Brackenbottom Rising. The two large phreatic ramps in Sleets Gill Cave, Littondale, appear to have been distributaries that rose from depth in a cave system that was more active prior to glacial rejuvenation of the dale, but it is uncertain if they were contemporary or sequential. The modern stream in the cave has developed its own route beneath the older passages, but water flows up the smaller ramp to emerge at the present cave entrance as a flood distributary.

The present cave systems clearly have an abundance of large trunk passages at altitudes close to the local resurgences; Kingsdale is an example with long sections of low-level main drain both above and below the Keld Head resurgence level.

Figure 7.40. The lower streamway in Penyghent Pot, one of the main feeders to the Brants Gill Head resurgence (TW).

These would be comparable to the 'levels' of development that might be recognized in the systems of large, old, high-level abandoned phreatic tunnels. But it is notable that the modern caves range between the resurgence-level water table and depths of about 40m, and also include trunk passages significantly above the local resurgences. In detail, the levels of cave development are primarily functions of the geological structure and stratigraphy, and not of resurgence levels. While the higher levels of cave development in the Yorkshire Dales do broadly represent past stages of drainage and dissolutional activity, they can only relate very roughly to the contemporary resurgence positions, except where detailed mapping of preserved underground morphology permits better correlations.

Many of the major active cave systems within the Great Scar Limestone drain to resurgences at or close to the base of the limestone. Little cave development is actually on the base of the limestone, largely because impure basal beds favour cave development at slightly higher stratigraphical levels. Only White Scar Cave has a largely vadose streamway through to its resurgence on the base of the limestone, because it lies in a position where it can drain down-dip into Chapel-le-Dale. Although the resurgence is at the contact with the impermeable basement, most of the cave lies some metres higher within the basal beds of the limestone (Waltham, 1977b). Most of the other major caves drain up-dip to the dale-floor resurgences, because they are at the lower ends of shallow phreatic loops where the drainage descends a joint and then rises along the bedding. Because these are phreatic they are not constrained towards the base of the limestone. Keld Head lies at the truncated end of a phreatic tube that happens to be about 40m above the base of the limestone where it has been breached by the incision of Kingsdale (Waltham *et al.*, 2010). Leck Beck Head resurges up a dipping bedding plane, while the God's Bridge risings, in Chapel-le-Dale, are also from bedding planes. Austwick Beck Head has an immature passage rising on a bedding plane about a metre above the base of the limestone, and appears to be a recent under-capture of another passage whose location is unknown.

Many of the smaller cave systems neither penetrate the full depth of the limestone nor reach down to the level of the dale floor. The caves around Birkwith, in Upper Ribblesdale, are the most conspicuous of these perched systems (Fig. 4.25). They are perched within the limestone largely because their passages developed along bedding planes or shale beds

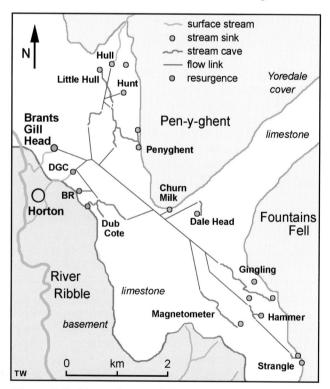

Figure 7.39. The underground drainage system behind Brants Gill Head, in Ribblesdale, with multiple tributaries from sinks on Pen-y-ghent and Fountains Fell, and its distributaries to the flood resurgences of Douk Gill Cave (DGC) and Dub Cote Cave, with base flow to Brackenbottom Rising (BR); the marked links are unknown in detail as they are only part of a complex hydrology within the flooded zone.

and failed to find joints that allowed them to descend to lower levels. One of these, the main streamway in Red Moss Pot, follows a single joint for more than 700m, but nowhere descends through the beds as it was all initiated on a single bedding/joint intersection. The Birkwith caves therefore drained out to the valley sides, though they may originally have continued further and perhaps reached greater depths before they were truncated at their current exits by surface erosion (Fig. 7.41).

A deep cave can form only where there are vertical (or inclined) geological structures (either fractures or bedding planes) to exploit and where the surface relief allows a long descent from sink to rising. In the Yorkshire Dales karst these two requirements are best met along the southern edge of the Askrigg Block, where fracture densities increase on approach to the Craven Faults and where the dales are entrenched deepest before emerging onto the Craven Lowlands. The deep shafts of southern Ingleborough make a clear contrast to the shallow caves of Ribblehead farther north. The scatter of deep caves that do occur further away from the Craven Fault zone are nearly all developed on isolated minor faults (Fig. 7.42). These include Alum Pot and Washfold Pot in Ribblesdale and most of the deeper caves in Upper Wharfedale, including Birks Fell Cave, Pasture Gill Pot and Strans Gill Pot, though all these caves also have some passages that are bedding-guided..

Filling and destruction of the caves

Once a cave passage has matured fully, with a significant stream flowing through it, there is a natural progression towards it losing its stream through rejuvenation and capture, eventually reaching a stage of old age that is distinguished by slow destruction or by infilling and choking. The internal processes of this stage are dominated by collapse and breakdown, and by filling with both clastic sediments and carbonate precipitates. At the same time, surface erosion can breach, un-roof and then totally destroy cave passages

Figure 7.42. The fluted walls of the main shaft in Hardrawkin Pot, Ingleborough, where the mismatch of the thin, dark shale beds indicate that the shaft was formed on a small fault that is roughly down the line of the rope (photo: Mark Shinwell).

Figure 7.41. The resurgence of Birkwith Cave where a cave stream emerges onto the surface well up in the limestone succession and above the floor of Ribblesdale (TW).

during landscape evolution. All these elements of destruction commence as soon as a cave is formed, when rock walls can be displaced between fractures and calcite can fill even a narrow fissure; but their roles increase with age, until they dominate in the older passages abandoned by streams that could have been capable of further enlarging them.

Bedrock breakdown and cave chambers

Breakdown and collapse of cave roofs and walls are inevitable in a bedded and fractured limestone such as that in the Yorkshire Dales. Though unsupported roof slabs can fall away, wall collapse is probably more widespread in the Dales caves. It is particularly prevalent in the zones of heavily fractured limestone that are commonly followed by cave passages, and makes a significant contribution to passage widening, especially where residual screens of rock fall away from passage walls or collapse between parallel rifts (Fig. 7.43). Extensions of the same process have contributed to formation of the larger cave chambers that lie within a number of the Dales caves. Collapse cannot form chambers, but can only modify them, as there has to be an earlier void into which broken material can fall. The collapse process is significant in that it supplies breakdown debris, which is then exposed to dissolution and erosion, but the ultimate size of a cave chamber is the product of rock removal, which is normally in solution in streams that flow across and through its debris floor. Roof stability over cave chambers

Figure 7.43. Wall collapse with a large limestone block toppling out into a cave passage in Scrafton Pot, Coverdale (TW).

Figure 7.44. The Main Chamber in Gaping Gill, looking towards the east with daylight shining down the waterfall shaft; both the vertical wall on the left and the sloping roof on the right are along minor faults or major joints; the floor is water-washed cobbles and sand overlying debris that may be 30m thick (TW).

can be related to bed thickness and span width (Waltham *et al.*, 2005), but this indicates only maximum spans in intact beds. Both in the Dales caves and elsewhere, nearly all roof failures are determined by the local situation with respect to the joints that break the beds.

Gaping Gill Main Chamber is the largest in the Dales, 130m long and about 30m high and wide, with its roof broken by the Main Shaft containing its 100m-deep waterfall where Fell Beck descends from daylight (Fig. 7.44). The chamber is formed at the intersection of various vertical and inclined faults and joints, and the ceiling profile (away from the Main Shaft) is clearly the result of many fracture-bounded blocks falling away (Murphy *et al.*, 2005). Most of the chamber floor is close to level on a thick clastic fill. Surveys of this, using ground-probing radar, suggest that the sediments are at least 30m deep, with layering defined by the signals from clay-rich horizons (Murphy *et al.*, 2005, 2008), but these surveys are difficult to interpret and have not been verified by any borehole or excavation. There are however no indications of large piles of fallen blocks.

The open pothole of Hull Pot, on Pen-y-ghent, is 90m long and 20m wide, with vertical walls dropping about 20m (Fig. 7.45). Whether it was initially developed as an open hole, or is an un-roofed cave chamber, is open to debate, but its genesis involves dissolution and wall collapse similar to that in underground chambers. It is formed in fractured limestone along a system of small splayed faults, and progressive wall failure has been recorded within the last hundred years (Murphy and Parr, 2004); this is a part of the process that has widened it from an initial one or two fissures. Its level floor is on clastic fill. A radar survey across this suggests a rock floor beneath about 30m of fill (Murphy *et al.*, 2008), though a breakdown pile is accessible from a side shaft at a depth of 40m at the eastern end (Pappard, 1976) (Fig. 4.31).

Also on Pen-y-ghent, Sell Gill Holes lead down to a single large chamber that has been heavily modified by collapse on multiple large fractures. Many other chambers within the Dales caves are little more than wider sections

Figure 7.45. Hull Pot, on the side of Pen-y-ghent, with the large tilted block at the western end showing the scale of wall retreat by successive failures on parallel fractures (TW).

along the large, old, phreatic, trunk passages. The Battlefield chamber in White Scar Cave is just such a larger section of the relict high-level passage, though its spaciousness has been enhanced by its floor of breakdown debris settling as some of the blocks have dropped into the younger stream canyon that winds its way beneath the large central section of the chamber (Waltham, 1977a).

Clastic cave sediments

Every cave in the Yorkshire Dales has clastic sediment in some of its passages. Clay, silt, sand, gravel and cobbles are constantly in transit through the active stream caves, with their distribution frequently changed after the flood events during which most sediment transport occurs. Floods pass through, and many vadose canyons are notable for their lack of sediment in conditions of low stage, but easily disturbed mud is almost ubiquitous in the phreatic passages where water velocities are generally lower. Abandoned, high-level caves are characterized by an abundance of clastic sediments, which may completely fill passage segments until an invading stream cuts a channel into them, or until cavers excavate enough of the sediment to allow access to open passages beyond.

Most cave sediment is allogenic, in that it has been carried into the caves by sinking streams. The sand, gravel and coarser materials in the Dales caves are derived largely from the Carboniferous grits and sandstones that crop out in the stream catchments. Fragments of limestone (known as clasts), derived from wall and roof breakdown, form a significant proportion of the coarser material in most stream caves, but are proportionally less abundant in trunk conduits beneath the dale floors where additional coarse material has been carried in by the larger sinking streams. The active phreatic conduit in Joint Hole, beneath Chapel-le-Dale, has gravel as its current sediment bed-load, and this moves as dune forms only during flood events (Fig. 7.46). The low gravel dunes migrate over the top of a cemented cobble deposit that is not involved in the active sediment transport (Murphy, 1999). Protected beneath the cobbles

Figure 7.46. Low banks of gravel being washed through the main phreatic conduit in Joint Hole, beneath the floor of Chapel-le-Dale (photo: John Cordingley).

Figure 7.47. The old phreatic trunk passage of Duke Street, in Ireby Fell Cavern, with a thick bank of sand, silt and clay eroded by a stream that subsequently invaded the passage (TW).

are pale clays that form no part of the modern sediment regime and may be remnants surviving from the glacial environments of the Pleistocene. Pebbles and cobbles, particularly those of sandstone, commonly acquire black coatings of compound oxides of iron and manganese, largely goethite. These coatings accumulate to create a partial cement in sediment banks, which then become more resistant to erosion and develop into semi-permanent features in some cave streamways. The rapid deposition of coarse sediment in some caves is demonstrated in Mongo Gill Cave where stratified gravels include layers with minerals derived from miners' waste dumps left in the Greenhow Hill area only a few hundred years ago.

Accumulations of clastic sediment within cave passages lead to paragenetic processes whereby walls or ceilings of the passages are eroded by flowing or effectively static water that is impounded above or behind the sediments (Farrant and Smart, 2011). Wall notches are the clearest indicators of paragenesis (Fig. 7.14) but these have not yet been identified widely within the Dales caves. If they can be distinguished from dissolution notches along horizontal bedding planes, they could indicate detail in the stages of passage evolution.

In the relict high-level caves, the coarser clastic sediments have a wide range of lithologies. Poorly sorted material, with more angular clasts, is less mature and was deposited more rapidly, probably in flood events, and notably during phases of de-glaciation. Great banks of coarse, poorly-sorted sediment in Stream Chamber in the Gaping Gill System indicate powerful stream flows that were capable of transporting this material in the past (Ford, 2001). Only 100m from that site, the stratified sands in Sand Cavern may represent a downstream extension of the same sediments that were deposited where water was ponded in the chambers; these sands contain grains of goethite that appear to have been re-worked from elsewhere. The well-sorted sand is more than 10m thick, largely in beds about 50 mm thick that are separated by thin partings of clay. Banded sediments in Sand Cavern, and in other caves, may be varves, but the timing of the cycles has not been investigated and they may represent random flood events rather than being annual features.

Thick sequences of stratified sediments are exposed in many of the large, old, trunk passages. Besides sand, there are massive quantities of silt and clay (Fig. 7.47). These appear to be derived largely from both the Yoredale shales of

Figure 7.48. Desiccation cracks in a patch of dried mud in the Battlefield chamber in White Scar Cave (TW).

the stream catchments and also from the loessic soils washed from the limestone outcrops, but no sedimentological studies have yet revealed the details of their origins. Many of the clay deposits in the Dales caves are laminated, but whether the individual layers represent flood events, seasonal changes or longer periods of climatic fluctuation has not been determined. Exposed tops of the clays are commonly distinguished by deep desiccation cracks (Fig. 7.48). It has been suggested that such may have been deposited beneath subglacial lakes during warm-based glacial maxima or beneath ice-dammed lakes during de-glaciation (Faulkner, 2011). Varved clays in Victoria Cave are also thought to have formed in cave lakes when warm-based ice covered the terrain during at least four glacial maxima (Lundberg *et al.*, 2010).

Whereas the sorted and bedded sediments are of largely fluvial origins, some caves in the Yorkshire Dales also contain clastic sediment that displays little or no sorting, and may therefore be described as diamicton. Some of this has been labelled as boulder clay or glacial till, but this cannot have been pushed far into caves by glacier ice, even in the coldest of Pleistocene Ice Age conditions. Except for debris that chokes or partially chokes many entrances, and may be till that has been dragged, squeezed, dropped or washed a few metres into the caves and potholes, much of this material may be better described as glaciofluvial, because it originated from

glaciers and ice sheets but was finally emplaced by meltwater (Fig. 7.49). However, similar unsorted fills that choke many entrance shafts can be younger and much later than the glacial activity; debris in the entrance to Shuttleworth Pot, on Leck Fell, contains Bronze Age artefacts less than 4500 years old. A variation in the mode of transport and deposition may be represented by the sediments in the far reaches of Dale Barn Cave where they lie beneath the slopes of Kingsdale. These are thick diamictons interbedded with cross-bedded sand and gravel, and are very similar to debris deposited in pipe-full glacier tunnels and subsequently exposed in eskers; they are interpreted as sub-glacial, phreatic deposits (Murphy *et al.*, 2001). A stalagmite, dated to 343 ka, was eroded by the flow that emplaced these sediments, indicating that they originate from a post-Anglian glaciation.

Burial in a cave of the quartz grains within clastic sediments can be dated by the unequal decay of aluminium and beryllium isotopes (see Chapter 10), but no age determinations have yet been obtained for clastic sediments in the Dales caves. Dating the thick clastic sequences in some of the old trunk passages might indicate stages in the caves development that pre-date glaciations prior to the Anglian, but there may be serious problems in defining the burial history of sediment that may have been derived from older tills before being washed into the caves.

Cave deposits from solution

Calcite deposits are virtually ubiquitous in limestone caves. Most are formed where percolation water, rich in biogenic carbon dioxide from its seepage through a soil cover, becomes saturated with carbonate (largely in its transit through the epikarst) before entering open cave passages. There it precipitates the calcite in response to partial loss of its carbon dioxide in order to achieve equilibrium with the cave air. Nearly all the Dales caves contain some calcite deposits, since few extend far beneath the impermeable shale cap that might prevent percolation water reaching the open passages. The decorative calcite speleothems occur in a huge variety of forms (Fig. 7.50). In response to the cool climates, past and present, of the Dales karst, they are generally less massive than their counterparts in karsts of warmer environments (where percolation waters pick up more biogenic carbon dioxide from the soil cover, because biological activity is greater, and can therefore dissolve more carbonate prior to precipitation when it de-gasses on entering open caves).

Straw stalactites are the most widespread and the most numerous calcite deposits in the Dales caves, with many occurring in large clusters and reaching more than a metre long. Stalagmites are far less numerous, and if any shape is typical in the Dales caves it is a stumpy column with little taper and only about half a metre tall; the Colonnades in Lancaster Hole are exceptional, reaching 5m tall and only about 120 mm in diameter. Large gour barriers are not common, but the largest of nine in Ingleborough Cave were about two metres high and wide before they were broken through in 1837 to gain access to the cave beyond (which is now the show cave passage). The original extent of those gour pools is now indicated by the sub-aqueous 'cave coral' coating the passage walls. Elsewhere in the Dales caves, small pool deposits include crystal linings and rare clusters

Figure 7.49. Poorly sorted sediment left by inflows of meltwater into the Broadway passage beneath the Ease Gill surface channel (TW).

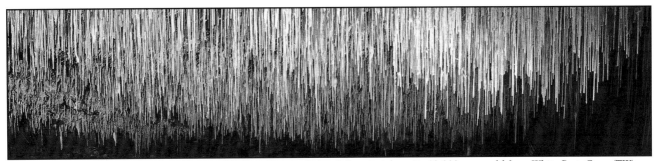

Above: straws in Glover's Chamber, Gaping Gill Cave System. Below left: cut stalagmite 12,000 years old from White Scar Cave (TW).
Below: straws and stalagmites in Easter Grotto, Ease Gill Caverns. Below right: straw bell in Shep Pot, Leck Fell (Mark Richardson).

Left: curtains in Gavel Pot. Above: stalagmites in Cape Kennedy,
Lancaster Hole. Right: stalagmites in Slug's World, Lancaster Hole.
Below left: flowstone in Ingleborough Cave (John Cordingley).
Below: pool deposits in Lancaster Hole (Mark Shinwell).
Bottom: cave pearls in Avalanche Inlet, Gaping Gill (TW).
Below right: gours in Gour Chamber, Bull Pot of the Witches.

Figure 7.50. *Calcite speleothems in the Dales caves (photos by John Forder except where labelled otherwise).*

Figure 7.51. Remnants of false floors that indicate old sediment levels within the Main Chamber of Yordas Cave, Kingsdale; one level is just above the person's head, and the other is as high again on the right (TW).

of cave pearls. False floors are common, and are important as indicators of past sediment levels, though many survive only as thin shelves of calcite projecting from passage walls, some with clastic sediment attached beneath (Fig. 7.51).

Pure calcite is white or translucent. Some completely white calcite speleothems do occur in the Dales caves, but most are of various hues from off-white, through cream and yellowish, to various shades of red and brown, all stained by traces of hydrated iron oxides in the water and in the calcite. Dirty greys and brown are due largely to included clay. Some red and yellow colourations are organic staining, and rare pale blues and pale greens are probably due to hydrated iron sulphates and carbonates, though some may contain traces of similar compounds of copper and other metals (Fig. 7.52).

Figure 7.52. Calcite at the Painter's Palette, in Lancaster Hole, stained by mineral oxides primarily of iron (photo: John Forder).

Gypsum is not common in the Dales caves. Crystals of gypsum, also known as selenite, can grow in the muds and silts left in passages where there is any sulphate present from the oxidation of pyrite within the shale beds through the limestone succession. Gypsum Cavern, in the high-levels of the Ease Gill System, originally had thousands of tiny acicular (needle-shaped) crystals protruding from the clay banks, as well as small tabular crystals scattered across the cave walls, but this site is an exception within the known Dales caves.

Calcite stalagmites and flowstones contain traces of the unstable isotopes of uranium that decay at measurable rates and thereby allow estimation of their ages. The dating of stalagmites, and the interpretation of palaeo-environments from their contents of stable isotopes of oxygen, has led to caves being recognized as invaluable sources of geomorphological and palaeo-climatic data, both on a worldwide scale and in the Yorkshire Dales (see Chapter 10).

Evolution of the Dales caves

The earliest stages of cave genesis within the Dales limestones must date back to the expulsion of connate water during the late stages of diagenesis. This was followed by the very small groundwater flows that descended through faults or sandstone aquifers, ascended from hydrothermal sources, or entered laterally as connate waters from basins adjacent to the Pennines. All recognizable traces of these have now been lost, except for the imprint that they left on the patterns of cave inception (see Chapter 8). A landmark event was then the initial un-roofing of the limestone, simply in response to regional denudation and surface lowering.

These first exposures of the limestone were along the southern edge of the Askrigg Block, where the geological structures are highest against the Craven Faults, and where the adjacent topography is lowest in the Craven Lowlands. The first limestones exposed were the higher beds in the local Yoredale succession, but cave development in most of these is, and probably was, quite limited, so the main consideration is with regard to the Great Scar Limestone. It is reasonable to assume that the first outcrops of limestone appeared against the North Craven Fault where it was crossed by the deeper dales. Ribblesdale is the largest southbound dale, is probably among the oldest, and crosses the edge of the Askrigg Block near a structural high (Arthurton *et al.*, 1988); the top of the Great Scar Limestone is currently exposed at an altitude of about 550m on Dick Close, at the southern end of Fountains Fell. A broad concept of the Dales landscape evolution, based on an interpolation of incision rates deduced from dated stalagmites, places the early exposures of the limestone west of Ingleborough at about 1.3 Ma (see Chapter 4). The paucity of currently available data makes this a very approximate figure, which is perhaps best interpreted as 'some time before about a million years ago', and the limestone exposures in Ribblesdale may be estimated to date back to 1.5 Ma or probably even earlier.

It is even more difficult to estimate times for unroofing of the limestone across the interfluves, but outcrops on the high ground north of Malham, must have been among the earliest. An early outcrop of the limestone, reaching from Ribblesdale towards the Malham High Country, would have allowed the

Figure 7.53. The retreating margin of the Yoredale shale cover that unroofed the Great Scar Limestone and allowed sinking streams to develop the major caves in the Yorkshire Dales. The present margin is drawn along the line of stream sinks where water drops into the main limestone unit. The margin at 0.5 Ma is a reconstruction of conditions just prior to the Anglian glaciation (Waltham, 1990), based partly on the positions of large and old potholes including Rumbling Hole, Great Douk Cave and Alum Pot. Known fragments of large old phreatic cave passage are probably of similar age. The margin at 1.3 Ma is taken from the interpretation of earliest exposures as in Figure 4.13; this is roughly comparable to the outcrop of the present base of the limestone, because it precedes denudation by about 200m, which is close to the thickness of the limestone. No details are known or indicated south of the North Craven Fault. Rivers are shown only at their present positions to aid readability.

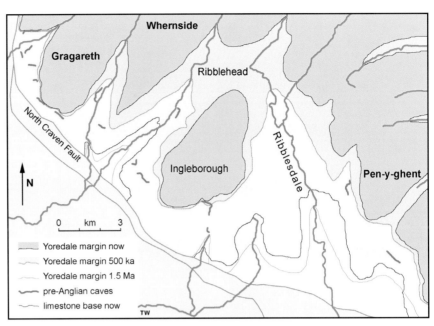

first development of karst (Fig. 7.53), other than small-scale features on the thin Yoredale limestones. This could have been drained underground towards Ribblesdale, and the first caves in the Dales are likely to have developed in this area. Alternatively, the first caves may have been in the smaller limestone outcrop between the North and Middle Craven Faults, reaching from the high ground of the Attermire Scar area again to the floor of Ribblesdale. Victoria Cave may be a remnant of this first generation of caves. It does contain the oldest cave sediments yet dated in the Dales (Lundberg *et al.*, 2010), but, determined only as >600 ka, these give little indication of the time when the cave was part of an active conduit. These two parallel sites in the flank of Ribblesdale were not linked as there is no continuity across the North Craven Fault, because its throw locally exceeds the thickness of the limestone.

As the dales were incised deeper into the limestone by surface erosion that was both glacial and fluvial, early phases of caves developed along newly available flow lines. Caves formed beneath and parallel with the trunk streams on the dale floors were doomed to total destruction when the dales were subsequently deepened and widened. Many of the earliest

Figure 7.54. Victoria Cave, a truncated fragment of cave passage that is at least 600,000 years old, in Attermire Scar 300m above the floor of Ribblesdale (TW).

caves, draining from sinks on the shoulders of the interfluves and down to the dale floors, would also largely have been removed by subsequent enlargement of the dales, though some passage fragments could have survived at sheltered locations. Victoria Cave is a very early remnant (Fig. 7.54), but recognition of more of these in the modern landscape is surrounded by uncertainty. Ribblesdale was almost certainly the site of the earliest cave development. Wharfedale (with its Littondale tributary) is another major feature that is likely to have been deep enough to become another site of early karst development, particularly in the Yoredale Middle Limestone, which locally is of significant thickness and is also at high altitude. Chapel-le-Dale and Kingsdale are smaller valleys that were probably later to develop their own cave systems. The age of initial limestone exposure at around 1.3 Ma is largely based on the morphology and the incision rates of these two dales (see Chapter 4), implying that the karst around Ribblesdale dates from well before that. The outer dales, Dentdale, Wensleydale, Swaledale and Nidderdale, all lie where the main limestones are at lower altitudes, so were probably later to develop their first significant karst.

The first generation of caves

The oldest surviving passages can be recognized within many of the Dales cave systems, because they are isolated segments that lie at high levels and bear little relationship to the later cave development that has intersected them by chance. A number of large, old, high-level passages can be ascribed to pre-Anglian development due to their positions in relation to the glaciated troughs and the depths that they are likely to have achieved prior to Anglian deepening. These provide part of the evidence for the reconstruction of the 0.5 Ma karst margin (Fig. 7.53). It is however very difficult to identify remnants of cave systems that developed in the early part of the time interval between 1.3 and 0.5 Ma, for which no absolute chronology of events yet exists.

Jupiter Cavern (in Ireby Fell Cavern) appears to be very old, and its presence suggests that there was an early outcrop of the limestone in the lower end of Ease Gill. The 1.3 Ma interpretation is too generalised to show this outcrop (Fig. 7.53),

Figure 7.55. High Level Mud Caverns, an old abandoned passage in Mossdale Caverns, high above Wharfedale (photo: Dave Judson).

following initial exposure of the Great Scar Limestone in Clapdale at around 1.3 Ma (Fig. 7.53). Pikedaw Calamine Caverns lie between the North and Middle Craven faults and may have very early origins, perhaps related to Victoria Cave when karst development linked the Ribblesdale and Malham inliers (Fig. 4.13). The inner ramp in Sleets Gill Cave also appears to be unrelated to the present topography, and may be very old, but there is no dated material associated with it. Beneath Grassington Moor, the Mossdale High Level Mud Caverns are relict phreatic tunnels at high altitude (Fig. 7.55), but they lie within the Middle Limestone and cannot be related to any known contemporary caves within the Great Scar Limestone. Each of these fragments of cave passage appears to be very old, but their potential ages are barely constrained, and they could date from any time within about half a million years, from well after 1.3 Ma until well before the Anglian glaciation (which started around 478 ka).

How these early caves related to each other is completely unknown, but long cave systems may have been a conspicuous feature of the earliest karst development when there were few outlets southwards from the Great Scar Limestone aquifer. It is likely that initial dissolutional opening of joints and bedding planes developed into very extensive networks of passages that were mainly of small cross section; but widespread enlargement of their passages was terminated when efficient conduits drained over shorter distances to a scatter of resurgences against the Craven Lowlands. The result was the series of isolated cave systems that are now known. Though the Three Counties Cave System (Brook, 1968), wrapped around Gragareth, is now a reality, and may one day extend to Chapel-le-Dale with the exploration of further links, the concept of a 'trans-Craven cave system' (Brook, 1971) is still very short of solid evidence.

A major stage of cave development in the Yorkshire Dales is clearly recognizable as pre-dating the major deepening of the glaciated troughs that subsequently evolved into the main dales in the modern landscape. These caves post-date exposure of the limestone at around 1.3 Ma, and pre-date the Anglian glaciation that started at about 478 ka, but currently

but it could have developed at an early stage on the folded limestones against the Dent Fault. The phreatic trunk route of Duke Street, which underlies Jupiter Cavern, does indicate early karst development between Kingsdale and Ease Gill, which is likely to pre-date 0.5 Ma (Waltham *et al*, 2010), but this was preceded by Jupiter Cavern. East Passage appears to be one of the older parts of the Gaping Gill System, but it is difficult to see how this could have developed before most of the shale cover had been removed from southeastern Ingleborough; that would have taken some considerable time

Figure 7.56. Monster Cavern, a part of the ancient high-levels of the Ease Gill Cave System that has been modified by extensive roof breakdown (photo: Ray Duffy).

available data allow no tighter constraint on their likely ages. Caves of this stage include the large, abandoned, high-level phreatic trunk passages that are a conspicuous feature of many of the known cave systems. They include Montague East Passage in Lancaster Hole and the high-level route through to Ease Gill (Fig. 7.56), various passage segments beneath Leck Fell and Ireby Fell, the Battlefield passages in White Scar Cave (Fig. 7.57), much of the main passage network in the Gaping Gill System, the Passage of Time in Strans Gill Pot, and many more. Stalagmites from these passages that have been dated include a number with ages that could only be recorded as >350 ka (see Chapter 10). The suite of samples is small and none has yet been dated by modern methods that can indicate more precise ages of the older material, but the available data support the concept of pre-Anglian development of many or all of these large old phreatic caves.

These systems all lay below contemporary dale floor levels, and deep phreatic lifts, notably in Gaping Gill and Sleets Gill, indicate that some, and probably most, were at significant depths below their resurgences. These caves may not necessarily have been contemporaneous, but could represent many phases within a very broad, post-1.3-Ma, 'pre-dales' stage. Dated stalagmites from many of these old passages indicate that they were drained prior to about 350 ka (see Chapter 10), and most of the phreatic trunk routes appear to have been active prior to the Anglian glaciation, which started at about 478 ka. They could be even older. It is possible that one of the Cromerian glaciations was more profound than the Anglian, and could have been responsible for major deepening of the dales, in which case these relict, high-level, phreatic caves would pre-date its start at around 659 ka. Flowstone on the wall of the chambers above Aven Pot in Simpson Pot, Kingsdale, yielded a date of 424 ka (Smart *et al.*, 1988), which could imply that the main level of old phreatic passages was drained prior to the Anglian. However, this was a single date by an experimental method using electron spin resonance (see Chapter 10), with an error bar of +/-57 ka, and the calcite deposition could have followed drainage of the cave consequent on Anglian rejuvenation.

Subsequent surface denudation rejuvenated the karst as the dales were progressively entrenched into the Great Scar Limestone. This occurred in repeated cycles throughout much of the Quaternary. Long interglacial phases of slow, fluvial denudation alternated with shorter phases of glacial denudation that caused major deepening of the U-shaped dales. The rejuvenations allowed new suites of caves to develop along drainage lines to lower resurgences, and the multiple phases saw progressive development of the modern, active cave systems. Notably, the greater relief within the karst landscape permitted deeper and more extensive vadose development. White Scar Cave's Main Streamway became vadose right through to its resurgence, as did various small systems that have perched resurgences in the dale sides. However, the dominant pattern became one of vadose caves draining mainly northwards (down the dip) into shallow phreatic loops that turn more to the south and extend to the resurgences; Keld Head and God's Bridge provide the finest examples. The end result is the suite of cave systems within the present karst of the Yorkshire Dales. Most of the caves that are currently active are reasonably well known from their intensive explorations by cavers, but there are still unanswered questions concerning the role, extent and evolution of the earlier Dales caves.

The caves beneath the Pleistocene ice

Most of the larger Dales cave systems have passages that pre-date the Devensian glaciation, and many also pre-date some earlier glaciations. It is clear that much of the cave development took place during warmer, interglacial stages of the Pleistocene, when dissolutional processes were driven by the available biogenic carbon dioxide that became a component of the karst groundwater. The distribution of stalagmite ages confirms that dissolution and precipitation processes were confined largely to these warmer stages (see Chapter 10). Conversely, major reductions in the scale of karst activity during the cold stages of the Pleistocene are indicated by the lack of dated stalagmites from these cold intervals. Colder climates minimized karst dissolution through a reduction of plant cover and consequent reduction of biogenic carbon

Figure 7.58. The static ice plug that blocks the end of Castleguard Cave where it meets the underside of the Columbia Icefield in the Canadian Rockies (TW).

dioxide. The extreme situation was provided by the periods of maximum ice cover when plant activity declined virtually to zero, and, perhaps more significantly, water flows were reduced to little or nothing.

A key question concerning the Dales caves during the Pleistocene glaciations was whether they became blocked and inactive beneath the ice or remained open as sub-glacial meltwater drains. The classic analogy is with Castleguard Cave, which lies partially beneath the Columbia Icefield in the Canadian Rocky Mountains (Ford, 1983; Ford *et al.*, 2000; Waltham 1974c). The long main passage of Castleguard, and its many tributaries end at plugs of ice and debris beneath the icefield floor (Fig. 7.58); they transmit no water into the cave. However, an unseen conduit lies beneath the main cave, and feeds powerful springs below the entrance with flows that show rapid response to melting by solar radiation on the icefield; floodwaters even back up into the older cave system above the active route. Castleguard Cave therefore demonstrates both sub-ice scenarios, of sealed inactivity and of meltwater activity; it also reveals the scale and importance of localized variations. However, it still does not represent an ice sheet that seals the sinks and resurgences of all underlying caves, as occurred in the Dales during the peaks of their major glaciations.

Both the modern Castleguard Cave and the Pleistocene Dales caves respond to the contrasting environments of warm-based ice (also known as temperate ice) and cold-based ice. Warm-based ice has its lower layers at temperatures above the pressure melting point, so meltwater is generated, the glaciers can slide over the terrain and there is considerable erosion of the bedrock. Conversely, cold-based ice does not reach its pressure melting point, so generates no meltwater, and is frozen to the bedrock so that any glacier movement is by deformation of higher ice layers and there is minimal erosion (see Chapter 3). A pattern of activity, with selective erosion by powerful flows of ice along and over the main valleys between areas of slow-moving ice on relatively unscathed highlands, is well-documented in glaciated terrains (Staiger *et al.*, 2005).

Pleistocene ice covered the entire karst of the Yorkshire Dales during the maxima of the cold stages. This ice was cold-based on the high plateaus, and was warm-based at lower elevations within the dales and their ancestral valleys (see Chapter 3). While the archetypal glaciated trough of Littondale was being deepened by a powerful flow of ice, dolines were preserved on the Malham High Country when they were buried by slow-moving ice that had spread from Littondale but had lost its erosive power where it was largely frozen to the limestone. In detail, the limestone outcrops of the Dales were probably covered by a complex mosaic of cold-based and warm-based ice that varied in space and time during the growth and decay stages of each major glaciation, as has been recognized more readily in the uplands of Scandinavia (Klemen *et al.*, 2008). In broad terms, the implications of ice temperatures and erosive impact are that the plateaus and benches on top of the Great Scar Limestone were mainly covered by slow-moving, cold-based ice. Frozen to the ground, any movement in the ice would easily have plucked off thin upper beds of the limestone, and thereby left the great stratimorphic benches on the highest bed that was thick and strong. In the main mass of the limestone, most caves were probably sealed off and dry through most of the cold stages of the Quaternary.

Figure 7.59. A part of Gypsum Cavern, in the high levels of the Ease Gill Cave System, a cave passage formed prior to the Anglian glaciation, partly filled with mud and sand during later stages that included the Devensian glaciation, before being decorated with calcite straws largely since the last retreat of the Dales glaciers; the chamber was named after gypsum crystals that were growing in its floor sediments (photo: Mark Shinwell).

Cave passages close to the dale floors may well have carried meltwater from the soles of the more active ice flows, but even they would have had their entrances easily blocked by injected glacial till, as has been recorded in glaciated karst in Newfoundland (Karolyi and Ford, 1983). Till blockages are known where Dales caves were truncated by glaciers, most famously where the Valley Entrance in Kingsdale was excavated by cavers to gain access to the old Roof Tunnel behind a surface layer of till. Glacio-fluvial sediments left by sub-glacial meltwater have not yet been demonstrated conclusively in the Dales caves. The poorly sorted material in Broadway, in County Pot (Fig. 7.49), may be the result of limited meltwater activity beneath the sluggish ice that occupied the Ease Gill valley in Devensian or earlier times, and unsorted sediments in the Kingsdale end of Dale Barn Cave appear to have been emplaced by sub-glacial water under pressure (Murphy *et al.*, 2001). Sub-glacial environments and meltwater activity would have seen major local variations beneath the Pleistocene ice sheets. There was clearly a boundary between cold-based ice on the Malham High Country and warm-based ice in the Malham Tarn basin if the latter was the source of jökulhlaup floods that enlarged Malham Cove (see Chapter 4). The impact of those floods on the caves behind the Cove remains unknown.

Whereas inactivity was perhaps widespread during the glacial maxima, the caves must have been invaded by meltwater from moulin streams, glacial lakes and glacier snouts during various parts of the retreat phases of each glaciation. Renewed flows of underground water were fed from a landscape devoid of plant cover, plastered with moraines or sheets of loess, and charged by floods of spring snow-melt. They could have carried huge amounts of sediment into the caves, and may account for a large proportion of the stratified muds, sands and gravels that are now distributed through many of the older passages. Ice-dammed lakes may also have been a feature of tributary valleys on and above the limestone when the ice sheets waned and reduced to valley glaciers between nunataks that were gaining in size. Though no firm evidence of such lakes has yet been found in the Yorkshire Dales, they are considered to have been significant features during de-glaciation of the Scandinavian karsts (Faulkner, 2007). As ephemeral features they could have had significant but local impact on some of the caves.

Only when the ice had completely disappeared did the caves and karst of the Dales emerge into something like the modern environment, where they continue to evolve in interglacial conditions.

References

Arthurton, R S, E W Johnson and D J C Mundy, 1988. Geology of the country around Settle. *Memoir of the British Geological Survey*, Sheet 60, 148pp.
Ashmead, P, 1974. The caves and karst of the Morecambe Bay area. 201-226 in Waltham, *op. cit.*.
Atkinson, T C, R S Harmon, P L Smart and A C Waltham, 1978. Palaeoclimatic and geomorphic implications of ^{230}Th/^{234}U Dates on speleothems from Britain. *Nature*, 272, 24-28.
Bögli, A, 1964. Mischungskorrosion: ein Beitrag zur Verkarstungsproblem. *Erdkunde*, 18, 83-92.
Bretz, J H, 1942. Vadose and phreatic features of limestone caverns. *J. Geol.*, 50, 675-811.
Brook, D (B), 1968. The Three Counties System. *Univ. Leeds Spel. Assoc. Review*, 3, 15-19.
Brook, D (B), 1969. The drainage and development of West Kingsdale. *Univ. Leeds Spel. Assoc. Explorations Journal*, 70-73.
Brook, D (B), 1974. Cave development in Kingsdale. 335-342 in Waltham, *op. cit.*.
Brook, D C, 1971. Trans-Craven Cave System. *Bull. Bradford Pothole Club*, 5 (8), 1-4.
Coe, R G, 1968. Birks Fell Cave extensions. *J. Craven Pothole Club*, 4, 11-120.
Cordingley, J N, 1991. Water stratification in active phreatic passages. *Cave Karst Science*, 18, 159.
Curl, R L, 1974. Deducing flow velocity in cave conduits from scallops. *Nat. Spel. Soc. Bull.*, 36, 1-5.
Davies, M, 1974. New Goyden Pot. *Univ. Leeds Spel. Assoc. Review*, 13, 22-24.
Davis, W M, 1930. Origin of limestone caverns. *Bull. Geol. Soc. Am.*, 41, 475-628.
Dreybrodt, W, 1987. The kinetics of calcite dissolution and its consequence to karst evolution from the initial to the mature state. *Nat. Spel. Soc. Bull.*, 49, 31-49.
Dreybrodt, W, 1990. The role of dissolution kinetics in the development of karst aquifers in limestone: a model simulation of karst evolution. *J. Geol.*, 98, 639-655.
Dwerryhouse, A R, 1907. Limestone caverns and potholes and their mode of origin. *J. Yorks. Ramblers Club*, 2 223-228.
Farrant, A R and P L Smart, 2011. Role of sediment in speleogenesis; sedimentation and paragenesis. *Geomorphology*, 134, 79-93.
Faulkner, T, 2006. Limestone dissolution in phreatic conditions at maximum rates and in pure, cold, water. *Cave Karst Science*, 33, 11-20.
Faulkner, T, 2007. The top-down, middle-outwards model of cave development in central Scandinavian marbles. *Cave Karst Science*, 34, 3-16.
Faulkner, T, 2009. Relationships between cave dimensions and local catchment areas in Central Scandinavia: implications for speleogenesis. *Cave Karst Science*, 36, 11-20.
Faulkner, T, 2010. An external model of speleogenesis during Quaternary glacial cycles in the marbles of central Scandinavia. *Cave Karst Science*, 37, 79-92.
Faulkner, T, 2011. Ice-dammed lakes in the central Swedish Mountains. *Grottan*, 46(1), 16-25.
Foley, I, 1930. Lost John's Cave. *J. Yorks. Ramblers Club*, 6, 44-59.
Ford, D C (ed.), 1983. Castleguard Cave and karst, Columbia Icefields area, Rocky Mountains of Canada: a symposium. *Arctic Alpine Res.*, 15, 425-554.
Ford D C and R O Ewers, 1978. The development of limestone cave systems in the dimensions of length and depth. *Can. J. Earth Sci.*, 15, 1783-1798.
Ford, D, S-E Lauritzen and S Worthington, 2000. Speleogenesis of Castleguard Cave, Rocky Mountains, Alberta, Canada. 332-337 in Klimchouk *et al., op. cit.*.
Ford, T D, 2000. Vein cavities: the early evolution of the Castleton cave systems. *Cave Karst Science*, 27, 5-14.
Ford, T D, 2001. Sediments in caves. *BCRA Cave Studies*, 9, 32pp.
Gabrovsek, F and W Dreybrodt, 2000. Role of mixing corrosion in calcite-aggressive $H_2O-CO_2-CaCO_3$ solutions in the early evolution of karst aquifers in limestone. *Water Resources Research*, 36, 1179-1188.
Gascoyne, M and D C Ford., 1984, Uranium-Series dating of speleothems, part II: results from Yorkshire Dales and Implications for cave development and Quaternary climates. *Cave Science*, 11, 65-85.
Gascoyne, M, D C Ford and H P Schwarcz, 1983. Rates of cave and landform development in the Yorkshire Dales from speleothem age data. *Earth Surf. Proc. Land.*, 8, 557-568.
Gascoyne, M, H P Schwarcz and D C Ford, 1983, Uranium-Series ages of speleothem from Northwest England: Correlation with Quaternary climate. *Phil. Trans. Royal Soc. London*, B301, 143-164.
Glover, R R, 1974. Cave development in the Gaping Gill System 343-384 in Waltham (ed.), *op. cit.*.
Halliwell, R A, 1974. A history of karst studies in Yorkshire. *Trans. Brit. Cave Res. Assoc.*, 1, 223-230.
Halliwell, R A, 1979. Influence of contrasted rock types and geological structure on solution processes in north-west Yorkshire. 51-71 in Pitty, A F (ed.), *Geographical Approaches to Fluvial Processes*, Geo Books: Norwich.
Halliwell, R A, 1980. Karst waters of the Ingleborough area, North Yorkshire. *Proc. Univ. Bristol Spel. Soc.*, 15, 183-205.
Harrison, T, 2006. Further phreatic cave systems in Swaledale, North Yorkshire, UK. *Cave Karst Science*, 33, 65-72.
Harrison, T, 2012a. Further phreatic cave systems under the Swaledale-Wensleydale surface watershed in the Yorkshire Dales, UK. *Cave Karst Science*, 39, 23-33.
Harrison, T, 2012b. Phreatic maze caves, Grinton Moor, Swaledale, UK: survey of the Devis Hole Mine Caves. *Cave Karst Science*, 39, 59-62.

Hill, C A, 1987. Geology of Carlsbad Cavern and other caves in the Guadalupe Mountains, New Mexico and Texas. *New Mexico Bureau Mines Mineral Resources Bulletin*, 117, 1-150.

Jones, D M H, 1957. Fairy Hole Cave, Weardale. *J. Yorks. Ramblers Club*, **8**, 118-126.

Karolyi, M S and D C Ford, 1983. The Goose Arm karst, Newfoundland, Canada. *Journ. Hydrol.*, **61**, 181-185.

Kleman, J, A P Stroeven and J Lundqvist, 2008. Patterns of Quaternary ice sheet erosion and deposition in Fennoscandia and a theoretical framework for explanation. *Geomorphology*, **97**, 73-90.

Klimchouk, A B, 2007. *Hypogene Speleogenesis*. National Cave Karst Research Institute: Carlsbad NM, 106pp

Klimchouk, A B, D C Ford, A N Palmer and W Dreybrodt (eds.), *Speleogenesis*. National Speleological Society: Huntsville AL, 527pp..

Lauritzen S E, J Abbot, A Arnesson, G Crossley, D Grepperud, A Ive and S Johnson, 1985. Morphology and hydraulics of an active phreatic conduit. *Cave Science*, **12**, 139-146.

Lowe, D J, 1992. A historical review of concepts of speleogenesis. *Cave Science*, **19**, 63-90.

Lowe, D J, 2000. Role of stratigraphic elements in speleogenesis: the speleoinception concept. 65-76 in Klimchouk *et al.*, *op. cit.*.

Lundberg, J, T C Lord and P J Murphy, 2010. Thermal ionization mass spectrometer U-Th dates on Pleistocene speleothems from Victoria Cave, North Yorkshire, UK: implications for palaeoenvironment and stratigraphy over multiple glacial cycles. *Geosphere*, **6**, 379-395.

Monico, P (ed.), 1995. *Northern Sump Index*. Cave Diving Group: UK, 286pp.

Murphy, P J, 1999. Sediment studies in Joint Hole, Chapel-le-Dale, North Yorkshire, UK. *Cave Karst Science*, **26**, 87-90.

Murphy, P and J Cordingley, 1999. Some observations on the occurrence of channel karren-like features in flooded karst conduits in the Yorkshire Dales. *Cave Karst Science*, **26**, 129-130.

Murphy, P and A Parr, 2004. Late 19th or early 20th century photographs of Hull Pot, North Yorkshire, UK. *Cave Karst Science*, **31**, 91-92.

Murphy, P J, A M Hall and J N Cordingley, 2000. Anomalous scallop distributions in Joint Hole, Chapel-le-Dale, North Yorkshire, UK. *Cave Karst Science*, **27**, 29-32.

Murphy, P J, R Smallshire and C Midgley, 2001. The sediments of Illusion Pot, Kingdsale, UK; evidence for sub-glacial utilisation of a karst conduit in the Yorkshire Dales? *Cave Karst Science*, **28**, 29-34.

Murphy, P J, A Parr, K Strange, G Hunter, S Allshorn, R A Halliwell, J Helm and A R Westerman, 2005. Investigating the nature and origins of Gaping Gill Main Chamber, North Yorkshire, UK, using ground penetrating radar and lidar. *Cave Karst Science*, **32**, 25-38.

Murphy, P, J Cordingley and T Waltham, 2008. New uranium-series dates from Keld Head, Kingsdale, North Yorkshire, UK. *Cave Karst Science*, **35**, 111-114.

Murphy, P, A R Westerman, R Clark, A Booth and A Parr, 2008. Enhancing understanding of breakdown and collapse in the Yorkshire Dales using ground penetrating radar on cave sediments. *Eng. Geol.*, **99**, 160-168.

Myers, J O, 1948. The formation of Yorkshire caves and potholes. *Trans. Cave Res. Gp.*, **1**, 26-29.

Myers, J O, 1963. The major underground drainage systems in the Yoredale limestones of the Askrigg Block. *J. Northern Pennine Club*, **2 (3)**, 43-53.

Mylroie, J E and J L Carew, 1987. Field evidence for the minimum time for speleogenesis. *Nat. Spel. Soc. Bull.*, 49, 67-72.

Newson, M D, 1971. The role of abrasion in caver development. *Trans. Cave Res. Gp.*, **13**, 101-107.

Palmer, A N, 1975. The origin of maze caves. *Nat. Spel. Soc. Bull.*, **37**, 56-76.

Palmer, A N, 1987. Cave levels and their interpretation. *Nat. Spel. Soc. Bull.*, **49**, 50-66.

Palmer, A N, 1991. Origin and morphology of limestone caves. *Geol. Soc. Amer. Bull.*, **103**, 1-21.

Palmer, A N, 2003. Speleogenesis in carbonate rocks. *Speleogenesis*, **1** (1), 1-11.

Palmer, A N, 2007. *Cave Geology*. Cave Books: Dayton OH, 454pp.

Palmer, A N, 2011. Distinction between epigenic and hypogenic maze caves. *Geomorphology*, **134**, 9-22.

Palmer A N and C A Hill, 2005. Sulfuric acid caves. 573-581 in D C Culver and W B White (eds.), *Encyclopedia of Caves*. Elsevier: Burlington MA.

Pappard, P, 1976. Hull Pot. *Bull. Brit. Cave Res. Assoc.*, 15, 7-8.

Raistrick, A, 1954. The calamine mines, Malham, Yorkshire. *Proc. Univ. Durham Phil. Soc.*, **11**, 125-130.

Rauch H W and W B White, 1970. Lithologic controls on the development of solution porosity in carbonate aquifers. *Water Resources Research*, **6**, 1175-1192.

Rauch H W and W B White, 1977. Dissolution kinetics of carbonate rocks: effects of lithology on dissolution rate. *Water Resources Research*, **13**, 381-394.

Ryder, P F, 1975. Phreatic network caves in the Swaledale area, Yorkshire. *Trans. Cave Res. Gp.*, **2**, 177-192.

Ryder, P F, 1981. Cliff Force Cave. *J. Craven Pothole Club*, **6**, 132-135.

Simpson, E, 1935. Notes on the formation of the Yorkshire caves and potholes. *Proc. Univ. Bristol. Spel. Soc.*, **4**, 224-232.

Skoglund, R O, 2011. Subglacial maze origin in low-dip marble stripe karst: examples from Norway. *J. Cave Karst Studies*, **73**, 31-43.

Smart, P L, B W Smith, H Chandra, J N Andrews and M C R Symons, 1988. An intercomparison of ESR and uranium-series ages for Quaternary speleothem calcites. *Quat. Sci. Rev.*, **7**, 411-416.

Staiger, J K W, J C Gosse, J V Johnson, J Fastook, J T Gray, D F Stockli, L Tockli and R Finfel, 2005. Quaternary relief generation by polythermal glacier ice. *Earth Surf. Proc. Land.*, **30**, 1145-1159.

Sutcliffe, J R, 1985. Knock Fell Caverns. *J. Gritstone Club*, (1985), 70-74.

Sweeting, M M, 1950. Erosion cycles and limestone caverns in the Ingleborough district. *Geog. J.*, **115**, 63-78.

Sweeting, M M and G S Sweeting, 1969. Some aspects of the Carboniferous limestone in relation to its landforms. *Mediterranée*, **7**, 201-209.

Swinnerton, A C, 1932. Origin of limestone caverns. *Bull. Geol. Soc. Am.*, **43**, 663-693.

Thrailkill, J V, 1968. Chemical and hydrologic factors in the excavation of limestone caves. *Bull. Geol. Soc. Am.*, **79**, 19-45.

Waltham, A C, 1970. Cave development in the limestone of the Ingleborough district. *Geog. J.*, **136**, 574-585.

Waltham, A C, 1971a. Shale units in the Great Scar Limestone of the southern Askrigg Block. *Proc. Yorks. Geol. Soc.*, **38**, 285-292.

Waltham, A C, 1971b. Controlling factors in the development of limestone caves. *Trans. Cave Res. Gp.*, **13**, 73-80.

Waltham, A C (ed.), 1974a. *Limestones and Caves of North-west England*. David and Charles (for British Cave Research Association): Newton Abbot, 477pp.

Waltham, A C, 1974b. Speleogenesis of the caves of Leck Fell. 273-309 in Waltham (ed), *op. cit.*.

Waltham, A C, 1974c. Castleguard Cave, Canada. *Bull. Brit. Cave Res. Assoc.*, 5, 18-28.

Waltham, A C, 1977a. White Scar Cave, Ingleton. *Trans. Brit. Cave Res. Assoc.*, **4**, 345-353.

Waltham, A C, 1977b. Cave development at the base of the limestone in Yorkshire. *Proc. 7th Int. Spel. Cong.* (Sheffield, UK), 421-423.

Waltham, A C and R S Harmon, 1977. Chronology of cave development in the Yorkshire Dales, England. *Proc. 7th Int. Spel. Cong.* (Sheffield, UK), 423-425.

Waltham A C and P Hatherley, 1983. The caves of Leck Fell. *Cave Science*, **10**, 245-247.

Waltham, A C, D B Brook, O W Statham and T G Yeadon, 1981. Swinsto Hole, Kingsdale: a type example of cave development in the limestone of Northern England. *Geog. J.*, **147**, 350-353.

Waltham, A C, M J Simms, A R Farrant and H S Goldie, 1997. *Karst and Caves of Great Britain*. Chapman & Hall (for Joint Nature Conservation Committee): London, 358pp.

Waltham, T, F Bell and M Culshaw, 2005. *Sinkholes and Subsidence*. Springer: Berlin, 382pp.

Waltham, T and H Long, 2011. Limestone plateaus of the Yorkshire Dales glaciokarst. *Cave and Karst Science*, **38**, 65-70.

Waltham, T, P Murphy and A Batty, 2010. Kingsdale: the evolution of a Yorkshire dale. *Proc. Yorks. Geol. Soc.*, **58**, 95-105.

White, W B, 1988. *Geomorphology and Hydrology of Karst Terrains*. Oxford University Press, 464pp.

Worthington, S R H, 2004. Hydraulic and geological factors influencing conduit flow depth. *Cave and Karst Science*, **31**, 123-134.

Worthimgton, S R H, 2005. Evolution of caves in response to base-level lowering. *Cave and Karst Science*, **32**, 3-12.

Geological influences on the caves

David Lowe

Whereas the processes and mechanisms of cave development and passage enlargement, in the Yorkshire Dales and elsewhere, are fairly well known (see Chapter 7), there is still much to understand about the true origins of the caves and the factors that influence their first stages of growth. These first phases in the evolution of a cave are known as its inception, when dissolutional processes were initiated wherever groundwater could move across surfaces of the limestone. A cave's inception phase is influenced dominantly by geological features within the host limestone, because it is they that can be exploited to create drainage paths through a rock mass that is almost impermeable in its initial state. Once the tortuous inception phase is completed, through-drainage of chemically aggressive waters can enlarge and develop a cave system with relative ease, but the geological influences on the inception phase are inherited and are thereby imprinted on the patterns of subsequent cave development.

Open fractures in a limestone can be developed by tectonic stresses, as joints or faults, without any initial dissolutional activity, and can subsequently evolve into open caves. But a very large proportion of cave passages are developed on bedding planes and stratigraphical features that relate to the lithology of the limestone independent of any tectonic deformation. These bedding features that are favourable to speleogenesis are known as inception horizons, and are clearly fundamental to cave evolution and the subsequent development of large cave systems.

Inception horizons were first named and described in the limestones and caves of the Yorkshire Dales (Lowe, 2000, 2004; Lowe and Gunn, 1997). Concepts of cave inception took a step forward when it was recognised that cave passages following the bedding were not simply influenced by the thin shale beds that are conspicuous in nearly all Dales caves. Speleogenesis is dependent on inception horizons that relate to very subtle details of the limestone lithology, combinations of which can provide favourable conditions for the first stages of dissolutional activity.

The concept of the inception horizon is now widely accepted (Filipponi et al., 2009), but is still maturing and is under continuing review (Lowe and Waters, 2013). There is already a clear need for specific fieldwork in the Dales, on the surface and within the caves, to improve the related dataset and refine application of the inception concept within the karst where it originated. Consequently this overview is a report on progress in a key step towards understanding the caves and karst of the Dales.

Geological influences on caves, by David Lowe,
Nottingham; drdjlowe@yahoo.co.uk
Chapter 8, pages 147-152 in **Caves and Karst of the Yorkshire Dales**,
edited by Tony Waltham and David Lowe.
Published 2013 by the British Cave Research Association,
978-0-900265-46-4 and at www.bcra.org.uk

Inception horizons in limestone

Inception horizons are stratigraphical intervals that favour early void creation (Lowe, 2000, 2004; Lowe and Gunn, 1997). Most are strong lithological contrasts between limestone types or between limestone and non-carbonate rock, and where exposed in caves some appear as prominent bedding planes (Fig. 8.1). Reflecting the cyclic deposition of many carbonate successions, some inception horizons are marked by shale, micrite or dolomite-rich partings.

Deposition of the Dales limestones included major sea-level oscillations related to global changes that imposed depositional cyclicity (Ramsbottom, 1973; and see Chapter 2). During periodic regressions burial pressure drove connate fluids from the sediment pile, much of it along zones between relatively porous, coarse-grained sediment above and less porous, fine-grained sediment below; these zones were incipient inception horizons (Fig. 8.2). As each cycle terminated, fluid transfer continued during diagenesis, focussed mainly at the major cycle boundaries where lithological contrast was greatest.

On the southern Askrigg Block the entire limestone succession was eventually buried beneath at least 500m of younger Carboniferous rocks, and inception processes continued. More connate fluids bled from the rocks, following embryonic inception horizons along primitive regional hydraulic gradients towards outputs in adjacent basins, which might have been tens of kilometres distant. It is uncertain how long connate fluids alone were involved; meteoric water passing from adjacent porous rocks or entering the limestone via fractures might, in due course, have exploited and enhanced the immature karstic permeability. After initially slow imprinting of the inception horizons, speleogenesis accelerated when buried rocks were

Figure 8.1. *The entrance passage of Stonelands Cave, in Littondale, with its roof along a bedding plane that was the inception horizon on which the cave initially developed (photo: Dave Hodgson).*

Figure 8.2. A clean bedding plane roof over a small canyon passage in Southerscales Pot; a thin shale parting, barely exposed and partly obscured by flowstone on both walls, marks the inception horizon on which the cave originated (photo: Mark Shinwell).

uplifted and exposed by landscape denudation. Regional hydraulic gradients along inception horizons were dissected by surface valleys, creating local hydraulic gradients (Lowe and Gunn, 1997), but contemporary underflow continued towards remote outlets or into adjacent basins via deeper, less-efficient, inception horizons.

The limestones of the Yorkshire Dales are the products of several major depositional cycles, each beginning when the Carboniferous sea transgressed the existing basement landmass or pre-existing limestones, and ending when, eventually, the sea withdrew. Potentially, each major cycle included several minor cycles (see below), with variations that reflect water depth and environmental changes. After reaching a maximum early in the cycle, depth tended to decrease as sediment built up on the sea floor. The grading of minor cycles is reflected in the joint rhythms, with upper parts being characterised by a finer grain-size (Doughty, 1968). However, grading within minor and major cycles is complex and is generally less predictable than theoretical expectation.

Within the Great Scar Limestone, each major cycle ends with a bed of fine-grained, chemically precipitated limestone (originally overlain by more soluble evaporite salts that are rarely preserved) and is overlain by coarse detrital limestones of the next transgression (Table 8.1). Palaeokarstic surfaces are common at major cycle boundaries and some minor cycle boundaries, where the lower unit was temporarily above sea-level during marine regression, before re-submergence initiated deposition of the next cycle. Some karstified boundaries also include thin, or locally thick, beds of shale

or other clastic rocks. Interplay of external geographical, topographical, climatic and tectonic factors during deposition ensured that sequences are rarely simple and predictable; parts of some cycles were not deposited, other components were lost to dissolution, and still others were repeated.

Timescales of inception

It is safe to assume that deposition of the Dinantian limestones that now form the Dales was punctuated by long periods of non-deposition and erosion. During these phases all manner of changes, including karstic dissolution, affected the sediment and rocks from previous cycles. These processes contributed to the inception stage of caves that only evolved to maturity many millions of years later (Fig. 8.3).

Syngenetic development of caves within just a few thousand years in very young limestones on tropical islands is now well documented (White, 2000; Mylroie, 2004). During the Dinantian, similar conditions prevailed along the southern margin of the Askrigg Block, leading to development of the reef belt of the Cracoe Limestone Formation. The analogy implies that syngenetic cavities of cave dimensions almost certainly existed in the reef belt, if not also elsewhere, during the latter half of the Dinantian. It is also reasonable to assume that karstification, including at least primitive development of dissolutional permeability, was active across the Askrigg Block during regressional hiatuses. Whether any cave-sized voids survived a further three hundred million years of burial, diagenesis, tectonism and erosion remains unproven, but it is likely that permeability development was well under way before the end of the Dinantian.

Explaining how meteoric water remains aggressive, despite constant contact with excess limestone in fissures that initially are virtually closed, has been a major hurdle in understanding cave development by carbonic acid. The paradox is resolved by recognition that there are no threshold widths below which the karstification of laterally extensive but narrow fissures is impossible (Palmer, 1981; Dreybrodt, 1990; Palmer, 1991; Dreybrodt et al. 2005). Timescales of the earliest fissure widening are extremely long, and sub-micron-wide fracture systems several kilometres in length take up to 10 million years to achieve widths of 0.1 mm (Faulkner, 2006).

The reefs are a mixture of fine, calcite-mudstone and coarser fossiliferous lithologies. Appearing massive overall, they include random patches of bedded limestone, with traces of original depositional dips up to 35° in some hills. Everywhere the limestone is well fractured, with some mineralisation. A few caves are known within the reefs, and

lithology	permeability	inception role
shale, seatearth, coal	significant primary	sulphuric acid from pyrite
calcite mudstone (*micrite*) [dolomite, evaporites]	impermeable, or with palaeo-karstification	sulphuric acid from evaporites
oolitic limestone	some primary permeability	location for early dissolution
bioclastic limestone (*sparite*) pale and thickly bedded [*most of the cycle thickness*]	initially impermeable	dissolution only in tectonic fissures
dark, thin-bedded limestone	initially impermeable	dissolution only in tectonic fissures

Table 8.1. Lithologies that form a single depositional cycle within the Dinantian limestones of the Askrigg Block. The cycle evolved through progressively decreasing water depth, and was terminated by a phase of sea-level rise or tectonic subsidence. A complete cycle would have a thin mudstone at its base, but this is rarely present within the Dales karst. The dolomite and evaporite beds are commonly absent in the Dales, and any original evaporite salts may have been lost to early dissolution. The shale unit at the top of the cycle may include volcanic fallout (condensed from Lowe, 2000).

Figure 8.3. Monster Cavern, on the high-level passage between Ease Gill and Lancaster Hole, was formed along an important inception horizon that now forms the bedding plane roof of the chamber; a series of dissolutional openings and channels developed on the inception horizon are exposed in profile along the top of the chamber wall (photo: Mark Shinwell).

some have vein-related cavities with phreatic rock-pendants. Elbolton Pot and other caves in the reef belt possibly originated during or soon after reef growth; they resemble syngenetic cavities in young limestones on subtropical islands (Gunn and Lowe, 2000).

Shale beds as inception horizons

Non-carbonate rocks in the Dales succession comprise sandstones, siltstones, coals, cherts and shaley mudstones (commonly known as shales) (Fig. 8.4). The latter include bentonite-rich clays derived mainly as airborne fallout from distant explosive volcanoes, resembling, but less abundant than, Derbyshire's clay wayboards (Walkden, 1972, 1974; Ford, 1977). They also include residual soils and seatearths, related to palaeokarstic activity. Some Dales examples are associated with thin discontinuous coals. Mudstones also formed by slow accumulation of fine clastic debris derived from distant land areas; rare sandstone and siltstone beds had similar but more local origins.

Though long recognised as important, the speleogenetic role of shale beds was initially partly misunderstood. Shales exposed in Dales caves were described as aquicludes that caused perching of water moving downwards through the limestone (Waltham, 1971a, 1971b). Undoubtedly this was the case at some sites, but it demands that limestone must already be permeable before significant shale influence was possible; it also assumes that speleogenetic fluids inevitably move downwards. In some situations the role of shales is more complex, with involvement beginning far earlier in

the development of voids, in association with the initial imprinting of inception horizons (see below).

Clayey layers also facilitate slip during fold development and faulting. Slip of beds in folds can generate increased permeability within some zones along the contacts. In some situations folding creates open voids between beds in fold cores and adjacent to related fractures (Dodwell *et al.,* 2012). Shaley pods that are more susceptible to erosion than adjacent limestone are also commonly produced. Such possibilities have received little attention in the Dales, but the giant cave passages in Slovenia's Škocjanske jame cross 62 bedding planes whereas its development was guided by only three planes, which had suffered lubricated slip (Knez, 1998).

Some shale horizons provide atypical chemical conditions that enhance early dissolution within carbonate successions, notably with contained minerals that undergo chemical breakdown. Pyrite is common in shale beds, and is important because its weathering produces sulphuric acid, which can be a significant aid to early void creation (Durov, 1956).

Whereas shales can be aquicludes, their role in cave inception is more complex. Primitive void inception by enhanced dissolution at limestone contacts beneath and above shales possibly occurs during early dewatering. Interbedded shale, siltstone and sandstone sediments also provide relatively porous pathways for connate fluid movement before significant permeability develops in adjacent low-porosity limestones. Whereas laterally-persistent chert beds might also act as aquicludes, cherts within the main limestone succession tend to be discontinuous. Chemical reactions between clay minerals and adjacent carbonates, particularly dolomitic beds, accelerate permeability development and inception of proto-channels (Pezdič *et al.,* 1998).

Inception in the Great Scar Limestone

Many horizons potentially favour speleogenesis in the Dales, but few behave ubiquitously as preferred inception horizons across wide areas. Those so far identified correspond to major cycle boundaries or to particularly well-marked minor cycle boundaries within major cycles. Less favourable examples act as inception horizons under specific, locally advantageous, circumstances. Only some shale beds (Waltham, 1971a) are major inception horizons, but all potentially influence cave development when other factors are favourable, and some certainly act as minor inception horizons locally.

Figure 8.4. A shale bed about 40 cm thick at the top of the wall of a passage in the Ease Gill Cave System (TW).

Figure 8.5. The Porcellanous Bed, which is the major Inception Horizon 2, exposed at roof-level in the entrance passage of Scoska Cave, Littondale, where it was the guiding influence on development of the passage (TW).

The main sequence of the Great Scar Limestone in the southern Dales belongs to three major cycles (Ramsbottom, 1973), corresponding approximately to the Arundian, Holkerian and Asbian substages (see Chapter 2), and these contain four major inception horizons (Table 8.2).

Inception Horizon 4 is widely marked by non-carbonate beds, including the Salt Lake Mudstone around much of Ingleborough (Turner, 1968) and the Notts Pot coal on Leck Fell. Horizon 3 is distinguished by major palaeokarst at the mid-Asbian Break, between two minor cycles within the Asbian Gordale Limestone. It is commonly marked by a generally thin but locally abnormally thick shale related to high-relief palaeokarst, indicating longer periods of emergence and more extreme karstification than that between adjacent minor cycles.

Inception Horizon 2 (at the Asbian/Holkerian boundary) lies close to or locally coincident with a zone rich in micritic limestones, including the Porcellanous Bed (see Chapter 2). This bed has long been recognised as important to speleogenesis across most of the Craven Dales (Glover,

1973, 1974, 1976). It is not present everywhere, and locally develops as multiple horizons (see Chapter 2), but where recognised it indicates the approximate position of the cycle boundary, and bedding-related caves occur above, below or within it (Fig. 8.5). Elsewhere a notable palaeokarst marks the same cycle boundary, indicating prolonged emergence, dewatering and karstification. Inception Horizon 1 is the conspicuous lithological contrast between the dark and thinly bedded Kilnsey Formation and the overlying pale and massive Cove Limestone.

One more major inception horizon is likely to exist at the Holkerian/Arundian boundary within the Kilnsey Limestone (see Chapter 2), but this is widely cut out by relief of the basement rocks and has not yet been identified as influencing speleogenesis in the caves that do extend down to its level.

These four major inception horizons are each separated by about 50m within the Great Scar Limestone (Fig. 8.6), but considerable lateral variation within the sequence means that this is only an approximate figure (see Chapter 2). Another widespread marker horizon, known as the Girvanella Bed, is only a minor inception horizon and lies within the Hawes Limestone above the sequence shown in Table 8.2.

Further inception horizons and structures

Superimposed on and interleaving with the recognised major inception horizons, there are numerous minor inception horizons that are recognisable by their local influence on cave passages. Whereas their importance to cave inception and speleogenesis is undeniable, mapping and definition of them is fraught with problems, largely due to the difficulties of correlating them between individual exposures above and below ground. Existing geological data have not been integrated into a comprehensible record of the limestone stratigraphy. The single major cycle represented by the Asbian Gordale Limestone has been divided into ten minor cycles in Kingsdale (Murray Mitchell, *pers comm*), though farther east the same sequence was previously divided into nine minor cycles on the basis of both its lithology (Schwarzacher, 1958)

lithology	stratigraphy	examples of cave development
	Lower Hawes Limestone	
extensive shale beds Notts Pot coal Salt Lake Mudstone	**Inception Horizon 4**	Swinsto Hole Long Crawl Upper Long Churn Cave Penyghent Pot Canal
	upper Gordale Limestone	
thick shale bed with palaeokarst channels	**Inception Horizon 3**	Lost Johns Cave Shale Cavern Ireby Fell Cavern Glory Holes
	lower Gordale Limestone	
Porcellanous Bed, or prominent bedding plane where it is absent	**Inception Horizon 2**	Notts Pot Notts 2 streamway Ireby Fell Cavern Duke Street Kingsdale Master Cave and Roof Tunnel Gaping Gill Cave Hensler's Crawls, South Passages and Whitsun Series Scoska Cave
	Cove Limestone	
conspicuous bedding plane widely with shale and pyrite above darker limestones	**Inception Horizon 1**	Ingleborough Cave main passage Malham Cove Rising Sleets Gill Cave Hydrophobia
	Kilnsey Limestone	

Table 8.2. The four highest major inception horizons that have been a powerful influence on cave development across a large part of the Yorkshire Dales. Only a few examples of passages are listed for each horizon. Between these major horizons there are many minor inception horizons that have local influence and may be neither laterally extensive nor continuous. The major horizons are numbered only with respect to this table, and there is probably another beneath these shown.

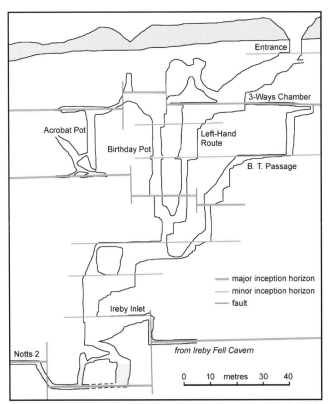

Figure 8.6. *Highly simplified profile, partly projected and partly extended, of some of the shafts and passages in the vertical maze of Notts Pot, on Gragareth. Major and minor inception horizons are indicated; some are displaced by minor faults that lie on various orientations relative to this profile; the various faults lie in different planes that are projected onto the profile, and the multiple passages are also projected, so not all the marked faults affect all the inception horizons; some thicknesses between horizons are only apparent where they are affected by fault displacements and the limestone dip.*

Figure 8.7. *Cave inception along the intersection of a vertical fracture and a bedding plane, which has evolved into a straight and level passage in Ingleborough Cave (photo: John Cordingley).*

Figure 8.8. *The daylight shaft of Jingling Pot, Kingsdale, with its lenticular section extended along the line of its inception fracture, which is probably a strike-slip fault with only a small vertical displacement (photo: Jerry Wooldridge).*

and its joint densities (Doughty, 1968). Neither the ten nor the nine cycles could be correlated with shale beds mapped within the caves (Waltham, 1971a), and subsequent better cave surveys have revealed even more complexity to the shale beds beneath Gragareth (Fig. 7.27); the surface mapping also indicated considerable variation between lithologies within the cycles. The exact structure, nature and distribution of the minor inception horizons within the Great Scar Limestone is not yet fully defined, though their local influence on cave development is clearly visible.

Difficulties in defining the minor inception horizons extend to defining details of the major horizons. This is significant where an horizon is masked within a cluster of closely spaced shale beds that exhibit marked variation between exposures in adjacent caves and there is no means of confirming any correlations through the unexposed rock sequence. Marking the four major inception horizons on the cave surveys shown in Figure 7.27 will only be possible after an underground field programme of re-survey and targeted geological mapping. The exception to that is Inception Horizon 2, which is on or close to the widely recognisable Porcellanous Bed, but even this has difficulties where the Bed is locally absent or split into multiple leaves.

Inception horizons have not been mapped within the Yoredale limestones, which are generally so thinly bedded that cave inception probably could have occurred at numerous horizons that are very closely spaced. Within most of the Yoredale limestones, cave inception and speleogenesis have been dominated by dense networks of joints, as is most obvious within the maze caves of the northern Dales.

Cave inception in the Great Scar Limestone has also taken place on many of the joints and faults that are conspicuous elements of the geology across the Dales. These structures provide important inception pathways that link the widespread inception horizons and thereby allow caves to develop right through the sequence of bedded limestones. Because they owe their existence to physical opening under tectonic stress they do not require any of the special chemical characteristics that distinguish an inception horizon, and there are therefore no parameters that can be used to identify or classify them. Numerous long and straight rift passages are clear evidence of cave inception on fractures either forming links between, or at intersections with, inception horizons (Fig. 8.7), and the waterfall shafts in almost every Dales cave evolved from inception on sub-vertical joints and faults (Figs 8.8 and 8.9).

Influence of the inception stage

Karst evolution depends upon establishment of a functional underground drainage system, and the Dales are well served by underground drains that follow local hydraulic gradients. Yet, visible or implied relationships of passage segments indicate that regional drainage systems existed long before the current landscape evolved. Dimensions reached by these drains before their interception by incising valleys are unknown, and it is unclear whether they originated solely by inception and dissolution prior to uplift and exposure. Such a primitive system, imprinted while the limestone was buried, presents interlinked implications for where and how the earliest surface karst features might have developed. Surface karstification began at structurally favourable points where the limestone was first unroofed (see Chapter 4), but how initial karst features impacted upon wider landscape development is unknown. Little effort has been focussed on such issues to date; it may be that innovative development modelling, on a scale that is now feasible, is a way towards gaining a full understanding of the geological features that influenced the origin and evolution of caves and karst in the Dales.

References

Dodwell, T, G Hunt, M Peletier and C Budd, 2012. Multi-layered folding with voids. *Phil. Trans. Roy. Soc.*, **A370**, 1740–1758.

Doughty, P S, 1968. Joint densities and their relation to lithology in the Great Scar Limestone. *Proc. Yorks. Geol. Soc.*, **36**, 479–543.

Dreybrodt, W, 1990. The role of dissolution kinetics in the development of karst aquifers in limestone: a model simulation of karst evolution. *J. Geology*, **98**, 639–655.

Dreybrodt, W, F Gabrovsek and D Romanov, 2005. *Processes of Speleogenesis: a Modeling Approach.* Zalozba ZRC: Postojna, 376pp.

Durov, S A, 1956. On the question about the origin of salt composition of karst waters. *Ukrainian Chemical J.*, **22**. [English translation in *Cave Geology*, **1**, 186–190, 1979]

Faulkner, T, 2006. Limestone dissolution in phreatic conditions at maximum rates and in pure, cold, water. *Cave Karst Science*, **33**, 11–20.

Filipponi, M, P-Y Jeannin and L Tacher, 2009. Evidence of inception horizons in karst conduit networks. *Geomorphology*, **106**, 86–99.

Ford, T D (ed.), 1977. *Limestones and Caves of the Peak District.* Geo Books: Norwich, 469pp.

Glover, R R, 1973, Gaping Gill – some underground controls of development. *Craven Pothole Club J.*, **5**, 8–11.

Glover, R R, 1974, Gaping Gill – some underground controls of development; part 2: the Porcellanous Band and its control of passage levels. *Craven Pothole Club J.*, **5**, 58–65.

Glover, R R, 1976. The Porcellanous Band in Yorkshire caves. *Brit. Cave Res. Assoc. Bull.*, 12, 11–12.

Gunn, J and D J Lowe, 2000. Speleogenesis on tectonically active carbonate islands. 238–243 in A B Klimchouk, D C Ford, A N Palmer and W Dreybrodt (eds), *Speleogenesis: Evolution of Karst Aquifers.* National Speleological Society: Huntsville AL.

Knez, M, 1998. The influence of bedding-planes on the development of karst caves (a study of Velika Dolina at Škocjanske Jame caves, Slovenia). *Carbonates and Evaporites*, **13**, 121–131.

Lowe, D J, 2000. Role of stratigraphic elements in speleogenesis: the speleoinception concept. 65–76 in A B Klimchouk, D C Ford, A N Palmer and W Dreybrodt (eds), *Speleogenesis: Evolution of Karst Aquifers.* National Speleological Society: Huntsville AL.

Lowe, D J, 2004. Inception of caves. 437–441 in J Gunn (ed.), *Encyclopedia of Caves and Karst Science.* Fitzroy Dearborn: New York.

Lowe, D J and J Gunn, 1997. Carbonate speleogenesis: an inception horizon hypothesis. *Acta Carsologica*, **26**, 457–488.

Lowe, D J and C N Waters, 2013. Geological influences on cave development in the Yorkshire Dales. *Cave Karst Science*, **40**, in press.

Mylroie, J, 2004. Speleogenesis: coastal and oceanic settings. 674–677 in J Gunn (ed.), *Encyclopedia of Caves and Karst Science.* Fitzroy Dearborn: New York.

Palmer, A N, 1981. Hydrochemical factors in the origin of limestone caves. *Proc. 8th Int. Spel. Cong.* (Bowling Green KY), 120–122.

Palmer, A N, 1991. Origin and morphology of limestone caves. *Geol. Soc. Amer. Bull.*, **103**, 1–21.

Pezdič, J, F Šušteršič and M Mišič, 1998. On the role of clay-carbonate reactions in speleo-inception: a contribution to the understanding of the earliest stage of karst channel formation. *Acta Carsologica*, **27**, 187–200.

Ramsbottom, W H C, 1973. Transgressions and regressions in the Dinantian: a new synthesis of British Dinantian stratigraphy. *Proc. Yorks. Geol. Soc.*, **39**, 567–607.

Schwarzacher, W, 1958. The stratification of the Great Scar Limestone in the Settle district of Yorkshire. *Liverpool Manchester Geol. J.*, **2**, 124–142.

Turner, J S, 1968. A note on the Meal Bank coal horizon around Ingleborough. *Trans. Leeds Geol. Assoc.*, **7**, 265–268.

Walkden, G M, 1972. The mineralogy and origin of interbedded clay wayboards in the Lower Carboniferous of the Derbyshire Dome. *Geol. J.*, **8**, 143–159.

Walkden, G M, 1974. Palaeokarstic surfaces in Upper Visean (Carboniferous) Limestones of the Derbyshire block, England. *J. Sedimentary Petrology*, **44**, 1232–1247.

Waltham, A C, 1971a. Shale units in the Great Scar Limestone of the southern Askrigg Block. *Proc. Yorks. Geol. Soc.*, **38**, 285–292.

Waltham, A C, 1971b. Controlling factors in the development of caves. *Trans. Cave Res. Gp. G.B.*, **13**, 73–80.

White, S, 2000. Syngenetic karst in coastal dune limestones: a review. 234–237 in A B Klimchouk, D C Ford, A N Palmer and W Dreybrodt (eds), *Speleogenesis: Evolution of Karst Aquifers.* National Speleological Society: Huntsville AL.

Figure 8.9. The main shaft of Alum Pot, 50m deep and open to daylight, is developed on the multiple fractures of a minor fault zone, but subsiduary inception horizons are indicated by the dissolutional notches along the bedding planes exposed in the shaft walls (photo: Dave Ryall).

CHAPTER 9

Hydrogeology of the karst

John Gunn and Simon Bottrell

In common with other Carboniferous age limestones in Britain the limestones in the Yorkshire Dales transmit groundwater through underground flow-paths that range in size from millimetres to cave passages (Fig. 9.1). The most important groundwater unit is the Great Scar Limestone which forms such a conspicuous component of the Dales landscape. The Dales limestones are classed by the Environment Agency as being local aquifers, with springs and small numbers of boreholes that provide water for agriculture and domestic supply, but the area's limestone groundwater is of far greater importance in providing base flow to the surface rivers that drain out of the area.

Porosity and permeability of the limestone

The key hydrogeological characteristics of the Great Scar Limestone are its porosity and its permeability. Porosity is the ratio of the volume of voids in the rock mass to the total bulk volume; normally expressed as a percentage, in a saturated rock this is the amount of water stored within it. Permeability indicates the ease with which a fluid can flow through the rock mass; it is measured as the rate at which a volume of fluid can pass through a cross-sectional area of rock, and is expressed in units of length per unit time (conventionally metres per second, though metres per day can provide more accessible numbers). Though these units are the same as those for velocity, they do not indicate the speed with which the water actually moves. That depends on the rock porosity and the gravitational forces driving the flow. In general, the permeability of a rock mass depends on the aperture of the largest voids that traverse it. Thus the permeability due to cave passages is many times larger than that of fractures, which in turn is much greater than the permeability of very small intergranular pore spaces within the rock itself. A distinction is therefore made between primary porosity and permeability (measured in solid, unfractured rock) and secondary porosity and permeability (referring to flow through planar voids such as bedding planes, joints and faults). The term 'permeability' is used here in an informal sense to describe the ease with which water can flow through the ground, which is formally known as hydraulic conductivity (in the technical literature, permeability has a more specialized meaning where it can also describe the movement of fluids with differing viscosities, such as oil or gas).

The primary properties are commonly referred to as the matrix porosity and matrix permeability. The latter is dependant on the absolute value of the former, but is also controlled by the pore geometry within the rock, particularly the degree to which pores are interconnected and the size of the throats between pores through which flowing water has to pass. Secondary porosity, commonly described as fracture porosity, can make it significantly easier for a fluid to pass though a body of rock, and thereby supports much higher values of secondary, or fracture, permeability. The presence of these two forms of porosity and permeability leads to the development of a dual-porosity aquifer, in which groundwater is present both in primary porosity (where it is relatively immobile due to lower primary permeability) and in secondary porosity (where it is relatively mobile in a fracture network that offers a higher permeability). This applies to most dense rocks, including most well-lithified sedimentary rocks, and is a key feature of the Dales limestones.

A third type of porosity and permeability is developed in limestones and other rocks that are subject to dissolution by groundwater, where the most active flow routes become enlarged over time, resulting in a highly heterogeneous and anisotropic tertiary porosity. Water flows through dissolutionally enlarged openings in interconnected systems of channels. As these channels mature, the flows become more directed and convergent towards a spring or a group of springs.

Figure 9.1. *Groundwater cascades down a chamber wall in Marble Steps Pot, under the slopes of Gragareth (TW).*

Hydrogeology of the karst, by John Gunn and Simon Bottrell,
John Gunn, University of Birmingham; j.gunn.1@bham.ac.uk
Simon Bottrell, University of Leeds; s.bottrell@earth.leeds.ac.uk
Chapter 9, pages 153-168 in **Caves and Karst of the Yorkshire Dales**,
edited by Tony Waltham and David Lowe.
Published 2013 by the British Cave Research Association,
978-0-900265-46-4 and at www.bcra.org.uk

Figure 9.2. The Main Drain in the Ease Gill Cave System is the master conduit of a large dendritic cave system, and lies about 300m away from (to the left in this view looking upstream), and 60m below the level of, the valley of Ease Gill, which is dry except after heavy rainfall events (TW).

When a channel's diameter becomes large enough (generally >10 mm) for turbulent flow it is commonly referred to as a conduit, and when conduits become sufficiently large for human exploration they are known as caves. Such is the case in any karst limestone, and the hydrogeology in the Yorkshire Dales of both the Great Scar Limestone and the limestones of the overlying Yoredale Group have to be viewed in terms of these three types of porosity and permeability.

Channels, conduits and caves are three points along a continuum of void sizes, and they are commonly referred to as the conduit porosity and permeability. Within a karst aquifer, a useful distinction can be made between diffuse flow within the matrix and fractures of the limestone, and conduit flow through the caves (Atkinson, 1977). However, it is recognised that these are also points on a continuum of flow paths. The underground drainage systems of the Dales are characterised by having conduit flow, but they do have important tributary elements within the limestone matrix and its fractures.

Based on sound understanding of the processes of carbonate rock dissolution, numerical models can simulate the development of permeability in carbonate rocks (Worthington and Gunn, 2009). The general conclusion of these models is that, within most natural situations, channels with apertures as narrow as 0.1 mm can reach conduit dimensions within periods of 10,000 to a million years. Conduits can subsequently be enlarged much more rapidly, potentially reaching cave dimensions in only a few thousand years. However, only a small proportion of channels become conduits and only a small proportion of conduits become caves (Fig. 9.2), so that any cave must be visualised as part of a network of tributary conduits and channels. Flow through carbonate rocks leads to the formation of self-organized channel networks with rapid groundwater flow (Worthington and Ford, 2009). The drainage networks within the Dales limestones are highly anisotropic and are broadly akin to those of surface streams, albeit in three-dimensions. They bear little resemblance to the coherent bodies of groundwater moving through porous aquifers such as sandstone.

In unconfined aquifers in porous rocks the interface between the unsaturated (vadose) and saturated (phreatic) zones is called the water table, but typically this is poorly defined in karst. Phreatic conduits, full of water, are commonly found above the zone where all the matrix and fracture voids are water-filled, and vadose conduits may pass beneath other vadose conduits or beneath surface streams. The cave

systems of the Yorkshire Dales include examples of every combination of dry galleries, open streamways and flooded passages above and below each other. In some lithologies a water table can be identified by drawing contours based on readings of water level in wells and boreholes (provided that they are unaffected by artificial pumping). However, this is less successful in karstified limestone where the water levels in wells and boreholes that are in close proximity may differ markedly depending on whether or not they connect to conduit porosity. In any event, there are few monitored boreholes in the limestones of the Yorkshire Dales. By definition, the water table is at surface where springs occur, but in the Dales many springs, particularly those in Yoredale limestone are perched on less permeable strata. If these are excluded, the altitudes of springs may be used to define the low points of a conceptual water table within the Great Scar Limestone. Most of the individual Yoredale limestones are thin and freely drained, so that concepts of water tables within them are barely appropriate.

Figure 9.3. Haws Gill Wheel in dry conditions and in flood; this is one of a group of sinks that swallow the headwater streams in Chapel-le-Dale, at various stage levels (TW).

One of the major features of the Yorkshire Dales is that the limestone outcrop is traversed by a series of glacially deepened valleys. Each of these is occupied, for at least part of the year, by a surface stream that originates on the overlying impermeable rocks. Surface flows on the limestone are a consequence of sinks being either too immature or partially choked, albeit temporarily, so that flood flows cannot pass through, though impermeable glacial deposits account for surface flows over limestone on parts of some dale floors. A hydrological gradation is apparent from Wharfedale, which has a perennial river with surface flow except in times of severe drought, and Littondale, where dry-weather flow is engulfed for 3.5 km, to Kingsdale, which is dry above the Keld Head resurgence under most weather conditions, and Chapel-le-Dale, where the channel is dry above the God's Bridge resurgence except in times of high flood (Table 4.3, Fig. 4.16).

Recharge into the limestone

Across some parts of the Yorkshire Dales karst, the limestone crops out at the surface and rainfall can enter it directly, but this is not the dominant situation because so much of the limestone is overlain by soil and drift deposits. Rain falling onto unsaturated soil infiltrates so that it enters the soil moisture store, although very heavy rainfall may exceed the soil's capacity to absorb it, in which case the excess becomes surface run-off as overland flow. Once it has entered the soil, a proportion of the water is utilised by plants and is returned to the atmosphere by evapotranspiration. The remainder moves laterally downslope as through-flow, or percolates vertically through unconsolidated glacial deposits and alluvial sands and gravels to enter the underlying rock. Autogenic recharge is the rainfall that lands directly on the limestone or on the unconsolidated sediments and soil that overlie the limestone. This is in contrast to the rainfall that lands on outcrops of other rocks, mostly forms streams that then flow onto the

Figure 9.5. A typical small sink that provides allogenic recharge to the limestone; the stream at Middle Washfold, above Chapel-le-Dale, drains off Yoredale shales in the background, flows on the top of a strong bed of limestone and then drops into the head of a small canyon passage formed by waterfall retreat from an initial fissure on a joint (TW).

limestone, and so becomes the allogenic recharge into the limestone aquifer. Both types of recharge, autogenic and allogenic, can be either concentrated or dispersed, depending on local details of the geology and geomorphology (Fig. 9.4).

Allogenic recharge into the karst

Within the Dales, most of the allogenic recharge into the limestone is concentrated, as it is dominated by the many small streams that gather on the overlying shales and sink within short distances of crossing the boundary onto the limestone (Fig. 9.5). The largest single sink into the Great Scar Limestone is Hull Pot, with a mean flow of well over 100 L/s from a catchment of 4.75 km² on the northwestern slopes of Pen-y-ghent. However, the two largest sinking streams in the Dales, the River Nidd at Goyden Pot and Mossdale Beck at its eponymous Scar (with catchments of about 34 km² and 6 km² respectively), both drain into the Middle Limestone of the Yoredale sequence (Fig. 9.6).

All these sinking streams of allogenic drainage form a conspicuous component of the karst recharge, as they are the streams that can be followed down through the many cave systems. Allogenic recharge accounts for about half the total input to the Dales caves, though the ratio varies

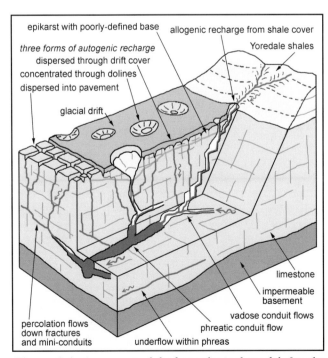

Figure 9.4. A conceptual hydrogeological model for the Great Scar Limestone of the Yorkshire Dales.

Figure 9.6. The River Nidd at a stage of moderate flood when a large flow sinks into the main entrance of Goyden Pot (TW).

between sites that have higher or lower proportions of shale outcrop in their catchments. Flow data gathered under a range of stage conditions in part of the West Kingsdale catchment indicate that only about 20% of the total annual flow is derived from the concentrated allogenic inputs of sinking streams (Halliwell, 1980). However, this swallet input by the visible streams is not all the allogenic flow, as there are also numerous small inputs, unseen beneath the soil cover under the lines of shakeholes along the shale margins. The allogenic component also varies with stage; at the Newhouses rising in Ribblesdale, flow from the sinks in Sell Gill accounts for 45% of the resurgence discharge during flood events, but declines to less than 15% in conditions of low flow (Halliwell, 1980).

Dispersed allogenic recharge occurs where the limestone is overlain by a permeable caprock that allows the percolating water to continue its downward path. In the Yorkshire Dales there is no dispersed allogenic recharge to the Great Scar Limestone as the overlying shales have very low permeability. Within the repetitive cyclic sequences of the Yoredale rocks, the limestones are normally overlain by shales, thereby again precluding dispersed allogenic recharge. An exception is where the Grassington Grit cuts unconformably down through the succession in the Nidderdale area, so that water may drain down from it into the Middle Limestone where this locally lies directly beneath. Such dispersed recharge may have contributed to inception of the cave passage that has a long section in limestone beneath an unbroken grit outcrop on its route through to the Nidd Heads resurgence (Waltham *et al.*, 1997).

Whereas the Yoredale limestones are generally overlain by shale, they are widely underlain by sandstone. Dispersed allogenic recharge can be an important process in the development of network caves (Palmer, 1975, 2007), and upward flow from the sandstone might have contributed to the development of some or all of the North Pennine maze caves (Ryder, 1975). This would have been prior to the Pleistocene excavation of the dales, after which most of the Yoredale limestones could drain down-dip to outcrops along the dale sides. It has also been suggested that the morphology of Knock Fell Caverns, a maze cave in the Great Limestone within the Yoredale succession on the Alston Block, is compatible with development by rising groundwater of deep-seated hypogene origin (Klimchouk, 2007). Phreatic shafts below the main passage mazes in the Devis Hole

Mine Caves may have been the sites of rising water input but the morphological evidence is not conclusive (Harrison, 2012). Though dispersed upward recharge, of either shallow phreatic or hypogene origin, into the Yoredale limestones is likely to have occurred, there is as yet no firm evidence for its role in cave development in the karst of the northern Dales.

Autogenic recharge into the karst

With precipitation landing on wide outcrops of the Great Scar Limestone, autogenic recharge is an important component of the Yorkshire Dales karst hydrogeology. Whether dispersed or concentrated to some degree, this may also be known as the percolation input, to distinguish it from the allogenic stream input. Some of the dispersed autogenic recharge enters the limestone through fissures in the bare limestone pavements and rock scars, and this is very different from the dispersed recharge that percolates through the extensive soil cover.

On the many limestone pavements within the Dales karst, each grike has a small catchment made up of surrounding clints that are commonly etched with karren. Though these do channel some of the surface flow, recharge from the areas of bare limestone pavement can be regarded as dispersed in the sense that there is little concentration of rainwater prior to its passing beneath the surface. However, the extensive network of dissolutionally enlarged grike fissures allows precipitation to move rapidly underground, where it may subsequently be concentrated into fast-flowing percolation streams.

Figure 9.7. Bare limestone pavements on Scales Moor, where dispersed autogenic recharge enters the limestone (TW).

The limestone bench of Scales Moor, between Kingsdale and Chapel-le-Dale has an extensive area of bare limestone pavement but no sinking streams and few dolines (Fig. 9.7). Despite there being no concentrated recharge in the strict sense, the risings at the foot of Scales Moor show a rapid increase in discharge shortly after rainfall events that create rapid recharge (Halliwell, 1980). The bare rock clint surfaces are dried soon after rain ceases, though the same may not apply in winter when grikes may be filled with snow that melts relatively slowly to yield a steady flow of water. As the grikes are formed on joints, the recharge from rainfall onto the Dales pavements may enter the limestone's secondary porosity that is provided by the narrow fissures. However, the rapid response of the springs below Scales Moor suggests that much of the pavement drainage runs directly into the tertiary porosity where flow is faster through dissolutionally enlarged conduits.

Across large areas in the Dales where the limestone is overlain by loessic soils that are less than a metre thick, dispersed autogenic recharge takes place through the soil on relatively flat areas of land between any dolines, and may enter the matrix, fissure or conduit porosity. After percolating through the soil cover, this water is generally enriched in biogenic carbon dioxide from the soil atmosphere, before it dissolves limestone from fissure walls. It is then conspicuously influential in the underlying caves as it is the dominant source of carbonate precipitation to form stalactites and other speleothems when the carbon dioxide is expelled to achieve equilibrium with the cave atmosphere.

Concentrated autogenic recharge occurs primarily into dolines that gather rainwater from surface flow on low-permeability glacial sediments and from lateral flow through the more permeable loessic soils. This is widespread in the Yorkshire Dales karst where the main sites of concentrated recharge are recognisable as the thousands of small subsidence dolines that are known within the Dales as shakeholes (Fig. 9.8). Beneath the lowest point of each shakehole, surface and soil drainage recharge the conduit porosity of the underlying limestone. Bedrock is exposed in the floors of some shakeholes, and some fissures within it are large enough to be the entrances to extensive cave systems. However, most shakeholes are floored by slumped soil and sediment through which water infiltrates, but the unseen openings below must have been dissolutionally enlarged to conduit size to permit the suffosional loss of the soil to form the shakeholes. The extent of dispersed recharge beneath the glacial soils and between the shakeholes is unknown, but virtually all of it must enter the fracture or conduit porosity given the very low matrix permeability of the intact limestone. The Long Crawl in Swinsto Hole, Kingsdale, lies only a few metres below the surface for nearly 300m. In dry weather it has no visible inflows from the numerous small shakeholes in the thin till cover, but following rainfall many tiny inlets provide a combined water input greater than that at the main sink adjacent to the entrance (Halliwell, 1980). The amounts of water entering the matrix porosity are negligible because of the extremely low permeability of the intact limestone.

In addition to the many small shakeholes, there are smaller numbers of larger solution dolines, notably on the Malham High Country, most of which are clearly pre-Devensian

Figure 9.8. A small shakehole above Clapdale, where autogenic recharge enters the limestone that lies beneath the thin cover of glacial till (TW).

(see Chapter 4). Soils and glacial sediments within them are pitted by the smaller shakeholes, but rainfall events also create surface flows on these fills. The larger dolines then have small ephemeral streams draining to their low points, and these constitute larger points of concentrated autogenic recharge to the conduit porosity of the limestone beneath.

Water storage within the limestone

Besides the water that is stored in the soil and in any unconsolidated sediments, water is stored in three zones within the bedrock. These are the uppermost few metres of weathered limestone known as the epikarst, the freely-draining vadose zone above the conceptual water table, and the flooded or saturated phreatic zone (also known as the phreas) below that water table. Within each zone, water is stored within all three elements of the limestone porosity – matrix, fracture and conduit. There are however significant differences between the water stored within each type of porosity, as their huge contrasts in permeability define the flow conditions and availability of the limestone's groundwater.

Matrix porosity is represented by the tiny spaces between calcite crystals and grains within the rock matrix. It can be measured by laboratory oven drying of intact rock samples that are devoid of fractures, but there are few available records for the Carboniferous Limestone. An average value of 1.3% is recorded from four outcrops and 1% from three boreholes in the Yorkshire–Lancashire Pennines (Jones *et al.*, 2000). Similar values have been obtained for comparable limestone in the Mendip Hills (David Drew, *pers. comm.*), though these rocks are tectonically more disturbed that those of the same age in the Dales.

Fracture porosity encompasses the narrowest fissures that have not undergone significant dissolutional enlargement, and this can be estimated from field abstraction tests, notably pump tests on wells and boreholes. Though a scatter of boreholes in the Yorkshire Dales yield usable supplies, there are no records of such tests on them, but an acceptable estimate for the Carboniferous Limestone in England is about 0.03%. Pump tests in comparable Palaeozoic limestones commonly indicate values of <0.1%, but many of these are from folded and fractured rocks that would be expected to have higher values than those from most of the Dales limestone that lies relatively undisturbed on the top of the Askrigg Block.

Conduit porosity refers to all openings wide enough to transmit turbulent flow, so generally >10 mm wide. Part of this, in the smaller conduits, is probably included within the fracture porosity that is determined by field tests involving pumped drawdown. The other part includes cave passages, defined as conduits large enough for human exploration. As a part of the conduit porosity, cave porosity can be estimated from cave surveys, and calculations within the Dales karst yield a cave porosity of 0.04% for the Kingsdale caves (Worthington, 1999), and 0.048% for the phreatic zone draining to Leck Beck Head (Worthington and Ford, 2009). In contrast, the large quarry at Horton-in-Ribblesdale has intersected only a single, very small, stream cave while removing limestone to depths of about 50m over an area of 20 ha, thereby indicating a negligible cave porosity. The higher values are very subjective as they depend on the size and shape of the box or envelope of limestone that is drawn around the caves to make the volume calculations. Estimates with tighter envelopes around the caves have yielded figures about three times higher in comparable karst terrains: by drawing an envelope tightly around a small area of maze cave, a cave porosity of 10% was calculated for Knock Fell Caverns in the Great Limestone in the northern Pennines (Klimchouk, 2007). This is however an exceptional figure, applicable only to a small area of caves within a thin band of limestone, and is not matched in any of the dendritic cave systems traversed by sinking streams in the Great Scar Limestone (Fig. 9.9).

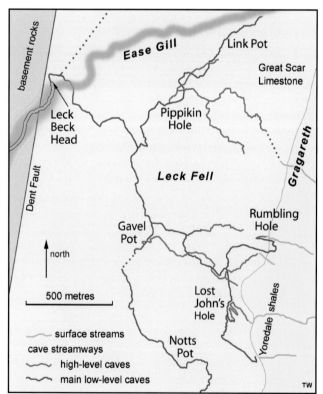

Figure 9.9. The larger known active conduits beneath Leck Fell that constitute part of a dendritic cave system draining to Leck Beck Head; the main cave streamways are in the lowest 50m of the limestone, whereas the high-level streamways are in the upper 100m; the latter follow bedding planes until they descend on shafts formed on joints; deflections in plan view are largely created by segments of passage being aligned on joints; not marked are many very small cave streams that are active only in wet weather.

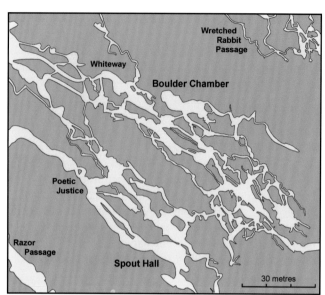

Figure 9.10. Outline map of a small part of the Three Counties Cave System, close inside the County Pot entrance. The narrow passages are mainly canyon streamways, 3–5m tall, but most of the wider passages are bedding plane openings less than 1m high. Though the passage density in the zone between Spout Hall and Boulder Chamber constitutes a high conduit porosity, this is a local feature, as large areas of limestone on each side of this zone have no known cave passages, and no indication of any awaiting exploration and mapping. All the passages are within a zone of limestone less than 30m thick, and there are no known passages in the 60m of limestone above, nor in about 50m of limestone that lies below (after survey by Red Rose Cave and Pothole Club).

All these figures for measured conduit porosity omit unexplored caves and also the conduits of sub-cave dimensions, both of which are of major significance. Each new exploration increases the perception of the cave porosity; cave maps of Gragareth from the 1950s, the 1970s and 2012 indicate progressively greater volumes of known cave, while predictions of future situations or of the real cave porosity are next to impossible. There is also no method of measuring the total conduit porosity represented by voids too small for direct exploration and measurement. Those in the phreatic zone may be recorded as part of the total porosity determined in pump tests, but such assessments take no account of porosity in the vadose zone. The highest values are likely to be found in the fissured epikarst, but this occupies only a very small proportion of the total karst aquifer.

As the matrix has the greatest porosity of the three elements it can store the largest volume of groundwater. However, most of the pores in the matrix of the Great Scar Limestone are very small and are poorly connected, so they cannot readily be drained. The Dales limestones have such extremely low matrix permeability that the role of the matrix in karst water circulation can be safely ignored. An exception to this virtual dismissal of matrix permeability may have to be made where groundwater pollution occurs, as pollutants may move slowly into part of the matrix and then take a very long time to be flushed clear.

Specific yield is a measure of the available water that is transferable or extractable from an aquifer, and is therefore very much less than the total porosity that includes the unconnected pores. It is also known as effective porosity, and is a useful term in practical hydrogeology. Most fractures connect within networks created by the intersections of the various joint systems and the bedding planes; consequently they can be drained and refilled, and are a major location of useable storage in the Dales limestones. Conduits, including large cave passages, in the phreatic zone also offer storage capacity. However, the amount of water stored in even the largest cave streamways in the vadose zone is negligible. Measurements of specific yield are lacking from the Dales, but analogies with monitored karsts in potentially comparable limestones elsewhere suggest that the combined fracture and conduit porosity of the Dales limestone is well under 1%, and may be as low as a tenth of that figure. This lack of data again reflects the very limited information that is available on the Dales hydrogeology in general, and there is considerable scope for further research.

Flow through the limestone

Matrix permeability of the dense Yoredale and Great Scar limestones is extremely low, but there are no recorded measurements from within the Dales karst. A median permeability of 3×10^{-6} m/d was derived from limestone cores at Sellafield on the Lake District margin (Allen *et al.*, 1997).

Hydraulic tests in boreholes give an approximation of fracture permeability. Values from 46 boreholes in the Carboniferous Limestone in the Mendip Hills ranged from <0.01 m/day to >100 m/day, with a geometric mean of 0.2 m/day (Smart *et al.*, 1992). The lower values represent boreholes that encountered only narrow fractures, whereas the higher values represent boreholes with fractures that have experienced substantial dissolutional enlargement. The four orders of magnitude of variation in fracture permeability reflect the extreme heterogeneity of the limestone, and the higher conduit permeabilities further extend that range.

Permeability in the conduit system varies widely. Tracer velocities in excess of 1000 m/d from sink to spring have been recorded at sites in the Dales. Overall velocities relate to the local hydrology, because flow is generally faster down vadose streamways than it is through flooded passages within the phreas. Tracer velocities along the largely phreatic route from the Malham Tarn Water Sinks to Aire Head were measured as 1.9 and 2.7 km/day at low and high stage respectively, while velocities of 2.9 and 9.8 km/day were recorded for flow from Smelt Mill Sink to Malham Cove where there appears to be a greater length of vadose conduit (Smith and Atkinson, 1977).

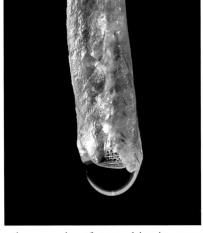

Figure 9.11. Water that enters an open cave passage by percolation flow, to form a drop of water hanging on the end of a straw stalactite in Shuttleworth Pot, Leck Fell (photo: Mark Shinwell).

Tracer velocities from the ground surface to drips in caves are lower, but these may include flow through the fracture porosity where velocities are lower than in conduits.

Significant insights into percolation flow and storage in the vadose zone were obtained from a long programme of tracer tests through the limestone above White Scar Cave in Chapel-le-Dale (Bottrell and Atkinson, 1992). Fluorescent dyes were placed in fissures beneath the soil and monitored at 24 inlets, each of which was a drip point or a minor fissure inlet in the cave passage at depths of 31 to 65 m below the injection points. The percolation flow was found to be via networks and systems of interconnected fractures that have very little interconnection between adjacent individual networks. Flow paths are not necessarily directly downwards, but can extend over horizontal distances of up to 100m, and can diverge to more remote distributaries under flood conditions (Fig. 9.12). The vadose flow above White Scar Cave was considered to have three components:

• Rapid, gravity-driven throughflow with optimally short paths through interconnected fractures and fissures, typically within periods of about three days.

• Short-term storage along slower flow paths within the networks of water-filled fractures and fissure, with residence times of 30 to 70 days.

• Long-term storage within water-filled fractures and fissures where water is flushed out only during widely spaced periods of high flow after residence of 160 days to more than 75 months.

Groundwater in the Yorkshire Dales limestones follows a spectrum of flow patterns and permeabilities that are largely related to the void widths. Flows through cave passages form only one end-point of that spectrum.

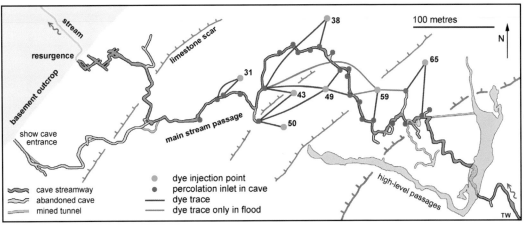

Figure 9.12. Flow paths of percolation water traced from the limestone fell to drips and small inlets in White Scar Cave; figures beside each dye injection point indicate its height in metres above the roof of the adjacent part of the cave streamway (after Bottrell and Atkinson, 1992).

Discharge from the limestone springs

The great majority of the water, both allogenic and autogenic, that sinks into the limestone of the Yorkshire Dales karst eventually emerges at numerous springs (Fig. 9.13). Flows into surrounding buried aquifers have not been measured but are likely to be very small as a proportion. There is no comprehensive inventory of springs, and the total number discharging from the Great Scar Limestone is roughly matched by the number in the various Yoredale limestones, both within the area of Figure 9.13 and to the north and east. The springs discharge varying proportions of allogenic and autogenic recharge. Those springs fed primarily by allogenic recharge are commonly referred to as resurgences and those fed largely or wholly by autogenic recharge may be called risings (though this term is also a synonym for springs).

Resurgences are dominated by allogenic water from sinking streams, and are so named because their cave streams resurge to the surface at these sites. They do have significant components of autogenic water that drain into the limestone outcrop and add to the cave streams between sink and spring. Proportions of allogenic and autogenic flows from resurgences vary over time, and autogenic recharge may dominate during dry periods. With mainly rapid flow through large conduits, these springs show rapid response to flood inputs; flow from White Scar Cave rose from 22 to 530 L/s in less than 10 hours in a flood in 1974. They also have considerable variations in flow, hydrochemistry and water temperature over time (Halliwell, 1980). This group includes most of the larger springs in the Dales, and flow data for some representative examples are given in Table 9.1.

Figure 9.13. Distribution of the larger springs across the southern part of the Yorkshire Dales karst; many smaller springs, and many more that flow for only short periods after rainfall events, are not marked on this map; catchment boundaries are drawn for only some of the larger springs referred to in the text.

Figure 9.14. A spring with only autogenic recharge emerges from an enlarged bedding at Kilnsey Crag, Wharfedale, after rainfall (TW)..

Risings are fed, largely or wholly, by autogenic recharge on the limestone, as they have little or no impermeable outcrop within their catchments and have no known stream sinks draining to them. The proportions of dispersed recharge through soils and grikes, as opposed to concentrated recharge through dolines, has not been determined or even estimated. Though the input to these springs may be described as percolation water, a large part of its flow paths to the risings is in conduits that permit rapid through-flow (Halliwell, 1980). Their flows tend to be less variable than those of the resurgences, though risings fed by recharge through limestone pavements can respond very rapidly to rainfall events. Flow data for representative examples of some larger risings are given in Table 9.1. This group includes most of the smaller Dales springs that have individual catchments of only small sectors of limestone plateau and hillside (Fig. 9.14). Also included is Aire Head, which is a hydrogeological exception in that its recharge is largely autogenic, but its catchment includes the large sink that swallows the outflow stream from Malham Tarn.

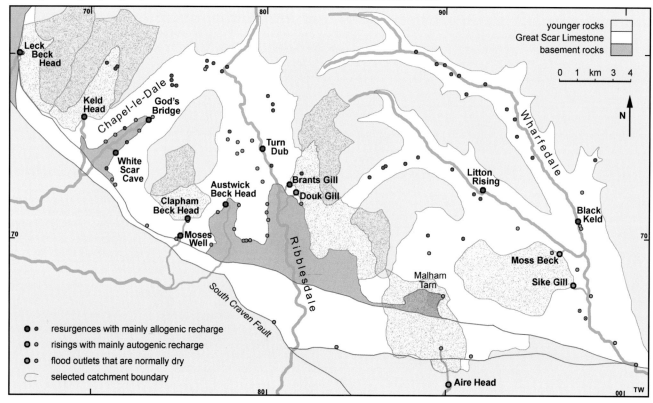

younger rocks
Great Scar Limestone
basement rocks

0 1 km 3 4

N

Leck Beck Head

Keld Head

Chapel-le-Dale

God's Bridge

Turn Dub

White Scar Cave

Austwick Beck Head

Brants Gill

Douk Gill

Clapham Beck Head

Moses Well

Ribblesdale

Litton Rising

Wharfedale

Black Keld

Moss Beck

Malham Tarn

Sike Gill

South Craven Fault

● ● ● resurgences with mainly allogenic recharge

◐ ◦ risings with mainly autogenic recharge

◉ ◦ flood outlets that are normally dry

⌒ selected catchment boundary

Aire Head

TW

Many resurgences and risings are also part of distributary systems where large springs with perennial flow are connected to one or more intermittent overflow springs that discharge during high flows. God's Bridge, Moses Well, Turn Dub, Brants Gill Head, Aire Head, and Moss Beck Rising are among those that each has one or more overflow springs.

The distribution of springs across the southern Dales (Fig. 9.13) is distinctive in that there are only a few large resurgences west of Ingleborough, where groundwater flows converge within dendritic cave systems, each feeding to a single dale-floor outlet in conditions of normal stage (Fig. 9.15). Conversely, Upper Wharfedale has many, smaller resurgences, each fed by only one or a few sinking streams, though there may be some links between catchments in flood conditions. Most of the smaller springs discharge autogenic drainage from small catchments along the dale-side limestone outcrops, and much of the autogenic water drains into cave streamways where it is mixed with the allogenic flows from stream sinks. The only large autogenic risings are those around the wide outcrop of limestone forming the Malham High Country (Fig. 9.13), where the lack of shale outliers precludes the formation of allogenic streams that can flow onto the limestone.

Figure 9.15. Austwick Beck Head, which lies at the base of the limestone and is the resurgence for allogenic streams sinking on the Ingleborough Allotment; however, passages behind the resurgence are so small and immature that flood flows back up, and excess water is diverted elsewhere, probably to Ringle Mill Cave (TW).

site	location	input L/s	outflows, L/s mean	outflows, L/s normal	outflows, L/s min	outflows, L/s max	catchments, km² total	catchments, km² limestone	NGR (all SD)	notes, sources	
resurgences											
Leck Beck Head	Ease Gill	500		75			18.7	4.7	660800	1	**A**
Keld Head	Kingsdale	400		~300	~40	3500	15.3	6.8	696766	2	**B**
White Scar Cave	Chapel-le-Dale	90		60	3	>1200	3.4	1.9	713746	3	**C**
Engine Shed Rising	Chapel-le-Dale	30	48	31	6	392	1.2	1.0	720752	4	**B**
Clapham Beck Head	Ingleborough	200		~50	5	2500	8.1	3.9	754711	5	**D**
Brants Gill Head	Ribblesdale	700		~150	~50	>>1500	26.3	12.7	812729	6	**E**
Black Keld	Wharfedale	500		~150	~40	>>400	18.2	5.9	974709	7	**F**
risings											
Aire Head	Malham	450		~130	5	>>500	17.6	14.5	901622	8	**G**
Light Water Spring	Chapel-le-Dale	15	28		0	364	~0.5	all	727758		**H**
Moss Beck Rising	Littondale	250	192		21	692	~10	all	964693	9	**H**
Sike Gill Rising	Wharfedale	300	230		29	673	~12	all	971675	9	**H**

Table 9.1. Available flow data for some representative resurgences and risings within the Yorkshire Dales. Other major springs exist, but flow records are not available. Resurgences have both allogenic flow from streams sinking at the shale margin and also autogenic recharge by rainfall onto the limestone outcrops. Risings are fed, largely or wholly, by autogenic recharge on the limestone, as they have little or no impermeable outcrop within their catchments.

All catchment areas are approximations, as the boundaries of their percolation recharge are not known.

Inputs are derived from assumed mean rainfalls of ~1500 mm/y = ~45 L/s/km² and estimated losses by evapotranspiration of about 40%, to give runoff of about 27 L/s/km² from the catchment areas. Inputs include flood flows and are therefore higher than the normal flows from the springs. Inputs that differ greatly from mean flows question the estimates of their poorly defined catchment areas.

Flow data are from various sources, and mean values are from limited lengths of recording. Normal flow figures are spot measurements or estimates in stable conditions, as are observed for about 90% of the time, ie except through flood events or prolonged droughts.

Sources of data (both published and unpublished): A: Bowser, 1973. B: Ric Halliwell (1970). C: Waltham, 1977. D: John Cordingley (2011). E: Tony Waltham (2012). F: Myers, 1950. G: Smith and Atkinson, 1977. H: Halliwell et al., 1974.

Notes

1. Outflow excludes floodwater that flows down the Ease Gill surface channel.

2. Outflow excludes floodwater that stays in the Kingsdale surface channel; this may be as much as half the theoretical input figure. Catchment excludes 1.64 km² captured by the leat to Masongill.

3. Outflow excludes floodwater that flows down Crina Bottom into the Skirwith catchment.

4. Catchment may be increased by flood overflow from Quaking Pot.

5. Catchment is poorly constrained across Newby Moss where flows from the known potholes diverge.

6. Includes flows from the flood risings of Douk Gill and Dub Cote.

7. Catchment excludes an estimated 3.8 km² on the Great Scar Limestone outcrop that drains to the percolation risings of White Keld and Spring Trap Cave while the conduit flow to Black Keld passes beneath with little or no hydrological connection. Flow figures are only from a few observations.

8. Catchment includes Malham Cove Rising, but flow data do not; flow from the Cove is about equal to that from Aire Head at low stage, but does not rise above a low maximum even at high stage.

9. Catchment areas are little more than rough estimates, as the two risings account for most of the drainage from the Malham High Country, but neither the overall nor the dividing boundaries have been determined.

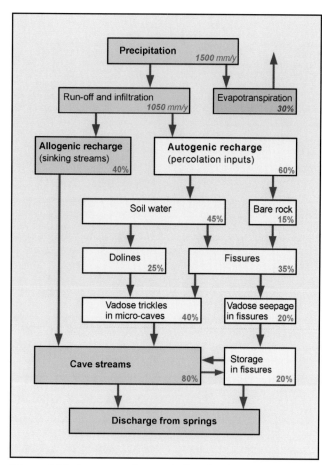

Figure 9.16. *A conceptual water budget for the Dales limestone, based largely on Halliwell (1980), modified so that the allogenic input is not only the swallet water but includes unseen allogenic drainage into lines of shakeholes along buried shale boundaries.*

There are insufficient available data to construct accurate water budgets for the Yorkshire Dales karst, but Figure 9.16 presents a conceptual outline; it is largely an extension and modification of a model for the Ingleborough area that was based on extensive monitoring of a large selection of springs (Halliwell, 1980). This concept budget is largely applicable to catchments west of the Pennine watershed, because there is more perennial surface flow in Wharfedale and the other dales east of the divide. Extreme conditions always distort the figures; in the dry summer of 1976 there were no sinking streams in most catchments (Halliwell, 1980), whereas extreme floods maintain surface flows that exceed the capacities of sinks along the floors of all the main dales.

The chemistry of water emerging from karst springs across the Dales is largely a function of their mode of recharge. Allogenic recharge from streams that originate on the outliers of Yoredale rocks is aggressive, and its low carbonate concentration increases rapidly as the stream moves through the limestone. As much of the Dales karst is free-draining, underground flow times are generally short, and concentrations of calcium carbonate at the major resurgences are only 80–140 mg/L (Halliwell, 1980). Where the allogenic catchments include Yoredale limestones, carbonate concentrations in the sinking streams are higher and there is proportionately less increase along cave streams. The larger risings with discharges that are wholly or largely autogenic typically carry 100–200 mg/L of calcium carbonate (Halliwell, 1980); these concentrations, which are low for

autogenic karst drainage, reflect the low levels of biogenic carbon dioxide within the poorly drained soils on the glacial till that overlies much of the limestone outcrop. Many of the smaller risings that are supplied almost entirely by dispersed autogenic recharge drain from richer agricultural land and consequently have calcium carbonate concentrations of 200–300 mg/L (see also Table 4.1).

Geological influences on the karst drainage

The principal geological influences on the patterns of underground drainage in the Yorkshire Dales are essentially those that have influenced the inception and development of the caves (see Chapters 7 and 8). These influences are the inception horizons and features of the limestone bedding, the structural dip of those bedding features, the networks of joints and faults, the morphology of the limestone's basement unconformity, and the development of multiple phases of passages through the history of Pleistocene glaciations and landscape rejuvenations.

Most vadose cave streams flow down the dip, which is to the north and northeast at many sites across the Dales. However, the regional drainage is towards the south, from the Craven Uplands to the Craven Lowlands, and consequently most of the cave streams feed into low-level phreatic conduits that flow along the strike or back up-dip towards the risings on the floors of the dales. The cave system from the Swinsto Hole sink to the Keld Head resurgence provides an example of the characteristic influences on underground water movement and cave development in the Yorkshire Dales (Waltham *et al.*, 1981). By following gently dipping bedding planes and shale beds, its active vadose cave extends towards the northeast for 1200m, from a stream sink close

Figure 9.17. *The lip of the 45m-deep shaft where the stream in Diccan Pot meets the Alum Pot Fault (TW).*

to the shale–limestone boundary; it also descends 130m by dropping vertically or obliquely down joints. Downstream of the vadose cave, the active phreatic cave is nearly 1800m long, with the stream flowing towards the southwest and passing through shallow loops by descending joints and then rising up bedding planes. This two-part pattern is repeated in many of the caves that drain through the Dales limestone.

The numerous joints and small faults in the limestone exert local rather than regional influence on the hydrology. In profile, joints determine the locations of most of the steps that become waterfall shafts in the descents of the typical Dales cave stream passages. Faults are fewer in number, but tend to be the sites of most of the deepest shafts in the Dales caves; Growling Hole, Spectacle Pot, Long Kin East Pot and Diccan Pot are among those that have no substantial depth development until their streams each reach faults where they descend to considerable depths (Fig. 9.17). Some faults are also conspicuous in plan view where they determine the alignment of considerable lengths of cave passage, as in the parallel streamways in the caves of Birks Fell and Birks Wood (Fig. 7.25).

A feature of the Dales karst is that the impermeable rocks underlying the limestone are exposed in some of the dale floors, where they form the local base level for drainage and determine the positions of numerous springs. Including the smallest of ephemeral flows, there are more than thirty springs along the margins of the basement outcrop in Chapel-le-Dale. Once the cave drainage has reached depth and is close to the base of the limestone, its flow path may be influenced by the local relief that is a feature of the basement

Figure 9.19. The large Duke Street passage with its underfit stream in Ireby Fell Cavern (TW).

on the Askrigg Block. This relief is largely a feature of the pre-Carboniferous landscape, but some of it was also created by post-Carboniferous folding. Basement highs appear to separate some of the drainage lines within the lowest beds of the limestone, so that springs are concentrated in the basement lows. Skirwith Cave, White Scar Cave and Granite Quarry Risings all lie in basement lows where their waters emerge into the south side of Chapel-le-Dale (Halliwell, 1979). On a larger scale, all the drainage from the western slopes of Fountains Fell heads north and northwest to emerge from Brants Gill Head some 4 km further up Ribblesdale, close to the lowest outcrop point of the limestone in the dale (Fig. 9.18). The underground flow is primarily down-dip, and lies behind a major basement ridge north of Stainforth that is partly created by a flexure in the northward dip, but is enhanced by the basement relief where the Kilnsey Limestone is absent over its crest.

An additional influence on cave drainage can be created where a stream invades an older passage that had developed in a previous hydrogeological environment. Duke Street, in Ireby Fell Cavern, is the best example of a large, old cave passage that now carries an underfit stream (Fig. 9.19). Passage invasion can also lead to flow reversal, as in Dale Barn Cave where the large, old, Expressway passage was formed by drainage westwards into Kingsdale, but now carries a stream eastwards towards Chapel-le-Dale (Murphy *et al.*, 2001). The perched rising of Ringle Mill, in Ribblesdale, is notable for its very large flood flows, which may be due to invasion or re-occupation of old passages by water from the Allotment when flows exceed the capacity of the immature passages to the modern outlet at Austwick Beck Head. Magnetometer Pot, under Fountains Fell, has a number of small streams draining through cave passages that may pre-date the deepening of Ribblesdale, and is just one more example of the complexity of the hydrogeology resulting from the multi-stage evolution of the Dales karst.

Most of the cave drainage in the Yoredale limestones is distinguished by its small stream flows and its constraint within the thin beds underlain and overlain by shales and sandstones. Consequently, the typical Yoredale cave is a small passage draining from a single sink, roughly down-dip to its resurgence high in a dale side. The notable exceptions are the caves in the Middle Limestone under Grassington Moor and Nidderdale. Both Langcliffe Pot and Mossdale Caverns

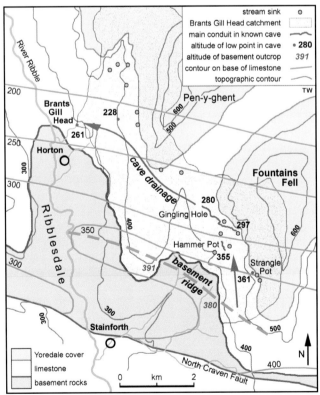

Figure 9.18. Cave drainage from Fountains Fell, north then northwest to the Brants Gill resurgence, behind the ridge in the unconformity at the base of the limestone that keeps outflow away from the nearer and lower part of Ribblesdale; structure contours on the base of the limestone are only generalised as they are interpreted from minimal data (after Jack Soper and Glyn Edwards).

Figure 9.20. *The Victorian masonry housing the pool with variable level at the Ebbing and Flowing Well, Giggleswick Scar (TW).*

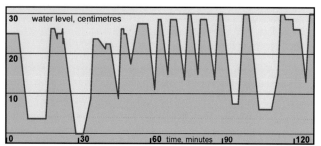

Figure 9.21. *Fluctuations of water level within the Ebbing and Flowing Well, recorded in August 1804 when it was more active than it is has been in recent years (after Gough, 1813).*

have long streamways aligned down-dip in the Middle Limestone, though their waters eventually resurge at Black Keld, low down in the Great Scar Limestone sequence. The drainage route down through the intervening non-carbonates can be followed only in Langcliffe Pot (Fig. 7.27), but the geological structure is obscured by a massive boulder choke whose scale suggests that it is in a local fault zone (Brook, 1989). Beneath the floor of Nidderdale, the many parts of the Goyden Pot Cave System carry the largest underground flow in the Dales, where the River Nidd drains through the faulted inliers of Middle Limestone.

As is characteristic of karst terrains, there are many sites in the Yorkshire Dales where underground drainage is at variance with the surface topography. Drainage passes between surface divides, notably where streams within the Yoredale limestones drain from Wensleydale beneath the divide into Swaledale, and where Dale Barn Cave carries a stream from Kingsdale beneath Scales Moor into Chapel-le-Dale. In the side of Wharfedale, much of the stream in the Dowber Gill valley sinks underground and flows beneath a ridge to a resurgence in the parallel valley of Caseker Gill, 1300m to the north, passing along the very straight, fault-guided Dowber Gill Passage into Dow Cave. In contrast, some cave drainage passes beneath valley floors. Much of the water sinking along the eastern bench above Kingsdale drains through a phreatic tunnel that passes beneath the dale floor and resurges from Keld Head on the western side of Kingsdale Beck (Fig. 9.22). Water from Alum Pot passes beneath the River Ribble to resurge at Turn Dub in its eastern bank, though floodwaters rise from the normally static pool at Footnaw's Hole in its western bank before passing beneath the surface river. Within the multiple levels of the larger Dales cave systems there are many examples of drainage routes that cross over or under other drainage routes, with a complexity that distinguishes karst groundwater systems from aquifers in homogenous rocks (Fig. 9.9).

An unusual feature of the Dales karst is the Ebbing and Flowing Well, midway along Giggleswick Scar (Fig. 9.20). This is a reciprocating spring, in that its flow can fluctuate rhythmically (Fig. 9.21), though it is not a true intermittent spring as it does not run completely dry in each cycle (Stevens, 1964). Its flow pattern is a consequence of a siphon passage that drains a small chamber each time that it is filled to a certain level. The Well was a significant local tourist attraction until the nineteenth century when the level fluctuated by 20 cm or so in a stone-lined pool that responds to flow because of its V-notch outlet. Activity declined over the years, though by 1900 it could still exhibit cyclic flow for a month at a time. The Well now pulses only during a narrow range of moderate stage, and its flow is uniform at both lower and higher stages. In fairly dry weather conditions in 2012, the pool level was seen to fluctuate by about 12 cm over repeated cycles each lasting about 8 minutes. The long-term change in the flow pattern may be due to dissolutional modification of the siphon conduits, or is more likely to be due to sediment accumulation within them.

Hydrogeology of Keld Head, Kingsdale

Keld Head is the large resurgence in the floor of Kingsdale. It is representative of the large springs within each of the main dales that are cut deep into the limestone of the Craven Uplands, but is distinctive in that a very large proportion of its underground drainage routes have been explored and mapped (Fig. 9.22). More than 30 km of cave passages are known under Kingsdale (Brook, 1969; Monico, 1995), and these collect nearly all the allogenic drainage that enters sinks along the shale margins behind the limestone benches on both sides of the dale. They all drain ultimately to Keld Head, where they are joined by autogenic recharge from Kingsdale's entire limestone outcrop.

The natural catchment of Keld Head extends across nearly 17 km², but about 1.6 km² is taken out by a leat (an artificial channel) that was originally built to gather water from the high western slopes to supply Bideber Mill, below Masongill; some of its water is now piped into the public supply. The limestone outcrop extends to about 6.8 km², so autogenic recharge should account for about 44% of the current discharge, the remainder being allogenic flow from the shale above the limestone. However, flow measurements in Kingsdale indicate that only about 20% of the mean total discharge is derived from swallet water entering sinks along the shale boundary (Halliwell, 1980), suggesting that a significant part of the allogenic drainage flows in and beneath the soil cover and enters the limestone beneath the lines of dolines that trace the shale boundary.

The ratio of autogenic to allogenic flow in the Keld Head discharge is also affected by surface run-off in flood conditions. At the head of the dale, Kingsdale Beck drains into sinks that are partially choked with boulders and sediment and cannot swallow flood flows. Wetter conditions, which pertain through about half the year, create large flows down the surface channel (which has been artificially straightened along its lower part); there is also some floodwater leakage into the East Kingsdale Master Cave. Estimates of rainfall and evapotranspiration suggest a mean flow from the Kingsdale catchment of around 450 L/s. Significant flood flows down

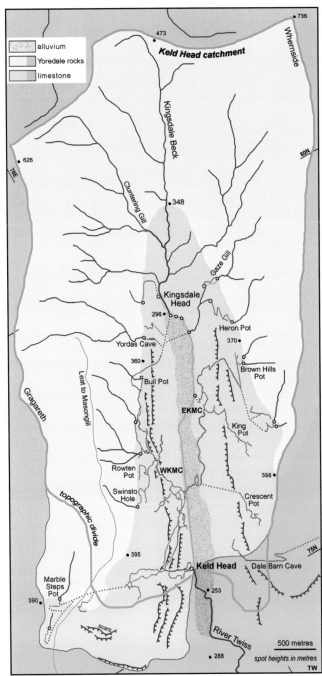

Figure 9.22. The streams and caves of Kingsdale that constitute the catchment of the Keld Head resurgence within the Great Scar Limestone; the only caves marked are those containing significant stream flows; dotted lines are dye traces; the alluvium indicates the extent of the floor of the dale; sinks and risings in the thin limestones within the overlying sequence of the Yoredale Group are not shown (after surveys by University of Leeds Speleological Association, Cave Diving Group, Northern Cave Club and others). WKMC and EKMC = West and East Kingsdale Master Caves.

and drain out to the resurgence pool. The gentle northerly dip of the bedding plane inception horizons means that most of the vadose drainage is towards the north, and the low-level conduits southwards to the resurgence are phreatic because they drain up-dip. A third major conduit carries drainage from the Marble Steps area, and all three main lines have braiding loop passages that carry parts of the conduit flows. The passage from East Kingsdale passes beneath the floor of the dale, with no link to or from the surface channel that is occupied in flood conditions. Autogenic water enters the cave conduits as numerous seepages and drips.

An extensive cover of till around Kingsdale Head keeps the upper Kingsdale Beck and Gaze Gill on the surface for a kilometre until they reach an area of multiple sinks through the alluvium. Flow from these enters the main upstream conduit in the West Kingsdale Cave System, which is phreatic along most of its length because it drains up-dip. Some or all of these sinks may also feed the Mud River conduit, whose source is unproven. Small sinks at the foot of Cluntering Gill take only a part of the flow, but drain beneath the till cover at Kingsdale Head to rejoin the main cave system.

The mapped southern boundary of the Keld Head catchment (on Fig. 9.22) is only approximate as the autogenic percolation recharge has not been traced. The boundary is interpreted as extending less on the east bank of the beck where surface run-off is locally dominant on the cover of moraine and alluvium. Dale Barn Cave drains east into Chapel-le-Dale but its passages extend beneath the mapped catchment of Keld Head. At low stage there is no significant flow in this part of the cave, but a static sump at its northern end (Boottrapper Passage) emits a large stream at high stage. This is a case of underground floodwater overflowing from the catchment across what is normally a hydrological divide. It is unknown if this flood flow is only from Crescent Pot, or if it is a distributary from the main conduits to Keld Head.

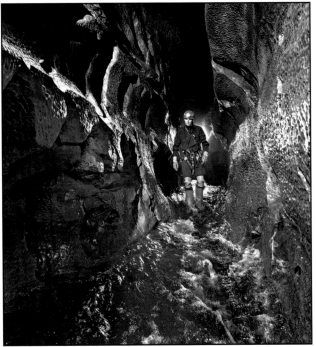

Figure 9.23. The vadose canyon that carries the large stream from the Master Junction towards the Downstream Sump within the West Kingsdale Master Cave (photo: Mark Shinwell).

the surface channel probably reduce the mean flow from Keld Head to little more than half of that figure, but no long records of flow are available. Flow from Keld Head probably exceeds 3500 L/s in flood, but declines to less than 50 L/s in long spells of dry weather.

Streams from sinks on the main benches descend through vadose caves, and many of these converge on the West and East Kingsdale Master Caves, which are the short lengths of vadose main drain under each side of the dale (Fig. 9.23). From the two main drains long phreatic tunnels converge

Groundwater flow at Malham

The karst around Malham was one of the first in Britain to have been subject to systematic water tracing (Fig. 9.24). Malham Tarn lies largely on an inlier of impermeable rock north of the North Craven Fault, and its outlet stream flows south to sink underground shortly after crossing the fault, at various points collectively known just as the Water Sinks (Fig. 9.25). One rising lies at the foot of the 70m-high cliff of Malham Cove (Fig. 9.26), 1.5 km south of the Tarn sinks, and a larger, double rising forms Aire Head, another 2 km to the south.

A connection from the Tarn sinks to Aire Head was proven in the 1870s by the monitoring of artificial flood pulses (Tate, 1879). Further pulse tests and the use of various chemical tracers, in 1899, confirmed that connection, proved drainage from the Smelt Mill Sink (west of Water Sinks) to the Cove rising, and also demonstrated a connection from the Tarn sinks to the Cove rising (Howarth *et al.*, 1900). From these grew the popular concept of crossing flow-paths at Malham. In the 1970s, traces with dyed *Lycopodium* spores, together with more pulse tests, confirmed connections from both sinks to both springs under certain stage conditions (Smith and Atkinson, 1977). The known limits of the catchment for the Malham Cove rising were then extended by multiple dye tests from a number of small sinks on the Grizedales slopes west of the Cove (Speight, 1994; Murphy, 2009).

The total catchment for the two risings is nearly 18 km², with only a small proportion providing allogenic recharge from the basement inlier at the Tarn and from a small part of the outlier of Yoredale rocks on Fountains Fell. Mean total discharge should therefore be around 350 L/s, and the larger proportion emerges from Aire Head. The phreatic conduit feeding Malham Cove Rising has been explored and mapped for 700m, and continues upstream beyond an underwater

Figure 9.25. The Water Sinks below Malham Tarn, where the tarn outflow sinks into the valley sediments at various points soon after crossing the buried North Craven Fault (TW).

boulder choke (Monico, 1995). No cave passage has been entered at Aire Head. Short lengths of cave are known at some of the sinks on Grizedales (Turton, 1994), and Malham Tarn Pot is a dry, choked shaft 27m deep, excavated in 1949 and subsequently back-filled.

The underground hydrology at Malham is relatively simple at low stage (Fig. 9.24), but the complexities of ephemeral underground connections and overflows under flood conditions have only been partially elucidated by quantitative pulse and tracer tests (Smith and Atkinson, 1977). A major unseen conduit extends from the Tarn sinks to Aire Head, and its rapid transmission of flood pulses indicates that much of its length is phreatic, presumably after a short and steep descent from the plateau level. From the quantitative dye traces, estimates of conduit volumes distinguish its

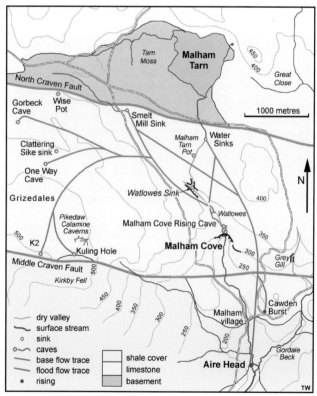

Figure 9.24. Underground flow paths in the Malham karst (after Smith and Atkinson, 1977, and Speight, 1994).

Figure 9.26. The limestone cliff of Malham Cove and the stream that flows from the rising at its base (TW).

vadose and the phreatic zones. Increased channel storage in the phreatic zone under conditions of higher discharge may be due to the presence of a maze passage network in the confined environment beneath the Bowland Shales between Malham Cove and Aire Head, where parts of the network only become active when flows are high. Increased storage is normal when the vadose zone is at flood stage.

Discharge from the Cove rising is dominated by recharge from the sinks at Smelt Mill and on Grizedales, and multiple dye tests did not reveal any flood overflows from the sinks on Grizedales into the Aire Head conduit (Speight, 1994); but see below. In all conditions of stage, a part of the Cove discharge is derived from the Tarn sinks. In very dry conditions, Aire Head can cease to flow, while the Tarn sinks still swallow a small stream and the Cove rising continues to flow. In moderately dry conditions dye traces have failed to indicate any flow through to the Cove, though arrivals of small artificial flood pulses confirm some activation of an overflow route to the Cove. In flood conditions, much larger flows cross from Water Sinks to the Cove, but still only represent a small proportion of the flow from the Cove rising. There would appear to be multiple distributary conduits off the trunk route from Water Sinks to Aire Head; each becomes active at its own particular stages of flood and thereby diverts underground flow away to the Malham Cove rising. Underground overflows also cross the hydrological divide in the opposite direction, as dye traces from the Smelt Mill Sink have proved positive to both Malham Cove and Aire Head at both high and low stage.

Subsequent traces with *Lycopodium* suggested that the two adjacent risings at Aire Head are fed by separate conduits, as traces from Smelt Mill Sink, Wise Pot and the Clattering Gill sink reached the southern rising and not the northern (Murphy, 2009), but these traces warrant confirmation.

Another distributary off the trunk route to Aire Head rises to the flood rising of the Cawden Burst. Perhaps once a year (though less frequently in the past), this produces a large flow from scree covering a slope on the side of Cawden Hill. For about a day, a sizeable stream runs down the road through the eastern part of Malham village, with a flow that far exceeds the potential local recharge from the Cawden reef knoll. A single dye test at high stage, when Tarn water was sinking all the way down its valley as far as the Watlowes Sink, proved the link to the Cawden Burst (Speight, 1994). Its multiple outpourings from the scree suggest a feed from a bedding plane cave that is a flood overflow 27m above the perennial rising at Aire Head.

It appears that there is some degree of connection between flows from both the Smelt Mill and Tarn sinks to both the Cove and Aire Head risings under all conditions of stage. This indicates a high level of maturity in the conduit network, with individual channels showing different levels of activity as stage increases. Constrictions do exist in some conduits, so that the Malham Cove rising is constrained to a modest flood peak while excess water is diverted to Aire Head; also, in extreme flood, the conduits to Aire Head are inadequate and water overflows from the Cawden Burst. Conduits that are almost unconnected at base flow are subject to increased flow integration when flood conditions are imposed. The Malham aquifer is considerably more complex than just having crossing flow-paths.

Karst water resources in the Dales

In the past, small springs from the limestone were utilised to supply water to villages, hamlets, farms and isolated dwellings across the Dales. Some still do provide supplies, but a better understanding of water-borne diseases has led to the water companies and local health authorities trying to eliminate many of these in favour of larger water undertakings with well-filtered supplies, mainly from surface catchments on the grit moors. This change of source has been carried out successfully in places such as Kettlewell, where the former supply from springs just south of Dowber Gill has been abandoned and replaced by a pumped main from the Embsay Reservoir. Ingleton used to take its supply from White Scar Cave, where a covered reservoir was later built for use in times of drought, but even this is no longer utilised. However, ten of the houses in Litton village are still reliant upon untreated water issuing from the valley-side spring of Litton Fosse, and the nearby group of farms and houses at Nether Hesleden has an untreated supply from the much smaller stream emerging from the nearby Mallender Cave.

The hamlet of Halton Gill, various hill farms and individual houses in many villages still rely on small springs to supply their water needs. A large proportion of these are outlets from fissure flows and small conduits perched on the shale horizons that act as aquicludes within the Great Scar Limestone. Others in the northern dales are outlets from the bases of the thin Yoredale limestones. At the other end of the scale, a part of Bradford's water supply is by abstraction from the River Wharfe at Lob Wood, near Addingham, where a high percentage of the water is from karst sources in Upper Wharfedale and Littondale. Bradford also takes water from

Figure 9.27. Kilnsey Trout Farm in Wharfedale, utilising clean, autogenic water from the Sike Gill Rising (TW).

Figure 9.28. *The partially choked shaft up which water rises to the Sike Gill Rising at Kilnsey (photo: John Cordingley).*

the Angram and Scar House reservoirs on the River Nidd, but these have catchments on shale and sandstone upstream of where their overflow water sinks into Manchester Hole and Goyden Pot.

Karst water from risings is also used by fish farms, which take advantage of the high and stable quality of emergent water that is derived largely or entirely from autogenic recharge into the limestone. In Wharfedale, the Kilnsey Park Trout Farm (Fig. 9.27) takes its water from the Sike Gill Rising with its catchment on the high limestone fells to the west (Fig. 9.13). Also in Wharfedale, trout hatcheries are sited to utilise water from the Moss Beck Rising, with some of its flow coming from Sleets Gill Cave, and from Brow Well, near Grassington, which is the known outlet for some of the water sinking on Grassington Moor.

Unlike the situation in the Peak District and the Mendip Hills, where groundwater is an important resource (Gunn, 1992), the overall usage of groundwater from the limestones of the Yorkshire Dales is modest, particularly since increasing demands for water quality have led to the abandonment of many small sources across the upland karst.

References

Allen, D J and 7 others, 1997. The physical properties of major aquifers in England and Wales. *Brit. Geol. Surv. Tech Report*, WD/97/34, 312pp.

Atkinson, T C, 1977. Diffuse flow and conduit flow in limestone terrain in the Mendip Hills, Somerset (Great Britain). *J. Hydrology*, 35, 93-110.

Bottrell, S. H. and T C Atkinson, 1992. Tracer study of flow and storage in the unsaturated zone of a karstic limestone aquifer. 207-211 in H Hötzl and A Werner (eds.), *Tracer Hydrology*. Balkema: Rotterdam.

Bowser, R, 1973. The Three Counties System. *J. London Univ. Caving Clubs*, 14, 8-13.

Brook, D, 1969. The drainage and development of West Kingsdale. *Univ. Leeds Spel. Assoc. Explorations Journal*, 70-73.

Brook, D, 1989. Langcliffe Pot. *Univ. Leeds Spel. Assoc. Explorations Journal 2*, 31-41.

Gough, J, 1813. Observations on the Ebbing and Flowing Well at Giggleswick, in the West Riding of Yorkshire, with a theory of reciprocating fountains. *Mem. Proc. Lit. Phil. Soc. Manchester*, 2, 354-383.

Gunn, J, 1992. Hydrogeological contrasts between British Carboniferous Limestone aquifers. *International Contributions to Hydrogeology*, 13, 25-42.

Halliwell, R A, J L Ternan and A F Pitty, 1974. Introduction to the karst hydrology of Northwest Yorkshire. 106-114 in A C Waltham (ed.), *Limestones and Caves of North-west England*. David and Charles: Newton Abbot.

Halliwell, R A, 1979. Influence of contrasted rock types and geological structure on solutional processes in North West Yorkshire. 51-71 in A F Pitty (ed.), *Geographical approaches to fluvial processes*. Geobooks: Norwich.

Halliwell, R A, 1980. Karst waters of the Ingleborough area, North Yorkshire. *Proc. Univ. Bristol Spel. Soc.*, 15, 183-205.

Harrison, T, 2012. Further phreatic cave systems under the Swaledale-Wensleydale surface watershed in the Yorkshire Dales, UK. *Cave Karst Science*, 39, 23- 33.

Howarth, J H, 1900. The underground waters of north-west Yorkshire. *Proc. Yorks. Geol. Polytech. Soc.*, 14, 1-44.

Jones, H K and 12 others, 2000. The physical properties of minor aquifers in England and Wales. *Brit. Geol. Surv. Tech. Report*, WD/00/04, 234pp.

Klimchouk, A B, 2007. *Hypogene Speleogenesis*. National Cave Karst Research Institute: Carlsbad NM, 106pp

Monico, P (ed.), 1995. *Northern Sump Index*. Cave Diving Group: UK, 286pp.

Murphy, P, 2009. Malham's missing miles of cave. *Speleology*, 13, 6-7.

Murphy, P J, R Smallshire and C Midgley, 2001. The sediments of Illusion Pot, Kingsdale, UK; evidence for sub-glacial utilisation of a karst conduit in the Yorkshire Dales? *Cave Karst Science*, 28, 29-34.

Myers, J O, 1950. The Mossdale problem: the problem of the underground water flows. *Trans. Cave Res. Gp.*, 1 (4), 23-30

Palmer, A N, 1975. The origin of maze caves. *Nat. Spel. Soc. Bull.*, 37 (3), 56-76.

Palmer, A N, 2007. *Cave Geology*. Cave Books: Dayton OH, 454pp.

Ryder, P F, 1975. Phreatic network caves in the Swaledale area, Yorkshire. *Trans. Brit. Cave Res. Assoc.*, 2, 177-192.

Smart, P L, A J Edwards and S L Hobbs, 1992. Heterogeneity in carbonate aquifers: effects of scale, fissuration, lithology and karstification. *Proc. 3rd Conf. on Hydrogeology, Ecology, Monitoring and Management of Groundwater in Karst Terranes, Nashville, Tennessee* (Water Well Journal: Dublin OH), 373-387.

Smith, D I and T C Atkinson, 1977. Underground flow in cavernous limestones with special reference to the Malham area. *Field Studies*, 4, 597-616.

Speight, A, 1994. Hydrology of the Aire River System, Malham. *J. Yorks. Subterranean Soc.*, 3, 55-60.

Stevens, G, 1964. Intermittent springs. *Trans. Cave Res. Gp.*, 7, 3-9.

Tate, T, 1879. The source of the River Aire. *Proc. Yorks. Geol. Polytech. Soc.*, 7, 177-187.

Turton, R, 1994. The Aire River System, Malham. *J. Yorks. Subterranean Soc.*, 3, 47-62.

Waltham, A C, 1977. White Scar Cave, Ingleton. *Trans. Brit. Cave Res. Assoc.*, 4, 345-353.

Waltham, A C, D B Brook, O W Statham and T G Yeadon, 1981. Swinsto Hole, Kingsdale: a type example of cave development in the limestone of Northern England. *Geog. J.*, 147, 350-353.

Waltham, A C, M J Simms, A R Farrant and H S Goldie, 1997. *Karst and Caves of Great Britain*. Chapman & Hall (for Joint Nature Conservation Committee): London, 358pp.

Worthington, S R H, 1999. A comprehensive strategy for understanding flow in carbonate aquifers. 30-37 in A N Palmer, M V Palmer and I D Sasowsky (eds.), Karst modelling. *Karst Waters Institute Spec. Pub.*, 5.

Worthington S R H and J Gunn, 2009. Hydrogeology of carbonate aquifers: a short history. *Ground Water*, 47, 462-467.

Worthington, S R H and D C Ford, 2009. Self-organized permeability in carbonate aquifers. *Ground Water*, 47, 326-336.

CHAPTER 10

Chronology of the caves

Alf Latham and Derek Ford

When the predecessor of this book was published nearly 40 years ago (Waltham, 1974) there was no dating method available to assign an absolute chronology to the caves and their deposits or to the karst landscapes. Many caves were known to pre-date the Devensian glaciation, but calendric dating of the British Quaternary was largely restricted to the radiocarbon method, which is limited to about 40 ka.

It was the advent of uranium-thorium (U–Th) dating of speleothems from the mid-70s that placed the successive phases of cave development on a firmer footing, and allowed their phase-chronology to be related to local landscape and, via stable isotopes, to palaeoclimates (see Chapter 11). As evolution of the karst within the Yorkshire Dales was expected, and has since been proven, to have been strongly influenced by the Pleistocene glaciations, it was recognised that dated speleothems provided an important record of landscape development through the glacials, interglacials, stadials and interstadials of the late Quaternary.

Uranium–thorium dating

The uranium–thorium method is the chief among several methods of dating that are based on the radioactive decay of unstable isotopes in speleothems (Fig. 10.1). It was first applied to cave calcite during work at the McMaster University uranium-series dating laboratory in Canada (Thompson et al., 1974; Harmon et al., 1975). The first chronology of British speleothems incorporated material from both the Yorkshire Dales and the Mendip Hills, with dates obtained in the McMaster laboratory (Atkinson et al., 1978), after preliminary reports had been published the previous year (Gascoyne, 1977; Waltham and Harmon, 1977). Those data were followed by greater numbers of speleothem dates from many more caves within the Dales (Gascoyne et al., 1983a; Gascoyne and Ford, 1984). All the early dates were obtained by alpha spectrometry. This method required samples of several grams of material, which limited precision in finely banded stalagmite, and also had an effective limit of about 350 ka.

A range of subsequent stalagmite dates emanated from various smaller projects pursued in the Dales caves. Most of these data were improved by the introduction of thermal ionization mass spectrometry (TIMS), which has a potential age limit of 600 ka, covering glacial and interglacial stages since Marine Isotope Stage (MIS) 15. This method also offers about ten times the dating precision, because it requires only very small samples that can encompass fewer growth layers (Fig. 10.2). Uranium-series dating has already enjoyed considerable success in its application to speleothems

(Ivanovich and Harmon, 1992; Bourdon et al., 1997; Latham, 2001; Dorale et al., 2007). The new and future emphasis is on inductively coupled plasma mass spectrometry, where still-smaller sample sizes present opportunity for even more detailed studies of palaeoclimates (Hoffmann, 2008).

Uranium in its oxidised hexavalent state is soluble in groundwater, so any speleothem initially incorporates small amounts of uranium, typically 0.15 to 5 ppm, into its growth layers. Within its decay series, uranium-238 is the long-lived parent isotope, with a half-life of 4468 Ma, and its alpha-decay daughter is uranium-234, with a half-life of 248 ka. The next alpha-decay daughter is thorium-230, with a half-life of 75.2 ka, but this is absent from cave dripwater because it is insoluble and is immobilized in the soil zone as thorium hydroxide. Consequently an initial radioactive disequilibrium exists in the calcite growth layer, in which the only thorium-230 present is that which has grown radiogenically with time from its two uranium parents. The known rate of production of thorium-230 from its parents constitutes the clock by which the speleothem can be dated. Due to the peculiar nature of weathering of uranium from initial rock sources, there is commonly an initial excess of uranium-234 over its parent uranium-238; it is the ratio of thorium-230 to uranium-234 that largely indicates the age, modified by the disequilibrium between the two uranium isotopes. Any contamination by detrital thorium also has to be taken into account, as failure to do so produces spuriously high age estimates; contamination is normally identified by the presence of thorium-232, which is not present in dripwater but occurs only in detritus. Many of the speleothems that began to form on a mud substrate are contaminated with sediment, and are consequently excluded from some statistical analyses (Baker et al., 1993a).

Figure 10.1. *Speleothems in Pippikin Pot, with a host of new straws and stalagmites forming over an older false floor of flowstone (TW).*

Chronology of the caves, by Alf Latham and Derek Ford,
Alf Latham: University of Liverpool; aa09@liverpool.ac.uk
Derek Ford: McMaster University, Canada; dford@mcmaster.ca
Chapter 10, pages 169-180 in **Caves and Karst of the Yorkshire Dales**,
edited by Tony Waltham and David Lowe.
Published 2013 by the British Cave Research Association,
978-0-900265-46-4 and at bcra.org.uk

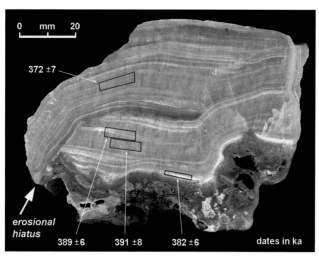

Figure 10.2. A piece of flowstone from Victoria Cave showing the very small sample sizes required for mass spectrometry uranium-series dating; the three dates in the older portion fall into age sequence within their error bars (photo: Joyce Lundberg).

In the laboratory the uranium and thorium have to be extracted from a speleothem sample by dissolution in acid, and then precipitated onto discs. Isotope analysis is then by computer counting of alpha emissions. In the original work with alpha spectrometry in the 1970s, this took many days, and its low precision was reflected in the large statistical error bars. The technique was greatly improved by the advent of mass spectrometry, but many of the dates for speleothems from the Yorkshire Dales were produced before this and before the development of multi-sample leaching. Some earlier analyses were corrected for detrital thorium-230 by relating them to the thorium-232, but that was recognised as only an approximation, and the estimated 'corrected' ages lacked precision. The lack of precision was more significant with younger ages, and dates produced by the older methods have been omitted from some chronological analyses for the last deglaciation (Baker *et al., 1993a*).

Uranium–lead dating

A well-established geological dating technique is based on the stable daughter lead-208 and its progenitor uranium-238. It was first used to date old speleothems with uranium-rich material from Winnats Head Cave, Derbyshire, where coincident ages from the uranium–lead and uranium–thorium methods demonstrated its applicability (Richards *et al., 1998*). Although both methods rely on the same parent uranium-238, the daughter products and half-lives are different and the clocks based on them are independent. Because uranium-238 has a very long half-life, of 4468 Ma, the amounts of accumulated daughter lead-208 are small. The method is therefore only applicable to speleothems with relatively high contents of uranium and lead, as are found in igneous rocks where it has long produced reliable results. Corrections for the lead that was co-precipitated from the original feedwater are achieved, with some difficulty, by using the non-radiogenic index isotopes lead-204 and lead-205.

Where concentrations of uranium and lead isotopes are sufficiently high, it may be possible to extend some speleothem-based records to more than 1 Ma using uranium–lead analyses. The method has been used successfully to date the Australopithecine cave sites, including Sterkfontein in South Africa, to about 2 Ma (Walker *et al., 2006*). For caves in the Dales, it remains uncertain whether the method could be applied to older flowstones such as those from Victoria Cave that contain only modest amounts of uranium.

Alternative dating methods

In parallel with research based on uranium–thorium dating, a large number of other dating methods have been tried, developed and applied to all kinds of deposits relevant to caves and to times that span much of the Quaternary. Most have been used more for archaeology and for dating other terrestrial deposits, and have so far yielded little data from the Dales caves, though several methods are still in development (Noller *et al., 2000*; Walker, 2005).

Carbon-14 dating

Until the 1970s, only the radiocarbon technique was available for dating material from the latter part of the British Quaternary, its dating limit being about 40 ka. Because the cosmogenic production rate of carbon-14 in the atmosphere has not been constant over time, radiocarbon dates have required calibration, first by dendrochronology (tree-ring counting) back to about 10 ka, and then by uranium dating back to 60 ka (Weninger and Jöris, 2008). Thus, raw carbon-14 ages of corals and speleothems are younger than equivalent uranium ages by about 1700 years at the start of the Holocene at 11.7 ka and by about 3500 yrs at around 40 ka. An internationally agreed model is used to recalibrate raw radiocarbon ages and they are then quoted 'before present' to 1950, in yrs cal BP (Reimer *et al., 2009*).

Figure 10.3. Tall narrow stalagmites, like these at Cape Kennedy in Lancaster Hole, are likely to hold detailed records of datable environmental changes, though these may only extend through the Holocene; collection of material has to be from less conspicuous sites (photo: John Forder).

Figure 10.4. The Jockey Cap stalagmite, which stands in the main gallery of Ingleborough Cave, and has been radiocarbon dated to nearly 4000 years old (photo: Don McFarlane).

The most common radiocarbon dating targets in caves and elsewhere are organic sediments with the protein collagen, which is found in bones that are not fully fossilised and in marine shells. A major problem is contamination by younger or older carbon introduced by groundwater, requiring careful screening of samples, extraction of particular parts of the collagen content, and checks for recrystallisation in shells.

For speleothems, the sources of the carbon in calcite are 50% from the host rock and 50% from atmospheric carbon dioxide and the organic soil zone. The feed-water, however, can continue to exchange carbon before precipitation of the calcite and so the carbon-14 component from organic materials is diluted by variable amounts from the carbon contributed by the rock. As radiocarbon dating is limited to ages younger than about 40 ka, the method has seldom been used for dating speleothems (Latham *et al.*, 1986). A carbon-14 date of 3123–3794 yrs cal BP was obtained for early material in the Jockey Cap stalagmite in Ingleborough Cave (Fig. 10.4), where excessive thorium contamination rendered uranium-series dating unusable, but problems of carbon contamination leave the interpreted dates open to question (McFarlane *et al.*, 2005).

Luminescence dating

Some radiogenic dose accumulation methods apply to certain buried materials, whose radiation-induced doses have been reset by initial exposure to heat or to light, and then accumulate a natural dose throughout their burial time. This is related to an external dose from cosmic rays and a mostly internal dose of alpha, beta and gamma emissions from naturally occurring uranium, thorium and potassium in the sediment matrix or in the target material itself. It results in an increasing number of electrons that are trapped at various types of lattice defects within crystalline material. Individual mineral grains of, for example, quartz, may inherit

a dose from earlier times, and some of the dose may reflect a complex history due to incomplete burial as the sediment moves from above ground to its final deposit. Single grain techniques have been developed to address these problems.

The methods involve the measurement of the trapped electrons that constitute the dose. It is recognised that the dose rate is dependent upon porosity of the surrounding matrix and hence upon the water content; it is generally assumed that the present-day water content is close to the long-term average. Phosphor dosimeters inserted in the sediment for a full year provide an estimate of the dose rate in burial, and the materials are given artificial doses from a cobalt-60 source in order to estimate the original dose.

Optically Stimulated Luminescence relies on the filling of electron traps that emit photons at optical wavelengths when stimulated; an alternative is Infra-Red Stimulated Luminescence, which can be used on single grains of quartz (Wintle, 2010). There is uncertainty about the accuracy of these methods at ages greater than 50 ka (Wintle, 1990), but they could be tried on the quartz grains bleached by exposure to sunlight prior to their incorporation in cave sediments. The former method has been used extensively on buried loess deposits, and loess horizons have been recognised in several palaeosol sequences in the Yorkshire Dales (Wilson *et al.*, 2008).

Thermoluminescence dating relies on measuring the accumulated dose by stepped heating to yield a luminescent glow curve (Wintle, 1978). The method was attempted to date stalagmitic calcite from Gavel Pot, but errors and problems rendered it inapplicable and the work was not pursued (Ann Wintle, *pers. comm.*).

Electron spin resonance dating

Another radiogenic method relies on the dose accumulated in material such as tooth enamel that has a zero dose during the life stage. It is measured by electron spin resonance. This method has a potential age limit of about a million years, so has been tried on speleothems. Dates of stalagmite from Simpson Pot and Victoria Cave (Fig. 10.5), among a suite of samples largely from caves outside the Dales, were in accord with uranium-series dates for the same material (Smart *et al.*, 1988), but uncertainties about the stability of the traps in calcite mean that the technique was not pursued.

Figure 10.5. The excavated entrance chamber in Victoria Cave (TW).

One date of 424 ka for flowstone in the abandoned high-levels of Simpson Pot may be indicative of pre-Anglian drainage of the passages, but the long error bar of ±57 ka limits the confidence in any such interpretation.

Another problem with all the dose-accumulation methods has been the chemical alteration of sediments in sites such as cave entrances that have been open to weathering and at locations subject to water infiltration. Methods were developed and tested on hominid sites in Israel. There was good concordance of their ages for Qafzeh Cave, near Nazareth. However, at the Neanderthal cave site of Tabun, near Haifa, thermoluminescence on burnt flint gave considerably greater ages for each stratum than those based on the electron spin resonance of teeth. The methods required a re-examination of experimental protocols and input parameters, in the light of a history of variable chemical alteration, before they could be reconciled (Grün et al., 1991; Mercier and Valladas, 2003).

Aluminium–beryllium dating

A promising methodology that can be applied to quartz-rich sediments in caves older than the Anglian glaciation is based on a comparison of the two cosmogenically-produced isotopes, beryllium-10 and aluminium-26 (Granger and Muzikar, 2001; Nishiizumi et al., 2007). As with carbon-14, these isotopes are produced, at rates that have varied over thousands of years, by cosmic-ray bombardment of weathering minerals in surface rock outcrops and soils, and quartz grains are the preferred target for measurement. The penetrating power of cosmic particles attenuates with depth, and is thought to be effectively zero beyond about 10m of rock. Hence, a fully exposed sediment load that is then quickly buried in a cave beyond this depth will have beryllium-10 and aluminium-26 that decay away completely without being renewed, with respective half-lives of 1.387 and 0.717 Ma. Thus, the age of the sediment burial can be estimated. The two isotopes together, expressed as the ratio $^{26}Al/^{10}Be$, compensate to some extent for the variable production rate of each considered alone, and the method has a potential age range up to several million years. However, few specialist, accelerator mass-spectrometry facilities are currently available, because initial capital expenditure and subsequent running costs are high.

***Figure 10.6**. The thick sequence of clastic sediments in the very old Duke Street 2 passage in Ireby FellCavern (photo: Dave Checkley).*

The method has been used successfully to estimate the incision rate of the Green River in Kentucky, by dating sediments in Mammoth Cave back to 3.5 Ma, which fits well with a previously established record of magnetic polarity reversals (Granger et al., 2001). It has also provided dates of over 2 Ma for sediments in the high-levels of the Mulu caves in Sarawak, these dates being compatible with the sequence of uranium–thorium dates in passages at lower altitudes (Pete Smart, pers.comm.). However, it has not been successful at other sites, where the cosmogenic age estimates are at variance from the more reliable uranium–lead dating. Sand and breccia from Kent's Cavern, in Devon, were dated to 0.95 and 2.32 Ma, but with very large error bars that minimised interpretation of the geomorphology (Lundberg and McFarlane, 2007). The aluminium–beryllium method has not yet been applied in the Yorkshire Dales, though thick and probably very old sequences of stratified quartz-rich clastic sediments in Lancaster Hole, Ireby Fell Cavern and Gaping Gill are among those that could provide useful material to contribute to a dated record (Fig. 10.6).

Cosmogenic chlorine dating

Assays of the cosmogenic isotope chlorine-36 in specimens from newly exposed surfaces in rocks has been used successfully to estimate erosion rates. The method has been used on the glacial erratics that stand on limestone plinths at Norber, on Ingleborough, yielding estimates of post-glacial exposure of around 18 ka, though without calibration for variable rates of isotopic evolution (Vincent et al., 2010). The record of chlorine-36 in stalagmite has the potential to yield reconstructions of solar irradiance that could extend back to 500 ka (Johnston and McDermott, 2009).

Palaeomagnetic dating

Polarity of the Earth's magnetic field has exhibited numerous reversals between periods of stability that have been either long or short. The last long-term change of polarity was at 780 ka, from the reversed Matuyama magnetic period to the present Brunhes, but smaller changes in declination and intensity and also short perturbations of polarity are superimposed on the long-term reversals. Clastic sediments containing iron oxide are orientated to the Earth's magnetic field at the time of deposition, and this orientation can be measured in suitably orientated laboratory samples. Dating then depends on the recognition of a match between the palaeomagnetic record of minerals in the target sequence of sediments with the bar-code-like changes of the age-calibrated Global Polarity Timescale (Gradstein et al., 2006).

The magnetic particles in a suitable sediment must have settled from the suspended load under the influence of the Earth's magnetic field, in practice in ponded, or slow-moving, water. Such fine-grained sediments are found in cave passages that have experienced backed up flood water. Sediments that have fallen down shafts, or that have slumped, are not likely to have magnetic records influenced only by the Earth's ambient field. Generally, cave sediment sequences are too short to record the long time-base changes of polarities (Stock et al., 2005). A notable exception is the succession of sediments in the multiple levels of the Mammoth Cave System in Kentucky, where those in the upper levels could be shown to date back to before 2.2 Ma (Schmidt, 1982).

Palynology

The readily identifiable pollen of different plant species create stratigraphical signals by their relative abundances, and are used to support the chronology of terrestrial sequences, when extracted from cores, particularly from bogs and lake floors (see Chapter 12). Pollen grains consist of shells of the carbon compound exine. These are generally resistant to degradation, except that the oxygenated, alkaline environment of caves is usually not conducive to their preservation. Nevertheless, some stalagmites and clastic sediments have been studied for their records, on the assumption that any contained pollen assemblage represents the contemporary regional vegetation (Caseldine *et al.*, 2008). The caveat is that some pollen survives for very long periods, so its presence in stalagmites may indicate past rather than contemporary conditions. There are fine-grained rhythmic sediments several metres thick in caves, including Ireby Fell Cavern and the Gaping Gill Cave System, that might also usefully be examined for pollen.

Speleothems and glacial cycles

The many speleothem ages from caves in the Yorkshire Dales, together with many more from caves elsewhere in Britain, have contributed significantly to an understanding of European terrestrial climate change. Many of the dates determined by alpha-spectrometry, between about 1977 and 1995, lack the precision of those derived subsequently by thermal imaging mass spectrometry, and this is especially pertinent for the dates around the end of MIS 2. Advances have also been made in mapping of Devensian glacial deposits and in carbon-14 dating that has led to refinement of the chronology of the end of MIS 2. The extent and duration of the last British–Irish ice sheet and its deglaciation were diachronous, and might not have coincided exactly with changes in global ice volume (Chiverrell and Thomas, 2010). Ice retreat from the Yorkshire Dales area is known to have taken place between about 18 and 16 ka (see Chapter 3).

The present interglacial setting of the Yorkshire Dales is referred to as a maritime climate consisting of warm, but not hot, summers and cool, but not cold, winters, with abundant rainfall and lacking a dry period; prevailing westerly winds bring moisture from the relatively warm North Atlantic Ocean. Deposition of speleothems is attributable both to above-freezing bedrock temperatures (in the absence of glacial cover and permafrost) and to plentiful rainfall. Whereas speleothem deposition over time may be thought to have tracked the oceanic changes in ice volume, their growth periods and isotope records have been modulated to some extent by more localised, terrestrial effects due to the position on the edge of the Atlantic Ocean. In addition, changes in seepage routing within the overlying limestone bedrock can influence patterns of speleothem deposition (Fig. 10.7).

Because stalagmites are formed from water seepage in the overlying rock mass, the base of each generally represents the end of a glacial period when bedrock temperature rose above freezing point for at least part of the year. Growth ceased when glacial or periglacial conditions returned. Hence it might be thought that speleothems accurately track the periods when the land surface was not covered by ice. A picture of speleothem growth coinciding with the warmer,

odd-numbered, marine isotope stages, and ceasing during the colder stages, is distorted by various factors. Although ground temperatures may rise above zero upon deglaciation, and speleothems may then form, masses of ice may remain on the surface for some time after ablation starts. Subsequent plant activity is also required to raise the levels of biogenic carbon dioxide in seepage waters, so that degassing in cave air causes calcite deposition. Conversely, it is likely that the initiation of a cold phase begins with permafrost, when soil formation greatly diminishes and speleothem growth ceases, and this may be some time before there is any significant covering of ice. Glacial initiation might also be caused by increased snowfall and snow-blow that persists through the summer into the next year, without the early periglacial phase, and it is also altitude-dependent.

The substantial formation of glaciers and ice sheets probably lags behind the decrease in temperature at the start of a glacial stage, and their ablation and melting almost certainly lag behind the rise in temperature at the end of a glacial or stadial. The marine isotope record is dominated by ice volume, so the speleothem record, were it to be dated rather more accurately than the early alpha-spectrometric method allowed, is likely to lag behind it at the onset of glaciation but to precede it as the ice disappeared. In addition to these factors, the Last Glacial Maximum is now known to be markedly diachronous in both its advance and retreat across Britain (Chiverrell and Thomas, 2010).

Figure 10.7. *Active deposition of calcite flowstone on the wall of the Main Streamway in White Scar Cave, as it appeared before the show cave walkway was installed (TW).*

location	NGR alt, m	sample number	part	U ppm	age ka	+/- ka	ref
Ibbeth Peril Cave 1	741864						
Entrance Passage	180	76110	top	0.72	10.1	0.5	2
Entrance Passage	180	76111	base upper	0.30 0.31	26.9* 13.7	3.4 1.3	2
Entrance Passage	180	76112	veneer	1.21	7.6	0.7	2
Lancaster Hole	664807						
Bill Taylor's Passage	245	76121	top base	2.42 1.49	113 114	8 7	2
Bill Taylor's Passage	245	76122	top base	2.59 2.12	70.6 90.8	3.4 5.3	2
Bill Taylor's Passage	245	76124	base	0.62	13.3	1.0	2
Bill Taylor's Passage	245	76125	top base	1.17 2.01	38.8 54.4	1.5 11.7	2
Bill Taylor's Passage	245	76135	top middle	1.32 0.97	85.7 94.7	2.6 4.4	2
Colonnade Passage	268	79005 77120	top upper lower base	0.43 0.41 0.43 2.71	43.0 62.3* 86.8 140	3.1 6.5 3.8 10	2
Colonnade Passage	268	LH906CT LH905CM LH905BM LH904BM	top upper lower base	1.56 1.70 4.82 5.49	36.1 57.8 84.5 126	0.7 1.7 0.7 3.4	7
Montagu East	245	76130	top base	1.90 2.77	5.5 9.6	0.2 0.3	2
Ease Gill Caverns	675805						
Stop Pot	265	76127	top middle base	13.1 14.5 5.8	225 238 >350	22 19	2
Stop Pot	265	76131	base	17.1	9.0	0.3	2
Easter Grotto	280	76128	base	18.3	11.5	0.5	2
Easter Grotto	280	76129	top base	3.1 1.8	0.5* 9.7*	0.3 1.0	2
Pippikin Pot	667800						
Whitehall	260		top base		4.3 9.5	0.1 0.2	12
Gavel Pot	666791						
Glasfurd's Passage	270	GP2	middle	0.85	14	9	1
Glasfurd's Passage	270	Y1	middle	0.28	131	18	1
Glasfurd's Passage	270	Y3	top middle base	0.19 0.13 0.15	61 92 112	4 5 5	1
Glasfurd's Passage	270	76190	top base	0.50 0.57	5.1 14.7	0.6 0.6	2
Lost John's Cave	670786						
Lyle Cavern High Level	272	76160	top base	0.18 0.20	123 127	26 12	2
Lyle Cavern High Level	272	76161	base	0.25	12.1	5.4	2
Leck Fell Master Cave	225	76164	top base	3.84 5.68	98.7 106	3.8 4	2
Valley Entrance	698774						
Roof Tunnel	263	KM1		0.10	>350		1
Roof Tunnel	263	KM2		0.10	239	23	6
Roof Tunnel	263	77240		0.20	324	>100	2
Roof Tunnel	263	77241		0.41	168	11	2
Roof Tunnel	263	77242		1.55	300	57	2
Roof Tunnel	263	77243		1.17	230	21	2
Keld Head	696766						
First Airbell	252	KH2			4.5	0.9	11
Marble Steps Inlet	248	MS2			89.4	1.0	11
Dale Barn Cave	700762						
Expressway	255	DB1			343	67	9
White Scar Cave	712745						
Main Streamway	264	WS5	top	0.38	225	60	1
Main Streamway	264	76100	top	0.88	>350		2
Battlefield	285	WS3	middle base	0.40 0.35	6 90	2 11	1
Battlefield	280		top base		6.8 10.7	0.1 0.5	12
Western Front	285	76102	top	0.06	>350		2
Western Front	285	WS8		0.25	26	6	5
Sleepwalker Yard	292	76106a	top base	0.58 0.61	218 255	26 51	2
Sleepwalker Yard	292	76106b	top	0.80	>350		2
Far Streamway	290	76108	top base	2.11 1.39	6.0 9.4*	0.3 1.2	2
Newby Moss Pot	738723						
Entrance Passage	450	76220	top	1.34	>350		2
Gaping Gill Cave	751727						
Mud Hall	325	76202	base	0.46	>350		2
Old East Passage	325	76209	top	0.25	312*	46	2
Old East Passage	325	76210	top base	2.38 1.39	37.7 38.5	1.4 1.5	2
Old East Passage	325	76211		0.39	253	27	2
Far East Passage	325	77200	top base	0.95 1.94	289 <350	22	2
Hensler's Dry Way	300	76206		1.81	43.5	1.2	2
Nevada Passage	285	76207	top base	0.30 0.89	135 114	15 8	2
Ingleborough Cave	754710						
Giant's Hall	265	76140	base	0.10	127*	38	2
Giant's Hall	265	77143	top upper lower base	0.06 0.07 0.14 0.12	93.9* 98.4 115 125	11.1 13.3 8.2 8.4	2
Victoria Cave	839650						
Loop Passage	440	76152	base	0.38	161*	43	2
Loop Passage	440	76153	top	0.18	11.4*	2.9	2
Loop Passage	440	76151	top base	0.43 0.24	202* 288	3 4	13
Loop Passage	443	VCB		0.38	118*	1	13
Main Chamber	440	79000		0.62	102	11	2
Main Chamber	440	79021		0.43	125	7	3
Main Chamber	440	77159	top base	0.32 0.39	92.5* 307	9 46	2
Main Chamber	430	63272		1.58	523*	17	13
Main Chamber	435	79155		0.14	467*	16	13
Main Chamber	440	77237	top base	0.44 0.50	372* 391	7 8	13
Rift	435	76155		0.62	>600*		13
Malham Cove Rising	897641						
Aire River Passage	224	MCS1		0.08	27.3	5.6	10
Stump Cross Caverns	089635						
Wolverine Cave	345	HAR2662 HAR2670 HAR2657	upper middle lower	0.15 0.09 0.11	42 57 93	6 10 14	4
Wolverine Cave	345	SURRC549		3.50	110	13	4
Wolverine Cave	345	HAR2672		2.84	172	7	4
Wolverine Cave	345	SURRC547		2.37	222	42	4
Wolverine Cave	345	SC906K SC906EM SC906M SC905A	top upper lower base	0.05 0.12 0.09 1.07	11.3* 52.7 76.7 169	2.8 1.4 2.6 4	8

Table 10.1. *Uranium–thorium age determinations of stalagmites in the Yorkshire Dales caves. These 107 records are only a selection of the data, and another 218 are recorded in the same set of published references; unlisted ages are either very similar to those listed above and from adjacent material, or are among a large number of samples that proved to be post-Devensian; all of these are included in the distribution histogram (Fig. 10.10).*
Uranium concentrations are low, with 62 at <1 ppm, 39 at 1.0–5.8 ppm, and 4 (all in Ease Gill Caverns) at 13–18 ppm.
* = corrected age with estimated compensation for detrital thorium.

Listed errors are mean values, but the older error is always greater than the younger.
Ages >100 ka are quoted to the nearest 1 ka.
NGRs are of the cave entrances; altitudes are of the sample sites within the caves; NGRs are in SD, except Stump Cross Caverns in SE.
*Sources: **1**: Atkinson et al., 1978. **2**: Gascoyne et al., 1983a. **3**: Gascoyne et al., 1984. **4**: Sutcliffe et al., 1985. **5**: Atkinson et al., 1986. **6**: Waltham, 1986. **7**: Baker et al., 1995. **8**: Baker et al., 1996. **9**: Murphy et al., 2001. **10**: Murphy and Latham, 2001. **11**: Murphy et al., 2008. **12**: Daley et al., 2011. **13**: Lundberg et al., 2010.*

Dales caves and the Quaternary record

The Quaternary record for the British Isles has been based largely on the recognition of tills, moraines and associated interglacial biostratigraphical sequences, and until recently many have lacked assignments of absolute age. This has been partly due to the 40 ka limit of radiocarbon dating of extant organic remains, and partly due to the lack of suitable materials for dating by other methods such as volcanic ash for potassium–argon dating or correlation with known eruptions. This situation changed for the better with the advent of uranium–thorium dating of speleothems. Speleothem dates and their underlying deposits may not easily be related to the record of surface geomophology, but the speleothem chronology is still a very useful adjunct to British Quaternary studies. It is significant that speleothem dates are not direct dates of the formation or the dewatering of cave passages, but are minimum dates only, and hence indicate only the earliest timings of related landforms; however, the age correspondence can be close if supported by appropriate geomorphological interpretation.

Starting with the first compilations of British speleothem dates (Atkinson *et al.*, 1978; Gascoyne *et al.*, 1983a; Gascoyne and Ford, 1984), there has been every emphasis on relating them to the wider geomorphology and regional evolutions of the landscapes. Much of the speleothem dating has been used climatologically to delineate interglacials and interstadials within the British Pleistocene. Compilations

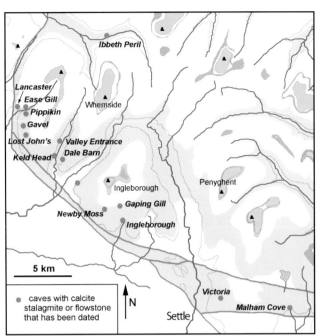

Figure 10.9. Locations of caves from which stalagmites or flowstones have been uranium–thorium dated; flowstones from Stump Cross Caverns have also been dated, but that cave lies east of the map coverage.

from wider coverage that included the Yorkshire Dales (Hennig *et al.*, 1983; Gordon and Smart, 1984) produced speleothem age frequency records from more than 400 dates, which were compared with the oxygen isotope record of glacial and interglacial stages, now referred to as Marine Isotope Stages (Fig. 10.8). Subsequent statistical studies with larger databases indicated the increase in post-glacial speleothem growth after about 18 ka (Atkinson *et al.*, 1986; Baker *et al.*, 1993a). Records from uncontaminated speleothems formed prior to the last glaciation recognised shorter periods of speleothem growth that are not seen in the pollen or beetle assemblage records (Gordon *et al.*, 1989), notably in the post-Wolstonian record of MIS 5e–3.

The timing of earlier glacial cycles has been greatly extended by the more precise mass spectrometry dating of the flowstones in Victoria Cave, above Ribblesdale (Lundberg *et al.*, 2010). Deposition was identified in all the warm stages of MIS 5, 7, 9, 11 and 13, and two speleothem samples indicated ages beyond the dating limit of 600 ka, testifying to the great antiquity of this cave.

More than 300 speleothems have now been dated from a total of 15 caves across the Yorkshire Dales (Table 10.1 and Fig. 10.9). Their age distribution is influenced by Quaternary palaeoclimates, but also shows smaller numbers of older speleothems, which is in part a function of sampling procedure and the difficulties in recognising old material suitable for dating (Fig. 10.10). Growth periods, recognisable by the frequencies of occurrence, match the interglacial and interstadial marine isotope stages back to about 180 ka, and they also match the pattern recognised in a wider sample of speleothems from numerous caves in all parts of northwest Europe (Fig. 10.8).

The cold stage (MIS 6) that included the final 'Wolstonian' glaciation, and extended through 186–126 ka, is barely identifiable in the stalagmite record from the

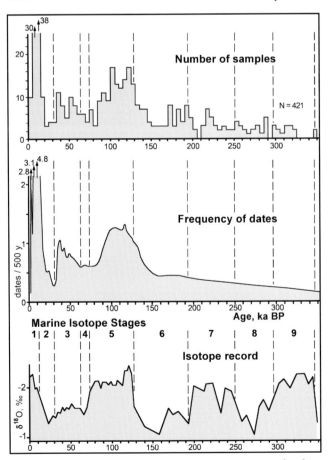

Figure 10.8. Speleothem frequency against age in samples from northwest Europe, as numbers of samples and frequency of dates, correlated with the Marine Isotope Stages and the oxygen isotope marine record where the smaller negative values indicate lower temperatures (after Gordon and Smart, 1984).

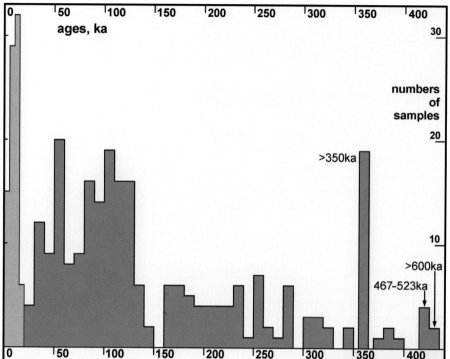

Figure 10.10. Distribution of the ages of 325 samples of stalagmite and flowstone from the Dales caves; the peak of post-Devensian records, at 0–15 ka, is reduced on this histogram because their records are for spans of 5 ka instead of 10 ka; the low number of records for 0–5 ka is an artefact due to sample collections that avoid damaging sites of active deposition.

Figure 10.11. Flowstone overlying sediments dated from around 83 ka, which were cut through by the trench to provide visitor access in the Wolverine Passage in Stump Cross Caverns (TW)

Dales caves, except for a brief reduction of deposition around 150 ka (Fig. 10.10). Subsequently, the distribution of speleothem dates confirms increased dissolutional activity in warmer environments of the two major interstadials, the Chelford (MIS 5c, at about 100 ka) and the Upton Warren Complex (MIS 3, with a peak at 43 ka, which was the warmest within a series of oscillations from about 60 ka to 30 ka). An intervening cold phase in MIS 5b is indicated by the teeth and jaws of wolverine found in Stump Cross Caverns with closely associated stalagmite dated to a mean of 83 ka (Sutcliffe *et al.*, 1985). Wolverine is indicative of a cold phase, but it is unclear whether breaks in flowstone deposition mark intervals cold enough to inhibit dissolution or were due to flooding of the cave (Fig. 10.11).

A single bank of flowstone from the Colonnade Passage in Lancaster Hole provided a more detailed set of growth bands and hiatuses spanning 135–37 ka (Baker *et al.*, 1995). The better definition and precision arise from the ion-counting capability of the mass spectrometry and from the fact that much smaller sample sizes means that fewer growth layers are represented in each sample. Although even these data are not precise enough to isolate the start and end of growth periods, it is clear from the best-fit growth lines that the contiguous calcite layers each represent up to just a few thousand years at most. The short periods of deposition correspond to the record of insolation maxima (Fig. 10.12), and not to interglacial stages indicated by global ice volume minima. However, the growth periods of speleothems covering a comparable time-span in Stump Cross Caverns do not coincide with those of the Colonnade flowstone, due to purely local site conditions (Baker *et al.*, 1996).

Dates older than 180 ka are fewer in number and most carry larger error bars, so the definition of earlier growth periods is poor. The low number of available samples, and hence dates, is partly due to erosion and burial within the caves, and partly due to some loss of older caves and their speleothems due to surface lowering. Furthermore, many

of the Dales caves are considerably older than the alpha spectrometry dating limit of 350 ka; these are only recorded on Figure 10.10 by the peak labelled as samples dated to >350 ka. Mass spectrometry has now provided eight dates between 372 and 523 ka for stalagmite from Victoria Cave, above Settle, together with two more samples that date back to more than 600 ka (Lundberg *et al.*, 2010).

The end of the Devensian is now seen to be not so well-defined by speleothem alpha-based ages in comparison with the newer, more precise dates obtained mainly by radiocarbon chronology. The earliest Holocene dates lacked precision because samples of about 10 grams, for alpha spectrometry, tended to include interlayered muds with detrital components that have the greatest impact on the calculation of the youngest dates. The limited bank of young dates from the Yorkshire Dales caves does indicate that post-glacial speleothem deposition was renewed by about 15 ka (Fig. 10.13). This is consistent with the finding that the Norber boulders were exposed from the ice as early as 18 ka, but probably remained in periglacial conditions until the start of the Windermere Interstadial at 14.7 ka (Vincent *et al.*, 2010). There is no recognisable reduction in the deposition of cave calcite during the subsequent Loch Lomond Stadial,

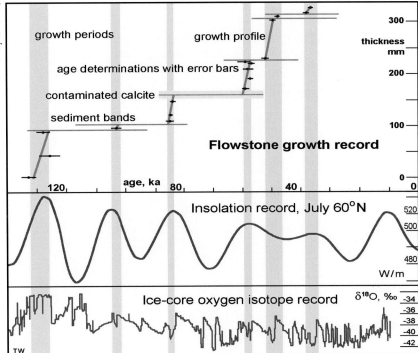

Figure 10.12. The record of interrupted deposition in a sequence of flowstones in the Colonnade Passage in Lancaster Hole; the pink shaded zones denote recognisable periods of calcite deposition; between them were longer intervals with no overall depositional growth (after Baker et al., 1995).

when small glaciers were temporarily established on some higher slopes within the Dales region, but the climatic warming at the start of the Holocene, now accepted to be at 11.7 ka (Walker *et al.*, 2009), is marked by more numerous dated speleothems from the caves (Fig. 10.13).

Rates of entrenchment of the dales

The accumulated record of speleothem dates confirms the long-held notion that the Dales caves developed during multiple cycles of glaciation and valley deepening through the Quaternary, but, apart from the dates from Victoria Cave, the record indicates little about landscape evolution prior to the Anglian glaciation. The Late Glacial Maximum peaked at around 26–21 ka (Chiverrell and Thomas, 2010; Clark *et al.*, 2011) and localised valley glaciers remained until their final disappearance at about 16 ka. Valley glaciers and the streams of faster flow within the ice sheets followed the lines of existing river valleys, thereby deepening them and enhancing the relief (see Chapter 3).

Mean rates of valley deepening, by the combination of glacial excavation with interglacial fluvial action, can be determined from the timing of abandonment of resurgences and the draining of related cave passages at various altitudes (Ford *et al.*, 1981). The method assumes that a cave passage could only be dry when it lay above the level of the valley floor into which its stream resurged. Basal dates of stalagmites in relict caves indicate the latest date at which their host passage could have been drained; however, calcite deposition might have started only after a long interval of inactivity within the cave, a factor that cannot be recognised until large numbers of samples have been dated. The speleothem dates represent only minimal ages for the caves and consequently only maximum rates for valley lowering. Furthermore, calculations yield only averaged erosion rates, and it is very likely that valley-floor lowering by glaciation was probably much faster than that by fluvial erosion during the interglacial stages.

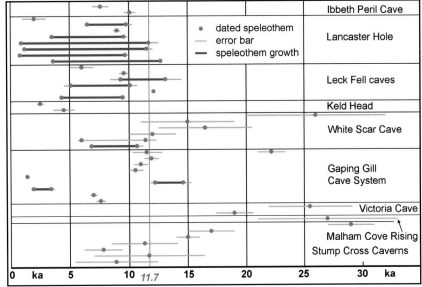

Figure 10.13. Speleothem dates that fall within the Devensian and Holocene stages from caves in the Yorkshire Dales, with a marked increase in calcite deposition after the last major climatic warming at the end of the Loch Lomond Stadial at 11.7 ka; any variations in calcite deposition through the Windermere Interstadial, prior to the Loch Lomond Stadial, are obscured by the long error bars and the detrital thorium that makes some of the dates less reliable (data from Gascoyne et al., 1983a; Atkinson et al., 1986; Baker et al., 1996; Murphy and Latham, 2001; Murphy et al., 2004).

Figure 10.14. *Stalagmites on ledges high in the main streamways of White Scar Cave, which allow estimation of canyon incision rates when dated (TW)*

Within White Scar Cave, the older phreatic passages of the Battlefield and Sleepwalker Series were drained by 350 ka, as indicated by two sampled stalagmites whose alpha spectrometry ages could only be determined to exceed that figure (Table. 10.1). These passages are at altitudes about 70m above that of the floor of Chapel-le-Dale immediately outside the cave, which indicate a maximum rate of valley deepening of 0.2 m/ka. A single stalagmite from near the roof of the main streamway in the same cave also yielded an age of >350 ka (Table 10.1), which indicates a lower level of drained passages at that time and a subsequent rate of valley deepening that is no more than 0.12 m/ka. A larger suite of samples, dated by mass spectrometry, is required to provide confidence in any geomorphological interpretation of this site. Both values are compatible with those estimated for incision rates in various of the dales west of Ingleborough (Gascoyne *et al.*, 1983b; Waltham, 1986).

Dated speleothems from Victoria Cave include a single flowstone sample that yielded two dates, from above and below a hiatus; both were older than 600 ka (Lundberg *et al.*, 2010). With the floor of Ribblesdale now 290m below the cave, this could imply a maximum rate of 0.48 m/ka for the valley deepening. However it is very likely that the dale floor was already below the cave altitude at that time, and the cave may have been dry for previous millennia. Relating the cave drainage to the level of the nearby Stockdale valley, with its floor now 120m below the cave, would indicate a maximum rate of surface lowering of 0.2 m/ka; this may also be high for an upland situation that is marginal to the zones of more rapid lowering where ice erosion was concentrated along the lines of the dales.

Rates of incision in cave streamways

More localised processes are involved in the estimation of incision rates for vadose passages using dated speleothems that are now out of reach of floods (Fig. 10.14). Speleothems can form only after phreatic passages have been drained and then at sites out of reach of all but the severest floods. Dated material taken from walls and ledges above active streamways can indicate the latest ages for the stream floor to have been at the sampled level, from which can be calculated maximum rates of incision to the present stream level (Gascoyne *et al.*, 1983b).

Incision rates have been determined for a number of cave streamways in the Dales (Table 10.2). The sample in Lost John's Cave was taken from the wall of the Leck Fell Master Cave, so gives a direct measurement of stream erosion in the same passage. Dated samples from the other caves were collected from phreatic roof passages, and the levels refer only to the incision depths within the adjacent stream canyons. The interpreted incision rates are only maximum values, as the caves may be much older that their speleothem deposits. They are also only mean values over the long periods of varying environmental conditions through the late Quaternary. All the incision rates for streamways in the Dales caves are more than an order of magnitude lower than the rate of 1200 mm/ka that was measured directly, by micro-erosion meter, in a comparable stream cave in West Virginia, USA (see Chapter 7). The latter figure was effectively a spot reading (over two years) in an environment of dissolutional activity, whereas the long periods covered by the Dales caves included considerable intervals of reduced or nil activity (Fig. 10.12). Cave floor incision is likely to have been at the higher rates for only a fraction of the total time involved.

Future prospects

Significant among the prospects for cave science is the use of speleothem stable-isotope data to elucidate the palaeo-temperature variations of interglacial periods. There is still the problem of separating out the temperature information from isotope variations due to other effects such as changes in storm track signatures, but there are many new developments in stable isotope analyses and interpretation (Fairchild and Baker, 2012). Following a few false dawns, a more reliable method for the extraction of absolute palaeo-temperature values from speleothem fluid inclusions has yet to be devised (McDermott, 2004; Zhang *et al.*, 2008).

It may be expected that developments in stable isotope studies coupled with mass-spectrometric dates will see a greater reliability for records of past climate and palaeo-temperatures. Had the precision of mass-spectrometry been

cave	sample number	height above stream (m)	basal age (ka)	maximum incision rate (mm/ka)
Ease Gill Caverns	76127	12	240	50
Lost John's Cave	77162	2.5	115	22
Kingsdale Master Cave	77242	11	300	37
White Scar Cave	76106	11	>350	>31
Ingleborough Cave	77143	4	120	33

Table 10.2. *Incision rates determined for vadose stream passages within Yorkshire Dales caves (after Gascoyne et al., 1983).*

Figure 10.15. Beneath the southwestern flank of Gragareth, Duke Street 2, in Ireby Cavern, is a remnant of a long-abandoned trunk route that may pre-date Anglian rejuvenation. The thick sediment banks that remain in parts of the cave include quartz materials that may be older than the limit of the uranium–thorium dating method (photo: Dave Checkley).

available for the major speleothem survey in the Dales during the 1980s, many of the stadials and interstadials within the last glacial cycle would have been much better defined. Further age estimates are likely to come from studies of the cosmogenic isotopes of aluminium, beryllium and chlorine, particularly with their useful application to older deposits. Caves will continue to be a valuable archive of geomorphology where the history of a given deposit can be elucidated with confidence. Development of the uranium-series chronology has undoubtedly advanced understanding of at least the later part of the Quaternary history of the Dales caves, and has contributed a new base for geomorphological interpretation of landscape evolution across the Yorkshire Dales. However, there are still further opportunities for valuable research in the caves of the Dales.

References

Atkinson, T C, P L Smart, R S Harmon and A C Waltham, 1978. Palaeoclimatic and geomorphic implications of 230Th/234U dates on speleothems from Britain. *Nature*, **272**, 24-28.

Atkinson, T C, T J Lawson, P L Smart, R S Harmon and J W Hess, 1986. New data on speleothem deposition and palaeoclimate in Britain over the last forty thousand years. *J. Quat. Sci.*, **1**, 67-72.

Baker, A, P L Smart and D C Ford, 1993a. Northwest European palaeoclimate as indicated by growth frequency variations of secondary calcite deposits. *Palaeogeography, Palaeoclimatology, Palaeoecology*, **100**, 291-301.

Baker, A, P L Smart and R L Edwards, 1995. Palaeoclimate implications of mass spectrometric dating of a British flowstone. *Geology*, **23**, 309-312.

Baker, A, P L Smart and R L Edwards, 1996. Mass spectrometric dating of flowstones from Stump Cross Caverns and Lancaster Hole, Yorkshire: palaeoclimate implications. *J. Quat. Sci.*, **11**, 107–114.

Bourdon B, S Turner, G M Henderson and C C Lundstrom (eds.), 1997. *Uranium-Series Geochemistry*. Reviews in Mineralogy and Geochemistry 52, Geochemical Society and Mineralogical Society of America.

Caseldine, C J, S F McGarry, A Baker, C Hawkesworth and P L Smart, 2008. Late Quaternary speleothem pollen in the British Isles. *J. Quat. Sci.*, **23**, 193–200.

Chiverrell, R C and G S P Thomas, 2010. Extent and timing of the Last Glacial Maximum in Britain and Ireland: a review. *J. Quat. Sci.*, **25**, 535-549.

Clark, C D, A L C Hughes, S L Greenwood, C Jordan and H P Sejrup, 2011. Pattern and timing of retreat of the last British-Irish Ice Sheet. *Quat. Sci. Reviews*, **10**, 1-35.

Dorale, J A, L Edwards, E C Alexander, Ch-Ch Shen, D A Richards and H Cheng, 2007. Uranium series dating of speleothems: current techniques, limitations and applications. 177-197 in Sasowsky and Mylroie, *op. cit.*

Fairchild, I J and A Baker, 2012. *Speleothem Science*. Wiley: London, 432pp.

Ford, D C, H P Schwarcz, J J Drake, M Gascoyne, R S Harmon and A G Latham, 1981. Estimates of the age of the existing relief within the Southern Rocky Mountains of Canada. *Arctic Alpine Research*, **13**, 1-10.

Gascoyne, M, 1977. Does the presence of stalagmites really indicate warm periods? New evidence from Yorkshire and Canadian caves. *Proc. 7th Int. Cong. Speleology* (Sheffield), 208-210.

Gascoyne, M and D C Ford, 1984. Uranium-series dating of speleothems, part II: results from Yorkshire Dales and implications for cave development and Quaternary climates. *Cave Science*, **11**, 65-85.

Gascoyne, M, H P Schwarcz and D C Ford, 1983a. Uranium-series ages of speleothem from Northwest England: correlation with Quaternary climate. *Phil. Trans. Roy. Soc.*, **B301**, 143-164.

Gascoyne, M, D C Ford and H P Schwarcz, 1983b. Rates of cave and landform development in the Yorkshire Dales from speleothem age data. *Earth Surface Processes Landforms*, **8**, 557-568.

Gordon, D and P L Smart, 1984. Comments on "Speleothems, Travertines, and Palaeoclimates" by G J Hennig, R Grün and K Brunnacker. *Quat. Res.*, **22**, 144-147.

Gordon, D, P L Smart, D C Ford, J N Andrews, T C Atkinson, P J Rowe and N S J Christopher, 1989. Dating of Late Pleistocene interglacial and interstadial periods in the United Kingdom from speleothem growth frequency. *Quat. Res.*, **31**, 14-26.

Gradstein, F M, J G Orr and A G Smith, 2006. *A Geologic Timescale 2004 (corrected edition)*. Cambridge University Press.

Granger, D E and P F Muzikar, 2001. Dating sediment burial with in situ-produced cosmogenic nuclides: theory, techniques, and limitations. *Earth Planetary Science Letters*, **188**, 269-281.

Granger D E, D Fabel and A N Palmer, 2001. Pliocene-Pleistocene incision of the Green River, Kentucky, determined from radioactive decay of 26Al and 10Be in Mammoth Cave sediments. *Geol. Soc. Amer. Bull.*, **113**, 825-836.

Grün, R, C B Stringer and H P Schwarcz, 1991. ESR dating of teeth from Garrod's Tabun cave collection. *J. Human Evolution*, **20**, 231-248.

Harmon, R S, P Thompson, H P Schwartz and D C Ford, 1975. Uranium-series dating of speleothems. *Bull. Nat. Spel. Soc.*, **37**, 21-33.

Hennig, G J, R Grün and K Brunnacker, 1983. Speleothems, travertines and paleoclimates. *Quat. Res.*, **20**, 1-29.

Hoffmann, D L, 2008. 230Th isotope measurements of femtogram quantities for U-series dating using multi-ion counting (MIC) MC-ICPMS. *Int. J. Mass Spectrometry*, **275**, 75-79.

Ivanovich, M and R S Harmon (Eds.), 1992. *Uranium-Series Disequilibrium: Applications to Earth, Marine, and Environmental Sciences*. Oxford University Press.

Johnston, V E and F McDermott, 2009. Cosmogenic Cl-36 in karst waters: quantifying contributions from atmospheric and bedrock sources. *Geophysical Research Letters*, **36**, L23705.

Latham, A G, H P Schwarcz and D C Ford, 1986. The paleomagnetism and U-Th dating of Mexican stalagmite, DAS2. Earth Planetary Science Letters, **79**, 195-207.

Latham, A G, 2001. Uranium-series dating. 63-72 D R Brothwell and A M Pollard (eds.), *Handbook of Archaeological Sciences*, Wiley: London.

Lundberg J and D A McFarlane, 2007. Pleistocene depositional history in a periglacial terrane: a 500 ky record from Kents Cavern, Devon, United Kingdom. *Geosphere*, **3**, 199-219.

Lundberg, J, T C Lord and P J Murphy, 2010. Thermal ionization mass spectrometer U-Th dates on Pleistocene speleothems from Victoria Cave, North Yorkshire, UK: implications for palaeoenvironment and stratigraphy over multiple glacial cycles. *Geosphere*, **6**, 379–395.

McDermott, F, 2004. Palaeo-climate reconstruction from stable isotope variations in speleothems: a review. *Quat. Sci. Rev.*, **23**, 901-918.

McDermott, F, T C Atkinson, I J Fairchild, L M Baldini and D P Mattey, 2011. A first evaluation of the spatial gradients in δ18O recorded by European Holocene speleothems. *Global Planetary Change*, **79**, 275-287.

McFarlane, D A, J Lundberg and J Cordingley, 2005. A brief history of stalagmite growth measurements at Ingleborough Cave, Yorkshire, UK. *Cave Karst Science*, **31**, 113-118.

Mercier, N and H Valladas, 2003. Reassessment of TL age estimates of burnt flints from the Palaeolithic site of Tabun Cave, Israel. *J. Human Evolution*, **45**, 401-409.

Murphy, P J and A G Latham, 2001. A uranium series date from Malham Cove Rising, North Yorkshire, UK. *Cave Karst Science*, **28**, 135-136.

Murphy, P J, R Smallshire and C Midgeley, 2001. The sediments of Illusion Pot, Kingsdale, UK: evidence for sub-glacial utilisation of a karst conduit in the Yorkshire Dales. *Cave Karst Science*, **28**, 29-34.

Murphy, P J, J Lundberg and J Cordingley, 2004. A uranium-series date from Keld Head, Kingsdale, North Yorkshire, UK. *Cave Karst Science*, **31**, 77-78.

Murphy, P, J Cordingley and T Waltham, 2008. New uranium-series dates from Keld Head, Kingsdale, North Yorkshire, UK. *Cave Karst Science*, **35**, 111-114.

Nishiizumi, K, M Imamura, M Caffee, J Southon, R Finkel and R McAnich, 2007. Absolute calibration of Be-10 AMS standards. *J. Nuclear Instruments and Methods*, **B258**, 403-413.

Noller, J, J M Sowers and W R Lettis (eds.), 2000. *Quaternary Geochronology: Methods and Applications*. American Geophysical Union: Washington, 582pp.

Reimer, P J and 8 others, 2009. IntCal09 and Marine09 radiocarbon age calibration curves 0-50,000 years cal BP. *Radiocarbon*, **51**, 1111-1150.

Richards, D A, S H Bottrell, R A Cliff, K Ströhle and P J Rowe, 1998. U-Pb dating of a speleothem of Quaternary age. *Geochimica Cosmochimica Acta*, **62**, 3683-3688.

Sasowsky I D and J Mylroie (eds.), 2007. *Studies of Cave Sediments: Physical and Chemical Records of Paleoclimate*. Springer: London, 329pp.

Schmidt, V A, 1982. Magnetostratigraphy of clastic sediments from within the Mammoth Cave National Park, Kentucky. *Science*, **217**, 827.

Shopov, Y Y, D C Ford and H P Schwarcz, 1994. Luminescence microbanding in speleothems: high resolution chronology and palaeoclimate. *Geology*, **22**, 407-410.

Smart, P L, B W Smith, H Chandra, J N Andrews and M C R Symons, 1988. An intercomparison of ESR and uranium-series ages for Quaternary speleothem calcites. *Quat. Sci. Rev.*, **7**, 411-416.

Stock, G M, D E Granger, I D Sasowsky, R S Anderson and R C Finkel, 2005. Comparison of U-Th, palaeomagnetism, and cosmogenic burial methods for dating caves: implications for landscape evolution studies. *Earth Planetary Science Letters*, **235**, 388-403.

Sutcliffe, A J, T C Lord, R S Harmon, M Ivanovich, A Rae and J W Hess, 1985. Wolverine in northern England at about 83,000 yr BP: faunal evidence for climatic change during isotope stage 5. *Quat. Res.*, **24**, 73-86.

Thompson, P, H P Schwartz and D C Ford, 1974. Continental Pleistocene climatic variations from speleothem age and isotopic data. *Science*, **184**, 893-895.

Vincent, P J, P Wilson, T C Lord, C Schnabel and K M Wilcken, 2010. Cosmogenic isotope (36Cl) surface exposure dating of the Norber erratics, Yorkshire Dales: further constraints on the timing of the LGM glaciation in Britain. *Proc. Geol. Assoc.*, **121**, 24-31.

Walker, J, R A Cliff and A G Latham, 2006. U-Pb isotopic age of the StW 573 hominid from Sterkfontein, South Africa. *Science*, **314**, 1592-1594.

Walker, M J C, 2005. *Quaternary Dating Methods*, Wiley: Chichester.

Walker, M and 16 others, 2009. Formal definition and dating of the GSSP (Global Stratotype Section and Point) for the base of the Holocene using the Greenland NGRIP ice core and selected auxiliary records. *J. Quat. Sci.*, **24**, 3-17.

Waltham, A C (ed.), 1974. *Limestones and Caves of North-west England*. David and Charles: Newton Abbot, 477pp.

Waltham, A C, 1986. Valley excavation in the Yorkshire Dales karst. 541-550 in K Paterson and M M Sweeting, *New Directions in Karst*, Geo Books: Norwich.

Waltham A C and R S Harmon, 1977. Chronology of cave development in the Yorkshire Dales, England. *Proc. 7th Int. Cong. Speleology* (Sheffield), 423-425.

Weninger, B and O Jöris, 2008. A 14C age calibration curve for the last 60 ka: the Greenland-Hula U/Th timescale and its impact on understanding the Middle to Upper Palaeolithic transition in Western Eurasia. *J. Human Evolution*, **55**, 772-781.

Wilson, P, P J Vincent, M W Telfer and T C Lord, 2008. Optically stimulated luminescence (OSL) dating of loessic sediments in northwest England. *The Holocene*, **18**, 1101-1112.

Wintle, A, 1978. A thermoluminescence dating study of some Quaternary calcite: potential and problems. *Can. J. Earth Sci.*, **15**, 1977-1986.

Wintle, A G, 1990. A review of current research on TL dating of loess. *Quat. Sci. Rev.*, **9**, 385-398.

Wintle, A G, 2010. Future directions of the luminescence dating of quartz. *Geochronometria*, **37**, 1-7.

Zhang R, H P Schwarcz, D C Ford, F Serefiddin-Schroeder and P A Beddows, 2008. Absolute palaeotemperature record from 10 to 6 ka inferred from fluid inclusion D/H ratios of a stalagmite from Vancouver Island. British Columbia. *Geochimica Cosmochimica Acta*, **72**, 1014-1026.

CHAPTER 11

Speleothems and palaeoclimates

Tim Atkinson and Phil Hopley

Most cave deposits, or speleothems, are deposited from dripping waters and the calcite of which they are formed builds up in successive layers that record changing conditions within the cave through their chemical composition. Conditions underground are the result of processes and conditions outside, from the large-scale circulation of the atmosphere, through the local climate and vegetation, down to the chemistry of the drip waters and the chemical composition of the air within the cave itself. Thus the chemistry of layered cave formations should record past climate, vegetation and hydrology, among other parameters, but such records can only be read backwards unambiguously if all the causative factors are well understood and can be unravelled; this is a daunting task that is not yet completed.

Stalagmites have the highest rates of growth and thus potentially record in greatest detail (Fig. 11.1). Their growth history can be dated by drilling out calcite from selected layers and using it for U–Th dating. The ages of levels in between the dates must be found by interpolation. Gross errors would arise if the stalagmite had ceased to grow at times between the dates, so any break in the calcite layering that might mark a hiatus in deposition must be identified, with dates obtained on either side of it to reveal the length of the gap in the record.

Features of past climates can be interpreted from the patterns of various stable isotopes that form tiny fractions of the bulk composition of various materials within the geological record (see box on next page). Though forming only about 0.2% of total natural oxygen, the heavy isotope oxygen-18 is an important indicator of palaeoclimate because of the selective evaporation and precipitation of the light and heavy isotopes in water. During glacial stages, the oceans become isotopically heavier than they are during interglacials due to the fact that the light isotope oxygen-16 is preferentially locked up in the expanding ice-sheets and glaciers, thereby leaving the ocean very slightly enriched in the heavier isotope oxygen-18 that is left behind. Palaeoclimatic signals are preserved in stratigraphical records, with colder conditions indicated by increased oxygen-18 in the foraminifera shells within ocean sediment cores and decreased oxygen-18 in polar ice cores. The stacked record of 57 marine cores now takes the marine isotope stages back to about 850 ka (Lisiecki and Raymo, 2005) (see Chapter 3).

The stalagmite record of stable isotopes, and of other chemical variables, is however immensely complicated. Palaeo-temperature has frequently been taken as the dominant factor in fractionation of the oxygen isotopes, but complex issues about other controls, their dominance and their duration are still not fully delineated (Williams *et al.,* 1998; McDermott *et al.,* 2011; Fairchild and Baker, 2012). The relationship between oxygen-18 and temperature seems to be positive in some cave stalagmite records, but negative in others. Three adjacent stalagmites from the Graveyard in Lancaster Hole exhibit a marked lack of coherence in their oxygen-18 profiles through the Holocene. Oxygen isotope records are now widely used as indicators of rainfall and moisture conditions, modifying or replacing the role they previously had as indicators of palaeo-temperatures (Lachniet, 2009; Polyak and Denniston, 2012). Some of these ambiguities are illustrated by details of a stalagmite from Lancaster Hole whose deposition spanned cold and warm intervals at the end of the Late Glacial period.

A stalagmite from Lancaster Hole

A single stalagmite (LH-70s-1) from the Graveyard area in Lancaster Hole has yielded the first long record of recent palaeoclimates from a Dales cave. Nearly half a metre tall, it was cut along its length (Fig. 11.3) and sampled for 16 age determinations and more than 300 analyses of isotopes and trace elements. The stalagmite began its life just prior to 12,750 years ago, at a time when the climate is known to have been deteriorating sharply into the Younger Dryas

Figure 11.1. *The tall stalagmite columns of the Colonnades in Lancaster Hole are likely to contain a long record of the Dales palaeoclimates, but significant and iconic cave features such as these are just not suitable for present analytical studies that require their removal to a laboratory (photo: Paul Deakin).*

Speleothems and palaeoclimates, by Tim Atkinson and Phil Hopley
Tim Atkinson, University College London; t.atkinson@ucl.ac.uk
Phil Hopley, Birkbeck College London; p.hopley@bbk.ac.uk
Chapter 11, pages 181–186 in **Caves and Karst of the Yorkshire Dales**, edited by Tony Waltham and David Lowe.
Published 2013 by the British Cave Research Association,
978-0-900265-46-4 and at www.bcra.org.uk

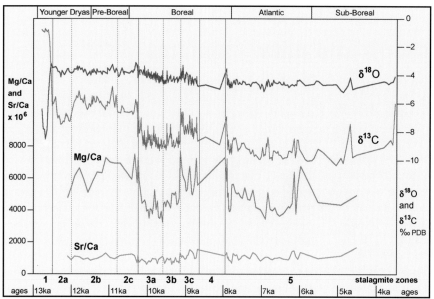

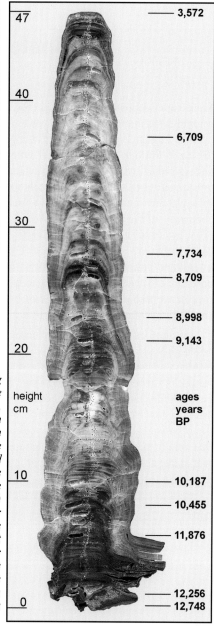

Figure 11.2. *Stable isotope and trace element records from LH-70s-1, the stalagmite from Lancaster Hole. Timescale is based on 16 U–Th dates. Isotope ratios δ18O and δ13C of the calcite were measured on samples drilled at 2 mm intervals up the axis of growth. Ratios of Mg/Ca and Sr/Ca were measured on separate holes drilled at intervals from 3 to 6 mm. Time zones, labelled at the foot, are zones based on these records and described in the text.*

(Loch Lomond) Stadial following the warm interval of the Windermere Interstadial; it ceased its growth about 3500 years ago, late in the Holocene. Its rate of deposition did vary, and was very slow between 8650 and 7950 years ago, but the stalagmite contains no obvious sign of a complete hiatus.

Four chemical signals were measured on the stalagmite: the concentrations of magnesium and strontium in the calcite (expressed as the ratio of each element to calcium) and the ratios of stable isotopes of oxygen and carbon in the calcite. The chemical and isotopic ratios (Fig. 11.2) are each controlled by different sets of factors, with considerable overlap between the sets, so the four variables show considerable similarity as well as differences in their records.

Magnesium and strontium

The magnesium (Mg) and strontium (Sr) contents are controlled by the concentrations of those elements in the drip water from which the stalagmite was deposited. These in turn have been found to depend on the length of time the water has spent in contact with the rock above the cave, as well as on the amount of each element available to be dissolved as the water percolates downwards from the surface, *i.e.* its concentration in the rock itself. This second factor is more or less constant for any one drip, though it can vary greatly from one drip to another, so different stalagmites forming in the same cave may have different levels of trace elements. Water takes less time to reach the cave when conditions on the surface are wet than when soils are dry and little rainwater enters the underlying rock. As a result the Mg and Sr concentrations in drip water sometimes vary seasonally, with lower values in winter when rainfall exceeds evaporation, soils are fully wetted and surplus rainfall percolates quickly through the bedrock. Higher values occur in summer when the reservoir of water stored in the fractured and fissured rock above the cave is replenished only a little if at all, and the intervals between drips onto the stalagmite become longer as the volume of water stored in the reservoir is drawn upon and reduced.

Figure 11.3. Long section through the stalagmite, LH-70s-1, 47 cm tall, from the Graveyard in Lancaster Hole; the small, round drilled holes (just visible along the centre line of the stalagmite) are sample sites for the stable isotope and trace element analyses; the larger elongate holes are sample sites for the uranium–thorium dating (photo: Saskia Kars).

Some stalagmites record such seasonal variation in the drip water chemistry as cycles of Mg/Ca and Sr/Ca values, the thickness of calcite containing each cycle representing a year's growth. Changes in Mg/Ca and Sr/Ca ratios over longer periods are thought to reflect the same factors, and can therefore be interpreted in terms of the wetness of the climate, with low values suggesting a climate with greater water surplus and high ones a reduced surplus. As the water surplus that enters the bedrock over a whole year is essentially the balance between annual rainfall and annual evaporation, low values could be due to a rainier climate, but they might also reflect a cooler one with less evaporation. Other ambiguities arise if there is a possibility that the drip water deposits calcite before reaching the stalagmite itself, for example on a stalactite. Such prior precipitation takes up Mg and Sr in different proportions, altering the composition of the drip water in ways that may be quite unrelated to the climatic water surplus, and weakening the tendency for Mg and Sr concentrations in the stalagmite to be correlated. Variations in the growth rate of calcite crystals during the lifetime of each drop of water on the stalagmite can have a similar effect.

Carbon-13

Variations in the ratio of stable isotopes of carbon are equally difficult to unravel unambiguously. They are also controlled in part by the drip-water hydrology and the climatic water surplus, but through rather complex mechanisms in which other factors play a part. The $\delta^{13}C$ of carbon-bearing ions dissolved in the drip water (chiefly carbonate and bicarbonate ions with the total referred to as DIC, or dissolved inorganic carbon) depends on the relative contributions of carbon dioxide from the soil air and from the free atmosphere, as well as on the exact sequence of chemical reactions that have occurred while limestone has been dissolved. Oxidation of organic matter washed down into the bedrock fractures by infiltrating water can also play a role.

Even once the drip water enters the cave, the complications are not over. As it hangs as a droplet from the roof (or from a stalactite), or once it has fallen and lies in a film over the stalagmite surface, the water loses carbon dioxide to the cave air. This loss is the mechanism that actually drives the formation of solid calcite and the growth of the stalagmite, but it also changes the $\delta^{13}C$ of the DIC and therefore of the calcite that is formed. The longer the interval between drops, the more degassing of CO_2 can occur, and the higher the value of $\delta^{13}C$ in the calcite will be. In this way, $\delta^{13}C$ values reflect the average drip interval, which in turn reflects the climatic water surplus, and thus there could be expected to be some correlation between the records of $\delta^{13}C$ and Mg/Ca and Sr/Ca. When all three move in harmony, probably the drip hydrology is the common cause.

Isotopes

The term *isotope* is used to denote atoms of an element that differ from each other in mass because they contain different numbers of neutrons, but have very nearly identical chemical behaviour because they possess the same numbers of protons and electrons.

The element oxygen has three naturally occurring isotopes with masses of 16, 17 and 18 atomic mass units, the heavier ones containing one and two extra neutrons in their nuclei. There are roughly 500 oxygen-16 atoms for every oxygen-18, but the exact ratios found in nature vary by several tenths of a per cent, depending on the substance in which the oxygen occurs, the conditions it was formed under and the materials it was formed from. The actual measured ratio for any particular calcite sample, such as a calcite powder drilled from a stalagmite, is expressed in the units known as a delta (δ) scale. Negative values of $\delta^{18}O$ (as in Figure 11.2) mean that the ratio of oxygen-18 to oxygen-16 is less than that in a standard calcite material.

All laboratories compare their samples with the same standard calcite that is known as PDB (named from its original source in a Cretaceous fossil belemnite from the Peedee Formation in South Carolina), and also use the standard to compare data between laboratories. Some records of $\delta^{18}O$ are related to SMOW, which is Standard Mean Ocean Water. The units are in parts per thousand (‰), so a value of −2‰ means that the ratio was two parts per thousand (0.2%) less in the sample than in the standard calcite.

Carbon has two stable isotopes with mass 12 and 13, with mass 12 being around 100 times more abundant. The standard, scale and units are the same as for oxygen. A third naturally occurring isotope, carbon-14, is radioactive (see Chapter 10), but its atoms have extremely low abundance.

But further complicating factors may intervene. The degassing rate is strongly influenced by the CO_2 concentration in the cave air, because it is driven by the difference between the pressure of CO_2 in the air and the pressure exerted chemically by the DIC in the water. Both quantities may vary through the year, especially the concentrations in cave air, which for many caves are high in summer and low in winter; so the chemical driver for degassing varies seasonally, but is out of phase with the drip interval that controls the time for which degassing occurs. A complex signal that is difficult to interpret may result.

Oxygen-18

The last variable, $\delta^{18}O$, is perhaps the most complex of all. Oxygen atoms occur in the dissolved carbonate and bicarbonate ions and in dissolved CO_2, so $\delta^{18}O$ is affected by degassing in the same way as $\delta^{13}C$, producing a correlation between the two. But the $\delta^{18}O$ variations are far smaller in amplitude than those of $\delta^{13}C$ because the water itself comprises a large reservoir of oxygen atoms that can exchange with the oxygen atoms in the DIC, tending to restore the latter towards a constant value. However the exchange is a rather slow chemical reaction, so the $\delta^{18}O$ of the DIC can only re-establish complete equilibrium with the water if the drip rate is very slow, with intervals of an hour or more between drips. Most drips are faster than this, so the $\delta^{18}O$ of stalagmites that they deposit is normally out of equilibrium and reflects in part the amount of degassing that has occurred as well as the incomplete but simultaneous reaction between DIC and water. Thus variations in $\delta^{18}O$ to some extent follow those in $\delta^{13}C$ and reflect drip hydrology and climatic water surplus.

In addition, there are two other factors. These are the $\delta^{18}O$ composition of the drip water itself and the cave temperature. Unpublished studies in Lancaster Hole, White Scar and other Dales caves have shown that drip waters have $\delta^{18}O$ that varies little during the year and approximates to the average value for rainfall, while temperatures far from the entrance zones remain constant through the year and are close to mean annual temperature on the surface. It is to be expected that large changes in average surface temperature, such as occurred in climatic transitions between glacials and interglacials, would be tracked by deep cave temperatures, but virtually nothing is known of the lags in response that are likely. If the cave temperature rises, the $\delta^{18}O$ of calcite tends to fall by about −0.24‰ per °C. However, the annual average $\delta^{18}O$ of rainfall is also related to climate. It is influenced by several climatic factors that include the pattern of atmospheric circulation, the amount of rainfall in relation to the humidity of the atmosphere, and the temperature range through which the rain-bearing air has cooled from the region of the ocean where its vapour originated.

In Britain these factors seem to combine to produce a dependence upon average annual temperature such that for each °C of warming the annual average of $\delta^{18}O$ increases by about +0.2‰. This direct climatic influence on the $\delta^{18}O$ of drip water is opposite to the effect of cave temperature, and therefore tends to cancel it out. This cancellation makes $\delta^{18}O$ in calcite rather unresponsive to climatic changes in temperature, and it is perhaps relatively more dependent on the drip hydrology.

Interpretation of the climatic signals

Clearly, the principles by which stalagmite chemistry can act as indicators of cave environment and external climate have a high degree of built-in ambiguity and this inevitably makes the climatic signal very difficult to unravel. Nevertheless, it is worth examining the records in Figure 11.3 in the light of these principles, because they cover a period in which very large climatic changes are known to have occurred and they provide an illustration of the potential and the limitations of speleothems as palaeoclimatic archives.

Stalagmite LH-70s-1 commenced growth around the start of the Younger Dryas period of intense cold, when niche glaciers re-formed in some high-level corries in the Dales (see Chapter 3). For about 2000 years before the Younger Dryas, Britain had enjoyed a mostly temperate climate, and before that was the long, intense cold of the Last Glacial period. The cold Younger Dryas episode ended with abrupt warming at about 11,500 years ago, the start of the Holocene period. Holocene climates may have varied in both temperature and moisture, but have been generally humid and temperate throughout the whole period.

An obvious feature of Figure 11.3 is that all four variables show similar patterns (only a part of the stalagmite has been analysed for Mg/Ca and Sr/Ca, and the spacing of the data for these two variables is different from that for the stable isotope ratios). The timings of all the major changes match very well for $\delta^{13}C$ and Mg/Ca, which show much larger ranges of variation than the other two variables, but these generally follow the same patterns including the timing of smaller peaks and troughs. The major features have been used to divide the record into five major time zones (Fig.11.3). Minor features have been used to define sub-divisions.

Zone 1, 12,775 – 12,500 BP

At the base of the stalagmite the calcite fills a hollow, possibly a drip-pit, in the underlying sediment. The lowest 7 mm have the highest $\delta^{13}C$ and lowest $\delta^{18}O$ of the entire record. The $\delta^{18}O$ shows a minimum around 12,690 years ago, and then rises rapidly to reach the values seen in Zone 2 by 12,500 BP. Over the same interval $\delta^{13}C$ falls steeply. This zone is the only one in which the generally positive correlation between $\delta^{18}O$ and $\delta^{13}C$ breaks down. The reason for the high $\delta^{13}C$ is not clear, but the exceptionally low $\delta^{18}O$ might be a reflection of low values in rain, snow and infiltrating water at the onset of the cold Younger Dryas period. If the cave temperature at the time of the $\delta^{18}O$ minimum in the calcite was slightly cooler than the modern value of 8.7°C, calculation suggests that the drip water might have had $\delta^{18}O$ of about –10‰ on the SMOW scale, compared with the modern average of –6.9‰. This would suggest a very much colder climate at the surface (annual average values of –10‰ for $\delta^{18}O$ are today typical of northern Scandinavia, Spitzbergen or southern Greenland), while cave temperatures might have remained relatively warm because of the large amount of heat stored in the 50m depth of bedrock above the stalagmite cavern.

If this were correct, then the rise in $\delta^{18}O$ values of the calcite towards 12,500 BP might have been due in part to cave temperatures falling as the bedrock cooled. However, the temperature must have remained at or above 0°C to

Figure 11.4. The Graveyard with its distinctive stalagmites in the high-level passages of Lancaster Hole (photo: John Cordingley).

permit a stalagmite to form at all, and this limits the part of the rise that might have been due to falling cave temperature to 40% of the total. The remaining 60% must have been due either to an increase in the $\delta^{18}O$ of drip water or to another factor such as imperfect isotopic equilibrium between water and calcite because of degassing. Depending on the importance of the second of these, the rise in $\delta^{18}O$ of drip water from its minimum may have been up to 3% if cave temperatures were at freezing point by the end of the zone, and could have been more if temperatures were higher than this. These considerations suggest that $\delta^{18}O$ of drip water may have risen to values not far from the modern value by the end of Zone 1.

Zone 2, 12,500 – 10,250 BP

In this zone the $\delta^{18}O$ of calcite shows a level trend with minor oscillations around an average value of about –3.7‰. The zone includes the end of the Younger Dryas around 11,500 BP when an abrupt warming occurred and average surface temperatures rose by around 13°C, but this is reflected by neither the $\delta^{18}O$ nor the $\delta^{13}C$ of the calcite. The failure of the isotope chemistry to signal such a major change makes the record for the zone very difficult to interpret in climatic terms. Presumably, the flat trend of $\delta^{18}O$ in calcite is due to the interplay of factors that almost exactly compensated one another. Cave temperatures probably fell and later rose again as a consequence of the cold Younger Dryas climate and then the warming that brought it to an end, but the amplitude of this oscillation may have been muted by the heat stored in the surrounding rock and changes within the cave would have lagged behind those on the surface. Alongside these, the isotopic composition of drip water may have varied, also as a consequence of climatic change. This would have acted in an opposite sense to the changes in cave temperature, in terms of their effect on the calcite $\delta^{18}O$, so the two effects may have compensated one another.

The $\delta^{13}C$ values in Zone 2 are generally higher than in any later part of the record. The zone can be sub-divided into three parts on the basis of variations in these values (Fig. 11.3). The early part of the zone has the lowest values; they are highest in the middle part and intermediate in the last part. The oscillations in $\delta^{13}C$ are closely reflected by minor oscillations in $\delta^{18}O$, which suggests that they are both due to variations in the degassing of CO_2 from the drip water during deposition of the calcite. Other factors being equal, this would likely reflect the drip rate, with more degassing taking place when drip intervals were longer (and the water discharge less). Thus, the fluctuations in δ^{13}C may to some extent reflect variations in the amount of water infiltrating the limestone bedrock. This interpretation is strengthened by the fact that Mg/Ca and Sr/Ca ratios both have levels in this zone that are high in relation to the later parts of the record, suggesting relatively long contact between water and rock in the transit from the surface down to the cave. Thus, the climates of Zone 2 were such as to limit drip rates and infiltration to relatively low levels. The lack of infiltration during the cold climates of the Younger Dryas (i.e. before 11,500 BP) may have been due to snow melt being diverted into surface runoff over frozen soils. But the climate after the warming of 11,500 BP must have been dry enough to have restricted infiltration to much the same extent, possibly even slightly more, as Mg/Ca and Sr/Ca are both highest after this.

Zone 3, 10,250 – 8,650 BP

During this Zone, the stalagmite grew steadily at an average rate of 117 μm per year (8.5 years to grow 1 mm), 3.6 times more than during Zone 2. All four variables show the same general pattern, and the zone is sub-divided by their common variations. All four were reduced in value during the first sub-division (Fig. 11.3), with δ^{13}C and Mg/Ca showing very steep initial declines at around 10,250 BP followed by slower downward trends to minima at the end of the sub-division 9600 years ago. The δ^{18}O does not show the initial steep decline, but is reduced steadily throughout, also reaching a minimum at 9600 BP. The Sr/Ca ratio follows a different path, declining sharply at the start of the zone, but increasing again during the first sub-division, then falling sharply at 9600 BP and the start of the second sub-division. The low values of δ^{13}C and Mg/Ca in the first sub-division are likely to reflect faster drip rates and a climate with a more positive water balance than at the end of Zone 1, perhaps due to higher rainfall, although cooler summers with less evaporation would be another possible cause. The reason for the decline in δ^{18}O is not clear, though it is presumably due to the factors that had balanced one another previously now failing to do so.

During the second and third divisions of Zone 3 (9600–9150 and 9150–8650 BP respectively) the δ^{13}C, Mg/Ca and Sr/Ca all rise, the latter two reaching values comparable with those in the second half of Zone 2. This suggests that drip rates reduced and the climatic water surplus was less than during the first sub-division. Again, this could have been due to changes in rainfall or to greater evaporation in summer, or to a combination of the two. The δ^{18}O varies in sympathy with δ^{13}C, suggesting an influence of degassing on δ^{18}O values.

Zone 4, 8,650 – 7,950 BP

During this interval of 700 years the stalagmite grew extremely slowly, at about 11 μm per year. The zone can be recognised on the sectioned stalagmite (Fig. 11.2) as a band of dark calcite at about 26.5 cm from the base. There are only two sampled points within this band (and none for trace elements), but both δ^{13}C and δ^{18}O have lower values than immediately before and after this zone, suggesting that drip rate and water surplus may have temporarily increased. The

period between about 8500 and 8000 BP is thought to have been a time of cooler climate, with a brief cold event lasting less than a century around 8200 BP. This event is reflected by marked excursions to low values of δ^{18}O in stalagmites from Pippikin Pot and White Scar Cave (Fig. 11.5), but the stalagmite from Lancaster Hole grew too slowly for the sampling to register it.

Zone 5, 7,950 – 3,500 BP

For the first 230 years of this Zone, the stalagmite grew at around 385 μm per year reaching a height of about 32 cm above its base (Fig. 11.2). Thereafter its growth slowed down to about 62 μm per year until about 6000 BP, some time after which it slowed again before eventually ceasing altogether about 3500 years ago. The δ^{18}O shows a flat trend with the lowest values of the entire record, but is punctuated by small peaks that coincide with much larger peaks in the other three variables. The δ^{13}C also has generally low values compared with previous zones, and declines to the lowest in the record at about 5000 BP. Though the trace elements do not show quite such low values relative to previous zones, Mg/Ca mirrors the declining trend in δ^{13}C, and both show peaks that coincide with short upwards excursions in δ^{13}C and δ^{18}O. Once again, this pattern is suggestive of predominantly wet conditions with relatively little degassing required to cause calcite deposition, punctuated by drier periods that may have lasted for one or two centuries.

Beyond Lancaster Hole

The Late Glacial and Holocene record from the Lancaster Hole stalagmite is one of the most detailed and complete for any cave in the Yorkshire Dales, or in Britain. Few other records that have been made in Dales caves have been published in detail, though isotope studies have been made of several stalagmites and flowstones from Lancaster Hole and also one each from Pippikin Pot and White Scar Cave. Records from the latter two sites (Fig. 11.5) span the

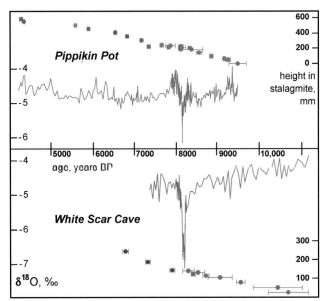

Figure 11.5. *Dated oxygen isotope records from two stalagmites, from White Scar Cave (Battlefield chamber) and Pippikin Pot (White Wall Chamber), that identify the brief period of cooling at 8200 years BP; age determinations with error bars are identified by their heights on the stalagmites.*

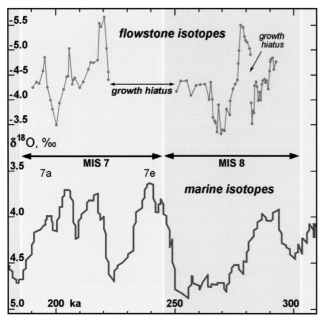

Figure 11.6. *The oxygen isotope record from a short flowstone sequence in Victoria Cave (after Gascoyne, 1981) compared with the modern chronology of the marine isotope record.*

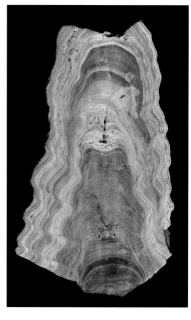

Figure 11.7. Closely spaced banding that is visible with the naked eye in a stalagmite 15 cm tall, with a basal age of about 15 ka, from a ledge in the Main Streamway of White Scar Cave (TW).

short cool period that was centred on 8200 years ago, when it is thought that the catastrophic emptying of ice-dammed lakes in North America released an enormous flood of fresh water into the North Atlantic, with subsequent effects on the climate (Daley *et al.*, 2011).

The only palaeoclimatic study of speleothems formed before the Last Glacial in the Dales is the pioneering work in Victoria Cave (Gascoyne, 1981). Tied to a sequence of seven sequential uranium–thorium dates, between 200 and 300 ka, a growth hiatus in a flowstone was correlated with a glaciation, but on the basis of an oxygen isotope chronology that was subsequently modified. Correlated with a modern marine isotope profile (Fig. 11.6), calcite deposition appears to have continued through most of the cold conditions of MIS 8 before ceasing. It then failed to restart in the warmer conditions of MIS 7e or its following cold phase, but restarted and continued with the subsequent warm phase. This would suggest that purely local conditions were influencing the flowstone growth, but any interpretation is limited by the low levels of precision on the isotope variations obtained with the old mass spectrometers (see Chapter 10). The oxygen isotope signal showed some correlation with the marine record, but it is now recognised that the stalagmite record is not just dependent on temperatures outside the cave. This flowstone formed part of a much longer sequence of flowstones and interbedded clays that have since been dated by more precise techniques than were available to Gascoyne. The whole sequence correlates well with the marine isotope record, and by inference with the history of glaciation in the British Isles (Lundberg *et al.*, 2010), and will repay further attention to the stable isotope records it potentially contains.

Banding in stalagmites (Fig. 11.7) is known to be annual at many sites, though a suite of 43 speleothems from British caves had detectable luminescence banding in only five samples (Baker *et al.*, 1993). The banding results from seasonal changes in the organics carried in seepage water as variations in fulvic and humic acid content, and counted

bands can be checked against high precision U–Th dates, but the processes behind the banding are not yet fully understood (Shopov *et al.*, 1994; White, 2007; Baker *et al.*, 2008; Crowell and White, 2012). There are to date no published studies of banded speleothems from caves within the Dales, but the stalagmite from White Scar Cave, whose isotope record is shown in Figure 11.5, displays banding at a microscopic scale. If these bands were annual they suggest that the episode of low $\delta^{18}O$ at about 8.2 ka may have lasted for about 110 years (Daley *et al.*, 2011). This is just one example of the level of data that is available to be extracted from stalagmites in the caves of the Dales.

References

Baker, A, P L Smart, R L Edwards and D A Richards, 1993. Annual growth banding in a cave stalagmite. *Nature*, **364**, 518-520.

Baker, A, C I Smith, C Jex, I J Fairchild, D Genty and L Fuller, 2008. Annually laminated speleothems: a review. *Int. J. Speleology*, **37**, 193-206.

Crowell, B E and W B White, 2012. Measurement of luminescent banding in speleothems: some techniques and limitations. *Int. J. Speleology*, **41**, 51-58.

Daley, T J and 16 others, 2011. The 8200 yr BP cold event in stable isotope records from the North Atlantic region. *Global Planetary Change*, **79**, 288-302.

Fairchild, I J and A Baker, 2012. *Speleothem Science*. Wiley: London, 432pp.

Gascoyne, M, 1981. A climate record of the Yorkshire Dales for the last 300,000 years. *Proc. 8th Int. Cong. Speleology* (Bowling Green KY), 96-98.

Lachniet, M S, 2009. Climatic and environmental controls on speleothem oxygen-isotope values. *Quat. Sci. Rev.*, **28**, 412-432.

Lisiecki, L E and M E Raymo, 2005. A Pliocene-Pleistocene stack of 57 globally distributed benthic $\delta^{18}O$ records. *Palaeoceanography*, **20**, 1003-1020.

Lundberg, J, T C Lord and P J Murphy, 2010. Thermal ionization mass spectrometer U-Th dates on Pleistocene speleothems from Victoria Cave, North Yorkshire, UK: implications for paleoenvironment and stratigraphy over multiple glacial cycles. *Geosphere*, **6**, 379–395.

McDermott, F, T C Atkinson, I J Fairchild, L M Baldini and D P Mattey, 2011. A first evaluation of the spatial gradients in $\delta^{18}O$ recorded by European Holocene speleothems. *Global Planetary Change*, **79**, 275-287.

Polyak, V J and R F Denniston, 2012. Paleoclimate records from speleothems. 577-585 in W B White and D C Culver (eds.), *Encyclopedia of Caves*, Academic Press: Waltham MA.

Shopov, Y Y, D C Ford and H P Schwarcz, 1994. Luminescence microbanding in speleothems: high resolution chronology and palaeoclimate. *Geology*, **22**, 407-410.

White, W B, 2007. Paleoclimate records from speleothems in limestone caves. 135-175 in I D Sasowsky and J Mylroie (eds.), *Studies of Cave Sediments: Physical and Chemical Records of Paleoclimate*. Springer: London.

Williams, M, D Dunkerley, P de Deckker, P Kershaw, and J Chappell, 1998. *Quaternary Environments*. Arnold: London, 352pp.

CHAPTER 12

Holocene environments

Margaret Atherden

The limestone areas of the Yorkshire Dales have a distinctive and beautiful landscape today, within which are some of the finest and most extensive areas of limestone pavement in Britain (see chapter 7). The dales support rich plant communities of hay meadows and limestone pastures, while surviving areas of deciduous woodland and scattered coniferous plantations provide habitats for a wide range of woodland animals and plants. However, all these habitats have been greatly modified by human actions and virtually none of the plant cover present across the Dales is truly natural. The soils and the plants have evolved and changed during the past 15,000 years or so, and climate and humans have combined to produce the modern landscape (Fig. 12.1).

Soil development

The underlying rocks have a fundamental role in soil formation and thus in the development of the plant cover. In turn, the soils play a considerable role in determining the nature and scale of limestone dissolution.

Within the Yorkshire Dales karst terrains, the soils have developed either directly over the limestone bedrock or on a drift cover. The calcium carbonate that makes up the bulk of the limestone is soluble in water, so where soils develop directly on the limestone it is largely the impurities in the rock that are left to provide the mineral fraction of the soils. Many of these impurities are blown away or washed down the grikes in the limestone pavements, so residual soils accumulate very slowly and lack well-developed horizons. These soils are known as rendzinas or humic rankers. They are typically very thin and freely draining, with an organic surface horizon directly overlying the limestone bedrock. They cover significant areas of the limestone outcrop in the southern Dales, particularly over the Malham High Country and on the Ingleborough massif. Smaller areas of these soils are scattered across the outcrops of the Yoredale limestones in Wensleydale and Swaledale.

Where glacial drift forms the parent material, soils are generally more acidic. Those with a clay matrix, which are dominant in the Dales, have very low permeablility, so are prone to seasonal water-logging and to the development of peaty surface layers. These soils are commonly thicker, with well-developed horizons, and are mapped as cambic stagnohumic gleys. They occur on many of the lower slopes of the uplands, on the limestone plateaus, on the higher slopes of the Yoredale rocks and on the dale floors. Brown earth soils have developed over drift that was derived from the sandstone and shale cover around Malham, across

much of Wensleydale east of Hawes and also in smaller areas in Swaledale (Bullock, 1971). Along the valley floors of Ribblesdale, Wharfedale and Wensleydale, there are groundwater gley soils that overlie river alluvium and also small patches of brown calcareous soils over some river-terrace gravels.

Loessic soils on the limestone

Silty soils on the limestone outcrops that are free of glacial till are largely loessic in origin (Pigott, 1962; Vincent, 2006). They consist almost entirely of silt-sized quartz grains with a narrow range of particle size that is typical of aeolian sediment (Fig. 12.2), and their lithology is very different from that of dissolutional residues from the limestone; the latter make only a very small contribution to the soils in the Dales karst. The loess weathers to a well-drained brown earth, which may contain a thin iron-pan underlying any cover of peaty soil.

The loess was carried onto the limestone uplands by winds that had crossed source areas of glaciofluvial outwash that were prone to deflation. These were extensive in the Irish Sea Basin both before and after its occupation by Devensian ice (see Chapter 3). Loess that preceded the glaciation has been recognised by dates of around 27,000 years for sediment in Dowkabottom, above Wharfedale (Telfer *et al.*, 2009). This was protected from ice erosion by its sheltered location within an old doline, and pre-Devensian loess is likely to be restricted to similar, protected sites elsewhere in the Dales.

Much of the loess appears to have been blown onto the Dales landscape in Late Glacial times, when low sea-levels exposed large source areas in the Irish Sea Basin, and limited

Figure 12.1. Upper Wharfedale, looking south from the hillside above Kettlewell; the green lane in the foreground was originally used to drive cattle between the upland summer pastures and their winter quarters in the valley; fields bounded by dry stone walls on the valley floor are used mainly for hay or silage production, and patches of ash woodland remain on the valley sides (MA).

Holocene environments, by Margaret Atherden,
York St John University; m.atherden@yorksj.ac.uk
Chapter 12, pages 187–198 in **Caves and Karst of the Yorkshire Dales**,
edited by Tony Waltham and David Lowe.
Published 2013 by the British Cave Research Association,
978-0-900265-46-4 and at www.bcra.org.uk

plant growth in the cold climates favoured aeolian deflation. However, dating of loess deposits by optically stimulated luminescence techniques indicates that most of the loess has only been buried since later in the Holocene (Vincent *et al.*, 2011). Five loess samples from the Malham High Country have dates from the Holocene between 6600 and 9200 years BP, while only two date from the Loch Lomond Stadial around 12,000 years ago in the Late Glacial. A similar age distribution is recorded for further samples from the karst around Morecambe Bay. It therefore appears that much of the loess was eroded and re-distributed as colluvial sediments during the Holocene.

A climatic interlude at about 8200 years BP is well-documented in the North Atlantic hinterlands and was probably related to a final collapse of the Laurentide ice sheet that caused widespread cooling by a few degrees as a consequence of the cold, fresh water added to the ocean (Alley *et al.*, 1997). The event is also recorded by isotope fluctuations in stalagmites in some Dales caves (see Chapter 10), and these indicate that the period of major cooling lasted little more than a hundred years (Daley *et al.*, 2011). Multiple dates of loessic sediments from the limestone uplands of the Dales, obtained by optically stimulated luminescence, confirms that extensive re-working of the loess appears to be related at least partially to this climatic event, when periglacial conditions briefly returned to the Yorkshire Dales (Wilson *et al.*, 2012).

Before, during and after that climatic interlude about 8200 years ago, the loessic soils were progressively eroded away from large areas of the limestone pavements in the Dales. Their early presence is indicated by the rounded features of the pavements (Fig. 12.4), which had formed beneath some type of soil cover, but subsequently much of the soil was lost into the limestone grikes. This soil loss was probably accelerated by woodland clearance and sheep grazing (see below), but the proportions of the losses that were natural or artificial remain open to debate (O'Connor, 2011).

Peat mires and blanket peat

Peat deposits are extensive across the Dales. Within the areas of limestone karst, thick lenses of Holocene peat form mires and raised bogs within many small basins. These all stand on floors of impermeable glacial till, and include some quaking bogs of deep, saturated *Sphagnum*, as well as dried areas of more stable raised bog. Successions within the peat commonly start with sedge or reed swamp and pass upwards into fen carr and then *Sphagnum* bog.

Tarn Moss, on the west side of Malham Tarn, has three low domes of raised bog, each rising to about 5m high (Fig. 12.5). Along their north side, a calcareous fen was partially

Figure 12.2. Exposed profile one metre deep through loessic soil on the floor of the Dowkabottom doline; two samples from below the position of the gamma spectrometer proved to be about 27,000 years old (photo: Matt Telfer).

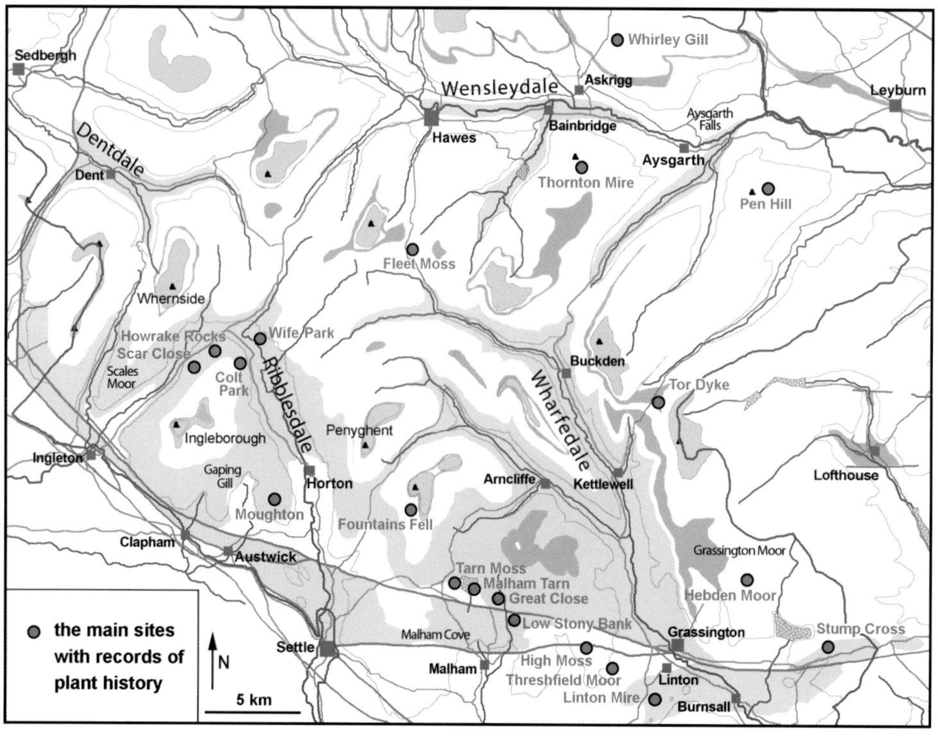

Figure 12.3. Locations of major sites where research on vegetation history has been undertaken, mostly with pollen analyses; data from Tor Dyke and Hebden Moor have not been published. Significant sites in the Craven Lowlands, at White Moss (Wigglesworth), Eshton Tarn (Airton) and Martons Booth (Bank Newton), all lie to the south.

inundated when the Tarn level was raised by about a metre in 1791 (Pigott and Pigott, 1959, 1963; Huddart, 2002). Each dome is built of peat up to 7m thick, and is directly underlain by Late Glacial silts that indicate the Tarn was originally about double its present size. The silts and the peat lie over an irregular surface of till, which also rises from the bog to form the Spiggot Hill drumlin. Exposures of the upper part of the peat profile reveal two paler bands of *Sphagnum*-rich peat that were preserved in wetter conditions. The second of these dates from about 2700 years ago (Swindles, 2009), which may correlate with a brief interlude of higher rainfall in response to an increase in North Atlantic ice produced by ice-shelf collapse. Within the sequence, a layer of tephra from the Icelandic volcano Hekla has been dated to the Glen Garry event of about 2100 years ago. The peat mire at Attermire has also yielded a core 2.4m long that dates back to 11.6 ka, very early in the Holocene (Rushworth *et al.*, 2012).

Figure 12.4. Rounded features in limestone pavement now exposed through a cover of soil and plants beside the Middle Washfold sinks, above Southerscales, Chapel-le-Dale (TW).

Plant research in the Dales

Some of the earliest research using pollen analysis in Britain was carried out in the Yorkshire Dales, including exploratory studies in the 1920s and 1930s by Woodhead, Godwin and Clark, and by Raistrick and Blackburn (Atherden, 1999). This established that even the higher parts of the area had formerly supported a woodland cover and, although the pollen diagrams were sketchy by modern standards, they laid the foundation for more detailed work that could include dating of the materials. In the late 1950s, Donald and Margaret Pigott (1959, 1963) produced pollen diagrams from Malham Tarn and Great Close Mire, spanning almost the entire Late Glacial and post-glacial Holocene periods. This was followed by Sheila Gosden's study (1968) of the peat deposits at Scar Close, Ingleborough.

Into the 1980s, pollen sequences were recorded at several sites in the Craven Lowlands (Bartley *et al.*, 1990), while data from the Ingleborough district, by Swales in 1987 and by Oybak in 1993, were never published. Subsequent research (Fig. 12.3) has included that by Margaret Bastow on Hebden Moor and at Tor Dike, above Wharfedale, but remains unpublished, while Graeme Swindles and Gary Rushworth have worked on peats around Malham and Settle (2009). High-resolution pollen diagrams have been combined with radiocarbon dating in Upper Ribblesdale by Helen Shaw and Ian Whyte (2010), and this work continues.

Unlike the larger areas of peat that are underlain by till, isolated islands of peat stand on many of the limestone pavements (Fig. 12.6), notably those around Ingleborough (Gosden, 1968). Though these appear to stand directly on the bare limestone, it is likely that their vegetation originally set roots into thin layers of the loessic soil that was widespread on the limestone before being partially or totally washed into the underlying grikes.

Right across the Yorkshire Dales, many of the highest plateau tops are covered with large expanses of blanket peat (Fig. 12.7). Fleet Moss is an unbroken area of very wet bog extending for more than 100 ha on the Wharfedale-Wensleydale watershed above Oughtershaw. These blanket peats developed largely on top of glacial drift that overlies sandstones, shales and limestones, mostly within the Yoredale Group. Regardless of the bedrock, the production of humic acids in the peat makes their soils extremely acidic. Many of the tracts of hill peat have been exploited for fuel by farmers and villagers who held turbary rights to cut peat from the high fells.

Figure 12.5. Tarn Moss, the large peat bog and wetland on the edge of Malham Tarn (photo: Rob Sutton).

Figure 12.6. Islands of drift and peat on the limestone pavements of Scar Close, above Chapel-le-Dale (TW).

Human influences on the soils

A generalised account of the soils gives only a broad picture of the relationship between soils and the underlying solid or drift geology. On the ground, the situation is much more complex, with variations in soil that relate to details that include the extent of fissuring of the limestone, the depth of the drift cover, the existence of loess overlying glacial drift and the effects of spring flushing on lower ground. Malham Moor is notable for its contrasting soils that occur within a few metres of each other (Smith, 1991). The existence of prehistoric ('Celtic') field walls, above Malham Cove and elsewhere on the limestone, suggests that soils were deeper in the past, as some of these areas are now little more than limestone pavement. It is very likely that the prehistoric farming triggered increased erosion and subsequent loss of the soil cover (Smith, 1991). Any loss of soils from areas of thin drift over the limestone rock would have been difficult to replace, owing to its very low rate of accumulation.

The areas of prehistoric fields are not the only ones where there have been significant changes in the soil cover. On the limestone pavements there are some areas where soil cover is eroding and others where it is extending (Curtis *et al.*, 1976). Any excessive grazing pressure may diminish the plant cover and then expose the soil to both water erosion and aeolian deflation. Much of the original loessic soil on the limestone has been washed down the grikes, to be re-deposited within the cave systems, thereby increasing the extent of the bare pavements. In contrast, both soil and plant covers are expanding in other areas, notably where fencing excludes grazing animals. At these sites, the peaty top soil gradually extends laterally on to adjacent areas of limestone pavement. Individual sites with both retreating and expanding soil cover occur on the limestone benches of the Ingleborough massif.

Plant development

Colonisation by plants proceeds alongside soil development. On bare limestone areas, it is difficult for plant growth to start, as the surface of the limestone clints is both hard and dry. Colonisation usually begins on flat or concave surfaces that can retain some moisture. The first colonisers are microscopic algae, fungi and bacteria. These begin the process of attacking the surface of the limestone and gradually create conditions for ground-hugging lichens to form a vegetative crust over the surface of the clints. This layer in turn is colonised by foliose lichens and mosses, and gradually a thin layer of organic matter builds up. On this the higher plants can gain a foothold. However, the early stages of colonisation are vulnerable to erosion, so it may take many years for plant growth to become firmly established.

Limestone soils are rich in calcium, which can make other nutrients less available to plants. A specific group of plants, the calcicoles, are adapted to grow in these conditions; they include the rock rose (*Helianthemum nummularium*) (Fig. 12.8) and the blue moor grass (*Sesleria caerulea*) [Latin names in this chapter follow Stace, 2010]. On a cover of glacial drift or loess, plant colonisation is much faster and there are fewer calcicoles. Areas of the most acidic drift, and the peats of the plateau tops, may develop as moorland that is dominated by heathers; these are particularly extensive

Figure 12.7. Blanket peat at Fleet Moss, lying on thin drift over Yoredale shales on the watershed ridge between Wharfedale and Wensleydale (MA).

Figure 12.8. Rock rose in profusion on the limestone slopes of Conistone Old Pasture, Wharfedale (MA).

Figure 12.9. Purple saxifrage on a gritstone ledge high on the upper slopes of Pen-y-ghent (photo: Rob Sutton).

on the wider outcrops of the Yoredale gritstones above Swaledale, and also form the grouse beats on Leck Fell and Casterton Fell.

The most direct evidence for the Holocene history of the plant cover comes from the study of organic remains from buried soil horizons. These include wood fragments, fruits and seeds, and microscopic materials that include pollen grains and the spores of mosses and ferns. In general, plant material is best preserved in acid or water-logged conditions, so the limestone karst of the Dales does not constitute a very promising resource. However, there are numerous sites where plant remains, particularly pollen grains, have been preserved. These include peat soils overlying limestone pavements, blanket peats overlying glacial drift, individual shakeholes and dolines, and various lakes and former lakebeds (Smith, 1986). Pollen analysis is the main tool for reconstructing profiles of the past plant cover (Faegri and Iversen, 1989; Moore *et al.*, 1991). Carbon-14 dates of profiles through a number of peat bogs record deposition that started close to the beginning of the Holocene, but many of the earlier pollen records are un-dated because studies preceded the wide availability of radiometric dating. Furthermore, pollen analysis provides little direct evidence of insect-pollinated species, notably the hay-meadow flowers and the rare calcicoles, and yields scant evidence of arable cultivation, because most cereals are self-pollinating.

The Late Glacial period

The ice-sheets of the Devensian glaciation began their retreat from the Dales around 17,000 years ago, when the earliest rock outcrops appeared along the southern margin of the Craven Uplands (see Chapter 3). The first plants to colonise the ice-free ground were low-growing grasses, sedges and arctic-alpine species, notably mountain avens (*Dryas octopetala*) and cloudberry (*Rubus chamaemorus*). These contributed to a new tundra landscape across the Dales. Conditions were still too severe for tree and shrub growth, but the dwarf birch (*Betula nana*) was present, its prostrate habit allowing it to survive under the winter snow cover to avoid the low temperatures and biting winds. Some of these

first colonisers are still present, with the beautiful purple saxifrage (*Saxifraga oppositifolia*) growing on rock ledges high on Pen-y-ghent (Fig. 12.9).

By about 14,700 years ago, the climate had warmed sufficiently for trees and shrubs to invade the Dales. Tree birches (*Betula* spp) and juniper (*Juniperus communis*) were the most important pioneers, along with smaller numbers of aspen (*Populus tremula*) and willows (*Salix* spp). Plant colonisation during this period, the Windermere Interstadial, was fastest on areas of glacial drift in the valleys, but also began to spread on the limestone rocks of the Dales karst.

However, about 12,800 years ago plant succession was suddenly reversed with a return to cold conditions in the Loch Lomond Stadial. Also known as the Younger Dryas, this lasted for just over 2000 years. Ice cover was only re-established in a few small corries high on the western hills (see Chapter 3), but across the Dales landscapes trees and shrubs died out, soils were subject to solifluction over permafrost and rock surfaces were laid bare again. The plant community returned to tundra, dominated once more by grasses and sedges. Mugworts (*Artemisia* spp) were particularly common, as they thrive on disturbed, nutrient-rich ground in the steppe environments that pertained through the Younger Dryas.

The Early Holocene period

After this major setback to plant succession, the climate finally warmed about 11,700 years ago, thereby marking the beginning of the Holocene. The first stages were similar to those in the Windermere Interstadial, with juniper and tree birches the first to form a light woodland canopy. Hazel (*Corylus avellana*) was another early coloniser and may have grown in pure stands, comparable with those now on Mull and Skye. Later, as taller trees invaded the area, hazel became part of the woodland under-storey. All the indicators are that the climate was generally warm and dry, so woodland spread rapidly in the early Holocene, soon shading out the open tundra vegetation. The arctic-alpine species of the Late Glacial were gradually confined to rocky outcrops on high ground, while grasses and sedges found new niches in woodland glades and wetlands. Willows thrived in the many

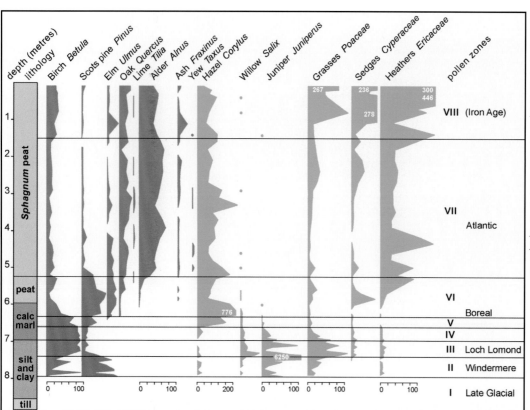

Figure 12.10. Sequence of changes in the trees, shrubs and grasses after the end of the Late Glacial period, indicated by the pollen record in the cored profile through the peat at Tarn Moss, Malham (after Pigott and Pigott, 1959); aspen is notable by its absence, but this is because its pollen is both rarely preserved and difficult to identify; scales are expressed as percentages of total tree pollen (darker green), and are the same for all taxa except hazel.

wetland sites. Plant distributions are generally limited more by competition from other species than by direct climatic factors; nearly all the plants of the Late Glacial period can survive in the present climate of the Dales, but they are restricted by the greater ability of other species to compete for the most favourable sites.

Trees dominated the Dales landscape from the early Holocene onwards, but some species took hundreds of years to reach the area from the warmer regions of southern England and continental Europe, where they had found refuge during the glacial periods. Scots Pine (*Pinus sylvestris*) was the next to arrive after birch and hazel, and it soon established dominance in the woodlands by its taller growth. Pollen sequences from Malham (Pigott and Pigott, 1963) show that pine grew on a wide variety of rock types, including the Carboniferous Limestone, where it seems to have thrived (Fig. 12.10). Birch, juniper and hazel formed the under-storey in the pinewoods, producing woodland similar to that still existing in parts of the Scottish Highlands. However, juniper was soon out-competed and virtually disappeared from the pollen record once the pinewoods were well established.

Elm (*Ulmus*), oak (*Quercus*) and lime (*Tilia*) were among the trees that gradually invaded the Dales, soon followed by alder (*Alnus glutinosa*). These competed well on the heavier soils over glacial drift, but found the well-drained limestone soils more difficult to colonise. Pine retained its dominance for longer on the limestone. This may have been a result of soil conditions alone, but it is also possible that fire played a part. Pine is partially fire-adapted, and sheds its seeds most readily after the cones have been heated by fire. The advantage of this to the tree is that the fire destroys the ground flora and recycles mineral nutrients from the soil in the ash, forming favourable conditions for seed germination. In the relatively dry climate of the early Holocene, lightning

fires were probably more frequent, but another possibility is that hunter-gatherers were using fire to drive game or enlarge natural woodland clearings (Simmons and Innes, 1981, 1987). Either way, pine would have had an advantage in areas that were regularly burned, and this may well have been a factor in its survival in the Yorkshire Dales. The balance of tree species within the woodland continued to change throughout the early Holocene, finally producing a mosaic of woodland types on different sites that were determined largely by geology and drainage.

The Mid-Holocene period

Following the rise in sea level that separated Britain from the continent about 8000 years ago, a wetter climate in the mid-Holocene gave a competitive advantage to oak and alder, and these came to dominate most of the woodlands. However, pine managed to cling on for several hundred years in the limestone areas of Craven. The Mid-Holocene woods had a wide variety of tree species, with yew (*Taxus baccata*), bird cherry (*Prunus padus*) and ash (*Fraxinus excelsior*) all as minor components. Hazel and other shrubs formed the understorey in the woods, and a ground flora of plants included primrose (*Primula vulgaris*), bluebell (*Hyacinthoides non-scripta*) and red campion (*Silene dioica*) growing where there was sufficient light, notably where a tree had fallen or along stream banks.

Pollen profiles indicate that a woodland canopy extended over nearly all of the Yorkshire Dales in the Mid-Holocene, even over some areas of limestone pavement. However, the canopy may not have been dense everywhere. Woodlands may have been relatively open, resembling parkland, as a result of grazing by wild herbivores (Vera, 2000). There was a rich fauna at the time, with grazing aurochs (wild catttle), deer and bison alongside omnivorous wild boar and

Figure 12.11. Old wood pasture among ash trees on the lower slopes of Wharfedale, down the valley from Kettlewell (MA).

brown bear. These were hunted by carnivorous grey wolf and European lynx, and also by humans. Consequently, there may have been a considerable grazing impact on the vegetation, producing some substantial open, grassy areas that were intermixed with denser woodland. The Mid-Holocene landscape of the Yorkshire Dales was probably a varied and rich environment, rather than a monotonous expanse of closed canopy woodland.

Traces of this former woodland cover still survive in parts of the Dales, notably on some of the benches along Upper Wharfedale (Fig. 12.11). Wood remains, including birch, oak, alder, pine and willow, are widely preserved under the blanket bogs on higher ground, and are revealed where streams cut down through the peat, or when severe burning strips the peat away. Large stumps can be preserved in their original positions of growth (Fig. 12.12), whereas other sites have only a scatter of smaller branches and twigs. Although more common on the gritstone moors, buried wood remains do also occur in limestone areas, bearing testimony to the existence of a wooded landscape that has subsequently disappeared from most of the Dales.

Figure 12.12. Buried tree remains, mostly pine stumps in position of growth and probably about 7000 years old, preserved beneath peat until revealed by erosion, on Blubberhouses Moor, between Wharfedale and Nidderdale (photo: Timothy Laurie).

The Late Holocene period

The advent of agricultural cultures in the Yorkshire Dales about 6000 years ago marks the beginning of the Late Holocene, when human impact on the environment became increasingly important. The effects were small-scale at first, but there is one feature on the pollen diagrams that provides a useful marker for the start of the period. The Elm Decline, probably the result of an outbreak of Dutch Elm Disease, is recognisable on pollen diagrams from all over northwestern Europe and has been dated to around 6000 years ago at many different sites, including several in the Dales. From the Elm Decline onwards, there are records of agricultural weeds. Ribwort plantain (*Plantago lanceolata*) and docks (*Rumex* spp) indicate pastoral agriculture, whereas members of the daisy (Asteraceae) and parsley (Apiaceae) families, are more often associated with arable farming. As well as native plants, which took advantage of the open ground created by farming, introduced plants began to colonise the area, especially cereals and the cornfield weeds. These appear in small numbers in the pollen record, and indicate a gradual decline of woodland and the expansion of grassland and arable land.

Within the Yorkshire Dales, such clearance episodes were characteristic of the late Neolithic and Bronze Age periods. The human population was probably small in number and impact on the plant cover was often temporary, but the cumulative effects of this early agriculture over several hundred years led to longer-term changes in the landscape. These included erosion and removal of some of the thin limestone soils, leaching of exposed soils on higher ground after the woodland cover had been removed, and re-colonisation with different plants after habitation sites were abandoned. Where woodland regenerated, it was often with a different combination of tree species, including more of the light-loving birch and ash. The Mid-Holocene woodlands had included relatively few of these trees, but they quickly colonised cleared land before the oak and alder could move in. Ash gradually increased in abundance throughout the Late Holocene, until it is now one of the most numerous trees in the Yorkshire Dales.

Figure 12.13. White wood anemone creates a carpet of flowers between clumps of hazel that were coppiced in the old woodland beside the Middle Aysgarth Falls, in Wensleydale (TW).

The human impact increased dramatically in the Iron Age, around 2500 years ago, when better technology allowed agricultural exploitation of the heavier soils over glacial drift within the dales. Another important development was iron smelting, which required large quantities of charcoal as fuel, and led to the first systematic management of the woodlands. When deciduous trees are felled, they re-grow from the cut stumps, producing within a few years many small shoots that are suitable for charcoal production. This tradition of coppicing can be traced back at least to the Iron Age (Fig. 12.13). The climate during the first millennium BC became cooler and wetter, as seen in the accumulation of wetter, less-decomposed peat layers in many bogs. This may have led to greater use of lowland sites for agriculture, along with abandonment of some farmland on higher ground (Mackay and Tallis, 1994). Re-colonisation into woodland was slower on the wetter upland soils of this period and this, combined with sustained grazing pressure from domestic stock, resulted in permanent changes in the landscape. It is likely that the extent of upland pastures and moorlands was similar to that of the present day by the end of the Iron Age (Tinsley 1975).

The arrival of the Romans in Britain in AD 43 coincided with a period of warmer climate, but the broad pattern of agricultural settlement probably changed little in the Dales. Archaeological finds confirm that the Romans used scythes for hay-making, though their use probably started in the Iron Age. Most of the familiar elements of the rural Dales landscape had thus emerged by Roman times, including arable land and hay meadows in the valleys, pastures on the higher ground and scattered small areas of deciduous woodland dominated by oak and ash. However, there is indirect evidence to suggest that some more substantial areas of woodland survived. Lynx bones, recovered from both Kinsey Cave and Moughton Fell Cave in the flanks of Ribblesdale and dated to about AD 500, show that this predator, which hunts exclusively in woodland, survived locally at least into the Anglo-Saxon period (Hetherington *et al.*, 2006). In many parts of northern England, there was a regeneration of woodland and scrub after the Romans left, but this is not very marked on pollen diagrams from the Dales, suggesting a broad continuity of land use over the next few centuries.

Anglo-Saxon and Viking settlers established villages in the Dales and gradually reduced the remaining woodland cover. The heavy clay soils of the Craven Lowlands were first farmed at this time. However, a more marked impact on the landscape came in medieval times, when the monastic centres at Furness, Fountains Abbey and Bolton Abbey established large-scale agricultural enterprises, with arable cultivation in the valleys, including the cultivation of hemp in Great Close Pasture, above Malham. Lynchets terrace many valley sides in the Dales where medieval cultivation took place on the steep slopes, but they are extremely difficult to date and many of them may be much older in origin (Fig. 12.14). However, the most significant impact was on the uplands, where the grazing of large flocks of sheep resulted in an expansion of grassland (Shaw and Whyte, 2010). The traditional herb-rich pastures (Fig. 12.15) of the Dales are direct descendants of these medieval grasslands. There is documentary evidence for transhumance in Nidderdale, with flocks grazed on upland pastures in the summer and moving to the lowlands in the winter. Deciduous woodlands were also exploited in medieval times. Some were coppiced to provide wood and charcoal, while others were managed as wood pasture, which offered shelter to grazing domestic animals as well as supporting timber production.

Figure 12.14. Lynchets set into the glacial till on the lower slopes of limestone east of Hawkswick, at the lower end of Littondale (TW).

Figure 12.15. Maintained by sheep grazing, and fertilised by sheep dung, grassland on the lower part of the Conistone Old Pasture, in Wharfedale, supports a rich assemblage of grasses and other plants, including abundant yellow rock rose (MA).

The last few centuries have seen further changes to the details of the landscape (Shaw and Whyte, 2010). Farming underwent a severe decline in the fourteenth century, owing to a combination of famine, animal disease, raids by Scots, the Black Death and the start of the cooler climate of the Little Ice Age. By the early sixteenth century, the familiar landscape of small farms and upland commons was largely established, and survives to modern times (Johnson, 2008). The field barns that form such a characteristic feature of the dales were established in the sixteenth and seventeenth centuries, and cattle droving became important in the seventeenth and eighteenth centuries (Shaw and Whyte, 2010). As the population increased, so the land was used more intensively, and this reflects in the pollen records, which show a growing dominance of grasses and a decline in woodland species.

More recently, there has been some planting of new woodlands on some of the large estates, often using non-native coniferous trees, but the extent of these plantations is less in the Craven district than it is in other parts of the Pennines. Moorlands on acidic soils have been used for grouse shooting since the mid-nineteenth century, leading to a loss of diversity of both plants and animals. Regular burning of the moorlands favours common heather (*Calluna vulgaris*) over other plant species, while gamekeepers have reduced the numbers of predators, especially birds of prey. Many of the grasslands have also lost species diversity over the past century, through more frequent use of artificial fertilisers that give a competitive advantage to a few grass species. Some hay meadows in the valleys have been ploughed up and re-seeded, making those traditional meadows that do survive particularly valuable in conservation terms. Although coppicing and wood pasture have declined as forms of woodland management, surviving deciduous woodlands are often used for pheasant shooting. It is apparent that all the habitats in the Yorkshire Dales have been significantly modified from their wild antecedents, and the present landscape is largely artificial (O'Connor, 2011).

The modern plant cover

The deciduous woodlands in the Dales are of three main types (Rodwell, 1991). On the limestone, ash woods predominate. Ash forms the main canopy species but is accompanied by a range of other trees and shrubs, including hazel, bird cherry, willows and hawthorn (*Crataegus monogyna*). Colt Park Wood (a National Nature Reserve on Ingleborough) has a dense cover of trees growing over deeply-fissured limestone pavement (Fig. 12.16), and some of the limestone pavements elsewhere on Ingleborough support scrub of ash, hazel, hawthorn and other species, mainly where grazing by sheep has been restricted. At Ling Gill, in upper Ribblesdale, the

Figure 12.16. Ash woodland and a rich ground flora that almost completely obscures the limestone pavement within Colt Park Wood, Ingleborough (TW).

Figure 12.17. Lady's slipper orchid, the jewel of the limestone Dales, photographed in 1976.

ash is accompanied by wych elm (*Ulmus glabra*), birch and aspen, while sycamore (*Acer pseudoplatanus*) has invaded some woods in the Malham area.

The ash woods have a rich ground flora and rarities include baneberry (*Actaea spicata*), herb Paris (*Paris quadrifolia*), Jacob's-ladder (*Polemonium caeruleum*) and meadow-rue (*Thalictrum flavum*). One of England's rarest plants, the lady's-slipper orchid (*Cypripedium calceolus*), survives at one closely-guarded site within the Yorkshire Dales (Fig. 12.17). It was a victim of its own beauty, when bunches of the flowers were sold in Settle market in the nineteenth century, until it was picked to the brink of extinction. Where ash woods were used as wood pasture, the ground flora tends to be less rich, dominated by grasses or bracken (*Pteridium aquilinum*), with meadowsweet (*Filipendula ulmaria*) in wet areas, such as below Gate Close Scar near Kettlewell.

On acid soils over shales or glacial drift, oak woodland predominates, as in West Wood and Preston Spring Wood, both near Redmire in lower Wensleydale. On the Yoredale rocks in upper Wensleydale, oak occurs on the wetter shale beds, with ash on the drier limestone terraces and scars. On wetter soils near rivers and on flushes around springs in the valley sides, alder is generally the dominant tree and willows are also common. Sepperdin Wood, near Redmire, is a fine coppiced alder wood. The moisture-loving ground flora includes meadow-sweet, marsh marigold (*Caltha palustris*) and sedges, and locally Indian balsam (*Impatiens glandulifera*), which then tends to out-compete other species.

On the limestone pavements, much of an ancestral soil cover has been washed down the grikes, where many plants subsequently take root. The moist, shady environment of the grikes resembles that of a woodland floor, and supports many woodland species among a large range of plants (Ward and Evans, 1976); dog's mercury (*Mercurialis perennis*) and hart's-tongue fern (*Asplenium scolopendrium*) are conspicuous at most sites (Fig. 12.18). Where vegetation has been undisturbed for centuries, mature woodland is developed even over deeply fissured limestone pavement. The preserved ash wood at Colt Park is a mature example

Figure 12.19. A limestone scar lies along the edge of the Colt Park Wood, on Ingleborough, with its mature woodland covering the limestone pavement that is immediately above it (TW).

(Fig. 12.19), and the thin scrub cover on Scar Close is a site less fully developed (Fig. 12.20).

There are many different types of grassland within the Dales landscape. Though dominated by the fescue and bent grasses (*Festuca* and *Agrostis*), the unimproved limestone pastures are some of the most botanically diverse grasslands in the country. Numerous grasses occur in the sward, conspicuous among which are the beautiful quaking-grass (*Briza media*) and the blue moor-grass, a species found only in a strip across northern England from Yorkshire to Lancashire. These limestone pastures need grazing to maintain their species diversity, which includes rock-rose, fairy flax (*Linum catharticum*), harebell (*Campanula rotundifolia*), salad burnet (*Poterium sanguisorba*) and felwort (*Gentianella amarella*). In Wharfedale, Conistone Old Pasture has grasslands that are often a carpet of yellow rock rose (Fig. 12.21).

Discontinuous grassland covers much of the limestone outcrop. This is largely the result of sheep grazing since prehistoric times and especially since the medieval period.

Figure 12.18. Hart's-tongue fern in a grike in the Southerscales limestone pavement above Chapel-le-Dale (TW).

Figure 12.20. Limestone pavement in Scar Close, Ingleborough; part of this is covered by peat, whereas part supports the scrub woodland that is rooted in the deep grikes (MA).

Figure 12.21. Colourful meadow flora with red clover, pignut and buttercups, on the floor of Arkengarthdale (TW).

Across the Malham High Country, plants surviving from the colder conditions of Late Glacial times include mountain avens, baneberry and spring-sandwort (*Minuartia verna*). The dark red helleborine (*Epipactis atro-rubens*) favours upper dale sides, but is not widespread. Other limestone treasures include lily-of-the-valley (*Convallaria majalis*) and bloody crane's-bill (*Geranium sanguineum*). Many grasslands on calcareous flushes are rich in species that include the carnivorous butterwort (*Pinguicula vulgaris*), the beautiful white-flowered grass-of-Parnassus (*Parnassia palustris*) and the delicate pink bird's-eye primrose (*Primula farinosa*).

Figure 12.22. Traditional hay meadows, rich in buttercups, with one of the many stone field barns, on the floor of Swaledale (TW).

Figure 12.23. A swathe of purple heather across the moorland above the village of Grinton in lower Swaledale (TW).

Neutral soils support a different type of grassland, notably the hay meadows that are so characteristic of the valley floors in the Yorkshire Dales (Figs. 12.21, 12.22). Traditionally-managed meadows have a wide variety of grass species. They grade into other types, generally dominated by perennial rye-grass (*Lolium perenne*), wherever fertilisers have been applied to improve the land for agriculture. Wetter soils support meadowsweet, great burnet (*Sanguisorba officinalis*), globe-flower (*Trollius europaeus*), wild angelica (*Angelica sylvestris*) and rushes (*Juncus*). Even-wetter areas have real mire communities, with important sites at Great Close Mire, Ha Mire and Tarn Moss above Malham. At these, sedges and bog-mosses (*Sphagnum* spp) abound, and their remains accumulate to form the peat deposits that preserve much of the evidence for past vegetation.

Acid soils over gritstones and sand-rich drift support heather moorland that turns the landscape purple in late summer (Fig. 12.23). Common heather is the main plant, with its dominance maintained by regular burning as part of grouse moor management. Two other heathers also occur frequently and flower earlier in the season; the bell heather (*Erica cinerea*) grows on well-drained soils, and the cross-leaved heather (*E. tetralix*) thrives in wetter situations. A range of berry-bearing dwarf shrubs accompanies the heathers, including bilberry (*Vaccinium myrtillus*), cowberry (*V. vitis-idaea*) and crowberry (*Empetrum nigrum*). On the highest ground, cloudberry may be more widespread, along with roseroot (*Sedum rosea*) and several species of saxifrage (*Saxifraga aizoides*, *S. hypnoides*) that survive on cliff ledges high on Ingleborough.

The future landscape

The survival of the plant communities owes much to the traditional farming methods that are still employed in the Dales, with sheep and cattle grazing on unimproved pastures and hay-making in the valleys (Fig. 12.24). However, the landscape is changing fast. Woodlands are commonly neglected and tree regeneration is limited by grazing pressure. Many pastures have been fertilised and thereby replaced by species-poor grasslands, while modern silage production has marked the demise of most of the colourful, traditional hay meadows. Grazing pressure and, to some extent, recreational pressure cause further erosion of soils and loss of plants on the limestone pavements. Added to these man-made threats is the impact of climate change. The first casualties of global warming in the Dales are likely to be the arctic-alpine survivors, but many other plant communities may also be threatened in the longer term. The rapid climate change will demand that many plant distributions shift northwards, but the fragmentation of the landscape by roads and settlements will leave some species unable to reach suitable new sites.

The priority for the future must be to create and enhance woodland corridors, especially along river valleys, to allow woodland flora and fauna to migrate. In contrast, grassland plants and animals may be able to migrate along the roadside verges that form a network linking unimproved grassland fragments within the different valleys. Sensitive management of road verge habitats is therefore another priority. It may also be possible to re-create some habitats, notably the hay meadows, by spreading seed from existing sites on to new ones. The present flora of the Yorkshire Dales has been subject to both environmental change and human impact for many millennia. The nature, value and diversity of the future flora will depend on man's ability to manage the landscape and adapt to even greater changes over the coming centuries.

Figure 12.24. *A landscape created by grazing with limestone pasture and enclosed grassland, above Caseker Pasture, Great Whernside; the green of the fescue grasses gives way to the yellow of the rushes on wetter ground (TW).*

References

Alley, R. B, P A Mayewski, T Sowers, M Stuiver, K C Taylor and P U Clark, 1997. Holocene climatic instability; a prominent, widespread event 8200 yr ago. *Geology*, **25**, 483-486.

Atherden M A, 1999. The vegetation history of Yorkshire: a bog-trotter's guide to God's own county. *The Naturalist*, **124**, 137-156.

Bartley D D, I P Jones and R T Smith, 1990. Studies in the Flandrian vegetational history of the Craven District of Yorkshire: the Lowlands. *J. Ecology*, **78**, 611-632.

Bullock, P, 1971. The soils of the Malham Tarn area. *Field Studies*, **3**, 381-408.

Curtis, L F, F M Courtney and S T Trudgill, 1976. *Soils in the British Isles*. Longman: Harlow, 364pp.

Daley, T J and 16 others, 2011. The 8200 yr BP cold event in stable isotope records from the North Atlantic region. *Global Planetary Change*, **79**, 288-302.

Faegri, K and J Iversen, 1989. *Textbook of Pollen Analysis*. Wiley: Oxford, 237pp.

Gosden, M S, 1968. Peat deposits of Scar Close, Ingleborough, Yorkshire. *J. Ecology*, **56**, 345-353.

Hetherington D A, T C Lord and R M Jacobi, 2006. New evidence for the occurrence of Eurasian lynx (*Lynx lynx*) in medieval Britain. *J. Quat. Sci.*, **21**, 3-8.

Huddart, D, 2002. Malham Tarn Moss. 512-518 in Huddart, D and Glasser, N F. (eds.). *Quaternary of Northern England*. Geological Conservation Review Series, 25, Chapman and Hall: London.

Johnson, D, 2008. *Ingleborough: Landscape and History*. Carnegie: Lancaster, 288pp.

Mackay, A W and J H Tallis, 1994. The recent vegetational history of the Forest of Bowland, Lancashire, UK. *New Phytologist*, **128**, 571-584.

Moore, P D, J A Webb and M E Collinson, 1991. *Pollen Analysis*. Blackwell: Oxford, 216pp.

O'Connor, T, 2011. The changing environment of the Yorkshire Dales during the Late and Post-Glacial periods. 1-12 in R D Martlew (ed.), Prehistory in the Yorkshire Dales, Yorkshire Dales Landscape Research Trust: York.

O'Regan, H J, T Faulkner and I R Smith (eds.), 2012. *Cave Archaeology and Karst Geomorphology of North West England*, Quaternary Research Association: London, 186pp.

Pigott, C D, 1962. Soil formation and development on the Carboniferous Limestone of Derbyshire. *J. Ecology*, **50**, 145-156.

Pigott, M E and C D Pigott, 1959. Stratigraphy and pollen analysis of Malham Tarn and Tarn Moss. *Field Studies*, **1**, 84-101.

Pigott, M E and C D Pigott, 1963. Lateglacial and postglacial deposits at Malham, Yorkshire. *New Phytologist*, **62**, 317-334.

Rodwell, J (ed.), 1991. *British Plant Communities. Vol.1. Woodlands and Scrub*. Cambridge University Press, 550pp.

Rushworth, G, G T Swindles and T Taylor, 2012. Late Quaternary vegetation history of Attermire, Yorkshire Dales. 151-153 in H O'Regan *et al.*, *op. cit.*

Shaw, H and I Whyte, 2010. Land management and biodiversity through time in upper Ribblesdale, North Yorkshire, UK: understanding the impact of traditional management. *Landscape Archaeology Ecology Review*, **20** (1, 2).

Simmons I G and J B Innes, 1981. Tree remains in a North Yorkshire Moors peat profile. *Nature*, **294**, 76-78.

Simmons I G and J B Innes, 1987 Mid-Holocene adaptations and later Mesolithic Disturbance in Northern England. *J. Archaeol. Sci.*, **14**, 358-403.

Smith, R T, 1986. Aspects of the soil and vegetation history of the Craven District of Yorkshire. 3-28 in T G Manby and P Turnbull (eds.), *Archaeology in the Pennines*, British Archaeological Reports, 158.

Smith, R T, 1991. Contrasted pedogenic pathways in the Craven highlands of North Yorkshire. *Proc. North of England Soil Discussion Group*, **26**, 69-73.

Stace, C, 2010. *New Flora of the British Isles*. Cambridge University Press, 1266pp.

Swindles, G, 2009. Palaeoclimatic significance of two major recurrence surfaces in Tarn Moss, Malham. *Proc. Malham Tarn Research Seminar* (Field Studies Council), 35-37.

Telfer, M W, P Wilson, T C Lord and P J Vincent, 2009. New constraints on the age of the last ice sheet glaciation in NW England using optically stimulated luminescence dating. *J. Quat. Sci.*, **24**, 906-915.

Tinsley, H M, 1975. The former woodland of the Nidderdale Moors (Yorkshire) and the role of early man in its decline. *J. Ecology.*, **63**, 12-16.

Vera, F W M, 2000. *Grazing Ecology and Forest History*. CABI: Wallingford, 498pp.

Vincent, P, 2006. Problems associated with the loess of the Craven Uplands. *Proc. Craven Historical Research Group Workshop*, 10-12.

Vincent, P J, T C Lord, M W Telfer and P Wilson, 2011. Early Holocene loessic colluviation in northwest England: new evidence for the 8.2 ka event in the terrestrail record? *Boreas*, **40**, 105-115.

Ward, S D and D F Evans, 1976. Conservation assessment of British limestone pavement based on floristic criteria. *Biological Conservation*, **9**, 217-233.

Wilson, P, M W Telfer, T C Lord and P J Vincent, 2012. Loessic sediments in northwest England. 143-150 in H J O'Regan *et al.*, *op. cit.*

CHAPTER 13

Subterranean biology

Graham Proudlove

Subterranean biology (also called biospeleology or speleobiology) is concerned with all parts of the Earth that are deemed to be below the level of the soil (or other surface covering). It includes studies of several different environments including caves, submerged bed-sediments in rivers, groundwater within aquifers, and mines (Culver and Pipan, 2009; Gibert *et al.*, 1994). There are extensive descriptions of subterranean biology in Great Britain and Ireland (Jefferson, 1976; Chapman, 1993).

For the Yorkshire Dales, an overview of the composition and distribution of animal communities within subterranean sites, both natural caves and man-made mines, can be assembled based on current knowledge. Beyond this the communities can be attributed to ecologically coherent groups and their origins examined within geological and ecological timeframes. When this is complete, knowledge gaps become apparent as do related important conservation issues. Whereas this book focuses on the Dales (Fig. 13.2), this review analyses data from subterranean sites across northern England, so that details from areas such as Morecambe Bay, Furness and the North York Moors are included. Data on bats are not included in this review, as they are covered by Chapter 14.

The most important information sources relating to cave and mine biology are the *Biological Records of the Cave Research Group of Great Britain* (CRG), the predecessor of the *British Cave Research Association*. From small beginnings in 1938 to completion in 1978, more than 5500 records of animals in British caves and mines were compiled by the CRG Biological Recorder, Mary Hazelton. These records were contributed by dozens of collectors during a 38-year period and constitute an invaluable quasi-random dataset. Records were published by Mary Hazelton in sixteen parts from 1955 to 1978 (see box in References list). All records are incorporated within a database now named *Hazelton* in honour of its main architect. Entries in the *Hazelton* database form the core of this analysis.

Several single-site studies undertaken by individuals and groups add valuable data to the *Hazelton* records, and provide snapshots of particular caves at particular times. Most were described in detail by Dixon (1974) and are discussed below following the analysis of the *Hazelton* dataset. Taken together the *Hazelton* data and single-site studies provide an invaluable overview of Dales cave and mine biology, with the following caveats. Firstly, most studies focused on macroscopic organisms, and microscopic animals (i.e. those smaller than c.0.5 mm) are therefore under-recorded. This applies most significantly to the small arthropods,

notably mites and Collembola in the terrestrial realm and various small Crustacea (especially Copepoda) in aquatic habitats. Secondly, the total number of records for all Dales underground sites is just over 1000. Thirdly, with relatively few notable exceptions, all records are more than 30 years old, because the *Hazelton* dataset stops in 1978. Even the single-site studies were primarily undertaken and published many years ago. Clearly there is a need for additional work, but with strict caveats concerning what should be done, and where.

Analysis of the *Hazelton* dataset

The *Hazelton* dataset provides records, samples and species for analysis. A record is the collection of a single species, in a single cave or mine, on a single date; for example, *Gammarus pulex* collected in Fairy Holes on 12/09/1954. Samples are the total number of records collected in a single cave or mine, on one single date, usually by one named collector; for example *Crenobia alpina* and *Calliphora vomitoria* collected in Fairy Holes on 14/06/1959; because no other animals were collected at this site on that date this constitutes the whole sample for that day. In this context, species refer to the total number of species recorded from a single cave or mine during the period covered by the *Hazelton* collection (1938 – 1976).

Placing species into the categories eutroglophile or trogloxene (see boxed text on page 201) is not an exact science and some species might be misclassified. Nevertheless, use of previous analyses (Hazelton and Glennie, 1953, 1962; Dixon, 1974; Hazelton, 1975, 1977; Jefferson, 1976, 1989; Chapman, 1993) and personal experience should lead to most being classified correctly. The analysis provided is kept simple, because it is designed only to show the nature of various trends.

Figure 13.1. Adult and immature springtails (Collembola) browse on fungi growing on a pool surface. Tiny, brown, mites (Acari) probably prey on immature springtails. A black rove beetle (Coleoptera: Staphylinidae) and a money spider (Arachnida: Lyniphiidae), both predators, dominate the image, along with the remains of a dead beetle. This might represent a typical food web in British caves. Fungi at the base of the web are browsed by Collembola, and various predators crop the browsers. This three-link web is typical of all food-limited caves (photo: Andrew Lewington).

Subterranean biology, by Graham Proudlove.
University of Manchester; g.proudlove@manchester.ac.uk
Chapter 13, pages 199–218 in **Caves and Karst of the Yorkshire Dales**, edited by Tony Waltham and David Lowe.
Published 2013 by the British Cave Research Association,
978-0-900265-46-4 and at www.bcra.org.uk

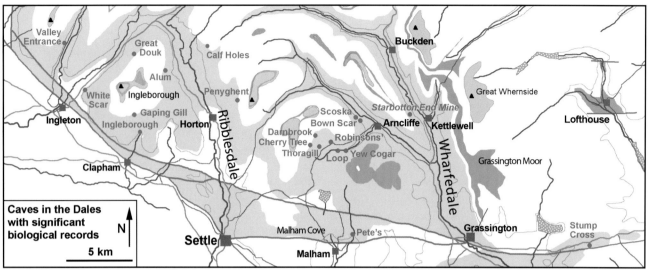

Figure 13.2. Locations of the caves and mines in the southern Yorkshire Dales area that are referred to in the text.

Dales cave faunas from the *Hazelton* dataset

From a total of about 2000 known caves in the Dales, only 98 (<5%) have been sampled (Table 13.1, which also shows numbers of records for each cave, total terrestrial and aquatic species known from that cave and a breakdown into ecological categories present). Most sites have less than 10 records, only 30 have 10 or more records, and only 7 have 20 or more. Caves with 20 or more recorded species provide 270 of the 829 records, or 32.57% of the total. Taken together these provide a reasonable picture of the area's biology (Figs 13.2 and 13.3).

Fairy Holes

This cave in Weardale has a single long streamway, and has yielded 13 samples, 30 records (3.62% of the Dales total) and 23 species (Table 13.2). Unsurprisingly, 11 of its total species are trogloxenes, 9 of them recorded as nymphs in the stream. It also contains typical eutroglophiles including

Speolepta leptogaster, *Heleomyza captiosa* and *Crenobia alpina*. Fairy Holes is one of the few caves to have a, probably transient, population of brown trout, *Salmo trutta* (see below). Though much of the downstream portion of this cave has been removed by quarrying it is unlikely that this has impacted significantly on the cave biology.

Gaping Gill

It is striking that 27 of 33 species (82%) recorded from Gaping Gill (16 samples, 58 records (7.00%), 33 species, 1 troglobiont; Table 13.3) are eutroglophiles, with only 5 trogloxene species (16%), and that 25 species (75%) are terrestrial with only 8 aquatic species (25%). This probably reflects the system's morphology. Among its 21 open entrances only Disappointment Pot descends relatively gradually; others drop almost directly to about 100m below moor level, and most of the system comprises extensive

---

Subterranean biology in the Yorkshire Dales

Subterranean biology was developing in continental Europe from around 1800, but it was around 1814 before any subterranean animals were discovered in wells in Great Britain. The first study of caves rather than wells, was concentrated in Mitchelstown Cave in Ireland, when an important series of papers (Carpenter, 1895; 1897a, 1897b; Jameson, 1896) demonstrated that this cave had a significant fauna including, most significantly, the troglobiont spider *Porrhomma rosenhaueri* (recorded then as *Porrhomma myops*). A great deal of work in 1946 allowed Glennie (1947) and Hazelton and Glennie (1947) to produce the first list of British cave fauna as early as January 1947. The first major review of the topic, in 37 pages, was published in *British Caving* by Hazelton and Glennie (1953). An overview of the literature is provided by Proudlove (2006b).

The first records of animals in caves of the Yorkshire Dales were taken in Ingleborough Cave and Marble Steps Pot by Hazelton and Glennie in 1938 (Hazelton, 1955). Samples were taken in Dales caves in most years thereafter, with the last three records being taken in White Scar Cave by the author in 1976 (Hazelton, 1978). Between 1938 and 1976 a total of 829 records from 98 caves and 309 records from 37 mines were collected in the Dales and other areas of northern England.

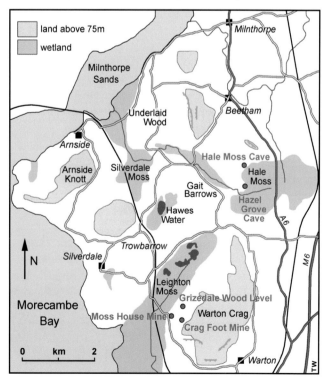

Figure 13.3. Locations of the caves and mines in the area east and northeast of Morecambe Bay that are referred to in the text.

Terminology and ecological classification

Several terms are commonly used to refer to the various parts of the Earth:

Epigean: the surface.

Endogean: the soil.

Hypogean: all regions below the soil, e.g. caves as normally defined, mines, and various smaller cavities including open fractures in lithologies such as chalk, and voids in porous media such as gravel bars in rivers.

Threshold: areas of caves or mines into which some light penetrates from the entrance.

Dark zone: Parts of caves or mines beyond the threshold, which receive no natural light.

Animals found in caves (and other subterranean voids) need not spend their full lifecycle underground. They might just be visiting, or they might have entered the cave accidentally. To understand the ecology of a cave or mine, and of individual faunal components, it is important to have the means to distinguish between permanent residents and visitors.

Classifications devised to aid labelling of various types of subterranean animals and denote their status have not always remained stable, and there has been little consensus concerning definition of the terms. These definitions derive from a recent review (Sket, 2008); alternative terms are shown in parentheses.

Troglobiont (Tb): species that are strongly bound to hypogean habitats (troglobite; stygobite).

Eutroglophile (EuT): species that are essentially epigean but are able to maintain permanent subterranean populations (troglophile; stygophile).

Subtroglophile (SuT): species inclined to inhabit subterranean habitats perpetually or temporarily but intimately associated with epigean habitats for some biological function that takes place daily, such as in feeding, seasonally, or during the life history, such as in reproduction (habitual trogloxene).

Trogloxene (Tx): species occurring sporadically in hypogean habitats but unable to establish or maintain permanent subterranean populations (accidental trogloxene; accidental).

Cave	Total records	TS	AS	Tb	EuT	SuT	Tx	Total species
Albert Cave	3	3	0	0	1	2	0	3
Allithwaite Cave	16	15	1	0	11	1	4	16
Alum Pot	12	9	3	0	8	1	3	12
Attermire Cave	4	4	0	0	3	1	0	4
Attermire Cave (Lower)	2	2	0	0	1	0	1	2
Ayleburn Mine Cave	2	1	1	0	2	0	0	2
Beck Head Stream Cave	1	1	0	0	1	0	0	1
Birkwith Cave	8	1	6	0	2	0	5	7
Birthday Cave	9	8	1	0	3	0	6	9
Black Reef Cave	3	0	2	0	1	0	1	2
Blackside Pot	18	13	1	0	6	2	6	14
Blackside Pot 2	2	2	0	0	1	0	1	2
Borrins Moor Cave	17	12	1	0	7	0	6	13
Bull Pot of the Witches	2	1	1	0	2	0	0	2
Calf Holes	14	6	7	0	5	0	8	13
Cave Hole	4	4	0	0	3	0	1	4
Combs Cave	1	1	0	0	0	0	1	1
Cappy Gill Cave	1	0	1	0	1	0	0	1
Cuddy Gill Cave	3	1	2	0	2	0	1	3
Dale Barn Cave	1	1	0	0	1	0	0	1
Dog Hole	3	2	0	0	2	0	0	2
Dow Cave	7	4	2	0	4	0	2	6
Dunald Mill Hole	12	9	3	0	6	1	5	12
Easegill Cave System	18	9	6	0	6	1	8	15
Eglins Hole	3	0	3	0	1	0	2	3
Elbolton Cave	8	7	0	0	5	0	2	7
Elpha Green Cave	10	9	0	0	4	2	3	9
Fairy Cave (Witherslack)	13	9	1	0	8	0	2	10
Fairy Holes	30 3.62%	9	12	0	8	1	12	21
Foss Gill Lower	6	4	2	0	3	1	2	6
Gaping Gill Hole	58 7.00%	25	8	1	27	0	5	33
Gill Rigg No 1	6	2	4	0	3	0	3	6
Gill Rigg No 2	3	1	1	0	1	0	1	2
Gods Bridge Caves	3	3	0	0	1	0	2	3
Goyden Pot	12	8	4	0	5	0	7	12
Greak Douk Cave	6	1	5	1	1	0	4	6
Greensett Cave	4	4	0	0	2	1	1	4
Greenwood Pot	4	4	0	0	3	0	1	4
Gunnerfleet Cave Lower	5	4	1	0	4	0	1	5
Gunnerfleet Cave Upper	4	2	1	0	1	0	2	3
Hale Moss Cave	10	9	1	0	7	0	3	10
Hazel Grove Main Cave	8	5	2	0	6	0	1	7
Heights Cave	4	4	0	0	1	1	2	4
Hell Hole	4	4	0	0	3	1	0	4
Henning Valley Cave	11	8	0	0	4	0	4	8
Holme Hill Cave	8	4	4	0	3	1	4	8
Ingleborough Cave	36 4.34%	16	5	0	18	0	3	21
Ireby Fell Cavern	7	7	0	0	4	1	2	7
Jack Scar Cave	1	0	1	0	1	0	0	1
Jacobs Well Cave	6	6	0	0	5	1	0	6

Cave	Total records	TS	AS	Tb	EuT	SuT	Tx	Total species
Jubilee Cave	5	5	0	0	2	1	2	5
Katnot Cave	1	0	1	0	1	0	0	1
Keld Head	7	0	5	0	2	0	3	5
Kingsdale Head Cave	2	0	2	0	1	0	1	2
Kirkdale Cave	11	11	0	0	6	2	3	11
Kirk Gill Cave	3	3	0	0	2	0	1	3
Little Hull Hole	1	1	0	0	1	0	0	1
Lost Johns System	4	3	1	0	3	0	1	4
Lower Hackergill Cave	1	1	0	0	0	0	1	1
Lower Ling Gill Cave	1	0	1	0	1	0	0	1
Lower Long Churn Cave	7	3	3	0	4	0	2	6
Lynnkirk Cave	17	10	4	0	8	0	6	14
Magnetometer Pot	7	3	3	0	4	0	2	6
Marble Steps Pot	4	2	2	0	2	0	2	4
Meregill Hole	4	1	3	0	0	0	4	4
Moking Hurth	1	1	0	0	0	0	1	1
Mossdale Caverns	2	1	1	0	0	0	2	2
Nippikin Hole	4	2	1	0	2	0	1	3
Old Ing Cave	1	1	0	0	1	0	0	1
Pate Hole	2	1	1	0	2	0	0	2
Petes Pot	2	0	2	0	2	0	0	2
Pikedaw Calamine Caverns	10	6	0	0	3	0	3	6
Pool Bank Cave	39 4.70%	24	1	0	15	2	8	25
Rift Pot	5	0	3	0	2	0	1	3
Roudsea Wood Cave	3	2	1	0	2	0	1	3
Rowten Cave	10	10	0	0	3	0	7	10
Runscar Cave	2	0	2	0	2	0	0	2
Scald Bank Cave	5	0	5	0	2	0	3	5
Scoska Cave	28 3.38%	19	3	0	9	2	11	22
Sell Gill Holes	17	11	3	0	7	1	6	14
Silverdale Cave	1	1	0	0	1	0	0	1
Silverdale Gill Pot	2	1	1	0	1	0	1	2
Simpsons Pot	1	0	1	0	0	0	1	1
Sleets Gill Cave	7	5	1	0	5	0	1	6
Sowan Burn Cave	2	2	0	0	1	0	1	2
Storrs Cave	9	9	0	0	5	1	3	9
Stump Cross Cavern	32 3.86%	18	2	0	16	1	3	20
Swinhope Cave	11	8	1	0	5	3	1	9
Tailbrigg Pot	2	2	0	0	1	0	1	2
Trollers Gill Cave	11	10	0	0	5	3	2	10
Twin Bottom Scar Cave	11	6	1	0	2	2	3	7
Upper Hackergill Cave	12	12	0	0	6	0	6	12
Upper Long Churn Cave	16	9	5	0	5	1	8	14
Victoria Cave	4	4	0	0	3	1	0	4
White Scar Cave	47 5.67%	18	8	1	21	0	4	26
Wilson's Cave	5	3	2	0	2	0	3	5
Wise Eel Cave	3	3	0	0	2	0	1	3
Yordas Cave	14	13	1	0	7	2	5	14

Table 13.1. *All caves in the Yorkshire Dales and adjacent areas for which there are records in the Hazelton dataset. TS = terrestrial species, AS = aquatic species, Tb = troglobiont, EuT = eutroglophile, SuT = subtroglophile, Tx = trogloxene. These terms are defined in the text after Sket (2008). Caves with 10 to 20 recorded species are shaded yellow; caves with 20 or more species, and those with troglobionts, are shaded blue.*

Eutroglophiles	
Diptera	**Araneae**
Speolepta leptogaster	Metellina merianae
Scoliocentra caesia	
Heleomyza captiosa	
Oligochaeta	**Crustacea**
Octolasion lacteum	Gammarus pulex (A)
Collembola	**Tricladida**
Folsomia sp.	Crenobia alpina (A)
Subtroglophiles	
Trichoptera	
Stenophylax vibex	
Trogloxenes	
Ephemeroptera	**Plecoptera**
Heptagenia lateralis (A)	Dinocras cephalotes (A)
Ecdyonurus sp. (A)	Protonemoura praecox (A)
Baetis rhodani (A)	Leuctra geniculata (A)
	Amphineura sulcicolis (A)
	Isoperla grammatica (A)
	Nemoura cambrica (A)
Diptera	**Teleostei**
Sphraeroceridae sp.	Salmo trutta (A)
Calliphora vomitoria	

Table 13.2. *Species recorded from Fairy Holes, Weardale. (A) = aquatic species; all other species are terrestrial.*

Troglobiont	
Coleoptera	
Hydroporus ferrugineus (A)	
Eutroglophiles	
Collembola	**Acari**
Megalothorax minimus	Eugamasus loricatus
Agrenia bidenticulata	Rhagidia terricola *
Folsomia sp.	Rhagidia spelaea
Arrhopalites pygmaeus	Rhagidia gelida
Pseudosinella alba	Rhagidia intermedia
Isotoma notabilis	Eugamasus tragardhi
Lepidocyrtus sp.	
Coleoptera	**Diptera**
Quedius mesomelinus	Speolepta leptogaster
Octhephilus aureus *	Trichocera maculipenis
Lesteva pubescens	Mycetophilidae larva
Agabus guttatus (A)	
Oligochaeta	**Triclada**
Eisenia rosea	Crenobia alpina (A)
Dendrobaena subrubicunda	Phagocata sp. (A)
Dendrobaena veneta	
Crustacea	**Mollusca**
Gammarus pulex * (A)	Pisidium obtusale (A)
Trogloxenes	
Plecoptera	**Diptera**
Leuctra inermis (A)	Bradysia sp.
Dinocras cephalotes (A)	Spaniotoma sp.
Coleoptera	
Dianous coerulescens	

Table 13.3. *Species recorded from the Gaping Gill System. (A) = aquatic species; all other species are terrestrial. * = species also recorded from Ingleborough Cave.*

Eutroglophiles	
Collembola	**Acari**
Deuteraphorura cebennaria	Rhagidia terricola *
Anurida granaria	Rhagidia sp.
Folsomia candida	Rhagidia sp. nov.
Folsomia quadrioculata	Eugamasus magnus
Oligaphorura schoetti	
Isotoma arborea	
Crustacea	**Oligochaeta**
Gammarus pulex * (A)	Allolobophora chlorotica
Acanthocyclops viridis (A)	Allolobophora sp.
Macrocyclops fuscus (A)	
Diptera	**Coleoptera**
Trichocera sp.	Ochthephilus aureus *
Diplopoda	
Nanogona polydesmoides	
Trogloxenes	
Ephemeroptera	**Diptera**
Ecdyonurus venosus (A)	Bradysia sp.
Trichoptera	
Plectrocnemia conspersa (A)	

Table 13.4. *Species recorded from Ingleborough Cave. (A) = aquatic species; all other species are terrestrial. * = Species also recorded from the Gaping Gill System.*

Figure 13.4. *Worm casts of* Allolobophora *sp. (Annelida: Oligochaeta: Lumbricidae) on a silt bank in Cellar Gallery, Ingleborough Cave; composed of aggregates of shiny, smooth rounded lumps of various sizes, sticky to the touch. EuT (photo: Jackie Paice).*

sub-horizontal passages at this level (Glover, 1974). Many such passages are remote from surface influence, so the number of immigrant trogloxenes is small. The eutroglophile community contains many common British species, and Gaping Gill probably provides a typical example of faunal communities in northern caves. It can be considered as a 'reference community' – a type of community anticipated in the absence of anthropogenic and/or other confounding factors.

Ingleborough Cave

Though it is the downstream end of the Gaping Gill Cave System, Ingleborough Cave (9 samples, 36 records (4.34%), 19 species; Table 13.4) contains a set of species different from its upstream counterpart. In common with Gaping Gill it has many eutroglophiles and relatively few trogloxenes. Once again this might be because most of its passages are remote from the surface. Two of the eutroglophiles, earthworms and the freshwater shrimp, *Gammarus pulex*, have been studied. The Ingleborough Cave *G. pulex* population was shown to

Figure 13.5. *A technique to determine cast accumulation rates in Ingleborough Cave's Cellar Gallery involves smoothing a 10x10cm area and recording subsequent cast build-ups. Those seen accumulated in seven months (photo: Trevor Piearce).*

be notably paler in colour that normal, epigean, populations (Piearce, 1972, 1975; Piearce and Cox, 1977a, b). More work is required to demonstrate conclusively whether this is because the population is more isolated than those in other caves. Earthworms in Cellar Gallery (Piearce, 1972, 1975; Piearce and Wells, 1977) form long-term populations breeding within the cave (Figs 13.4, 13.5). Study of the brown trout *(Salmo trutta)*, a trogloxene species, has confirmed that these fishes feed within the darkness of the cave, but it is unlikely that they breed (Proudlove, 1979, 1982, 2006; Gidman, 1975).

Pool Bank Cave

With 4 samples, 39 records (4.70%) and 25 species (Table 13.5), more than half of the cave's total known species are eutroglophiles and this might be another typical reference cave community.

Scoska Cave

Scoska Cave has 5 samples, 28 records (3.38%) and 23 species. Its large open entrance allows immigration of many trogloxenes, but eutroglophiles are plentiful and it is best known for subtroglophiles (Hodgson, 2004, 2005a, 2008). Many tissue moths *(Triphosa dubitata)* and herald moths *(Scoliopteryx libatrix)* hibernate here over winter. Tissue moths prefer to roost on cave walls in the deep (darkest) threshold, whereas heralds prefer cave ceiling sites in the near (lightest) threshold. Tissue moths also use the cave for mating during late summer. Surprisingly, they are not recorded among the *Hazelton* data (Table 13.6).

Stump Cross Caverns

This cave system, which includes Mongo Gill Hole, has yielded 8 samples, 32 records (3.86%) and 20 species (Table 13.7). The system provides another reference community for eutroglophile species.

White Scar Cave

This extensive stream cave, with 26 samples, 47 records (5.67%), 26 species and 1 troglobiont (Table 13.8), is notable for its relatively large collembolan fauna (Schofield, 1964). All of these species are common eutroglophiles.

Eutroglophiles	
Collembola	Crustacea
Onychiurus sp.	Gammarus pulex (A)
Araneae	Diplopoda
Meta menardi	Nanogona polydesmoides
Metellina merianae	Blaniulus guttulatus
Nesticus cellulanus	Archiboreoiulus pallidus
Diptera	
Speolepta lepogaster	
Tarnania fenestralis	
Scoliocentra villosa	
Limonia nubeculosa	
Heleomyza captiosa	
Rhymosia fasciata	
Exechiopsis subulata	
Subtroglophiles	
Diptera	Lepidodoptera
Culex pipiens	Scoliopteryx libatrix
Trogloxenes	
Diptera	Coleoptera
Copromyza roserii	Choleva glauca
Exechia contaminata	
Leptocera flaviceps	
Calyptotoma lynceum	
Megaselia sp.	
Mollusca	Araneae
Arion hortensis	Labulla thoracica

Table 13.5. *Species recorded from Pool Bank Cave; (A) = aquatic species, all other species are terrestrial.*

Eutroglophiles	
Diptera	Araneae
Heleomyza captiosa	Metellina merianae
Crumomyia nigra	
Oligochaeta	Collembola
Allolobophora chlorotica	Oligaphorura schoetti
Crustacea	Diplopoda
Gammarus pulex (A)	Tachypodoiulus niger
Mollusca	Hemiptera
Pisidium sp. (A)	Velia caprai (A)
Subtroglophiles	
Lepidodoptera	Diptera
Scoliopteryx libatrix	Culex pipiens
Trogloxenes	
Hemiptera	Diptera
Stenodema holsatum	Scatophaga stercoraria
Philaenus spumarius	Hydrotaea irritans
Cixius distinguendus	
Opiliones	Mecoptera
Mitopus morio	Panorpa germanica
Araneae	Coleoptera
Linyphia triangularis	Loricera pilicornis
	Trechus secalis

Table 13.6. *Species recorded from Scoska Cave; (A) = aquatic species; all other species are terrestrial.*

Eutroglophiles	
Diptera	Collembola
Copromyza nigra	Hypogastrura purpurescens
Trichocera maculipennis	Deuteraphorura cebannaria
Trichocera regelationis	Oligaphorura schoetti
Heleomyza captiosa	Tomocerus minor
Coleoptera	Acari
Ochthephilus aureus	Rhagidia spelaea
Agabus guttatus (A)	Eugamasus sp.
Quedius mesomelinus	
Crustacea	Diplopoda
Gammarus pulex (A)	Tachypodoiulus niger
Oligochaeta	
Eiseniella tetraedra	
Subtroglophiles	
Diptera	
Culex pipiens	
Trogloxenes	
Diptera	Mecoptera
Bradysia sp.	Boreus hyemalis
Ormosia pseudosimilis	

Table 13.7. *Species recorded from Stump Cross Caverns and Mongo Gill Hole. (A) = aquatic species; all other species are terrestrial.*

Troglobionts	
Crustacea	
Antrobathynella stammeri (A)	
Eutroglophiles	
Diptera	Acari
Trichocera regelationis	Tyrophagus dimidiatus
Speolepta leptogaster	Soldanellonyx chappuisi (A)
Oligochaeta	Collembola
Nias elinguis	Folsomia candida
Tubifex tubifex (A)	Arrhopalites coecus
Bimastus eiseni	Oligaphorura schoetti
	Deuteraphorua cebannaria
	Megalothorax sp.
	Isotoma olivacea
	Hypogastrura purpurescens
	Anurida granaria
	Schaefferia emucronata
	Folsomia fimetaria
Crustacea	Coleoptera
Gammarus pulex (A)	Agabus guttatus (A)
Acanthocyclops viridis (A)	Lesteva pubescens
Trogloxenes	
Diptera	Acari
Chironomid sp.	Tydeus sp.
Trichoptera	
Philopotamus montanus	
Polycentropus sp. (A)	

Table 13.8. *Species recorded from White Scar Cave. (A) = aquatic species; all other species are terrestrial.*

Dales mine faunas from the *Hazelton* dataset

The number of mines throughout the Dales and adjacent areas is unknown with certainty, but runs to many hundreds. Of these, 37 have *Hazelton* records (Table 13.9). Most sites have less than 10 records, 8 mines have 10 or more records, and 4 have 20 or more. Only mines with 20 or more recorded species are considered, and these four mines provide 137 of 309 records, or 44.34% of the total, so they should provide a reasonable overview of the mine biology of the area.

All these mines contain characteristic eutroglophile faunas, with sporadic trogloxenes and subtroglophiles. The eutroglophile species are similar to those found in caves, indicating that they have a strong affinity (association) with subterranean sites, and are mobile. All of the mines are less than c.250 years old, compared to a minimum age of several thousand years for even the youngest cave passages.

Crag Foot Mine

With a dataset comprising 15 samples, 38 records (12.30%) and 20 species (Table 13.10) this site provides a typical reference subterranean community.

Mine	Total Records	TS	AS	Tb	EuT	SuT	Tx	Total species
Aragonite Band Mine	2	1	1	0	2	0	0	2
Barnry Craig Mine	3	3	0	0	1	1	1	3
Barrow Scout Mine	2	1	1	0	2	0	0	2
Blind Gill Level	1	1	0	0	0	0	1	1
Blockley Level	5	5	0	0	3	0	2	5
Boggs Level	1	1	0	0	1	0	0	1
Buckden Gavel Mine	8	8	0	0	4	1	3	8
Calvert Mine	6	6	0	0	4	1	1	6
Clough Head Level	6	5	1	0	4	0	2	6
Cononley Lead Mine	16	8	0	0	5	0	3	8
Crag Foot Mine	38 (12.30%)	16	4	0	17	0	3	20
Daylight Hole	15	9	3	0	10	0	2	12
Dosey Level	4	3	1	0	2	0	2	4
Firestone Mine	3	3	0	0	2	0	1	3
Gilbert Level	9	9	0	0	4	2	3	9
Gillfields Level	6	6	0	0	4	1	1	6
Gorton Level	2	2	0	0	1	0	1	2
Grizedale Wood Level	39 (12.62%)	18	3	0	12	3	6	21
Hood Crag Mine	10	7	3	0	7	1	2	10
Jack Scout Mine	8	8	0	0	2	0	6	8
Moss House Mine	28 (9.06%)	21	1	0	17	2	3	22
Priscilla Level	3	3	0	0	2	1	0	3
Ramp Gill Mine	6	6	0	0	5	0	1	6
Ray Gill Sike	5	5	0	0	3	2	0	5
Red Rake Mine	11	6	1	0	4	2	1	7
Richmond Copper Mine	4	4	0	0	2	2	0	4
Scrait Hole Mine	5	5	0	0	4	1	0	5
Sea Wood Copper Mine	1	1	0	0	1	0	0	1
Sir Francis Level	3	3	0	0	3	0	0	3
Small Clough Level	4	4	0	0	3	1	0	4
Starbotton End Mine	32 (10.36%)	18	5	0	13	4	6	23
Tyne Head Mine	4	4	0	0	3	0	1	4
Un-named trial level 1	8	8	0	0	4	0	4	8
Un-named trial level 2	3	3	0	0	1	0	2	3
Un-named trial level 3	1	1	0	0	1	0	0	1
Wet Groves Mine	6	6	0	0	2	1	3	6
Windy Scout Mine	1	1	0	0	1	0	0	1

Table 13.9. *All mines in the Yorkshire Dales for which there are records in the Hazelton dataset. TS = terrestrial species, AS = aquatic species, Tb = troglobiont, EuT = eutroglophile, SuT = subtroglophile, Tx = trogloxene. These terms are defined in the text after Sket (2008). Mines with 10 to 20 recorded species are shaded yellow; mines with 20 or more species are shaded blue. No mines contain troglobionts.*

Grizedale Wood Drainage Level

Among 11 samples, 39 records (12.62%) and 21 species (Table 13.11) this contains species characteristic of northern subterranean sites plus the coastal isopod *Trichoniscoides saeroeensis,* which is thought to be colonising inland habitats via subterranean passages (Moseley, 1969, 1970, 2000; Gregory, 2009).

Eutroglophiles	
Collembola	**Acari**
Tomcerus minor	*Eupodes variegatus*
Deuteraphorura cebennaria	*Linopodes motatorius*
Oligaphorura schoetti	*Rhagidia intermedia*
Schaefferia emucronata	
Crustacea	**Coleoptera**
Acanthocyclops bisetosus (A)	*Agabus guttatus* (A)
Trichoniscoides saeroeensis	*Quedius mesomelinus*
Diplopoda	**Tricladida**
Nanogona polydesmoides	*Phagocata vitta* (A)
Trogloxenes	
Isopoda	**Oligochaeta**
Trichoniscus pygmaeus	*Enchytraeus albidus* (A)
Coleoptera	
Trechus sp. larva	

Table 13.10. *Species recorded from Crag Foot Mine; (A) = aquatic species, all others are terrestrial.*

Eutroglophiles	
Crustacea	**Araneae**
Gammarus pulex (A)	*Meta menardi*
Androniscus dentiger	*Metelina merianae*
Trichoniscoides saeroeensis	*Nesticus cellulanus*
Diptera	**Diplopoda**
Heleomyza captiosa	*Blaniulus guttulatus*
Speolepta leptogaster	*Polydesmus angustus*
Hemiptera	**Tricladida**
Velia caprai (A)	*Crenobia alpina* (A)
Subtroglophiles	
Trichoptera	**Lepidoptera**
Stenophylax permistus	*Scolioteryx libatrix*
Diptera	
Culex pipiens	
Trogloxenes	
Diptera	**Coleoptera**
Bradysia sp.	*Trechus fulvus*
Rymosia sp.	
Exechiopsis sp.	
Leptocera flaviceps	
Leptocera sylvatica	

Table 13.11. *Species recorded from Grizedale Wood Drainage Level; (A) = aquatic species, all others are terrestrial.*

Eutroglophiles	
Diptera	**Acari**
Rymosia fasciata	*Microtrombidium sucidum*
Heleomyza captiosa	*Rhagidia gigas*
Scoliocentra villosa	*Rhagidia diversicolor*
Tricladida	**Diplopoda**
Phagocata vitta (A)	*Blaniulus guttulatus*
Collembola	**Crustacea**
Schaefferia emucronata	*Androniscus dentiger*
Hypogastrura denticulata	*Trichoniscoides saeroeensis*
Hypogastrura purpurescens	
Pseudosinella sp.	
Deuteraphorura cebannaria	
Lepidocyrtus curicollis	
Oligaphorura schoetti	
Subtroglophiles	
Trichoptera	**Diptera**
Stenophylax permistus	*Culex pipiens*
Trogloxenes	
Coleoptera	**Crustacea**
Cantharis sp. larva	*Oniscus asselus*
Symphyla	
Symphylella isabellae	

Table 13.12. *Species recorded from Moss House Mine; (A) = aquatic species, all others are terrestrial.*

Eutroglophiles	
Diptera	**Crustacea**
Heleomyza captiosa	Gammarus pulex (A)
Scoliocentra caesia	Cyclops sp. (A)
Crumomyia nigra	Paracyclops fimbriatus (A)
Speolepta leptogaster	
Araneae	**Tricladida**
Meta menardi	Crenobia alpine (A)
Metellina merianae	Dendrocoelum lacteum (A)
Collembola	**Diplopoda**
Isotomurus pallustris.	Tachypodoiulus niger
Subtroglophiles	
Lepidoptera	**Diptera**
Stenophylax vibex	Culex pipiens
Scoliopteryx libatrix	
Triphosa dubitata	
Trogloxenes	
Coleoptera	**Chilopoda**
Nebria rufescens	Lithobius variagatus
Diptera	
Limosina larva	
Tipulidae larva	
Lipsothrix remota	
Lipsothrix sp.	

Table 13.13. Species recorded from Starbotton End Mine, also known as Springs Wood Level; (A) = aquatic species, all others are terrestrial.

Moss House Mine

Represented by 9 samples, 28 records (9.06%) and 22 species (Table 13.12), this locality is similar to Grizedale Wood Drainage Level, and also including the tiny woodlouse *Trichoniscoides saeroeensis* (Moseley, 1969, 1970, 2000; Gregory, 2009).

Starbotton End Mine

Also known as Springs Wood Level, this site has provided 7 samples, 32 records (10.36%) and 23 species (Table 13.13) (Dixon and Richardson, 1965; Dixon, 1966, 1974).

Comparison of caves with mines

Summary statistics calculated for caves (Table 13.1) and mines (Table 13.9) are compared in Table 13.14. There is no significant difference between the mean number of records per site and the mean number of terrestrial species per site. Mines have a smaller mean number of aquatic species, unsurprisingly, because mines normally carry less water than is carried by caves. The significance of the mean numbers of eutroglophiles, subtroglophiles and trogloxenes in caves and mines is discussed below.

Finally there is no significant difference between the mean numbers of species recorded per site. Clearly, the cave and mine datasets for the Dales and surrounding area are very similar in terms of records collected and species recorded. Whereas statistically it would be valid to combine all the data into a single pool of subterranean sites, this is avoided here in case new studies reveal differences between caves and mines; it is recommended that all future research continues this differentiation.

Species recorded from caves and mines

Because of the absence of light, plants are not normally found beyond the deepest penetration of daylight into cave threshold zones. The few exceptions are the lampenflora (lamp floras) found in the artificially lit tourist sections of Ingleborough, Stump Cross and White Scar caves (Pentecost, 2010). Little work has been carried out on the plants in Dales cave thresholds (Cubbon, 1970, 1972, 1976; Gidman, 1975), but plant species zonation against the reduction in light has been recognised (Pentecost and Zhang, 2001).

Recorded species of animals (Tables 13.15, 13.16, 13.17 and 13.18) can initially be differentiated by habitat and then by taxonomic group. This approach aids determination of which are the Dales' genuine subterranean species, as opposed to the many trogloxene species that also exist. Within caves, terrestrial species comprise 78% of the total (168 species from 215), whereas in mines the figure is 86% (79 species from 92). Aquatic species comprise 22% of the total within caves (47 species from 215) and the figure is 14% (13 species from 92) in mines.

Non-arthropod taxa

Tricladida (flat worms)

Only twelve species of Tricladida are known from Britain and Ireland (Reynoldson and Young, 2000) but three are known from subterranean sites. *Dendrocoelum lacteum* (Tables 13.15, 13.17) is classed, provisionally, as a eutroglophile because it undoubtedly feeds underground, although it is known from only one cave and one mine. Since its main habitat is productive lakes it might be a trogloxene in subterranean areas. The other two species, *Crenobia alpina* and *Phagocata vitta* (Fig. 13.6) are certainly eutroglophiles (Gourbault, 1986).

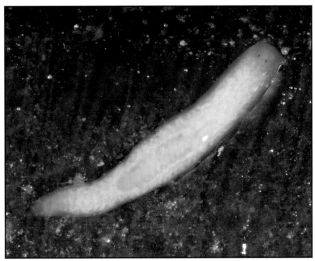

Figure 13.6. The eutroglophile flatworm Phagocata vitta *(Platyhelminthes: Turbellaria: Tricladida) in Pool Sink, Ease Gill. EuT (photo: Andrew Lewington).*

Table 13.14. Summary statistics for all caves and mines in the Yorkshire Dales area contained in the Hazelton dataset. TS = terrestrial species, AS = aquatic species, Tb = troglobiont, EuT = eutroglophile, SuT = subtroglophile, Tx = trogloxene. These terms are defined in the text, after Sket (2008). Note: no figures are provided for troglobionts because there are too few to require a statistical treatment.

	Caves		Mines		Combined	
Total sites	98		37		135	
Total records	829		309		1138	
Mean number records/site	8.46	(range 1–58)	8.35	(range 1–39)	8.43	(range 1–58)
Mean number TS/site	5.19	(range 0–25)	5.92	(range 1–21)	5.39	(range 0–25)
Mean number AS/site	1.67	(range 0–12)	0.65	(range 0– 5)	1.39	(range 0–12)
Mean number EuT/site	3.93	(range 0–27)	4.22	(range 1–17)	2.85	(range 0–27)
Mean number SuT/site	0.42	(range 0– 3)	0.70	(range 0– 4)	0.50	(range 0– 4)
Mean number Tx/site	2.49	(range 0–12)	1.65	(range 0– 6)	2.26	(range 0–12)
Mean number species/site	6.87	(range 1–33)	6.57	(range 1–23)	6.79	(range 1–33)

Figure 13.7. The land snail Oxychilus cellarius *(Mollusca: Pulmonata: Oxychilidae). EuT (photo: Andrew Lewington).*

In central European headwater streams, populations of *Crenobia alpina* are distinct from one another (Brandle *et al.,* 2007). It seems that there are many cryptic species, and that commonly they are very old. All are glacial relicts preferring cold water. Global warming might persuade more populations to migrate permanently into the more buffered temperatures of caves and springs.

Oligochaeta (including earthworms)

Within Ingleborough Cave, Oligochaeta appear to build long-term populations supported in rich sediments carried in by flooding (Gidman, 1975; Piearce, 1972, 1975; Piearce and Wells, 1977), but there might be alternative features behind their development (Thomas and Bottrell, 1992). Common eutroglophile species include *Allolobophora chlorotica*, *Aporrectodea rosea* and *Dendrobaena veneta*. Individuals of the first two species are recorded crawling on the surface of sediments in Ingleborough Cave (Piearce, 1975), behaviour not reported in epigean populations. Darkness and 100% humidity are probable factors in this unusual behaviour. (Figs 13.4 and 13.5).

Mollusca

Twelve species are recorded from caves, but none from mines. Two terrestrial species are probably eutroglophiles, *Oxychilus navvaricus* (previously called *O. helveticus* and recorded as such in *Hazelton*) and *O. alliarius*, though they might not be cavernicolous (Chapman, 1993). Another *Oxychilus* species, *O. cellarius* (Fig. 13.7) is certainly a eutroglophile (Thines and Tercafs, 1972; Chapman, 1993) and it seems sensible to consider both species as such until proven otherwise (Hazelton and Glennie, 1953, 1962). Two bivalve species, *Pisidium obtusale* and *P. personatum* are known from single records; these species could readily form permanent populations (Knight and Wood, 2000) and an abundant population of *P. personatum* is recorded in Hazel Grove Main Cave (Moseley, 1970).

Arthropoda: Arachnida

Acari (Mites)

Together with Collembola, the mites (Figs 13.8 and 13.9) are among the more important components of cave ecology in the Dales. Many species are eutroglophiles, as they are ideally adapted to subterranean conditions. Fifteen species are recorded from caves and twelve species from mines. Only two species, *Soldanelonyx chappuisi* and *S. monardi*, are aquatic. These are minute interstitial species that live between sand grains. *S. chappuisi* is recorded from Pete's Pot at Gordale and from White Scar Cave, and *S. monardi* only from Pete's Pot (Gerecke, 2007, 2010). These species and other interstitial mites, of which there are many, will probably be found elsewhere if searched for. Of the terrestrial mites, the genera *Eugamasus* and *Rhagidia* seem to be particularly suited to cave conditions, as three species of *Eugamasus* and seven species of *Rhagidia* are recorded (Zacharda, 1980).

All mite specimens from Dales caves and mines were identified and named many years ago in accordance with contemporary thinking. Several of the names applied (Tables 13.15, 13.17) have probably changed since then, but are retained here because there is no modern, accessible review of mite names. Any research on subterranean mites should investigate the nomenclature situation carefully.

Figure 13.8. Mite. EuT (photo: Andrew Lewington).

Figure 13.9. Mite. EuT (photo: Andrew Lewington).

Species	Records	EC
Tricladida	**16**	–
Crenobia alpina (A)	10	EuT
Phagocatta vitta (A)	5	EuT
Dendrocoelum lacteum (A)	1	EuT
Oligochaeta	**23**	–
Allolobophora chlorotica	5	EuT
Aporrectodea rosea	2	EuT
Allolobophoridella eiseni	1	EuT
Dendrodrilus rubidus	1	Tx
Dendrodrilus subrubicundus	1	Tx
Dendrobaena veneta	2	EuT
Eiseniella tetraedra	1	EuT
Octolasion tyrtaeum	1	Tx
Nais elinguis (A)	1	EuT
Stylodrilus herigianus (A)	3	EuT
Tubifex tubifex (A)	1	EuT
Other Oligochaeta	4	–
Mollusca	**21**	–
Deroceras reticulatum	2	Tx
Arion ater	1	Tx
Arion hortensis	4	Tx
Arion intermedius	1	Tx
Oxychilus alliarius	1	EuT
Oxychilus navvaricus	5	EuT
Galba trucatula	2	Tx
Pisidium obtusale (A)	1	EuT
Pisidium personatum (A)	1	EuT
Pisidium immature (A)	1	EuT
Arianta arbustorum	1	Tx
Discus rotundatus	1	Tx
Arthropoda: Arachnida: Acari	**28**	–
Calyptostoma velutinus	1	EuT
Calyptostoma lynceum	1	EuT
Eugamasus loricatus	3	EuT
Eugamasus magnus	1	EuT
Eugamasus tragardhi	1	EuT
Euryparasitus emarginatus	1	EuT
Pergamasus robustus	1	EuT
Rhagidia gelida	1	EuT
Rhagidia intermedia	1	EuT
Rhagidia spelaea	5	EuT
Rhagidia terricola	2	EuT
Soldanelonyx chappuisi (A)	2	EuT
Soldanelonyx monardi (A)	1	EuT
Tyrophagus dimidiatus	1	EuT
Veigaia herculaneus	1	EuT
Other Acari	5	–
Arthropoda: Arachnida: Araneae	**92**	–
Bathyphantes gracilis	1	Tx
Walckenaeria cuspidata	2	Tx
Walckenaeria nudipalpis	1	Tx
Diplocephalus cristatus	1	Tx
Labulla thoracica	1	Tx
Lepthyphantes mengei	1	Tx
Linyphia triangularis	2	Tx
Meta menardi	18	EuT
Metellina merianae	35	EuT
Nesticus cellulanus	9	EuT
Porrhomma convexum	10	EuT
Tmeticus affinis	1	Tx
Other Araneae	10	–
Arthropoda: Arachnida: Chelonethida	**1**	–
Neobisium carcinoides	1	Tx
Arthropoda: Arachnida: Opilionida	**1**	–
Mitopus morio	1	Tx
Arthropoda: Crustacea: Copepoda	**10**	–
Acanthocylops venustus (A)	1	EuT
Acanthocyclops viridis (A)	7	EuT
Macrocyclops fuscus (A)	1	EuT
Canthcamptus praegeri (A)	1	EuT
Arthropoda: Crustacea: Syncarida	**4**	–
Antrobathynella stammeri (A)	4	Tb
Arthropoda: Crustacea: Amphipoda	**71**	–
Gammarus pulex (A)	71	EuT
Arthropoda: Crustacea: Isopoda	**21**	–
Androniscus dentiger	6	EuT
Oniscus asellus	13	Tx
Porcellio scaber	1	Tx
Trichoniscus pusillus	1	Tx
Arthropoda: Insecta: Collembola	**87**	–
Agrenia bidenticulata	2	EuT
Anurida granaria	3	EuT
Arrhopalites caecus	1	EuT
Arrhopalites pygmaeus	3	EuT
Dicyrtoma fusca	1	EuT
Folsomia candida	9	EuT
Folsomia agrelli	1	EuT
Folsomia fimetaria	1	EuT
Folsomia quadrioculata	1	EuT
Hypogastrura purpurescens	4	EuT
Entomobrya multifasciata	2	EuT
Parisotoma notabilis	1	EuT
Desoria tigrina	6	EuT
Desoria violocea	3	EuT
Lepidocyrtus curvicollis	1	EuT
Megalothorax minimus	2	EuT
Onychiurus ambulans	1	EuT
Onychiurus arans???	2	EuT
Deuteraphorura cebannaria	7	EuT
Oligaphorura schoetti	17	EuT
Psedosinella alba	4	EuT
Schaefferia emucronata group	4	EuT
Tomocerus minor	5	EuT
Other Collembola	6	–
Arthropoda: Insecta: Ephemeroptera	**24**	–
Baetis rhodani (A)	3	Tx
Ecdyonurus venosus (A)	2	Tx
Habrophlebia fusca (A)	1	Tx
Electrogena lateralis (A)	6	Tx
Leptophlebia marginata (A)	1	Tx
Paraleptophlebia submarginata (A)	1	Tx
Rhithrogena semicolorata (A)	2	Tx
Siphlonurus lacustris (A)	1	Tx
Other Ephemeroptera	7	–
Arthropoda: Insecta: Trichoptera	**27**	–
Philopotamus montanus (A)	4	Tx
Plectrocnemia conspersa (A)	4	Tx
Plectrocnemia geniculata (A)	4	Tx
Stenophylax permistus	1	SuT
Stenophylax vibex	2	SuT
Other Trichoptera	12	–
Arthropoda: Insecta: Plecoptera	**30**	–
Amphinemura sulcicollis (A)	1	Tx
Siphonoperla torrentium (A)	2	Tx
Dinocras cephalotes (A)	12	Tx
Diura bicaudata (A)	1	Tx
Isoperla gramatica (A)	1	Tx
Leuctra fusca (A)	2	Tx
Leuctra geniculata (A)	1	Tx
Leuctra hippopus (A)	1	Tx
Leuctra inermis (A)	1	Tx
Nemoura cambrica (A)	2	Tx
Perlodes microcephala (A)	1	Tx
Protonemura praecox (A)	2	Tx
Other Plecoptera	3	–
Arthropoda: Insecta: Mecoptera	**2**	–
Boreus hyemalis	1	Tx
Panorpa germanica	1	Tx
Arthropoda: Insecta: Hemiptera	**13**	–
Cixius distinguendus	1	Tx
Philaenus spumarius	1	Tx
Psylla melanoneura	1	Tx
Stendomus holsatum	2	Tx
Velia caprai (A)	8	EuT
Arthropoda: Insecta: Diptera	**252**	–
Macropelopia nebulosa	3	Tx
Macropelopia notata	1	Tx
Calliphora vomitoria	4	Tx
Kowarzia bipunctata	1	Tx
Wiedemannia insularis	1	Tx
Boreoclytocerus ocellaris	1	Tx
Crumomyia nigra	7	EuT
Crumomyia nitida	2	Tx
Crumomyia roserii	1	Tx
Crumomyia fimetaria	1	Tx
Culex pipiens	31	SuT
Culicoides delta	1	Tx
Culiseta annulata	1	Tx
Diamesa tonsa	1	Tx
Eukiefferiella coerulescens	1	Tx
Eukiefferiella brevicalcar	1	Tx
Exechia contaminata	2	Tx
Exechia festiva	1	Tx
Exechiopsis subulata	2	Tx
Heleomyza captiosa	33	EuT
Hydrotaea irritans	1	Tx
Gigalimosina flaviceps	1	Tx
Terrilimosina racovitzai	1	EuT
Eloeophila submarmorata	1	Tx
Eloeophila trimaculata	1	Tx
Limnophora exuta	1	Tx
Limonia nubeculosa	6	SuT
Limosina silvatica	1	Tx
Lipsothrix remota	1	Tx
Molophilus curvatus	1	Tx
Mycetophila ornata	1	Tx
Mycetophila ruficolis (?)	1	Tx
Oecothea praecox	1	Tx
Ormosia pseudosimilis	1	Tx
Neomyia caesarion	1	Tx
Pedicia rivosa	1	Tx
Pedicia straminea	3	Tx
Trissopelopia longimana	1	Tx
Prodiamesa olivacea	1	Tx
Rymosia fasciata	3	Tx
Scatophaga stercoraria	1	Tx
Gymnomus caesius	3	Tx
Scoliocentra scutellaris	1	Tx
Scoliocentra villosa	5	Tx
Simulium argyreatum	1	Tx
Speolepta leptogaster	40	EuT
Tarnania fenestralis	1	Tx
Thienemanniella clavicornis	1	Tx
Copromyza equina	2	Tx
Trichocera maculipenis	11	EuT
Trichocera regelationis	6	EuT
Triphleba antricola	1	EuT
Other Diptera	54	–
Arthropoda: Insecta: Coleoptera	**61**	–
Agabus biguttatus (A)	1	Tx
Agabus bipustulatus (A)	1	Tx
Agabus guttatus (A)	9	EuT
Agonum muelleri	1	Tx
Anacaena globulus	1	Tx
Ochthephilus aureus	7	EuT
Atheta graminicola	1	Tx
Bembidion guttula	1	Tx
Catops nigricans	1	Tx
Choleva glauca	1	Tx
Choleva jeanneli	1	Tx
Dianous coerulescens	1	Tx
Enicmus testaceus	1	Tx
Geodromicus nigrita	2	Tx
Hydroporus aquaticus (A)	1	Tx
Hydroporus ferrugineus (A)	2	Tb
Hypolithus riparius	1	Tx
Lathrobium fulvipenne	1	Tx
Lathrobium geminum	1	Tx
Leptinus testaceus	1	Tx
Lesteva pubescens	9	EuT
Loricera pilicornis	1	Tx
Nebria brevicollis	4	Tx
Nebria rufescens	1	Tx
Olophrum piceum	1	Tx
Pterostichus madidus	1	Tx
Quedius mesomelinus	6	EuT
Trechus secalis	1	Tx
Other Coleoptera	1	–
Arthropoda: Insecta: Lepidoptera	**13**	–
Scoliopteryx libatrix	11	SuT
Triphosa dubitata	2	SuT
Arthropoda: Myriapoda: Chilopoda	**3**	–
Lithobius forficatus	2	Tx
Lithobius variegatus	1	Tx
Arthropoda: Myriapoda: Diplopoda	**28**	–
Archiboreoiulus pallidus	1	Tx
Blaniulus guttulatus	4	EuT
Brachydesmus superus	1	EuT
Cyclindroiulus parisiorum	1	Tx
Glomeris marginata	1	Tx
Ophyiulus pilosus	1	Tx
Polydesmus angustus	3	EuT
Polydesmus coriaceus	1	Tx
Nanogona polydesmoides	8	EuT
Tachypodoiulus niger	7	EuT
Chordata: Teleostei	**1**	–
Salmo trutta (A)	1	Tx

Table 13.15. Species recorded from Yorkshire Dales caves. EC = ecological classification, Tb = troglobiont, EuT = eutroglophile, SuT = subtroglophile, Tx = trogloxene. These terms are defined in the text, after Sket (2008). (A) = aquatic species; all other species are terrestrial. Troglobionts are shaded green, eutroglophiles pale orange and subtroglophiles pink.

Figure 13.10. *The common eutroglophile spider* Meta menardi *(Arachnida: Araneae: Tetragnathidae), which is found in cave and mine threshold zones. Threshold EuT (photo: Phil Chapman).*

Figure 13.11. *The common eutroglophile spider* Metellina merianae *(Arachnida: Araneae: Tetragnathidae), which is found in cave and mine threshold zones. Threshold EuT (photo: Phil Chapman).*

Figure 13.12. Nesticus cellulanus *(Arachnida: Araneae: Nesticidae), a eutroglophile spider occurs in both the threshold and dark zone of caves and mines. EuT (photo: Andrew Lewington).*

Figure 13.13. *Like other species in its genus, the small money spider* Porrhomma convexum *(Arachnida: Araneae: Linyphiidae) is found in the dark zone of caves and mines. EuT (photo: Phil Chapman).*

Araneae (Spiders)

Spiders are an important group in Yorkshire Dales caves and mines, as they are in all karst areas, and constitute 11% of all records. Twelve species are known, all but five being low-number record trogloxenes. Four eutroglophile species make up 78% of all spider records. Three of these, *Meta menardi* (Fig. 13.10), *Metellina merianae* (Fig. 13.11) and *Nesticus cellulanus* (Fig. 13.12), are very common threshold eutroglophiles, with *Nesticus* also found in the dark zone (Jefferson, 1976, 1983; Chapman, 1993; Smithers, 1996, 2004, 2005a, 2005b; Smithers and Fox Smith, 1998; Rogers, 1999). In the dark zone the spider fauna is dominated by money spiders (Linyphiidae) of the genus *Porrhomma*. In the Dales only one *Porrhomma* species, *P. convexum*, is recorded (Fig. 13.13).

Arthropoda: Crustacea

Copepoda

Only seven copepod species are recorded from Dales caves (10 records) and mines (6 records) (Tables 13.15 and 13.17) and only one species is common to both. These few records and species probably reflect the fact that most species are tiny and transparent, and all live in water – an under-recorded habitat in British caves and mines generally. However, worldwide, copepods are a highly significant component of the subterranean fauna. They are particularly prominent in the epikarstic zone, below the soil and above the cave roofs (Ford and Williams, 2007; Jones *et al.*, 2004; Pipan, 2005). In the light of these studies, in Slovenia and the USA, it would appear worthwhile to study the Dales epikarst, where many copepod species would probably be recorded.

Syncarida

Only one species of syncarid crustacean, *Antrobathynella stammeri*, is recorded. This minute troglobiont has been recorded within the Dales from White Scar Cave, Great Douk Cave (Gledhill and Driver, 1964; Serban and Gledhill, 1965), and recently from Scoska Cave (Lee Knight *pers. comm.*) and the hyporheic zone of the River Skirfare (Stubbington *et al.*, 2008). It is also know from several Lake District rivers (Gledhill, Sutcliffe and Williams, 1993; Proudlove *et al.*, 2003), just north of the Central Belt of Scotland (Maitland, 1962; Proudlove *et al.*, 2003) and from sites in southern England and Ireland (Proudlove *et al.*, 2003; Knight and Penk, 2010). Syncarid Crustacea have notably poor powers of dispersal and it is unclear whether they re-colonised the north of England and Scotland after the last glaciation or survived it in subterranean refugia (see below).

Taxa	Records	%	TS	AS	Number of species	%	Tb	EuT	SuT	Tx
Tricladida	16	1.93	0	3	3	1.40	0	3	0	0
Oligochaeta	23	2.77	7	4	11	5.12	0	8	0	3
Mollusca	21	2.53	9	3	12	5.58	0	5	0	7
Arthropoda: Arachnida										
Acari	28	3.38	13	2	15	6.98	0	15	0	0
Araneae	92	11.10	12	0	12	5.58	0	4	0	8
Chelonethida	1	0.12	1	0	1	0.47	0	0	0	1
Opilionida	1	0.12	1	0	1	0.47	0	0	0	1
Arthropoda: Crustacea										
Copepoda	10	1.21	0	4	4	1.86	0	4	0	0
Syncarida	4	0.48	0	1	1	0.47	1	0	0	0
Amphipoda	71	8.56	0	1	1	0.47	0	1	0	0
Isopoda	21	2.53	4	0	4	1.86	0	1	0	3

Table 13.16. A summary of the higher taxonomic faunal groups recorded from caves in the Dales and adjacent areas. Abbreviated terminology as for Table 13.17.

Taxa	Records	%	TS	AS	Number of species	%	Tb	EuT	SuT	Tx
Arthropoda: Insecta										
Collembola	87	10.49	23	0	23	10.70	0	23	0	0
Ephemeroptera	24	2.90	0	8	8	3.72	0	0	0	8
Trichoptera	27	3.26	3	2	5	2.33	0	0	2	3
Plecoptera	30	3.62	0	12	12	5.58	0	0	0	12
Mecoptera	2	0.24	2	0	2	0.93	0	0	0	2
Hemiptera	13	1.57	4	1	5	2.33	0	1	0	4
Diptera	252	30.31	52	0	52	24.17	0	7	2	43
Coleoptera	61	7.36	23	5	28	13.02	1	4	0	23
Lepidoptera	13	1.57	2	0	2	0.93	0	0	2	0
Arthropoda: Myriapoda										
Chilopoda	3	0.36	2	0	2	0.93	0	0	0	2
Diplopoda	28	3.38	10	0	10	4.65	0	5	0	5
Chordata										
Teleostei	1	0.12	0	1	1	0.47	0	0	0	1
TOTALS	**829**	—	**168**	**47**	**215**	—	**2**	**81**	**6**	**126**

Species	Records	EC
Tricladida	**10**	—
Crenobia alpine (A)	4	EuT
Phagocatta vitta (A)	4	EuT
Dendrocoelum lacteum (A)	1	EuT
Other Tricladida	1	—
Oligochaeta	**2**	—
Dendrodrilus rubidus	1	Tx
Enchytraeus albidus	1	Tx
Arthropoda: Arachnida: Acari	**14**	—
Eugamasus loricatus	1	EuT
Eupodes variegatus	1	EuT
Linopodes motatorius	1	EuT
Microtrombidium sucidum	1	EuT
Parasitus coleoptratorum	1	EuT
Pergamasus minor	1	EuT
Rhagidia diversicolor	1	EuT
Rhagidia gigas	1	EuT
Rhagidia intermedia	1	EuT
Rhagidia longipes	1	EuT
Rhagidia spelaea	1	EuT
Veigaia transisalae	2	EuT
Other Acari	1	—
Arthropoda: Arachnida: Araneae	**40**	—
Bathyphantes gracilis	1	Tx
Lepthyphantes mengei	1	Tx
Lepthyphantes zimmermanni	2	Tx
Meta menardi	7	EuT
Metellina merianae	19	EuT
Nesticus cellulanus	2	EuT
Porrhomma convexum	7	EuT
Other Araneae	1	—
Arthropoda: Arachnida: Opilionida	**1**	—
Mitastoma chrysomelas	1	Tx
Arthropoda: Crustacea: Copepoda	**6**	—
Acanthocyclops viridis (A)	1	EuT
Acanthocyclops bisetosus (A)	1	EuT
Eucyclops agilis (A)	1	EuT
Paracyclops fimbriatus (A)	2	EuT
Other Copepoda	1	—
Arthropoda: Crustacea: Amphipoda	**6**	—
Gammarus pulex (A)	6	EuT
Arthropoda: Crustacea: Isopoda	**19**	—
Androniscus dentiger	4	EuT
Oniscus asellus	5	Tx
Trichoniscus pygmaeus	3	Tx
Trichoniscoides saeroeensis	7	EuT
Arthropoda: Insecta: Collembola	**49**	—
Folsomia candida	1	EuT
Folsomia fimetaria	1	EuT
Ceratophysella denticulata	2	EuT
Hypogastrura purpurescens	3	EuT
Isotomurus palustris	1	EuT
Lepidocyrtus curvicollis	1	EuT
Neanura muscorum	3	EuT
Onychiurus arans ???	1	EuT
Deuteraphorura cebannaria	9	EuT
Oligaphorura schoetti	5	EuT
Schaefferia emucronata group	5	EuT
Tomocerus minor	14	EuT

Species	Records	EC
Arthropoda: Insecta: Ephemeroptera	**1**	—
Siphlonurus armatus (A)	1	Tx
Arthropoda: Insecta: Trichoptera	**5**	—
Plectrocnemia conspersa (A)	1	Tx
Stenophylax permistus	4	SuT
Arthropoda: Insecta: Hemiptera	**4**	—
Velia caprai (A)	4	EuT
Arthropoda: Insecta: Diptera	**111**	—
Macropelopia goetghebueri	1	Tx
Calliphora vicina	1	Tx
Crumomyia nigra	6	EuT
Crumomyia fimetaria	1	Tx
Culex pipiens	19	SuT
Culiseta annulata	1	Tx
Diamesa bohemani	1	Tx
Heleomyza borealis	1	Tx
Heleomyza captiosa	18	EuT
Gigalimosina flaviceps	1	Tx
Leptocera syvatica	1	Tx
Limonia nubeculosa	3	SuT
Limosina silvatica	1	Tx
Lipsothrix remota	2	Tx
Paratanytarsus autriacus	1	Tx
Pedicia straminea	1	Tx
Rymosia fasciata	2	Tx
Gymnomus caecius	1	Tx
Scoliocentra villosa	1	Tx
Speolepta leptogaster	23	EuT
Sylvicola fenestralis	1	Tx
Tephrochlamis rufiventris	1	Tx
Trichocera maculipenis	1	EuT
Other Diptera	22	—
Arthropoda: Insecta: Coleoptera	**15**	—
Agabus guttatus (A)	2	EuT
Agonum albipes	1	Tx
Ochthephilus aureus	2	EuT
Hydroporus obseletus (A)	1	Tx
Lesteva pubescens	1	EuT
Nebria rufescens	1	Tx
Tachinus rufipennis	1	Tx
Trechus fulvus	1	Tx
Other Coleoptera	5	
Arthropoda: Insecta: Lepidoptera	**10**	—
Operophtera brumata	2	SuT
Scoliopteryx libatrix	5	SuT
Triphosa dubitata	3	SuT
Arthropoda: Myriapoda: Chilopoda	**1**	—
Lithobius variegatus	1	Tx
Arthropoda: Myriapoda: Diplopoda	**13**	—
Blaniulus guttulatus	3	EuT
Cyclindroiulus latestriatus	1	Tx
Polydesmus angustus	1	EuT
Nanogona polydesmoides	6	EuT
Proteroiulus fuscus	1	Tx
Tachypodoiulus niger	1	EuT
Arthropoda: Myriapoda: Symphyla	**2**	—
Symphylella isabellae	2	Tx

Table 13.17. Species recorded from Yorkshire Dales mines. EC = ecological classification, EuT = eutroglophile, SuT = subtroglophile, Tx = trogloxene. These terms are defined in the text, after Sket (2008). (A) = aquatic species; all other species are terrestrial. Eutroglophiles are shaded pale orange and subtroglophiles are shaded pink.

Taxa	Records	%	TS	AS	Number of species	%	Tb	EuT	SuT	Tx
Tricladida	10	3.24	0	3	3	3.26	0	3	0	0
Oligochaeta	2	0.65	2	0	2	2.17	0	0	0	2
Arthropoda: Arachnida										
Acari	14	4.53	12	0	12	13.04	0	12	0	0
Araneae	40	12.94	7	0	7	7.61	0	4	0	3
Opilionida	1	0.32	1	0	1	1.09	0	0	0	1
Arthropoda: Crustacea										
Copepoda	6	1.94	0	4	4	4.35	0	4	0	0
Amphipoda	6	1.94	0	1	1	1.09	0	1	0	0
Isopoda	19	6.15	4	0	4	4.35	0	2	0	2
Arthropoda: Insecta										
Collembola	49	15.86	12	0	12	13.04	0	12	0	0
Ephemeroptera	1	0.32	0	1	1	1.09	0	0	0	1
Trichoptera	5	1.62	1	1	2	2.17	0	0	1	1
Hemiptera	4	1.29	0	1	1	1.09	0	1	0	0
Diptera	111	35.92	23	0	23	25.00	0	4	2	17
Coleoptera	15	4.85	6	2	8	8.70	0	3	0	5
Lepidoptera	10	3.23	3	0	3	3.26	0	0	3	0
Arthropoda: Myriapoda										
Chilopoda	1	0.32	1	0	1	1.09	0	0	0	1
Diplopoda	13	4.21	6	0	6	6.52	0	4	0	2
Symphyla	2	0.65	1	0	1	1.09	0	0	0	1
TOTALS	309	—	79	13	92	—	0	50	6	36

Table 13.18. A summary of the higher taxonomic groups recorded from mines in the Yorkshire Dales. TS = terrestrial species, AS = aquatic species, EuT = eutroglophile, SuT = subtroglophile, Tx = trogloxene. These terms are defined in the text, after Sket (2008).

Amphipoda (freshwater shrimps)

Only one species, *Gammarus pulex* (Figs 13.14 and 13.15), is recorded. It is widespread in cave streams, being a common epigean species that drifts in the current so that if the stream enters a cave, so will *G. pulex*. Clearly this applies to all stream species, but *G. pulex* is large, active and easily collected, hence the many records. *G. pulex* is perfectly able to survive in caves and is undoubtedly a eutroglophile. It is suggested that some populations are depigmented, as within Ingleborough Cave, and might differ genetically from normal stream populations (Piearce, 1975; Piearce and Cox, 1977a, 1977b). Hypogean *G. pulex* are typically smaller than epigean specimens, and might be preferentially carnivorous or even cannibalistic as a strategy for overcoming poor food availability (Little *et al.*, 2006; Worrall and Wood, 2007). Many original records of this species in published Biological Records in the *Hazelton* database are under the generic name *Rivulogammarus*, which is now an invalid name, so its use should be discontinued (Stock, 1969).

Isopoda (Woodlice)

Six isopod species are recorded but only two are of interest. The common rosy woodlouse, *Androniscus dentiger* (Fig. 13.16) is a eutroglophile both in caves and mines.

Figure 13.14. Depigmented and white eyed Gammarus pulex (Crustacea: Amphipoda: Gammaridae). Whereas most cave populations of this common amphipod are normally pigmented and have normal eyes, some populations, including one in Ingleborough Cave, have much reduced pigmentation and the eye facets are white rather than black. EuT (photo: Phil Chapman).

Individual populations of this species, in separate caves in Italy, are highly distinct and do not exchange genes with other cave populations, or with surface populations (Gentile and Sbordoni, 1998). In this situation the populations are effectively troglobionts. A similar study in the Dales might provide interesting results.

The second species of interest is *Trichoniscoides saeroeensis,* which was first recorded in England in mines in the Morecambe Bay area to the west of the Dales (Moseley, 1970; Sheppard, 1968, 1971). It is now recognised as a relatively common coastal species, also known from limestone uplands in Britain and Ireland (Gregory, 2009). It is suggested that this species is spreading from the coastal areas and is actively colonising caves and other hypogean habitats, (Moseley, 2000).

Arthropoda: Insecta

Collembola (Springtails)

The taxonomy and nomenclature of Collembola have altered significantly since the publication of the Biological Records. All names reported here have been updated using Hopkin (2007, and roehampton.ac.uk/collembola). Collembola are, with the mites, the predominant group within the ecology of British caves and mines. They are eminently suited to hypogean conditions. Twenty-three Collembola species are recorded from caves and twelve from mines, most of them recorded only a few times.

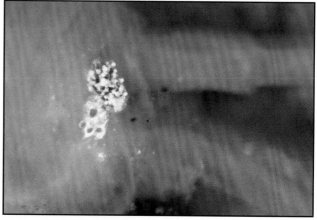

Figure 13.15. A close-up view of the eye of the depigmented Gammarus pulex of Figure 13.14. EuT (photo: Phil Chapman).

Figure 13.16. The rosy woodlouse Androniscus dentiger *(Crustacea: Isopoda: Trichoniscidae). EuT (photo: Phil Chapman).*

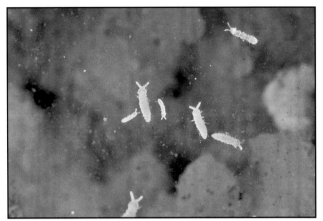

Figure 13.18. Collembola (springtails), probably browsing for food on the water surface . EuT (photo: Phil Chapman).

The most-collected Collembola species from caves are *Folsomia candida, Deuteraphorura cebennaria* (previously referred to as *Onychiurus fimetarius*) and *Oligaphorura schoetti* (previously known as *Onychiurus schoetti*) (Figs 13.17, 13.18).

In mines the commonest Collembola species are *D. cebennaria, O. schoetti* and *Tomocerus minor*. It is not surprising to find *T. minor* and *F. candida* present; they are ubiquitous and highly aggressive colonisers of many different habitats (Hopkin, 1997). *Deuteraphorura cebennaria* is also a common species but seems to favour caves particularly.

All known records of *Oligaphorura schoetti* are from caves (Hopkin, 2007), and it accounts for 20% of all cave Collembola records and 11% of all mine records. It was recognised as a member of the British fauna only in 1958 when it was collected in Pen Park Hole at Bristol in May, in the Dales at White Scar Cave in November, and in Becks Shaft, Derbyshire, also in November (Lawrence, 1960). It appears that *O. schoetti* might be a troglobiont in British caves and mines. However, Collembola are small, difficult to identify and very under-recorded in this country. It is therefore possible that the species exists in other, so-far unknown, epigean areas and thus it is considered here as being a eutroglophile.

One other species, *Folsomia agrelli*, is also known only from caves within Britain and Ireland. It is recorded from Beck Head Stream Cave (part of Ingleborough Cave) in the Dales. Because it is even less well known than *O. schoetti*, it too is retained here as a eutroglophile.

Ephemeroptera (mayflies)

All Ephemeroptera recorded in the Yorkshire Dales are trogloxenes, found as nymphs in cave or mine streams where they arrive by drift from upstream epigean reaches.

Trichoptera (caddis flies)

Only five caddis flies have been recorded in the Dales. Three of these are trogloxenes, washed into caves and mines as larvae in streams.

Two species, *Stenophylax permistus* (Fig. 13.19) and *Stenophylax vibex*, are subtroglophiles, which aestivate in caves and mines during the summer. This period of diapause is probably to allow the ovaries to mature before mating and egg-laying in the autumn (Chapman, 1993; Thines and Tercafs, 1972). The Spanish species *Mesophylax aspersus* has been shown to break its aestivation in order to leave the cave to breed, and this activity is prompted by changes in air currents within the cave (Salavert *et al.,* 2008).

Plecoptera (stone flies)

All Plecoptera recorded in the Dales are trogloxenes that were found as nymphs in cave streams where they arrived by drift from epigean reaches upstream of the cave.

Hemiptera (true bugs)

As a whole this group appears to be unimportant within subterranean habitats in the Dales. One species, *Velia caprai,* has been recorded sufficiently frequently to suggest that it is a eutroglophile.

Figure 13.17. Collembola. EuT (photo: Phil Chapman).

Figure 13.19. Stenophylax permsitus *(Insecta: Trichoptera: Limnephilidae); a female using a cave for aestivation. SuT (photo: Phil Chapman).*

Figure 13.20. Culex pipiens *(Insecta: Diptera: Culicidae). SuT (photo: Phil Chapman).*

Figure 13.21. The common two-winged fly, Heleomyza captiosa *(Insecta: Diptera: Heleomyzidae). EuT (photo: Phil Chapman).*

Figure 13.22. The adult of Speolepta leptogaster *(Insecta: Diptera: Mycetphillidae). EuT (photo: Phil Chapman).*

Diptera (two-winged flies)

By a considerable margin the Diptera are the commonest recorded animals in Dales caves and mines (Hutson and Proudlove, 2010). It is likely (see above) that Collembola and Acari are as common as Diptera but the latter are larger and generally easier to collect and identify (at least to Family level). Caves support 52 species (252 records) and mines 23 species (111 records). However, if taken at face value these long species lists are highly misleading. Most species are known from single records; only a few have between one and five records. In fact, of all these species, only four are of major importance. The subtroglophile *Culex pipiens* (Fig. 13.20) is a common winter visitor as it hibernates in caves (usually threshold zones) to allow eggs to mature before the spring mating. Hibernating populations are well known in man-made subterranean shelters (Sulaiman and Service, 1983) and within the London Underground (Byrne and Nichols, 1999).

Three species are eutroglophiles in British and continental caves and mines. *Trichocera maculipennis* is widely found deep in caves, where it is more common than on the surface (Chapman, 1993). Larvae are recorded and it is certain that these animals breed in caves. *Heleomyza captiosa* (Fig. 13.21) (recorded in *Hazelton* and all earlier literature as *Heleomyza serrata*; Papp, 1978) is also common, but its status is in dispute. Some authors consider it a eutroglophile (Papp, 1978), some a threshold subtroglophile (Leruth, 1939; Hazelton and Glennie, 1953, 1962), and some a trogloxene (Jefferson, 1981; Chapman, 1993; Jefferson *et al.*, 2004). More work is needed to confirm its status, which could include all three options in different places. In contrast, *Speolepta leptogaster* (Figs 13.22, 13.23 and 13.24) is unquestionably a eutroglophile and is the commonest species in Dales caves and mines. Though rare outside caves it is known from man-made subterranean structures such as cellars (Laurence, 1982, 1989; Matile, 1962).

Coleoptera (beetles)

Surprisingly few species of Coleoptera, the largest order of insects, are recorded from subterranean sites – only 28 (23 terrestrial, 5 aquatic) in caves and 8 (6 terrestrial, 2 aquatic) in mines. Most are trogloxenes, recorded only once or twice. Five species are noteworthy. Three terrestrial beetles belonging to the family Staphylinidae, *Ochthephilus aureus* (Fig. 13.25) (previously named *Ancyrophorus aureus*), *Lesteva pubescens*

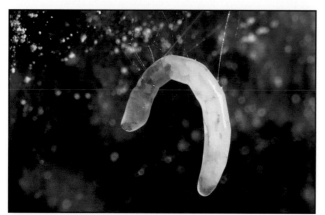

Figure 13.23. The larva of Speolepta leptogaster *in characteristic pose suspended from its silken threads. It browses for algae, fungi and bacteria on cave walls. EuT (photo: Phil Chapman).*

Figure 13.24. Another view of the larva of Speolepta leptogaster *showing some details of the mesh of silken threads on which it lives. EuT (photo: Phil Chapman).*

Figure 13.25. The terrestrial beetle Ochthephilus aureus *(Insecta: Coleoptera: Staphylinidae) is a eutroglophile that is common in caves throughout Britain. EuT (photo: Phil Chapman).*

Figure 13.26. The tissue moth Triphosa dubitata *(Insecta: Lepidoptera: Geometridae) (photo: Phil Chapman).*

and *Quedius mesomelinus,* are eutroglophiles, common in caves and mines throughout Britain. Curiously, no members of the Caribidae, a large family of mobile ground beetles, are common in underground habitats.

Two water beetles, both in the family Dytiscidae, are significant. *Agabus guttatus* is widespread and common, and is a eutroglophile. The other, *Hydroporus ferrugineus,* might be a troglobiont in Britain. In the Dales it is recorded only from the Gaping Gill Cave System. All records of the small (3.5 mm) flightless adults are associated with springs and other subterranean sites. It would be valuable to search other caves for this nationally notable beetle (Alarie *et al.,* 2001).

Lepidoptera (moths)

Three Lepidoptera species, *Triphosa dubitata* (the tissue moth, Fig. 13.26), *Scoliopteryx libatrix* (the herald moth, Fig. 13.27) and *Opheroptera brummata* (the winter moth) use cave entrances, and, in some cases, deeper areas of caves and mines for winter hibernation. In Scoska Cave, bats might be feeding on hibernating herald and tissue moths (Hodgson, 2004, 2005a, 2008), a phenomenon also recorded in Japanese caves (Sano, 2006).

Arthropoda: Myriapoda

All recorded examples of Chilopoda (centipedes) in the Yorkshire Dales are considered to be trogloxenes.

Of 12 recorded species Diplopoda (millipedes) only three are recognised eutroglophiles. The most important species, *Nanogona polydesmoides* (Fig. 13.28), is relatively widespread in subterranean sites throughout Britain. It is common in Ingleborough Cave, where it leaves distinctive casts on mudbank surfaces.

Other eutroglophile species include the common spotted snake millipede, *Blaniulus guttulatus,* and the large black millipede *Tachypodoiulus niger.* Two other species, *Brachydesmus superus* (Fig. 13.29) and *Polydesmus angustus* are represented by just a few samples in the Dales but are common elsewhere as eutroglophiles. It is interesting to compare these *Hazelton* data with the atlas of Diplopod distribution (Lee, 2006), which records 13 species from caves; *Nanogona polydesmoides* is most common, with several records of *Tachypodoiulus niger, Blaniulus guttulatus* and *Brachydesmus superus.*

Figure 13.27. The herald moth Scoliopteryx libatrix *(Insecta: Lepidoptera: Noctuidae). SuT (photo: Phil Chapman).*

Figure 13.28. The eutrogrophile millipede Nanogona polydesmoides *(Myriapoda: Diplopoda: Chordeumatida) is widespread across Britain . EuT (photo: Phil Chapman).*

Figure 13.29 Less common than other millipedes in British caves and mines, Brachydesmus superus *(Myriapoda: Diplopoda: Polydesmida) has been found at relatively few Dales sites. EuT (photo: Andrew Lewington).*

Chordata: fishes

Fishes (Teleostei) are not an important component of the Dales subterranean fauna, but their presence in caves is of interest, from both ecological and physiological perspectives (Chapman, 1993; Glover, 1978; Proudlove, 1979, 1982, 2006).

Brown trout

Brown trout (*Salmo trutta*: Salmonidae) are recorded in several Dales caves including Penyghent Pot (Fig. 13.30), Ingleborough Cave, Fairy Holes, the Alum Pot system and Calf Holes. The stomach of a single specimen from Ingleborough Cave contained insect and crustacea fragments, along with small stones (Glover, 1978). This confirmed that this fish must have fed in the cave, because food only remains in the stomach of trout for a short time. Moreover, the stones show that it was feeding on the bottom, which is unusual for trout but presumably the only option in total darkness.

Trout in caves commonly look white but this is not due to evolutionary pigment loss as in true troglobiotic fishes (Proudlove, 2006a). Black melanin pigment can fill its cell (a melanophore) to create a dark fish, or shrink into a small ball in the centre of the cell to create a pale-looking animal. This is the state of trout that have been examined from caves and they would probably regain a darker colour if flushed out from the cave.

Within the Alum Pot system, trout have regularly been seen in the Borrins Moor Cave lower streamway, and in Dr Bannister's Handbasin in Upper Long Churn Cave. In August 2010 six trout were counted in the Handbasin pool, with sizes ranging between 10 cm and 15 cm, but a return to the site in September 2010 found that no fish were present (Jes Hart, *pers. comm.*). Three sizeable floods between the visits might account for the contrast in fish populations.

Bullhead

The only other fish commonly seen in Dales caves is the bullhead (*Cottus gobio*: Cottidae). Unlike cave trout, these small fishes are not white but remain darkly coloured. Many were seen in an inlet in Ibbeth Peril Cave in 2005 after a significant dry spell with unusually low water levels (Jes Hart, *pers. comm.*). They are also known from the Kingsdale Master Cave.

Ecological composition of the subterranean fauna

Among the four ecological categories in caves and in mines (Table 13.19), there are few troglobionts and subtroglophiles, so their proportions are expectedly small. The proportions for eutroglophiles and trogloxenes seem, at first sight, to be the opposite of expectation. Caves, having been present in the landscape for much longer than mines, might be expected to contain proportionally more eutroglophiles. This apparently unlikely result is explained by the presence in caves of many aquatic trogloxene larvae and insect nymphs, which drift accidentally into caves in the stream current (downstream drift). Clearly, few mines have the same magnitude of water flow as even small cave streams, and none has sinking streams. The best description of the current subterranean fauna of the Dales is that it is *"a predominantly post-glacial colonising fauna with possible trans-glacial elements"*.

Further studies of Dales caves and mines

Several significant single-site, or single-area, studies in the Yorkshire Dales and adjacent areas enhance the knowledge gained from study of the *Hazelton* data.

Morecambe Bay limestones

The fauna of Hale Moss Cave, near Beetham, is influenced by the fact that the passages lie close beneath the surface where comparatively large amounts of food can be washed down by rainfall. Additionally, temperatures are more variable than in most caves and there is a continual interchange between surface and cave terrestrial fauna. A faunal list shows that the terrestrial specimens are very similar to those of the endogean domain (Moseley, 1970). Aquatic species in these caves occupy isolated pools with no direct connection with surface populations. Expectation in such conditions is of numerous specimens of a few species. This was borne out by one pool examined, which supported a flourishing colony of *Gammarus pulex*, a colony of *Pisidium personatum* (Mollusca: Bivalvia) and very little else.

Both the aquatic and terrestrial fauna are helped in survival by the presence of a plentiful food supply. In the case of terrestrial fauna this is primarily organic matter carried down through various openings by seepage water. The pools, also fed by seepage water, are lined with rich deep mud containing a high proportion of organic matter. This is broken down by bacteria, providing food for protozoa. Numerous ciliates – revealed by microscopic examination of a water sample – are presumably eaten by the *Pisidium*, which is a filter feeder. *Gammarus pulex*, which is known to be carnivorous, may feed on the *Pisidium*.

Within the hypogean environment of the caves and mines near Morecambe Bay, each biotope shows a characteristic fauna (Moseley, 1969, 1970). Dark zone terrestrial species occur in mine timbers, which form a very rich habitat. The fauna consists mostly of lumbricid earthworms, isopods, diplopods and Collembola. Vegetable detritus supports isopods (*Androniscus dentiger*) and diplopods (*Nanogona polydesmoides* and *Blaniulus guttulatus*), in turn preyed upon by Coleoptera (*Quedius mesomelinus*). All these are characteristic eutroglophiles in Britain.

***Figure 13.30.** A pale-coloured brown trout* (Salmo trutta) *from the canal in Penyghent Pot. Tx (photographer unknown).*

	Tb	EuT	SuT	Tx
Caves	0.93	37.67	2.79	58.60
Mines	0.00	55.32	6.38	38.30

Table 13.19. Percentages of each ecological classification in Yorkshire Dales caves and mines. These figures are discussed and interpreted in the text.

Rock surfaces are dominated by adult and larval Diptera; isopods and diplopods also occur locally. Surface filmwaters are mainly occupied by Collembola, but mites and symphyla are also present. No direct evidence is available regarding interstitial fauna, but the isopod *Trichoniscus saeroeensis* might be primarily interstitial (Moseley, 2000). Dark zone aquatic fauna found in pools are mainly planarians, copepods and *Gammarus pulex*. Flowing water has not been investigated. Seepage water and springs within the cave and mines did not yield fauna, but a single specimen of *Hydroporus obsoletus* might indicate the presence of a phreatic fauna. Threshold-region terrestrial fauna found on rock surfaces are typically species of Diptera and, in winter, Lepidoptera, together with accidental fauna. Surface water films support Hemiptera (*Velia caprai*) and various Collembola. *Gammarus pulex* is common in the threshold-region aquatic zone.

Caves in Cowside Beck

Six caves resurge into Cowside Beck. Few cavers visit these systems so they are in a largely natural condition and contain fine calcite formations (Hodgson, 2005b).

The 2500m of passages in Robinsons' Pot were first surveyed for cave life in 1975, when the fauna was considerably richer than currently, with 30 cavernicolous species found, including 7 caddis fly larvae compared to just one caddis recently. In 2002 a strong smell of sheep-dip was noticed underground, and water contaminated by sheep-dip was found to be entering the system at several points. Its widespread distribution was confirmed using a conductivity meter, and it is suspected that its presence accounts for the sharp fall in faunal diversity. A fish seen at the start of Sump 1 in Robinsons' Pot was probably a trout.

Flies caught deep underground during two visits to Cherry Tree Hole were identified as *Heleomyza captiosa*. Larvae and adults of the stonefly *Dinocras cephalotes* extend throughout the Robinsons' Pot system, and a web-spinning caddis fly larva *(Plectronemia conspersa)* occurs in the same cave. The herald moth *(Scoliopteryx libatrix)* uses Loop Cave for hibernation. This cave is also home to a breeding colony of the spider *Meta merianae*.

Freshwater shrimps, *Gammarus pulex*, still inhabit the same site in Robinsons' Pot where first discovered in 1975, as do *Crenobia alpina* flatworms. The latter is a cold water species; the water temperature in the cave averages 8.8°C. Mud banks on both sides of the Worm Series, a side passage off the main Robinsons' Pot stream passage, show abundant worm casts produced by a large and healthy population of an albino form of the green earthworm *Allolobophora chlorotica*. This species is common in limestone soils in the Malham area where it displays a greenish pink colour. It can survive and breed for at least 50 weeks totally submerged beneath aerated water. Unpigmented cave populations are otherwise known only from Ingleborough Cave.

Figure 13.31. The main streamway in White Scar Cave as it was in the 1960s before the Show Cave raised pathway was extended through it as far as the tunnel up into the Battlefield (TW).

White Scar Cave

Biological recording in White Scar Cave during the 1960s revealed that species and relative sizes of populations differed between the Show Cave streamway and the further reaches of the cave that were at that time rarely visited (Schofield, 1964). It was unexpected that the larger and more numerous colonies, with the sole exception of Diptera species, are in the unvisited parts of the cave rather than in its commercialised section with its relatively higher levels of organic contamination.

During 1960 a visit to White Scar Cave was organised on behalf of the Freshwater Biological Association, with the aim of determining whether the cave's lakes supported fish. No fish were caught, but collections made during the visit yielded specimens of the troglobiont crustacean *Antrobathynella stammeri*, a first-time record of this species for Yorkshire. Following this discovery, another single specimen of *A. stammeri* was found in the silt of a wall pool in May 1960, and eleven additional specimens were collected in stream gravels and wall pools during May 1961 (Gledhill and Driver, 1964).

Stump Cross Caverns

Springtails (Collembola) were studied in Stump Cross Caverns during 1961–1962 at one location in the Show Cave and another in a seldom-visited passage (Dixon, 1974). Contrary to the findings in White Scar Cave, this study revealed greater concentrations of Collembola in the commercialised section of the cave than in the unvisited area. During the study it was also noted that the springtails tended to congregate at the ends of the pools closest to artificial light sources in the Show Cave.

Scoska Cave

Between 1965 and 1967 a comprehensive biological survey carried out in Scoska Cave (reported by Dixon, 1974) was facilitated by dividing it into zones, so that each zone could be examined and recorded carefully. Three bats were seen during the survey and local information implies that Scoska supported a significant bat colony until 1964. Evidence of digging and burying was found on a mudbank within a zone 70–95m from the entrance, and hazel nuts were found hereabouts on several occasions. This suggested the presence of long-tailed field mice *(Apodemus sylvaticus)*, which dig burrows and store nuts for winter use. This part of the cave is relatively dry and is not flood-liable (Fig. 13.32). Moth counts were made during the winter months and the threshold flora was recorded, including several species of moths and liverworts. Recent collections by Lee Knight have found the syncarid crustacean *Antrobathynella stammeri* and the collembolan *Folsomia agrelli*, both of which are troglobionts.

Scoska Cave's flora was also studied in detail (Pentecost and Zhang, 2001, 2004). Scoska is one of the best-studied caves in the Dales, but much remains to be learned about its species and communities.

Springs Wood Level

For the first biological survey of Springs Wood Level (or Starbotton End Mine), the adit was divided into 15m-zones, working inwards from the entrance (Dixon and Richardson, 1965; Dixon, 1966). Diptera and Araneae were predominant in the deep threshold zone up to 60m. Spiders were rare beyond this, but flies remained common to 90m and occurred sporadically to 180m. Tissue moths *(Triphosa dubitata)*, which hibernate in the mine, occurred between 75m and 135m from the entrance. Beyond 180m only a few *Sciara* larvae were found. Stream samples revealed *Gammarus pulex*, cyclopoid and harpacticoid copepods, and lumbricid and enchytraeid worms. In October 1969 seven pairs of tissue moths were found *in copula*. Many moths not copulating were in pairs on the rock surface. Numbers of moths present varied from 50 to 300 in mid-winter. A few herald moths *(Scoliopteryx libatrix)* are also present in the mine in winter months. The level's aquatic fauna includes ostracods, cyclopoid and harpacticoid copepods, ciliate protozoa, free-living nematodes, small specimens of *Gammarus pulex* and small planaria (probably *Crenobia alpina)*. Adult caddis flies *(Plectrocnemia conspersa)* are present during the summer, usually averaging thirty.

Diptera have been recorded, with *Speolepta leptogaster* seen *in copula* on several occasions. A station survey showed that *Heleomyza captiosa* tend to occur mainly in the 30–75m zone. Abundant *Crenobia alpina* are present at all times and appear to wander at will through the level, specimens being found in different areas at different times. A small colony of *Dendrocoelum lacteum* was found in only one location, not in conjunction with *Crenobia*. Several specimens of the spiders *Meta menardi* and *Metellina merianae* have been found on well-developed webs, with some feeding on Diptera.

Figure 13.32. Part of the threshold area of Scoska Cave, Littondale (photo: John Altringham).

Origin of the Dales subterranean fauna

Geological and geomorphological events have influenced the composition of the subterranean fauna. The Dales were affected extensively by several Pleistocene glacial advances (see Chapter 3), which probably eradicated any pre-glacial or interglacial fauna that existed in the caves, with the possible exception of *Antrobathynella stammeri*. Immediately after the final retreat of Devensian ice, caves were almost certainly devoid of life, providing a possible explanation for a virtually total absence of troglobionts and concomitant predominance of eutroglophiles within the present cave fauna.

The presence of *A. stammeri* in the Dales and farther north is perplexing because it is unlikely that these areas could have been colonised since the end of the Devensian. The much larger, more mobile hypogean amphipod *Niphargus aquilex* has not been recorded farther north than Anglesey and the River Humber (Bratton, 2006), presumably marking the northern limit of its post-Devensian expansion. If *N. aquilex* has not reached Yorkshire, it is pertinent to ask how *A. stammeri* could do so. One possibility is that the species survived in sub-glacial refugia below Pleistocene ice (Proudlove *et al.*, 2003), but more work is needed to confirm this. Evidence from molecular studies (Kornobis *et al.*, 2010, 2011; Hanfling *et al.*, 2008) confirms that some troglobiotic species in Iceland and Ireland survived in sub-glacial refugia.

Details of how eutrogrophilic populations originate still await elucidation from among a spectrum of possibilities. A current eutroglophile population (e.g. *Gammarus pulex*) might have arrived in the cave recently by migration from the surface, with no in-cave birth for several generations, many generations, or ever. Alternatively, a current eutroglophile population (e.g. *Speolepta leptogaster*) might be derived totally from birth within the cave, with no migratory individuals for several generations, many generations, or since initial colonisation (in principle as long ago as 10,000 years). Clearly there is also a strong possibility that current cave populations might contain some individuals born in the cave and some that arrived by migration from the surface.

Different species in any cave may have differing origins. For example, Collembola might exist as permanent populations with little migration, whereas *Gammarus pulex* in streams may be replenished by migration from upstream. It seems likely that terrestrial and pool-living species might exist as quasi-permanent reproducing populations, whereas stream species might receive a regular supply of migrants from upstream. Eutroglophiles have a predominant position within the Dales, making the area a perfect place to study the migration, or not, of animals into and out of subterranean sites.

Research and conservation

There is a clear need and ample scope for additional studies of Dales subterranean biology. Such research should balance what is already known against what needs to be known, in the light of conservation principles and good practice. The analysis provided here confirms what has long been acknowledged, that Dales caves and mines contain many trogloxenes (accidentals), as is common among all other caves and mines in Great Britain and Ireland. Clearly little will be gained by further collection and study of such animals.

The three most important taxa, the Collembola, mites and Diptera, should be targeted for research. Detailed ecological studies within these groups would increase understanding of the population and colonisation dynamics of eutroglophile populations. Two other animals, easy to collect and identify, are the rosy woodlouse, *Androniscus dentiger* (Fig. 13.16) and the flatback millipede *Nanogona polydesmoides* (Fig. 13.28). Study of these species could make ideal beginners' projects. Potentially, populations in larger and deeper caves are less transitory than those in smaller, shallower systems, so it makes sense to examine some large systems in detail. In particular the Three Counties Cave System (including Kingsdale) and the Gaping Gill Cave System should be surveyed comprehensively to determine their total species composition.

All collection must be carried out strictly within the principles of conservation (Price, 1997; Tercafs, 2001; Hildreth-Werker and Werker, 2006). Thus, animals that can be identified *in situ* should not be collected. For example, large spiders in cave thresholds are readily identified using a large plastic tub and a reference book; they should not be killed and removed. Equally, many animals cannot be identified *in situ* and must be collected. This should not be done without the right equipment for collection and for subsequent identification. Identifications within some taxa require expert involvement. In such cases agreement of a suitable expert to examine a specified number of samples should be gained before collecting. With careful research and due attention to conservation there is still much to be learned about the biology of the Dales caves

References

Alarie, A, P J Wood, A M H DeBruyn and J G N Cuppen, 2001. Description of the larvae of *Hydroporus ferrugineus* Stephens and *H. polaris* Fall (Coleoptera: Adephaga: Dytiscidae). *Aquatic Insects, 23*, 123–133.

Bate, C S, 1859. On the genus *Niphargus. Proc. Dublin University Zoological Botanical Assoc., 1*, 237–240.

Brandle, M, R Heuser, A Marten and R Brandl, 2007. Population structure of the freshwater flatworm *Crenobia alpina* (Dana): old lineages and low gene flow. *J. Biogeography, 34*, 1183–1192.

Bratton, J, 2006. Occurrence of the well shrimp *Niphargus aquilex* (Crustacea: Niphargidae) in Anglesey, North Wales. *Cave Karst Science, 33*, 29–30.

Byrne, K and R A Nichols, 1999. *Culex pipiens* in London Underground tunnels: differentiation between surface and subterranean populations. *Heredity, 82*, 7–15.

Carpenter, G H, 1895. Animals found in the Mitchelstown Cave. *The Irish Naturalist, 4*, 25–35.

Carpenter, G H, 1897a. The collombola of Mitchelstown Cave. *The Irish Naturalist, 6*, 225–233.

Carpenter, G H, 1897b. The collembola of Mitchelstown Cave. Supplementary Note. *The Irish Naturalist, 6*, 257–258.

Chapman, P, 1993. *Caves and cave life.* Harper Collins: London.

Cubbon, B D, 1970. Flora records of the Cave Research Group of Great Britain from 1939 to June 1969. *Trans. Cave Res. Gp. G. B., 12*, 57–74.

Cubbon, B D, 1972. Flora records for 1969–70. *Trans Cave Res. Gp. G. B., 14*, 201–203.

Cubbon, B D, 1976. Cave flora. 423–452 in T D Ford and C H D Cullingford (Eds), *The Science of Speleology.* Academic Press: London.

Culver, D C and T Pipan, 2009. *The biology of caves and other subterranean habitats.* Oxford University Press.

Dixon, J M, 1966. Biological survey of Springs Wood Level, Starbotton, Yorks. *Northern Cavern Mine Research Society Individual Survey Series, 1*, 9–14.

Dixon, J M, 1974. Biospeleology in north-west England. 150–181 in A C Waltham (Ed.), *Limestones and Caves of north-west England.* David and Charles: Newton Abbot.

Dixon, J M and D T Richardson, 1965. Starbotton End Mine (Springs Wood Level): a preliminary biological report. *Memoirs Northern Cavern and Mine Research Society, 1965*, 54–57.

Ford, D and P Williams, 2007. *Karst hydrogeology and geomorphology.* Wiley: Chichester.

Gentile, G and V Sbordoni, 1998. Indirect methods to estimate gene flow in cave and surface populations of *Androniscus dentiger. Evolution, 52*, 432–442.

Gerecke, R (Ed.), 2007. Chelicerata: Araneae, Acari I. *Susswasserfauna von Mitteleuropa* 7/2–1. Spektrum Akademischer: München.

Gerecke, R (Ed.), 2010. Chelicerata: Acari II. *Susswasserfauna von Mitteleuropa* 7/2–2. Spektrum Akademischer: München.

Gibert, J, D L Danielopol and J A Stanford, 1994. *Groundwater Ecology.* Academic Press: London.

Gidman, C, 1975. Biological studies in Ingleborough Cavern. *Trans. Brit. Cave Res. Assoc., 2*,116–122.

Gledhill, T and D B Driver, 1964. *Bathynella natans* Vejdovsky (Crustacea: Syncarida) and its occurrence in Yorkshire. *Naturalist, 809*, 104–106.

Gledhill, T, D W Sutcliffe and W D Williams, 1993. British freshwater Crustacea Malacostraca: A key with ecological notes. *Freshwater Biological Association Scientific Publication, 52*.

Glennie, E A, 1947. Cave fauna. *Cave Res. Gp. G. B. Publication*, No.1, Part 1.

Glover, R R, 1974. Cave development in the Gaping Gill System. 343–384 in A C Waltham, (Ed.), *Limestones and Caves of north-west England.* David and Charles: Newton Abbot.

Glover, R R, 1978. The blind white fish of Ingleborough Cave. *Craven Pothole Club J., 5*, 309–311.

Gourbault, N, 1986. Turbellaria Tricladida. 57–71 in L Botosaneanu, (Ed.), *Stygofauna Mundi. A faunistic, distributional and ecological synthesis of the world fauna inhabiting subterranean waters.* E J Brill: Leiden.

Gregory, S, 2009. *Woodlice and waterlice (Isopoda: Oniscidea and Asellota) in Britain and Ireland.* British Myriapod and Isopod Group. Biological Records Centre: Wallingford.

Hänfling, B, I Douterelo-Soler, L R F D Knight, and G S Proudlove, 2008. Molecular studies on the *Niphargus kochianus* group (Crustacea: Amphipoda: Niphargidae) in Great Britain and Ireland. *Cave Karst Science, 35*, 35–40.

Harmer, S F, 1899. On the occurrence of the "well shrimp", *Niphargus,* near Norwich. *Trans. Norfolk Norwich Naturalists Society, 6*, 489–491.

Hazelton, M, 1975. The biology of Mendip caves. 313–351 in D I Smith and D P Drew (eds), *Limestones and Caves of the Mendip Hills.* David and Charles: Newton Abbot.

Hazelton, M, 1977. Life underground – biospeleology. 251–261 in T D Ford (Ed.), *Limestones and Caves of the Peak District.* Geo Abstracts: Norwich.

Hazelton, M and E A Glennie, 1947. Cave fauna. Preliminary list. *Cave Research Group Publication* No.1, Part 2.

Hazelton, M and E A Glennie, 1953. Cave fauna and flora. 247–283 in C H D Cullingford (Ed.), *British Caving: An introduction to speleology.* Routledge and Kegan Paul: London.

Hazelton, M and E A Glennie, 1962. Cave fauna and flora. 347–395 in C H D Cullingford (Ed.), *British Caving: An introduction to speleology.* Second Edition. Routledge and Kegan Paul: London.

Hildreth-Werker, V and J C Werker, 2006, *Cave conservation and restoration.* National Speleological Society: Huntsville.

Hodgson, D, 2004. Scoska Cave revisited. *Craven Pothole Club Record, 76*, 16–18.

Hodgson, D, 2005a. Scoska Cave moths again. *Craven Pothole Club Record, 77*, 23–25.

Hodgson, D, 2005b. Cave studies. 27–28 in A Pickles (Ed.), *The ecology of Cowside Beck, a tributary of the River Skirfare in the Malham area of Yorkshire.* Field Studies Council: Malham.

Hodgson, D G, 2008. Aestivation, dormancy, no sex. *Craven Pothole Club Record, 80*, 18–20.

Hogan, A R, 1859. On the habits and localities of *Niphargus fontanus* (n s), *N. kochianus* (n s) and *Crangonyx subterraneus* (n g & n s) Spence Bate. *Natural History Review and Quarterly Journal of Science, 6*, 166–169.

Records of cave biology published by Mary Hazelton

Biological Supplements of the Cave Research Group of Great Britain.
1955, Part 1 (1938–1939). Issued with Newsletter 52.
1956, Part 2 (1940–1946). Issued with Newsletters 58 to 61.
1958, Part 3 (1947). Issued with Newsletters 72 to 77.
1959, Part 4 (1948–1949). Issued with Newsletters 79 and 80.
1960, Part 5 (1950–1953). Issued with Newsletter 81.

Biological Records of the Cave Research Group of Great Britain.
1960, Part 6 (1954–1956).
1961, Part 7 (1957–1959).
1963, Part 8 (1960–1962).

Hypogean fauna and Biological Records of the Cave Research Group of Great Britain.
1965, Part 9 (1963).
1967, Part 10 (1964–1966). *Trans. Cave Res. Gp. G. B., 9*, 162–241.
1968, Part 11 (1967). *Trans. Cave Res. Gp. G. B., 10*, 143–165.
1970, Part 12 (1968). *Trans. Cave Res. Gp. G. B., 12*, 3–26.
1971, Part 13 (1969). *Trans. Cave Res. Gp. G. B., 13*, 167–197.
1972, Part 14 (1970–1971). *Trans. Cave Res. Gp. G. B., 14*, 205–230.
1974, Part 15 (Ireland 1952–1971). *Trans. Cave Res. Gp. G. B., 15*, 225–253.
1978, Part 16 (1972–1976). *Trans. Brit. Cave Res. Assoc., 5*, 164–198.

Hogan, A R, 1860. Notice of British well shrimps. *British Association Report* 1860:116–117.

Hopkin, S P, 1997. *Biology of the springtails*. Oxford University Press.

Hopkin, S P, 2007. A key to the Collembola (Springtails) of Britain and Ireland. *Field Studies Council Occasional Publication*, **111**.

Hutson, A M and G S Proudlove, 2010. Caves and other underground habitats. 288–295 in P J Chandler (Ed.) *A dipterist's handbook*. The Amateur Entomologists' Society: Orpington.

Jameson, H L, 1896. On the exploration of the caves of Enniskillen and Mitchelstown for the R.I.A. flora and fauna committee. *Irish Naturalist*, **5**, 93–100.

Jefferson, G T, 1976. Cave faunas. 359–422 in T D Ford and C H D Cullingford (eds), *The Science of Speleology*. Academic Press: London.

Jefferson, G T, 1981. Diptera in British caves. *Proc. 8th Int. Cong. Speleology* (Bowling Green KY), 106–107.

Jefferson, G T, 1983. The threshold fauna. A neglected area of British cave biology. *Studies in Speleology*, **4**, 53–58.

Jefferson, G T, 1989. Cave biology in South Wales. In T D Ford (Ed.), *Limestones and caves of Wales*. Cambridge University Press.

Jefferson, G T, P Chapman, J Carter and G S Proudlove, 2004. The invertebrate fauna of the Ogof Ffynnon Ddu cave system, Powys, South Wales, UK. *Cave Karst Science*, **31**, 63–76.

Jones, W K, D C Culver and J S Herman (eds), 2004. *Epikarst*. Karst Waters Institute Special Publication, 9.

Kane, W F, 1904. *Niphargus kochianus*, Bate, in an Irish lake and *N. subterraneus*, Leach, in Kent. *Annals Magazine Natural History*, **14**, 274–283.

Knight, L and P J Wood, 2000. Bivalves (Pisidiidae) in English Caves. *Cave Karst Science*, **27**, 89–90.

Knight, L R F D and M R Penk, 2010. Groundwater Crustacea of Ireland: a survey of the stygobiotic Malacostraca of caves and springs. Biology and Environment. *Proc. Royal Irish Academy*, **110B**, 211–235.

Kornobis, E, S Palsson, B K Kristjansson and J Svavarsson, J, 2010. Molecular evidence of the survival of subterranean amphipods (Arthropoda) during Ice Age underneath glaciers in Iceland. *Molecular Ecology*, **19**, 2516–2530.

Kornobis, E, S Palsson, D A Sidorov, J R Holsinger and B K Kristjansson, 2011. Molecular taxonomy and phylogenetic affinities of two groundwater amphipods, *Crangonyx islandicus* and *Crymostygius thingvallensis*, endemic to Iceland. *Molecular Phylogenetics Evolution*, **58**, 527–539.

Laurence, B R, 1982. A cave dwelling Mycetophilid in central London. *Entomologist's Monthly Magazine*, **117**, 198.

Laurence, B R, 1989. The ecology of a cave-dwelling fly, *Speolepta leptogaster* Winn. (Dipt., Mycetophilidae) in central London. *Entomologist's Monthly Magazine*, **125**, 89–93.

Lawrence, P. N, 1960. The discovery of *Onychiurus schoetti* (Lie-Pettersen, 1896), *sensu* Stach, 1947 (Collembola) in British caves. *The Entomologist*, **93**, 36–39.

Lee, P, 2006. *Atlas of the millipedes (Diplopoda) of Britain and Ireland*. Pensoft: Sofia.

Leruth, R, 1939. La biologie du domain souterrain et la faune cavernicole de la Belgique. *Memoires du Musee Royal d'Histoire Naturelle de Belgique*, **87**.

Little, S, T Haslehurst and P J Wood, 2006. Intraspecific predation and survivorship of *Gammarus pulex* (Crustacea: Amphipoda) within aquatic karstic habitats. *Cave Karst Science*, **33**, 73–76.

Maitland, P S, 1962. *Bathynella natans*, new to Scotland. *The Glasgow Naturalist*, **18**, 175–176.

Matile, L, 1962. Morphologie et biologie d'un diptere cavernicole *Speolepta leptogaster* Winnerz (Mycetophilidae). *Memoires du Museum National d'Histoire Naturelle Series A*, **20**, 219–242.

Moseley, M, 1969. The metalliferous mines of the Arnside – Carnforth districts of Lancashire and Westmorland. *Northern Cavern Mine Research Society Individual Survey Series*, **3**.

Moseley, M, 1970. The fauna of caves and mines in the Morecambe Bay area. *Trans. Cave Res. Gp. G. B.*, **12**, 43–56.

Moseley, M, 2000. *Trichoniscoides saeroeensis* Lohmander (Isopoda: Trichoniscidae) in the British hypogean fauna. *Cave Karst Science*, **27**, 127–128.

Papp, L, 1978. Some cavernicolous Diptera of the Geneva Museum. *Revue Suisse de Zoologie*, **85**, 99–106.

Pentecost, A, 2010. Some 'lamp floras' from tourist caves in northern England. *Cave Karst Science*, **37**, 93–98.

Pentecost, A and Z Zhang, 2001. The distribution of plants in Scoska Cave, north Yorkshire, and their relationship to light intensity. *Int. J. Speleology*, **30A**, 27–37.

Pentecost, A and Z Zhang, 2004. The distribution of plants in Scoska Cave, north Yorkshire, United Kingdom, and their relationship to light intensity. *Cave Karst Science*, **31**, 19–22.

Pearce, T G, 1972. Fauna of Ingleborough show cave. *Lancaster Univ. Spel. Soc. J.*, **2**, 27.

Pearce, T G, 1975. Observations on the fauna and flora of Ingleborough Cavern, Yorkshire. *Trans. Brit. Cave Res. Assoc.*, **2**, 107–115.

Piearce, T G and M Cox, 1977a. Distribution and response to light of unpigmented and pigmented *Gammarus pulex* L. (Crustacea, Amphipoda). *Proc. 7th Int. Spel. Cong.* (Sheffield), 351–353.

Piearce, T G and M Cox, 1977b. The distribution of unpigmented and pigmented *Gammarus pulex* L. in two streams in northern England. *Naturalist*, **102**, 21–23.

Piearce, T G and E J Wells, 1977. The activity of Lumbricidae in a northern English cave. *Proc. 7th Int. Spel. Cong.* (Sheffield), 353–355.

Pipan, T, 2005. *Epikarst - a Promising Habitat*. ZRC: Ljubljana.

Price, G (Ed.), 1997. *Cave Conservation Handbook*. National Caving Association: London.

Proudlove, G S, 1979. Fishes in British caves. An interim report. *Craven Pothole Club J.*, **6**, 10–12.

Proudlove, G S, 1982. Cave life. Part 2: Cave fish. *Caves and Caving*, 15, 6–7.

Proudlove, G S, 2006a. *Subterranean fishes of the world. An account of the subterranean (hypogean) fishes described up to 2003 with a bibliography 1541 – 2004*. International Society for Subterranean Biology: Moulis.

Proudlove, G S (Ed.), 2006b. Essential sources in cave science. A guide to the literature of cave science. *Brit. Cave Res. Assoc. Cave Studies*, 16.

Proudlove, G S and 5 others, 2003. A review of the status and distribution of the subterranean aquatic Crustacea of Britain and Ireland. *Cave Karst Science*, **30**, 53–74.

Reynoldson, T B and J O Young, 2000. A key to the freshwater Triclads of Britain and Ireland with notes on their ecology. *Freshwater Biological Association Scientific Publication*, **58**.

Rogers, C, 1999. *Meta menardi* in underground systems in the south west of England. *Studies in Speleology*, **11**, 13–41.

Salavert, V, C Zamora-Munoz, M Ruiz-Rodriguez, A Fernandez-Cortes and J J Soler, 2008. Climatic conditions, diapause and migration in a troglophile caddis fly. *Freshwater Biology*, **53**, 1606–1617.

Sano, A, 2006. Impact of predation by a cave-dwelling bat, *Rhinolophus ferrumequinum*, on the diapausing population of a troglophilic moth, *Goniocraspidum preyeri*. *Ecological Research*, **21**, 321–324.

Schofield, P C S, 1964. Notes on recent fauna studies in Yorkshire. *Proc. Brit. Spel. Assoc.*, **2**, 63–69.

Serban, E and T Gledhill, T, 1965. Concerning the presence of *Bathynella natans stammeri* Jakobi (Crustacea: Syncarida) in England and Rumania. *Annals Magazine Natural History*, **8**, 513–522.

Sheppard, E M, 1968. *Trichoniscoides saeroeensis* Lohmander, an isopod new to the British fauna. *Trans. Cave Res. Gp. G. B.*, **10**, 135–137.

Sheppard, E M, 1971. *Trichoniscoides saeroeensis* Lohmander, an isopod crustacean new to the British fauna. *Int. J. Speleology*, **3**, 425–432.

Sket, B, 2008. Can we agree on an ecological classification of subterranean animals? *J. Natural History*, **42**, 1549–1563.

Smithers, P, 1996. Observations on the prey of the cave spider *Meta menardi* (Latreille, 1804) in south Devon. *Newsletter British Arachnological Society*, **77**, 12–14.

Smithers, P, 2004. Myriapods as prey of the cave spider *Meta menardi*. *Bulletin British Myriapod Group*, **20**, 17–19.

Smithers, P, 2005a. The early life history and dispersal on the cave spider *Meta menardi*. *Bulletin British Arachnological Society*, **13**, 6.

Smithers, P, 2005b. The diet of the cave spider *Meta menardi* (Latreille 1804) (Araneae, Tetragnathidae). *J. Arachnology*, **33**, 243–246.

Smithers, P and M Fox Smith, 1998. Observations on the behaviour of second instars of the cave sipder *Meta menardi* (Latreille, 1804). *Newsletter British Arachnological Society*, **81**, 4–5.

Stock, J H, 1969. *Rivulogammarus*, an amphipod name that must be rejected. *Crustaceana*, **17**, 106–107.

Stubbington, R, M P Dunscombe and T Gledhill, 2008. Occurrence of *Antrobathynella stammeri* (Jakobi, 1954) (Crustacea: Syncarida: Bathynellidae) in the hyporheic zones of two English karst rivers. *Cave Karst Science*, **35**, 59–62.

Sulaiman, S and M W Service, 1983. Studies on hibernating populations of the mosquito *Culex pipiens* L. in southern and northern England. *J. Natural History*, **17**, 849–857.

Tercafs, R, 2001. *The protection of the subterranean environment. Conservation principles and management tools*. P.S.: Luxembourg.

Thines, G and R Tercafs, 1972. *Atlas de la vie souterraine. Les animaux cavernicoles*. N. Boubee: Paris.

Thomas, R and S H Bottrell, 1992. The role of Oligochaeta in the ecology of Speedwell Cavern, Derbyshire. *Cave Science*, **19**, 21–23.

Westwood, J O, 1853. [Discovery of *Niphargus* in Great Britain]. *Proc. Linnean Society*, 1853, 218–219.

Worral, T P and P J Wood, 2007. Cannibalism within freshwater shrimp populations (*Gammarus duebeni*, Crustacea:Amphipoda) from spring, riverine and subterranean habitats, Marble Arch Cave System (Northern Ireland). *Cave Karst Science*, **34**, 33–36.

Zacharda, M, 1980. Soil mites of the family Rhagidiidae (Actinedida: Eupodoidea). Morphology, systematics, ecology. *Acta Universitatis Carolinae – Biologica*, **1978**, 489–785.

CHAPTER 14

Bats in the caves

John Altringham and Anita Glover

Bats evolved as night-flying insect-eaters, the combination of agile flight and an ability to orientate and navigate in the dark using high-frequency sonar giving them a unique ecological niche. These abilities made them pre-adapted to caves; they did not evolve these skills for use in caves, but having acquired them, caves became accessible, and bats moved in. Bats evolved in the tropics and tropical bats make use of caves year round, because they are warm and provide safety from the majority of predators.

As mammals, bats are endotherms and homeotherms: they generate heat internally to maintain a constant, high body temperature. This allows them to remain active all the time, so long as there is abundant food. To cope in regions where the weather was harsher and food supply unpredictable, some bats evolved the ability to lower their body temperature, thereby lowering their metabolic rate and saving valuable energy stores. This ability allowed insectivorous bats to spread from the tropics into temperate regions, where food was commonly non-existent during the long winter. What started as an ability to lower temperature a few degrees for a few hours, evolved into hibernation; some bats spend months at a time with a core temperature only a little above freezing (Fig. 14.1). Hibernation costs are lowest if bats can sleep undisturbed where the microclimate is stable, dark and damp. Many caves contain ideal overwintering sites, and bats are adept at finding passages that provide the stability and safety that they need to survive (Altringham, 2011).

A year in the life of a Dales bat

To know when to expect to see bats in the caves of the Yorkshire Dales and why they might be there, it is important to understand a little about their behaviour throughout the year (Altringham, 2003). On emerging from hibernation pregnant females gather into colonies in May and June to give birth to their single pups in a suitable roost site. Colony size typically ranges from twenty to two hundred individuals but may exceed a thousand. Single pups are born naked and blind in June and initially have a poor ability to maintain and regulate their body temperatures, so roosts at this time ideally need to be warm and dry. Most species therefore roost in tree holes, buildings and other built structures. The females occupy these roosts from May until August or September. The pups are independent in as little as six weeks. Caves are rarely used as nursery roosts in Britain and have never been recorded as such in the Dales. However, the same species may use caves in southern Europe where the temperatures are higher at low altitudes.

Bats in the caves, by John Altringham and Anita Glover,
John Altringham, University of Leeds; j.d.altringham@leeds.ac.uk
Anita Glover, University of Leeds; a.m.glover@leeds.ac.uk
Chapter 14, pages 219–224 in **Caves and Karst of the Yorkshire Dales**,
edited by Tony Waltham and David Lowe.
Published 2013 by the British Cave Research Association,
978-0-900265-46-4 and at www.bcra.org.uk

Whereas the females bear the burden of rearing the next generation, the males have only themselves to forage for, and generally they roost apart; they are solitary or form small colonies. Bats have the potential to lower their body temperature and go torpid whenever food is scarce or the weather prevents them feeding. Females are rarely able to do this during the summer, because it would slow the growth of the foetus or reduce the amount of milk they can produce for their young. Males (or non-breeding females) on the other hand do not have this constraint and this is commonly reflected in their choice of roost sites. A bat that wants to save energy using torpor can only let its temperature drop to that of its surroundings – they are not fridges. Cool roosts therefore offer greater energy saving potential when circumstances demand it, so males can be found in caves during the summer, as well as in a similar range of roosts as those used by females. When found in caves, they are typically deep in torpor and to all appearances dead – cold and inert. However, their internal clock, or disturbance, can initiate awakening and in twenty minutes they can be warm and active. Often therefore, males are more mobile than females, moving from roost to roost as the situation demands.

Nursery colonies begin to break up in August, and late summer or autumn are when most bats mate. Like many other mammals, bats have the ability to delay birth after mating. In the case of bats, this is done by delaying ovulation and fertilisation until the spring. Mating can take place in the summer roost, or in special mating roosts selected by the males. Only one of the many different mating systems that have evolved need be looked at here. Known as swarming, this mating system leads directly into hibernation, and caves are vital to these two life-history stages of bats in the Dales.

Swarming and hibernation

Summer colonies are generally small and isolated, with males and females typically living apart. A major change in behaviour in the autumn brings bats together to mate. At this time of year they also have to fatten themselves up and prepare for hibernation.

Figure 14.1 Hibernating Brandt's bats in the abandoned Buckden Gavel lead mine, Wharfedale (AG).

Suitable sites for the many bat species that hibernate underground are quite rare and scattered, so they may have to travel long distances to find them. This provides an elegant solution to the twin problems of dispersal for mating and hibernation; they start visiting hibernation sites early and mate there prior to hibernation (Thomas *et al.*, 1979; Parsons *et al.*, 2003; Rivers *et al.*, 2005, 2006). From August to October many caves are visited by large and transient populations of bats from up to 60 km away and probably much farther (Rivers *et al.*, 2006). The best examples in the Dales – those attracting the largest number of bats – include parts of the Ease Gill Cave System (e.g. Cow Pot, Mistral Hole, Link Pot, County Pot, Wretched Rabbit and Pool Sink), various Leck Fell caves (e.g. Death's Head Hole, Gavel Pot, Lost John's Cave and Notts Pot), Rift Pot (Gragareth), Rowten Pot and Bull Pot (Kingsdale), Gaping Gill (e.g. Bar Pot and Flood Entrance Pot), Cherry Tree Hole and Dow Cave. The primary function of this behaviour appears to be mating and there is genetic evidence to show that this ensures adequate gene flow among the bats from the numerous summer colonies that visit the caves (Kerth *et al.*, 2003, Rivers *et al.*, 2005). Swarming probably also serves to introduce the year's offspring to the caves for the first time. Bats visit the same caves year after year (a bat can live for ten to thirty years) and most are faithful to a single site (Glover and Altringham, 2008; Parsons *et al.*, 2003; Rivers *et al.*, 2006).

During the peak of the swarming season, from mid-August to mid-October several hundreds of bats may visit a cave each night, but virtually all leave again before the night is over. The bats 'swarm' outside and inside the cave, all of them involved in long and elaborate chases, before landing on the cave walls to mate (Thomas *et al.*, 1979). Only towards the end of October and into November, as the intensity of swarming activity declines, do bats begin to stay in the caves at the end of each night (Rivers *et al.*, 2006). It is difficult to be certain, because of the complex behaviour of the bats, but it is probable that at many caves a large proportion of those swarming at a site will later hibernate there.

British bat species

The status of bat species in the Dales; those species that are known to use caves regularly, though not necessarily in the Dales, are shown in bold type:

Lesser horseshoe bat, *Rhinolophus hipposideros*. Absent.

Greater horseshoe bat, *Rhinolophus ferrumequinum*. Absent.

Alcathoe bat, *Myotis alcathoe*. Discovered in Britain only in 2009, distribution unknown. Rare.

Bechstein's bat, *Myotis bechsteinii*. Absent.

Brandt's bat, *Myotis brandtii*. Widespread, rare.

Daubenton's bat, *Myotis daubentonii*. Widespread, common.

Natterer's bat, *Myotis nattereri*. Widespread, common.

Whiskered bat, *Myotis mystacinus*. Widespread, rare.

Common pipistrelle, *Pipistrellus pipistrellus*. Widespread, common.

Soprano pipistrelle, *Pipistrellus pygmaeus*. Widespread, common.

Nathusius' pipistrelle, *Pipistrellus nathusius*. Unconfirmed, but might be present.

Serotine, *Eptesicus serotinus*. Absent.

Noctule, *Nyctalus noctula*. Widespread, rare

Leisler's bat, *Nyctalus leisleri*. Unconfirmed, but may be present.

Brown long-eared bat, *Plecotus auritus*. Widespread, common.

Grey long-eared bat, *Plecotus austriacus*. Absent.

Barbastelle, *Barbastella barbastellus*. Absent

Hibernation is not a continuous process. Bats enter torpor more frequently and for longer periods as the nights get longer and cooler, but may still feed during warmer nights when food is available. By entering torpor soon after feeding, they quickly lay down fat for the winter. An 8g bat can put on 2–3g in less than two weeks. By December, in a typical year, the bats are in almost continuous deep torpor, with a body temperature only just above cave temperature. This continues until April or May.

A 3g fat build-up in late autumn can nourish the bat right through the winter, energy consumption being less than 1% that of a resting but warm bat. The physiology of torpor is extreme: heart rate drops from 1000 beats per minute in flight to 400 at rest and just 10–60 in torpor. A torpid bat might breathe only once in 90 minutes. However, even in mid-winter bats wake briefly at one- to four-week intervals. Though this may occasionally be to eat or drink, in many species the reasons are not obvious, but might relate to physiological or immunological maintenance. Waking is obviously important, because the energy cost is very high. The energy used during one awakening could keep a torpid bat alive for weeks. Bats can hibernate singly or, less commonly seen in Britain, in closely packed groups. This clustering is part of their strategy to minimize heat and water loss.

Bat species in the Dales caves

There are seventeen species of bat in Britain and eight of these are widespread in the Dales (see Box). Details of which species are found in which caves are not given, because all or most species present in the Dales can be found in the majority of suitable caves given adequate survey effort. Almost a hundred caves have been given at least a minimal survey.

The three *Pipistrellus* and two *Nyctalus* species are found elsewhere in Yorkshire, but there are no confirmed records from the Dales of Nathusius' pipistrelle or Leisler's bat. All typically hibernate in cool buildings or in tree holes and none make significant use of caves in any part of their range.

The lesser horseshoe bat and the barbastelle were present in the Helmsley area as recently as the 1940s and 1950s respectively, but have not been recorded reliably in the Dales. The former is said to have been seen in caves and mines in the Greenhow area in the nineteenth century, but there is no convincing evidence to support these claims. Only *Myotis* and *Plecotus* species are regular cave-users in the Dales and they have been observed at almost all sites investigated, but commonly only in very small numbers.

Daubenton's bat

This species is widespread and relatively common. It is a small bat (7–12g) that feeds almost exclusively over smooth-flowing water, catching insects in the air or off the water surface. It makes frequent use of its tail membrane and big feet, particularly when gaffing prey from the water. It also roosts close to water, in trees (in the Dales most commonly in holes and cracks in ash trees), the stone work of bridges (a significant proportion of Dales bridges) and occasionally in buildings. A few males and non-breeding females use caves throughout the year and both sexes swarm and hibernate in caves in large numbers. As the second most common species in Dales caves, it has been found in most of the caves surveyed. A detailed study of these bats in Wharfedale revealed a complex pattern of behaviour (Senior *et al.*, 2005) with much activity centred around Dow Cave and Buckden Gavel lead mine.

Natterer's bat

With large broad wings for slow, manoeuvrable flight, this 7–12g bat is adapted to feeding in woodland, where it frequently takes prey from the ground or from vegetation, usually plucking them up without landing. As well as eating flying and non-flying insects, it will take other invertebrates such as spiders. Nursery colonies are most commonly found in buildings (especially churches) but also in holes in trees. Some males share the nursery roost with the females, but most roost separately in tree holes. This is the most abundant species caught at swarming sites, despite it being rarer than both Daubenton's bat and the brown long-eared bat. Most appear to hibernate underground and it is the species most likely to be found in any Dales cave.

Brandt's bat and whiskered bat

In the Dales these two rarer species are close to the northern limits of their British range. Little is known about their detailed ecology, though their broad wings and varied diet suggest that, as with Natterer's bat, they feed in woodland and along hedgerows, commonly by gleaning prey from vegetation. They are smaller than Daubenton's and Natterer's bats at 6–8g (Figs 14.2 and 14.3). In common with other species in this genus they roost in buildings and trees, swarm at caves and hibernate underground. Swarming Brandt's and whiskered bats have been found at most well-studied caves and significant numbers have been found hibernating in Link Pot.

Alcathoe bat

This species was only recognised and described formally in 2001, on the basis of bats caught in Greece. It has since been found in isolated locations around Europe, but known distribution remains patchy. It was therefore something of a surprise when it was found at swarming sites in Sussex and the North York Moors in 2009 (Jan *et al.*, 2010). It almost certainly represents an overlooked resident species and is similar to Brandt's and whiskered bats, probably with a comparable ecology. It has not yet been identified definitively 'in the hand' in the Dales, but its distinctive echo-location call has been recorded at Link Pot.

Brown long-eared bat

Unmistakeable with its enormous ears (Fig. 14.4), this bat species commonly feeds in dense vegetation and is capable of hovering, landing and taking off in confined spaces. The brown long-eared bat specialises in preying on flying and stationary moths. Many moths have simple ears that can hear the ultrasonic echo-location calls of bats. This does not prevent bats from feeding on them, but may reduce the ease with which they can do so, because it enables the moths to take evasive action. Brown long-eared bats switch off their echo-location as they approach their prey, using their unusually large and sensitive eyes and ears to make the final approach unheard. This species also roosts in buildings and tree holes. Favoured roosting places in buildings are in loft apexes. Long-eared bats swarm at cave entrances and commonly hibernate underground. The species has been found at most of the Dales caves surveyed. It is more commonly found hibernating nearer to cave entrances than are other species, seeming to prefer the less stable microclimate.

Figure 14.2. Hibernating Brandt's bats in Buckden Gavel lead mine, Wharefdale; as one is small and grey, indicating that it is a juvenile, these bats may be mother and offspring (JA).

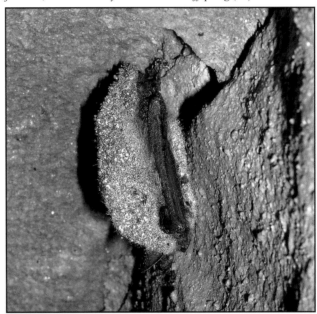

Figure 14.3 Hibernating whiskered bat in Link Pot, Ease Gill (JA).

Figure 14.4. Brown long-eared bat, clearly showing its characteristic ears and the smaller tragi, as described in the text (JA).

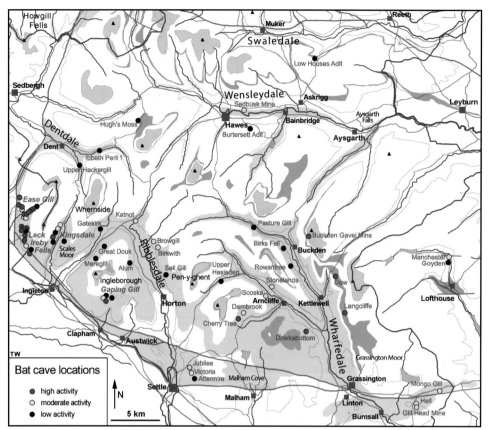

Figure 14.5. Yorkshire Dales caves (and mines) surveyed for bats to date; coloured symbols denote levels of bat activity, as shown in the key.

Individual cave entrances within the named site clusters in the west of the area are as follows:

Ease Gill:
Aygill, Bull Pot of the Witches, County Pot, Cow Pot, Lancaster Hole, Link Pot, Mistral Hole, Nippikin Pot, Pippikin Pot, Pool Sink, Swindon Hole, Top Sink, Wretched Rabbit.

Leck and Ireby Fells:
Big Meanie, Death's Head Hole, Gavel Pot, Ireby Fell Cavern, Lost John's Cave, Marble Steps Pot, Notts Pot, Rift Pot, Rumbling Hole, Short Drop Cave.

Kingsdale:
Bull Pot, Jingling Pot, King Pot, Rowten Pot, Valley Entrance, Yordas Cave.

Gaping Gill:
Bar Pot, Car Pot, Flood Entrance Pot, Gaping Gill.

Dales bats and Dales caves

Repeat surveys at almost sixty caves (Fig. 14.5), were carried out by Glover and Altringham (2008) using echo-location call loggers to estimate the level of autumn swarming activity (Fig. 14.6). To determine the species present bats were captured in the autumn at more than twenty caves, many of them receiving repeated visits. Additional caves have been logged since then, in particular those on Leck Fell and in Kingsdale (Fig. 14.5). From these broad surveys several conclusions can be drawn.

In small numbers at least, bats visit almost all of the caves surveyed, but there is considerable variation in activity levels, with only a minority of caves attracting large numbers (Fig. 14.5). Most caves are visited by more than one species and after several surveys it is not uncommon to have recorded four or five (the brown long-eared bat and three or four of the *Myotis* species). *Myotis* and *Plecotus* species may well visit most of the caves in the Dales. As the autumn progresses, the catch becomes increasingly dominated by Natterer's bat, which can make up more than 80% of all bats caught. Brandt's and Daubenton's bats appear to swarm significantly earlier than other species.

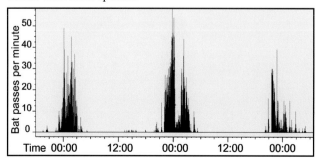

Figure 14.6. *Autumn swarming activity at Rumbling Hole, Leck Fell; echo-location call loggers reveal activity peaks 4–5 hours after dark.*

Counting the bats that are using a cave is not straightforward. Echo-location call recording overestimates numbers, because bats fly past the logger several times before entering the cave. Catching bats underestimates numbers, because only 5–20% are caught. Trapping efficiency (Fig. 14.10) varies with entrance size and shape and the aim is to minimize the disruption to most of the bats. By combining these two methods with an infra-red video camera at Slip Gill in the North York Moors, it has been calculated that three to four hundred bats visited the cave on an average night (Rivers *et al.*, 2006). Reliable data are not available for the Dales, but by extrapolation from similar but less extensive catch and logger data, similar numbers are visiting the more important caves in the Dales such as Link Pot and Bar Pot.

By ringing bats over several years the total number of individuals visiting a site each year can be calculated from the recapture data. Again, the best measurements come from Slip Gill and other windypits in the North York Moors, and these allow similar estimates to be made for the Dales from less extensive data. Slip Gill, Antofts, Helmsley and Ashberry windypits, in combination, are visited by four to six thousand bats each autumn. The numbers for individual caves in the Dales are on average much lower, but the larger systems, in particular Ease Gill, probably attract more. The windypits, despite their small size relative to Dales caves, are the biggest caves in a very cave-poor area and may be something of a magnet for bats. A much larger population of bats is spread across a very much larger number of caves in the Dales.

As swarming activity declines in October, there is a net influx of bats into the caves each night. The numbers are relatively small, but night after night, these small numbers accumulate to become significant. Survey of caves from November onwards reveals hibernating bats too: but far fewer than are probably there. Scatter several thousand of these inconspicuous, thumb-sized mammals among the cracks and crevices of the larger caves and even a thorough search is unlikely to reveal more than a few. The two species of horseshoe bat found in the caves of Wales and the southwest of England hang free from the ceiling, commonly in conspicuous groups. Dales species generally prefer to hide in bat-sized cracks and dissolution cavities, usually alone and rarely in groups of more than a few bats. They are not generally noticed except when in flight.

Among the caves (and mines) surveyed to date the most important swarming sites include two of the area's largest cave systems, Ease Gill and Gaping Gill. Not all entrances have been surveyed, but most of those that have (Fig. 14.5) attract significant numbers of bats. However, some smaller caves have also proven to be important, such as Rift Pot (Gragareth), Cherry Tree Hole and Dow Cave. Bats are attracted to caves with particular characteristics. Entrance size and orientation, altitude, habitat and remoteness appear to be unimportant. The bats are agile enough to fly into any cave a human explorer can enter (and probably into even smaller entrances that they cannot). Once inside, bats have a preference for the drier parts of systems with well-developed chambers (Glover and Altringham, 2008), although they are capable of flying deep into narrow and complex caves, such as Langcliffe Pot in Wharfedale. Bats and bat droppings have been found in the Easter Grotto area of the Ease Gill Cave System for example, and Sand Cavern in Gaping Gill. Droppings have been found in abundance all along the passages linking Short Drop Cave and Gavel Pot on Leck Fell.

There is considerable variation in activity between caves, and much of this remains unexplained. Dry systems are probably more stable thermally, because the water entering a cave is generally warmer or colder than the cave itself, so a significant change in flow will alter cave temperature. Water flow also increases airflow through the cave, again changing temperature. Rushing water is noisy too, with a significant high frequency component that could disturb bats. Water also brings the threat of flooding. Large chambers may be favoured for swarming behaviour and offer bats undisturbed hibernation sites with a wide choice of physical and microclimatic options. Although bats are found deep inside caves and their droppings are commonly very widespread, they are most commonly seen within the first few hundred metres from the entrance. This suggests that the bats deeper in the cave may be better hidden and awaken less frequently. They might be found everywhere, from the floor to the roof, but most commonly above head height. Brown long-eared bats are most commonly found on the open cave wall and will even hang free from the ceiling (Fig. 14.8). With their huge ears tucked under their wings, only the tragi are visible. Looking like small ears, the tragi can lead the inexperienced into misidentifying the bat as one of the *Myotis* species. The tragus is a projection of soft cartilage originating at the base of the ear. It helps the bat determine the precise direction of origin of echoes returning from echo-location calls. The *Myotis* species will also hang on open walls but more frequently crawl into narrow crevices or dissolution cavities, where they are more easily overlooked. *Myotis* species are not easy to identify unless seen close up, and even then positive identification is commonly not possible.

The most readily identified is Natterer's bat, since it has longer ears than other *Myotis* species (Fig. 14.9). Daubenton's bat has shorter, more rounded ears and is similar in size to Natterer's bat. Whiskered and Brandt's bats (Figs 14.1 and 14.2) are smaller with pointed ears, but are commonly very difficult to recognise with certainty even when wide awake in the hand. The Alcathoe bat is marginally smaller still and very similar in appearance to Brandt's and whiskered bats. Colour is an unreliable guide, because this can vary considerably in all of these species. Commonly the high humidity in caves deposits a glistening coat of water droplets on the bat, which obscures their coat, but can be astonishingly beautiful (Fig. 14.7).

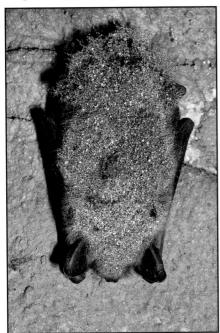

Figure 14.7. A whiskered bat covered in minute droplets of condensation water, in Link Pot, Ease Gill (JA).

Figure 14.8. Hibernating brown long-eared bat, with its ears tucked under its wings, in Short Drop Cave, Leck Fell (JA).

Figure 14.9. A ringed Natterer's bat, observed in Dowkabottom Cave, on the western side of lower Littondale (JA).

Figure 14.10. A harp trap flanked by mist nets at Link Pot in Ease Gill, set up to intercept visiting bats. Mist nets are very similar to those used to catch birds. The harp trap is designed specifically for bats and includes a double vertical bank of tensioned, fine fishing line to intercept bats, which then fall into the bag below. Echolocating bats can detect both mist nets and harp traps, so capture success is typically low (JA).

Conservation

In Britain all bat species and their roosts are protected by law, under both national and international legislation. At no time should bats be handled, or disturbed in any other way. This is particularly important between October and April, when they will probably be torpid and any accidental or intentional awakening by human intervention could lead to the loss of valuable fat reserves.

However, it would be a pity on finding a bat or bats not to take a careful look, because even for regular cavers it might be a rare sight. A short examination, carried out with appropriate precautions, should not disturb the bat. Do not touch. Illuminate the bat with the minimum light needed to see it. Do not breathe on the bat or stand unnecessarily close, and do not speak loudly. Touch, light, heat and noise can all awaken the bat, though this may not occur until some time later. Do not take photographs, with or without flash illumination, because this too is disturbing to bats and actually requires a licence.

Bats may be particularly obvious when they swarm during late summer and autumn evenings, but evening caving trips by small parties are unlikely to disturb them significantly. On the other hand, a major cave rescue practice, for example, could cause disturbance at major swarming sites if carried out after dark during the period between mid-August and the end of September.

In some parts of Britain gates have been erected over cave entrances, to restrict access to 'legitimate' users, prevent accidents to people or livestock, or to protect bats. Few Dales caves have permanent, lockable barriers and none has a gate to protect bats. This is a good thing: these barriers are rarely attractive and not usually needed. Where a barrier is needed, if at all possible it should not stop bats entering and leaving. The use of bat-friendly gates (Mitchell-Jones and McCleish, 2005; Pugh and Altringham, 2005), should be considered, even on recently excavated entrances. Bats are inquisitive and are constantly searching for new sites. Some of the most important known bat sites in the Dales, such as Link Pot and Cherry Tree Hole, were opened by cavers in the relatively recent past and were probably adopted by bats within a few years of opening.

The caves of the Yorkshire Dales are used by at least six of Britain's seventeen bat species, including one only recently discovered. A significant proportion of the caves are used, many by large numbers of bats, which visit from well beyond the Dales: they therefore support a substantial proportion of the British populations of some species. The caves are an integral part of the bats' life cycle: they are where the bats mate in the autumn and hibernate through the winter, whereas a smaller number of bats can be found roosting in them throughout the year. To sit outside Link Pot, or one of the other caves described, at night during late summer, as hundreds of bats chase each other in and out, is to witness some of Britain's wildlife at its best.

References

Altringham, J D, 1996. *Bats: Biology and Behaviour.* Oxford University Press. 262 pp.

Altringham, J D, 2003. *British Bats.* New Naturalist Series. Harper Collins: London. 218 pp.

Altringham, J D, 2011. *Bats: from Evolution to Conservation.* Oxford University Press. 352 pp.

Glover, A M and J D Altringham, 2008. Cave selection and use by swarming bat species. *Biological Conservation*, **141**, 1493–1504.

Jan, C and 9 others, 2010. *Myotis alcathoe* in the UK. *Acta Chiropterologica*, **12**, 471–483.

Kerth, G, A Kiefer, C Trappmann and M Weishaar, 2003. High gene diversity at swarming sites suggest hot spots for gene flow in the endangered Bechstein's bat. *Conservation Genetics*, **4**, 491–499.

Mitchell-Jones, A J and A P McCleish, 2004. *The Bat Workers' Manual.* Joint Nature Conservation Committee: Peterborough.

Parsons, K N, G Jones, I Davidson-Watts and F Greenaway, 2003. Swarming of bats at underground sites in Britain – implications for conservation. *Biological Conservation*, **111**, 63–70.

Pugh, M and J D Altringham, 2005. The effect of gates on cave entry by swarming bats. *Acta Chiropterologica*, **7**, 293–299.

Rivers, N M, R K Butlin and J D Altringham, 2005. Genetic population structure of Natterer's bats explained by mating at swarming sites and philopatry. *Molecular Ecology*, **14**, 4299–4312.

Rivers, N M, R K Butlin and J D Altringham, 2006. Autumn swarming behaviour of Natterer's bats in the UK – population size, catchment area and dispersal. *Biological Conservation*, **127**, 215–226.

Senior, P, R K Butlin and J D Altringham, 2005. Sex and segregation in temperate bats. *Proc. Roy. Soc.,* **B272**, 2467–2473.

Thomas, D W, M B Fenton and R M R Barclay, 1979. Social behaviour of the little brown bat, *Myotis lucifugus* I. Mating behaviour. *Behavioural Ecology and Sociobiology*, **6**, 129–136.

CHAPTER 15

Cave palaeontology

Terry O'Connor and Tom Lord

Cave palaeontology is the study of the fossil remains of plants and animals preserved in sediments contained within caves and cave entrances. Many different types of fossils have been found in cave sediments in the Yorkshire Dales. Best known are the bones of spectacular large mammals such as spotted hyaenas, brown bears and even hippopotamus, but there are also examples of small mammals, birds, reptiles, amphibians and fish, the shells of terrestrial snails, animal dung preserved intact and partially-digested bones. Some animals, especially large carnivores, may leave trace fossils such as tooth marks on the bones of their prey. Plant fossils by contrast are mostly represented by microscopic pollen and spores. Such plant remains can include specimens derived from much older geological strata, distinguished by identification to species or preservation condition. Rarely, impressions of plant soft tissue are preserved in travertine at cave entrances, and root impressions can be found etched into the surfaces of bones.

The remains and traces of vertebrate animals are the most abundant and best-understood part of the fossil record from caves in the Dales. But invertebrate animals, plants and fungi were also important components of the past environments and ecology. The record of bones from the caves of the Craven Dales has been known since the early 1800s, but it was neither appreciated nor understood prior to modern studies.

Cave palaeontology is concerned with fossils that accumulate as a result of natural processes rather than human activity, but considerable investigation may be required to make this distinction. Bones naturally accumulate in caves used by animals for shelter, feeding, sleeping, hibernating, giving birth and bringing up young. Bones also accumulate naturally where animals fall into a cave system or enter it and become trapped, and as part of the sediments brought into a cave by geomorphic processes such as down-slope colluviation and fluvial activity. Taphonomy is the study of how living organisms become preserved as fossils (Lyman, 1994), and its application to plant and animal remains in caves is essential to interpret these deposits correctly.

Despite the great age of many cave systems in the Dales, bone deposits older than about 6000 years are rare, so there is nothing like a complete sequence. The fossil record from caves in the Yorkshire Dales suggests that cave entrances were blocked and the interiors were inaccessible to surface-living animals for long periods of time. However, geomorphological processes have reworked cave sediments containing bone deposits so it has to be considered how these processes have shaped the faunal record.

People impacted upon bone deposits in caves millennia before they became the subject of scientific enquiry and excavation. In exploring caves or in blocking up cave entrances people can make the interiors accessible or inaccessible. Around 6000 years ago, the new beliefs and social systems connected with the beginning of farming included new ways of treating the dead, and this triggered an unprecedented phase of cave exploration and excavation in the Yorkshire Dales, one that lasted for possibly a few centuries and yielded the first evidence for people intentionally placing animal and human remains in caves (see Chapter 16). Further cave exploration and excavation connected with cult activity is detectable soon after the Roman conquest of the north of England around AD100 (Dearne and Lord, 1998). People continued to visit caves for cult purposes until well into historic times, deliberately reworking earlier bone deposits in caves, perhaps searching for older bones to use as talismans or as medicines. Largely as a result of six millennia of cult activity, people came to play a much more significant part in the formation of bone deposits in caves and on the formation of cave sediments generally.

People also affect the formation of bone deposits in more indirect ways. Once even small numbers of people are present in a limestone landscape, their activities can affect the behaviour of large carnivores such as brown bears and wolves that routinely use caves, and so change the pattern of bone deposition by these animals. In exploring and excavating caves, people might make them accessible to large carnivores such as wolf and lynx, which then displace smaller carnivores such as polecats and wildcats, thus changing patterns of bone deposition. Finally as people exterminate large carnivores altogether to protect their domestic livestock and themselves, predation by bears, wolves and lynx on

Figure 15.1*. Victoria Cave, a site of major importance for its bone material that dates from the Last Interglacial; its entrance was hugely enlarged by the large-scale excavations of the 1870s (TO).*

Cave palaeontology, by Terry O'Connor and Tom Lord
Terry O'Connor: University of York; terry.oconnor@york.ac.uk
Tom Lord: Settle; tomlord@daelnet.co.uk
Chapter 15, pages 225–238 in **Caves and Karst of the Yorkshire Dales**, edited by Tony Waltham and David Lowe.
Published 2013 by the British Cave Research Association,
978-0-900265-46-4 and at bcra.org.uk

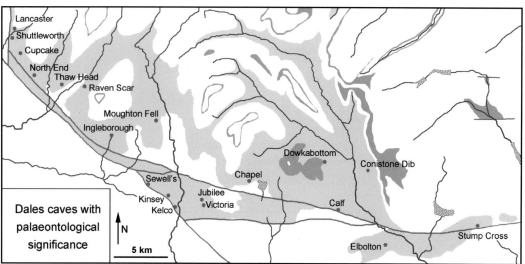

Figure 15.2. Locations of caves within the Yorkshire Dales that have yielded palaeontological material from excavation of their sediments. Raygill Fissure is 15 km south of the mapped area, and Rawthey Cave is 14 km to the north.

smaller bodied carnivores, especially foxes and badgers, is eliminated. These animals are now able to use caves without the threat of attack from larger carnivores and subject only to human persecution. People's elimination of large carnivores indirectly brings about further changes in patterns of bone deposition. These direct and indirect effects of human activity blur the distinction between cave archaeology and palaeontology.

Early excavations

It is difficult to put a start-date on cave palaeontology in the Dales. Ice Age hunters exploring the interior of Victoria Cave around 14,400 years ago would have found on the floor the bones of brown bears that had recently died in hibernation. In Roman times people may have searched caves for old bones. Two brown bear claws recorded from Roman age deposits outside Sewell's Cave had been brought there from another cave. Radiocarbon dating shows that these animals had died more than 13,000 years ago. Prehistoric, Roman and Mediaeval artefacts show that caves have been visited over the millennia by people who probably wondered about the bones that they encountered.

Current research is just the latest phase of human investigation of caves and their animal bones. Some of the first recorded investigations of what might be called the scientific era were undertaken by James Farrer of Ingleborough Hall; better and infamously known north of the border for his excavation of the great Neolithic chambered tomb of Maeshowe on Orkney (Farrer, 1862). He undertook measurements in Ingleborough Cave to determine the rate at which stalagmite formed (McFarlane *et al.*, 2005), and conducted excavations at Dowkabottom Cave in the 1850s and 1860s, believing the cave to pre-date the down-cutting of Littondale.

Nearby, mid-Victorian scientific cave excavations were undertaken in the intellectual context of three Big Questions: the age of the Earth, the place that some transmutation of species (i.e. evolution) might have played in the history of life on Earth, and evidence for a glacial period in the recent geological history of the higher latitudes (Dawkins, 1880; O'Connor, A. 2007). The first of these questions was largely in the hands of physicists, while the other two might be addressed through the palaeontological record

of the 'bone caves'. Thus in 1869, when the Settle Cave Exploration Committee published a Prospectus that aspired to "discoveries of great scientific interest", they began with the statement that "It has long been known, that in the District of Craven, there are many Bone Caves…". The Prospectus led to a programme of excavations, from 1870 to 1878, in Victoria Cave (Fig. 15.1), with the objective of establishing a sequence of pre-glacial and glacial mammals, and perhaps of resolving the antiquity of man in relation to this emerging (relative) chronology (Dawkins, 1872, 1874; Tiddeman, 1873, 1876, 1878a, 1879; Busk, 1874).

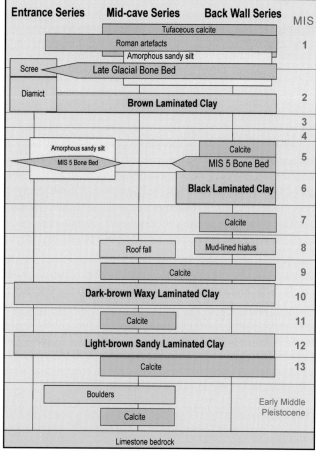

Figure 15.3. A sedimentary matrix for Victoria Cave, with its deposits and flowstones correlated with a timeline of the Marine Isotope Stages (after Lundberg et al., 2010).

Victoria Cave was the high-profile investigation of the later 19th century, but by no means the only one. Smaller-scale exploration of other 'bone caves' in the Dales began the process of collecting assemblages, some of them into private hands and others into museums. Some of those museums then exchanged specimens, resulting in the dispersal of materials with which researchers have to contend today. Archived assemblages may be the whole of the recovered assemblage, or an arbitrary sub-set, or a collection of selected specimens, and investigations have to proceed with appropriate caution. Similarly, chronology can be problematic. Over the last 20 years, considerable progress has been made in the reliable, absolute dating of key specimens and assemblages, and in dating depositional sequences in some caves. However, there remain too many assemblages that are dated by estimate and supposition. The cave animal bone archive from the Dales is a precious and informative archive that continues to yield important new information as modern dating and other techniques are brought to bear.

Pre-Last Interglacial fauna

The only faunal record that pre-dates the Last Interglacial is the report of "small wolf teeth" from Victoria Cave identified by the palaeontologist George Busk; these were found in January 1877 probably in the lowest part of what came to be assigned to the *Sandy laminated clay*, which has been dated to Marine Isotope Stage (MIS) 12 (Lundberg *et al.*, 2010). Excavation conditions in 1876–77 were difficult, with frequent records of excavated sections slipping. The teeth were recorded in the excavation register as the last upper molar of a large dog or wolf and a fragment of canine (Lundberg *et al.*, 2010). The first account of their discovery (Tiddeman, 1878b) specifically refers to *two teeth of a small wolf, a canine and molar*, though the Appendix to that account contains a letter from Busk that refers to *three or four specimens ... of a wolf of small size... .* The specimens cannot be located today, but Busk was an authority on bones from caves and his identification can be taken as reliable. The position of the teeth, if intercalated within the lowest layers of the *Sandy laminated clay*, could be interpreted as a very early MIS 12 fauna. However, it is more likely that the teeth were re-worked and mixed in with the clays when the cave became flooded in MIS 12, at about 440 ka BP, and they may be older than the calcite-coated boulders and large stalagmite bosses on the bedrock floor in the mid-cave area (Fig 15.3). The teeth are probably from an animal that lived before 440 ka, and possibly before the MIS 13 calcite from the cave dated to 490 ka. They are provisionally assigned to the extinct *Canis mosbachensis*, a small wolf-like species, recorded from the pre-MIS 13 West Runton Fresh Water Bed (Lewis, 2011; Penkman *et al.*, 2011) and from the early Middle Pleistocene cave deposits at Westbury-sub-Mendip (Turner, 2009).

After the MIS 12 glaciation, extensive calcite flowstone formed on the cave floor during interglacials in MIS 11, MIS 9 and MIS 7, from c.400–190 ka (Gascoyne and Ford, 1984; Lundberg *et al.*, 2010). These interglacials are known to have supported abundant large mammal populations in Britain (Ashton *et al.*, 2011), yet there is no evidence of them in Victoria Cave or elsewhere in the Dales. Flowstones

formed on the cave floor show that the cave was not flooded in these interglacials; so the explanation must be that the cave interior was inaccessible. The cave interior could have been sealed by the accumulation of limestone scree falling from the cliff above the entrance, and by the laminated clays formed during the glaciations in MIS 12 and MIS 10 when warm-based ice cover caused flooding in the cave. Successive glaciations have truncated Victoria Cave by cutting back the cliff line at its mouth, thus destroying older bone deposits close to the surface within the cave and on the screes outside it. Glaciation during MIS 6, at about 140 ka, removed the scree banks and the other clastic sediments that had blocked the cave entrance, and this enabled spotted hyaenas and brown bears to access the interior of the cave during the Last Interglacial, MIS 5e, beginning around 128 ka.

Last Interglacial

Faunas in the Dales during the Last Interglacial are known from two assemblages: the well-known Hyaena bone bed from the *Lower cave earth* in Victoria Cave, and a less well-known and poorly published assemblage from Raygill Fissure in Lothersdale. Fossil pollen, preserved in a flowstone dated by its uranium and thorium isotopes (U–Th dating) from Lancaster Hole, shows the presence of trees including oak, ash and hazel by about 126 ka, suggesting the vegetation underwent a rapid response to warming at the beginning of the interglacial (Caseldine *et al.*, 2008).

Victoria Cave

The assemblage from the *Lower cave earth* Hyaena bone bed in Victoria Cave was largely recovered during the 1870–78 campaign of excavations. Further work by Tot Lord in the 1930s yielded material directly overlain by calcite flowstone close to the back wall of the lower cave (Fig. 15.5). The Hyaena bone bed is dated to the Last Interglacial, MIS 5e, in part on the grounds of its highly characteristic species content (Currant and Jacobi, 2001) and in part by a U–Th date of ~115 ka on flowstone overlying a rhinoceros jaw found by Tot Lord (Gilmour *et al.*, 2007). Victoria Cave is one of only two caves in Britain where substantial amounts of flowstone formed during MIS 5e directly on top of a Last Interglacial bone bed. The other is Kirkdale Cave in East Yorkshire (McFarlane and Ford, 1998), which was famously excavated in the early nineteenth century by Dean Buckland (1823).

Figure 15.4. *Victoria Cave under excavation in 1870; comparison with Figure 15.1 shows how the present appearance of the cave entrance is largely a result of the 19th century excavations.*

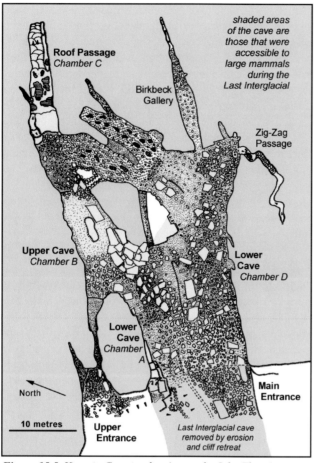

Figure 15.5. *Victoria Cave in plan (survey by John Thorp).*

Arvicola terrestris cantiana	water vole
Vulpes vulpes	red fox
Ursus arctos	brown bear
Crocuta crocuta	spotted hyena
Panthera leo	lion
Palaeoloxodon antiquus	straight-tusked elephant
Mammuthus sp.	mammoth
Stephanorhinus hemitoechus	narrow-nosed rhinoceros
Hippopotamus amphibius	hippopotamus
Megaloceros giganteus	giant deer
Cervus elaphus	red deer
Dama dama	fallow deer
Capreolus capreolus	roe deer
Bison priscus	bison

Table 15.1. *Provisional species list for the Last Interglacial assemblage from Victoria Cave.*

Victoria Cave is therefore of special interest in determining the age of MIS 5e faunas by stalagmite dating (Gascoyne *et al.*, 1981). Although the recovery, documentation and curation of the recovered assemblage in the 1870s were exemplary for their day, it cannot be assumed to be a completely unbiased sample of the in-ground assemblage. The bones show tooth-marks and splintering consistent with accumulation by hyaenas, and a number of hyaena coprolites were recovered from the deposits. The hyaena bones and teeth in the assemblage are greatly outnumbered by the bones of large herbivores (Fig. 15.6), indicating that the excavated areas of the cave were used as a den by hunting groups of hyaenas, rather than as a maternal den. However, the entirely unexcavated, narrow Zig-Zag Passage, discovered in the south wall at the rear of the lower cave in 1875, could have served as a maternal den, as the finds register places its entrance at the level of the Hyaena bone bed (Fig. 15.5).

In a provisional list of species (Table 15.1) large grazing mammals (bison and rhinoceros) are predominant in the assemblage, indicating rather open terrain around the site. Victoria Cave is located on the steep and broken topography near the Middle Craven Fault, so the immediate surroundings must have been quite diverse. Pollen from hyaena coprolites indicates largely open terrain with some deciduous and coniferous woodland. The presence of *Carpinus* pollen suggests a date late in MIS 5e (Lewis, 2011). Hippopotamus is represented only by two specimens, an ankle bone directly overlain by flowstone found by Tot Lord (Gascoyne *et al.*, 1981), and a fragment of canine found in 1874 (Tiddeman, 1878). This relative scarcity may be significant in comparison with the assemblage from Raygill Fissure.

Raygill Fissure

The bone assemblage from the Raygill Fissure is smaller and less well-known than that from Victoria Cave, but is none the less significant. The steeply descending fissure was discovered in the face of a quarry working limestone and baryte in the Embsay Limestone at Lothersdale, southwest of Skipton, in 1874 (Miall, 1878). The uppermost part was exposed first, and as the quarry expanded the fissure was exposed at ever greater depths. The upper part is recorded as about 8 feet (about 2.5m) high and wide, enlarging at depth to a height of nearly 9m (Davis, 1880). The fissure in the face of the quarry was photographed by the Yorkshire Geological and Polytechnic Society in 1875 and 1880. It was eventually explored to a depth of nearly 40m from the surface, at which point the fissure closed down and branched into a complex of smaller passages and fissures (Davis, 1882, 1887).

Most of the fissure was filled to the roof with water-lain clastic sediments. Rounded sandstone pebbles and disarticulated large mammal bones and teeth show that it had been formerly open to the surface. Unfortunately, access to the fissure high up in a working quarry face was difficult, and the considerable thickness of the deposits presented formidable challenges, hence incomplete investigation. By the mid-1880s the quarry had destroyed what must have been one of the richest Last Interglacial bone deposits from a cave in Britain.

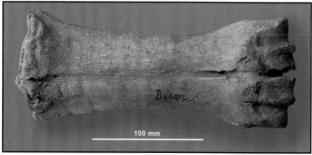

Figure 15.6. *Bison metacarpal from the Last Interglacial assemblage from Victoria Cave, showing the excellent preservation of some of the material from this deposit (TO).*

1. Laminated clay:	9 ft, 2.7m.
2. Sand, with layers of sandy clay, and numerous angular and sub-angular stones:	11 ft 6 in, 3.5m.
3. Sandy clay with rounded stones:	7 ft, 2.2m.

Table 15.2. The section exposed in sediments in the Raygill Fissure in June 1880 (after Davis, 1884).

The first report of bones from Raygill was published soon after the fissure was discovered (Plant, 1874). Specimens were collected sporadically by Richard Tiddeman, Louis Miall and others (Miall, 1878, 1880). The only attempt at systematic excavation took place in the early 1880s, supervised by James Davis, the Secretary of the Yorkshire Geological and Polytechnic Society (Davis 1880, 1882, 1884, 1885, 1886, 1887). The section exposed in the quarry face was recorded in June 1880 (Table 15.2), where these sediments filled the fissure to the roof that lay about 18m below the original ground level.

Last Interglacial large mammal remains were found in Davis's Unit 3, the *Sandy clay with rounded stones*, which was described as *brown sandy clay, containing numerous well rounded water worn pebbles of limestone and sandstone, apparently derived from rocks in the neighbourhood. Intermixed with these, especially near the base of the section, are numerous bones and teeth* (Davis, 1884). This fits modern descriptions of matrix-supported gravels deposited in caves under hydraulic conditions by flood pulses of moderate to high energy (Gillieson, 1996).

With the assistance of quarrymen, Davis was able to excavate the *Sandy clay with rounded stones* for a distance of some 4.5m in June 1880. This work discovered numerous elephant bones as well as teeth and tusks of hippopotamus, rhinoceros teeth, and hyaena teeth (Davis, 1882). Flowstone deposition had cemented the *Sandy clay with rounded stones* into a conglomerate. *The sands and clays surrounding or forming the matrix of the bones are cemented together, forming a hard mass enclosing the animal remains. The bones for the most part, when nearly exposed, are very soft and friable, and being cemented in the hard matrix, it rarely happens that a bone can be secured which retains its original form* (Davis, 1884).

The original published species lists were used to assign the Raygill fauna to the Last Interglacial (Ipswichian), with comment on the absence of horse (Sutcliffe, 1960). Similarly, the Raygill fauna has been included as a northern

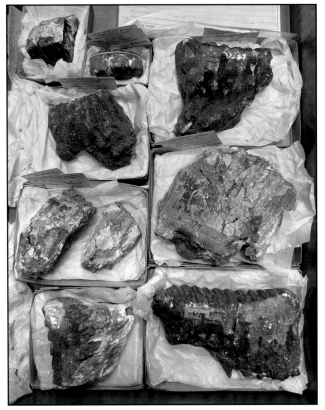

Figure 15.7. Part of the Raygill Fissure assemblage, curated at the Leeds Discovery Centre (TO).

outlier of the Joint Mitnor Mammal Assemblage Zone (Currant and Jacobi, 2001, 2011) assigned to MIS 5e, now dated to 126–114 ka in Northwest Europe (Meyer *et al.*, 2008; Sánchez Goñi *et al.*, 2005). Many of the finds from Raygill are now lost. The fifty or so specimens preserved in museum collections are nearly all robust large teeth or tooth fragments (Table 15.3; Fig. 15.7). Hardly any bones have survived. Understanding the taphonomy of the Raygill fauna is therefore very dependent upon observations reported in the contemporary publications.

The report of finding numerous elephant bones, including *fragments of a tusk 7 inches [175 mm] in diameter, and many molar teeth* (Davis, 1882) suggests the presence of elements representing substantial parts of adult elephant skeletons. Given the topography of the fissure, it is very likely that the elephant remains initially accumulated in the cave as a result of a vertical or sub-vertical opening to the surface acting as a natural pitfall trap. The presence of water in the cave may have attracted elephants and other large herbivores, and a steep-sided access prevented some animals from returning to the surface. Spotted hyaenas and lions scavenging the carcasses might have similarly become trapped (Sutcliffe, 1960, 1985). Raygill Fissure may have operated as a water-hole trap rather like a cenote (Simms, 1994). The remains of animals that were trapped and died there were then re-deposited by flood events as disarticulated elements deeper in the cave.

Re-examination of the Raygill material held at Leeds Discovery Centre and Cliffe Castle, Keighley, in 2011 confirmed that a high proportion of the surviving material assemblage consists of rhinoceros teeth, and also that much of the material has a somewhat battered, rolled appearance,

Bear	cf *Ursus arctos*
Spotted hyaena*	*Crocuta crocuta*
Lion	*Panthera leo*
Straight-tusked elephant*	*Palaeoloxodon antiquus*
Narrow-nosed rhinoceros*	*Stephanorhinus hemitoechus*
Hippopotamus*	*Hippopotamus amphibius*
Roe deer	*Capreolus capreolus*
Bison*	*Bison priscus*

*Table 15.3. The mammalian fauna from Unit 3, the sandy clay with rounded stones, in Raygill Fissure, with modern nomenclature, based on lists by Miall (1878, 1880), Dawkins (1880) and Davis (1882, 1884). Species marked * are held in museum collections.*

quite different from that of the Victoria Cave specimens. A hippopotamus lower molar tooth preserved in the Leeds Discovery Centre has been abraded by fluvial activity into a pebble-like shape (Fig. 15.8). Flood events at Raygill Fissure may have intensified with the shift to much wetter and colder winters in the later part of MIS 5e, as detected in Alpine speleothem records after c.119 ka (Meyer *et al.*, 2008).

The hypothesis that Raygill Fissure operated as a natural trap during the Last Interglacial implies that hippopotamuses moved onto higher ground in search of grazing, and were not restricted to areas immediately adjacent to rivers and floodplains. The altitude of the opening into the fissure would have been around 260m. This has considerable significance for understanding the ecology of the Last Interglacial in Britain. Competition from hippopotamus may be a factor in explaining the absence of horses during this period, or a general lack of dry open grassland early in the Last Interglacial may have militated against horses while favouring hippopotamus.

The interglacial environment

What these two assemblages show is that during the Last Interglacial, and probably late in that Interglacial, the Yorkshire Dales supported a diverse fauna of large mammals that included grazers, browsers (i.e. the deer) and their predators. Comparisons beyond the region are ambiguous and therefore interesting. The Dales material would fit with the Joint Mitnor Mammal Assemblage Zone, characterised by hippopotamus and fallow deer, but for the presence at Victoria Cave of mammoth and roe deer (Currant and Jacobi, 2001). Those two species are characteristic of the supposedly later Bacon Hole Mammal Assemblage Zone, which would be inconsistent with the >115 ka date for the Victoria Cave assemblage. Rather than shoe-horning the Dales assemblages into a faunal sequence within which they do not seem to fit, it is simpler to suppose that the karst region of northern England offered a mosaic of habitats and microclimates different from those in the more southerly regions on which the zonal sequence is based. In short, the Dales assemblages may be distinctive because the Last Interglacial faunas of the region were distinctive. Further research on the two assemblages needs to focus on chronology, in particular in dating the Raygill assemblage by some means other than biostratigraphical association. For now, the relative abundance

Figure 15.8. *Hippopotamus mandibular molar from the Raygill Fissure assemblage, showing a degree of rounding that is consistent with abrasion in flowing water (TO).*

of hippopotamus at Raygill compared with Victoria Cave, and the presence of mammoth and roe deer at Victoria Cave, appears to show that Raygill accumulated earlier, at the peak of MIS 5e, and Victoria Cave later, as cooling set in.

Different patterns of spotted hyaena behaviour are identified at the two sites. At Victoria Cave the evidence points to packs communally hunting large herbivores, especially bison, and using the cave as a den. At Raygill Fissure spotted hyaenas were in a scavenging role, attempting to access carcasses of mega-herbivores such as straight-tusked elephant, hippopotamus and narrow-nosed rhinoceros. However, there is evidence to suggest that spotted hyaenas were scavenging at Victoria Cave, but in a different context. The Hyaena bone bed includes substantial numbers of brown bear specimens, mostly isolated teeth and occasional chewed and splintered bones, greatly outnumbering the spotted hyaenas in the assemblage. It is possible that the Hyaena bone bed incorporates within it the remains of brown bears that died in hibernation and were subsequently scavenged by spotted hyaenas, thus replicating the observed pattern during the first part of the Lateglacial Interstadial at about 14.7–14.0 ka when wolves scavenged brown bear carcasses of animals that died in hibernation.

Available records of the internal stratigraphy of the Hyaena bone bed are too coarse to show chronological patterns in the use of the cave by hunting packs and the scavenging of bear carcasses. However the recognition of different facies within the bone assemblage shows how spotted hyaenas made different use of Victoria Cave during MIS 5e. Perhaps there was a more general shift in behaviour by spotted hyaenas, from a pattern of largely scavenging early in the stage to more pack hunting late in MIS 5e. If evidence that hippopotamus was a major component of the mega-herbivore guild in Britain is accepted, the body size of hippopotamus puts it beyond the scope of pack-hunting spotted hyaenas. This might have pushed spotted hyaenas into more of a scavenging role early in MIS 5e when hippopotamus numbers would have been at their greatest. Conversely as hippopotamus numbers fell as winters became colder late in MIS 5e, this could have left a niche for other herbivores. Species such as bison are of a body size that could be taken by spotted hyaena packs, so more pack-hunting by spotted hyaenas late in MIS 5e can be envisaged if bison numbers increased. This may be what is seen at Victoria Cave. The Last Interglacial bone assemblages at this site and Raygill Fissure may provide evidence for hitherto unrecognised changes in the ecology of Britain during MIS 5e.

Later MIS 5 from 114 to 74 ka

After the Last Interglacial in MIS 5e, the climate oscillated between increasingly cold stadials, in MIS 5d (114–105 ka) and MIS 5b (92–84 ka), and two relatively warm interstadials, in MIS 5c (105–92 ka) and MIS 5a (84–74 ka) (Bassinot *et al.*, 1994). The expansion of land ice in parts of the northern hemisphere caused sea levels to fall, so that they were 40–60m lower than today during the stadials, and 20–30m lower during the interstadials (Lambeck, 1993). Despite the lower sea levels, Britain was basically an island that was separate from mainland Europe, though it did have a land area greater than that of the present.

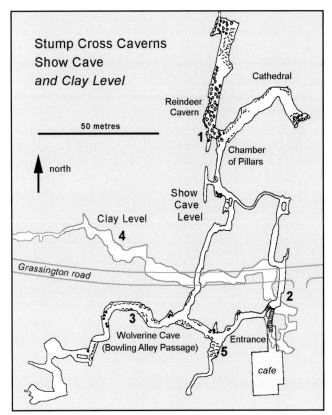

Figure 15.9. *The passages of the Show Cave Level in Stump Cross Caverns system, with numbered sites of the main palaeontological discoveries; the Clay Level passages lie 12m below the show cave.*

Figure 15.10. *A wolverine skull with intact incisor teeth, on the left, and the lower jaw of a wolf on the right, from the Clastic Horizon within Stump Cross Caverns (TW).*

Stump Cross Caverns

The caves of Stump Cross lie in the broad interfluve between Wharfedale and Nidderdale, close to the Middle Craven Fault, and include key sites for understanding events during later MIS 5. The extensive cave system has both active passages and relict phreatic passages formed at different levels in steeply dipping and fractured limestone. It was sealed by roof breakdown, clastic infill and speleothem until broken into by lead miners in the nineteenth century. The upper series of relict phreatic passages that lie about 16m below the surface are well decorated with speleothems and have been developed as a show cave for visitors since soon after their discovery (Fig. 15.9). The show cave is reached by steps that descend from an artificial entrance at 360m OD. It is highly significant that the sediment sequence in Stump Cross Cave has none of the laminated clays that characterise the Victoria Cave record (Lundberg *et al.*, 2010). This suggests that Stump Cross Cave was not covered by warm-based ice during glaciations (see Chapter 3), possibly because of its high interfluve setting.

Speleothems from passages at the show cave level in Stump Cross Cave must be the most intensely dated sediments from a British cave, with 55 age determinations. Beds of gravel, sands and silts were deposited before the MIS 7 interglacial, and more-localised beds of sands and silts were deposited after the Last Interglacial in the later part of MIS 5. Flowstones with fine clay layers, and scattered horizons with detrital speleothem, indicate that the cave flooded repeatedly from before 225 ka to the mid-Holocene. During the very driest events drip water routes switched and speleothem deposition was restricted to a few areas

(Sutcliffe *et al.*, 1985). More extensive flowstones formed in response to increased drip water flows, but were restricted to high points in the cave whenever pools formed on the cave floor. Multiple dating has identified a number of phases of flowstone growth on the floor of the show cave, beginning at around 225 ka (Sutcliffe *et al.*, 1985; Baker *et al.*, 1996).

Despite extensive sampling, there are no flowstones clearly dating to the interglacials at MIS 7 (210–190 ka) or MIS 5e (128–114 ka). Prolonged low-energy flooding may have prevented flowstone formation through much of these times (Baker *et al.*, 1996). A phase of higher-energy flooding in the later part of MIS 5, before about 80 ka, formed a laterally extensive but locally variable deposit containing mammal bones, detrital speleothems and fine clastic sediments. This is referred to as the *Clastic Horizon* (Table 15.4). The fresh condition of the bones, with the skulls of wolverine retaining their incisor teeth, indicates that the bones are contemporary with the high-energy flood phase, and are not a reworked older assemblage.

In 1956 parts of four reindeer skeletons were found in a narrow rift adjacent to the Show Cave (Collins, 1959). Bones from two wolverines and a skull embedded in flowstone were found in 1962 at the base of the rift where the steps descend into the show cave. In 1980, a reindeer bone and bones of wolverine and wolf were discovered in cutting through sediments to make a path for visitors into the Bowling Alley Passage (since renamed Wolverine Cave). Systematic excavation (by Tom Lord and the late Anthony Sutcliffe) then yielded disassociated parts of six wolverines, and bones from a wolf as well as a bison and fox bone. The bones were part of a clastic horizon with abundant fragments of detrital speleothem. Further bone discoveries include part of an associated wolverine skeleton found in digging to extend the cave in Clay Cavern in 1981 (site 4 on Figure 15.9), and an *in situ* wolverine tibia was discovered in the show cave (at site 5) in 2011. It is very likely that discoveries of bones at Stump Cross Cave will continue.

Wolf	*Canis lupus*
Fox	*Vulpes* sp.
Wolverine	*Gulo gulo*
Reindeer	*Rangifer tarandus*
Bison	*Bison priscus*

Table 15.4. *The fauna from the Clastic Horizon in Stump Cross Caverns, dated from the later part of MIS 5 before about 80 ka.*

The 1980s investigation used U–Th dating of associated speleothems to establish the age of the *Clastic Horizon* with its contained bone deposits. Based on 32 dates for speleothems from different parts of the cave, the fauna was attributed to the MIS 5b stadial at 92–84 ka (Sutcliffe *et al.*, 1985). Following the development of more precise dating techniques (see Chapter 10), an impressive series of dates for a flowstone sequence from Site 3/B in the Bowling Alley Passage provided an age of about 80 ka for flowstone overlying the *Clastic Horizon* (Baker *et al.*, 1996).

The modern dating shows that the flowstone above the *Clastic Horizon* in the show cave is diachronous; it formed at different times between 70 and 80 ka. Flowstone overlying the *Clastic Horizon* at a high point in the Bowling Alley Passage, Site 3A/B, is dated to 79.2 ± 2.4 ka (Baker *et al.*, 1996); and the date for flowstone overlying the same horizon some 60m distant at the foot of the entrance steps, Site 2, is 73.86 ± 1.20 ka (Gilmour *et al.*, 2007). Clear evidence of a further and longer hiatus between the deposition of the *Clastic Horizon* and the flowstone sequence overlying it comes from the lowest part of the show cave investigated in the 1980s, Site 3C in the Bowling Alley Passage, where Sample S.C.18 was dated to 15 ± 1 ka (Sutcliffe *et al.*, 1985). Here localised ponding and other factors had delayed the onset of flowstone formation above the *Clastic Horizon* until the Windermere Interstadial after the main glacial retreat.

Dating the *Clastic Horizon* fauna is made more difficult because of the hiatuses in speleothem growth resulting from local factors within the cave. The dated sequence from Site 3A/B shows a hiatus between about 165 and 80 ka. So, on this part of the cave floor there is no evidence for flowstone deposition in MIS 5 until part way through the MIS 5c interstadial. However, the 1980s investigation detected an earlier phase of speleothem growth in MIS 5 on the evidence of five dates, four of them for samples in stratigraphical relationship to the *Clastic Horizon* (Sutcliffe *et al.*, 1985). Two stalagmites in growth position from below the horizon at Site 3C have a mean age of 114 ka and two detrital speleothems within the *Clastic Horizon,* a stalagmite from Site 3C and a flowstone clast from Site 2, have a mean age of 109 ka. The fifth date of about 116 ka was for part of a stalagmite that grew on the cave floor at site 3A/B. Within the

Figure 15.11. *The trench cut through flowstone and the underlying, bone-bearing Clastic Horizon in Wolverine Passage in the Show Cave Level of Stump Cross Caverns (TW).*

uncertainties of the older dating methods all five speleothems appear contemporary. Three of the stalagmites grew on the floor of the cave at the lowest point of the Bowling Alley Passage, Site 3C, and so must have formed during a fairly dry climatic episode. The dating suggests these samples formed after the Last Interglacial, possibly in the drier MIS 5d stadial at 114–100 ka.

On present evidence, the following sequence of events can be reconstructed for the show cave passages during MIS 5. A prolonged phase of low-energy flooding during the Last Interglacial with no discernible inputs of clastic sediments was followed by a dry phase with local speleothem deposition during MIS 5d. Then came a return to low-energy flooding, but this time with inputs of sands and silts that buried the MIS 5d stalagmites at Site 3C, the lowest point of the Bowling Alley Passage. Nivation and frost activity enlarged openings into the highest parts of the cave system, and reindeer and bison were trapped in the openings. Attracted by the scent of carrion, scavenging carnivores descended into the cave. Unable to return to the surface some 16m above the cave floor, a number of wolverines and a wolf died of starvation or drowning. Water levels fluctuated. The remains of at least six wolverines and a wolf accumulated on the sands and silts at Site 3C, floating to this point during low-energy flood events before their flesh and soft tissues decayed. To combat starvation, live wolverines fed on wolverine and wolf remains at Site 3A/B, at the highest point in the Bowling Alley Passage. In short, the cave acted as a pitfall trap for large herbivores, and a baited trap for scavenging carnivores. This took place during a period of partial flooding when live wolverine were able to feed on the higher parts of the cave floor, and floating carcasses accumulated at the lowest point in the passage.

After the period of partial flooding when the cave acted as a trap for scavenging carnivores, there was a phase of high-energy flooding with floodwaters rising under hydrostatic pressure from deeper in the cave system to come up through the sediments on the cave floor. This was the flood phase responsible for the *Clastic Horizon*. The flooding moved pieces of flowstone and stalagmites. It broke straw stalactites on the cave roof, and generated a pipe over an enlarged joint in the cave floor at Site 3C, which cut through the clastic sediments at that point. Bones in the upper part of the sands and silts at Site 3C moved down into the pipe together with stalagmites and straw stalactites. The bones and stalagmites winnowed out as lag deposits in the pipe. The high-energy flood phase took place before about 80 ka, during the MIS 5a interstadial, when a dated flowstone formed over part of the *Clastic Horizon* and over its contained mammal fauna at Site 3A/B in the Bowling Alley Passage.

It appears that the high-energy flooding was generated by rapid snow-melt delivering fine clastic sediment and large volumes of water into the active cave stream. At the surface frost activity and long periods of annual snow cover mobilised soils and coarser materials that were washed into the cave in the spring snow-melt. Flood waters backed up into the passages at a higher level, especially the Clay Level at around 28m below the surface, which partly filled with fine sediment. Bones of a wolverine skeleton were found in the Clay Level sediments beneath 3m of sands and silts in 1981. As the inputs of fine sediment reduced the storage capacity in the passages beneath the show cave level, snow-melt flood waters rose under pressure into the passages at the show cave level, generating the high-energy flood phase that gave rise to the *Clastic Horizon.*

The publication of the 1980s investigations at Stump Cross Caverns prompted a re-analysis of deposits at caves and open sites with the same mammal fauna as the *Clastic Horizon* (Currant and Jacobi, 2001). It is a very unusual fauna characterised by having only two large herbivores, bison and reindeer, and a distinctive carnivore guild of brown bear, wolf and wolverine. Its low species-diversity is explained by its status as an "island fauna" during the oscillating climatic conditions in the later part of MIS 5 (Currant and Jacobi, 2011). The cave system at Stump Cross is a key site for understanding this low-diversity mammal fauna, and the conditions that gave rise to it.

Away from Stump Cross

In the north of England, it is not known when the fauna with only two large herbivores (bison and reindeer) replaced the Last Interglacial fauna of 126–114 ka with its many different species of large and mega-herbivores found at Victoria Cave and Raygill Fissure. Dated stalagmites from Tornewton Cave, in Devon, show that some of the Last Interglacial species lived in southwest England during the MIS 5c interstadial and possibly later (Gilmour *et al.*, 2007). This must be very close in time to the fossiliferous silts at Isleworth, in the lower Thames valley, which contain interstadial fossil pollen, beetles and abundant bison and reindeer bones (Coope and Angus, 1975) and are dated to after MIS 5e and before MIS 5a (Penkman *et al.*, 2011). The Isleworth silts might represent part of the MIS 5c interstadial when Last Interglacial species are recorded from Tornewton Cave, or one of the later short interstadials in MIS 5b identified by the higher resolution of the Greenland Ice Core Record.

However, instead of looking for an abrupt temporal boundary for the replacement of the Last Interglacial fauna, it is instructive to compare the faunal record alongside the ground-breaking work on fossil pollen preserved in the dated later MIS 5 flowstones from Lancaster Hole (Caseldine *et al.*, 2008). The Lancaster Hole flowstones show that oak, hazel and ash were present during the MIS 5c interstadial at around 100 ka, and oak and ash were present during the MIS 5a interstadial at about 84 ka. It is unlikely that the tree species came in from mainland Europe because Britain was an island. Instead the Lancaster Hole pollen record suggests that deciduous trees survived in local refugia, possibly the nearby Morecambe Bay area, during MIS 5d and MIS 5b stadials when sea levels were 40–60m lower than now, then spread out onto higher ground during the milder MIS 5c and MIS 5a interstadials. It is possible that the coastal areas of southwest of England, and possibly south Wales, acted as refugia for Last Interglacial mammals during cold events in MIS 5. It is even possible that Morecambe Bay provided a refugium for mammals as well as trees, though there is no fossil evidence for that from the caves there.

Bison and reindeer are capable of foraging under snow. Wolverine is also a specialised carnivore adapted to winters with long periods of snow cover (Telfer and Kelsall, 1984).

Figure 15.12. The Colonnades Passage in Lancaster Hole where pollen records were obtained from the flowstone (photo: Ray Duffy).

Recent research on wolverine ecology reveals that it requires persistent spring snow cover for successful reproductive denning. In North America and Scandinavia denning takes place from February to May, with natal and maternal dens up to 60m in length dug into the snow-pack for insulation and protection from other predators. Thus the presence of wolverine in the vicinity of Stump Cross in later part of MIS 5 indicates cold winters but with sufficiently high levels of precipitation to generate several months of snow cover lasting until May.

Using the temperature model to estimate annual snow cover for the 8.2 ka cold event in the early Holocene (Vincent *et al.*, 2011), a fall in mean annual air temperature at sea level of about 3°C, compared to present conditions, would be sufficient to generate this length of snow cover for high ground above 300m OD in northern England, at present-day lapse rates. If lapse rates were higher in the later part of MIS 5 then these conditions would be met with a smaller fall in temperature at sea level. During the later part of MIS 5 the Yorkshire Dales would frequently have experienced snow-pack across the uplands, and also on large areas of the lower ground, for the greater part of the year.

Rather than view the final demise of the Last Interglacial mammal fauna in Britain as a catastrophic collapse during the cold MIS 5b event as proposed by recent work (Currant and Jacobi, 2001, 2011), it is appropriate to envisage long periods with snow cover filtering out the Last Interglacial mammal species one by one according to their ability to cope with the conditions. The evidence from Stump Cross Caverns suggests that snow cover, rather than cold *per se*, was the key to the demise of the Last Interglacial mammal fauna. It was most likely a staggered process rather than an abrupt one, and was complicated by coastal refugia supporting populations of plants and animals.

The missing Mammoth Steppe Fauna

Low sea levels from c.60 ka and a succession of interstadials to c.30 ka enabled the Eurasian Mammoth Steppe fauna to colonise Britain. This included mega-herbivores such as mammoth and woolly rhinoceros, abundant cave-using top predators such as spotted hyaenas, and more rarely Neanderthals and anatomically Modern Humans (Currant and Jacobi, 2011). Remarkably, apart from a possible woolly rhinoceros tooth found in coarse fluvial sediments in Ingleborough Cave (Murphy, 2011), the Mammoth Steppe Fauna is not yet detected in caves in the Dales, even though dated woolly rhinoceros bones from beneath glacial sediments in Scotland show that elements of this fauna ranged much further north in Britain. The Ingleborough Cave rhinoceros could have fallen down or had its remains washed into a cave shaft; either way it suggests that cave shafts on Ingleborough were open before the Last Glacial Maximum. However, these were likely to have been active stream caves, so that animal remains in them would have been reworked during flood events or even destroyed altogether by erosion.

The lack of material attributable to the period of about 60–26 ka is a telling aspect of the Dales cave record. Despite a number of excavations down to bedrock in relict phreatic caves such as Jubilee Cave, which might have been used by spotted hyaenas and the other Mammoth Steppe top predators, there is no known evidence of them. Perhaps the entrances to these caves had been blocked by scree and were inaccessible at this time, as at Victoria Cave; or the Mammoth Steppe and other fossiliferous cave sediments could have been flushed out by later flooding caused by warm-based ice cover during the Last Glacial Maximum (Murphy *et al.*, 2001).

The Lateglacial Interstadial

The period of the Last Glacial Maximum, around 26–18 ka, saw the Dales extensively covered by ice and there is therefore a break in the palaeontological record. New data indicate that at least parts of the Dales were ice-free by 17±2 ka (Telfer *et al.*, 2009; Vincent *et al.*, 2010). At that time, the climate was still cold, and the rapid loss of ice cover was largely due to the reduced snowfall. The presence of extensive loess deposits may indicate the potential development of fertile soils (Wilson *et al.*, 2008), though these are likely to have been unstable in the cold, dry climate and so re-establishment of vegetation cover may have been patchy. That in turn

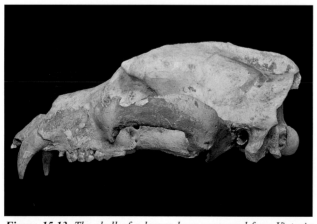

***Figure 15.13**. The skull of a brown bear recovered from Victoria Cave and dated from the Lateglacial Interstadial (TO).*

Victoria Cave	BP		
18992	14,707 ± 430	*Ursus* pelvis	D
15729	14,675 ± 428	*Ursus* mandible	D
20693	14,521 ± 434**	*Rangifer* (artefact)	B
15078	14,502 ± 438	*Equus* atlas with cut-marks	B
18993	14,029 ± 168	*Ursus* humerus	D
15728	14,028 ± 162	*Ursus mandible* (articulates with skull)	D
2457	13,534 ± 269*	*Rangifer* radius	E
12143	13,508 ± 154	*Bos primigenius* calcaneum	B
15170	13,252 ± 115	*Rangifer* metatarsal	E
2454	12,920 ± 242*	*Rangifer* mandible	E
20692	12,911 ± 203**	*Rangifer* artefact	C
14888	12,846 ± 153**	*Rangifer* artefact	E
Kinsey Cave			
16338	14,721 ± 435	*Ursus* partial skull	
19183	14,647 ± 436	*Ursus* femur	
16337	14,493 ± 448	*Ursus* mandible (with skull, Fig. 15.13)	
16339	13,469 ± 146	cf. *Bos primigenius* cervical vertebra	
11154	13,364 ± 158	*Rangifer* antler	
20694	13,359 ± 129**	*Rangifer* (artefact)	
Conistone Dib Cave			
18997	13,567 ± 160	*Ursus* ulna	
2847	13,024 ± 224*	cf. *Alces* (artefact)	
Sewell's Cave			
18996	14,249 ± 322	*Ursus* phalange	
18995	13,602 ± 160	*Ursus* phalange	
20698	12,844 ± 158**	*Equus* metatarsal	
16389	12,771 ± 138	*Equus* tibia	
8095	12,762 ± 150*	cf. *Bos primigenius* lumbar vertebra	
8096	12,720 ± 119*	*Rangifer* pelvis	
Moughton Fissure			
19164	13,122 ± 175**	*Equus* metatarsal	

***Table 15.5.** Radiocarbon dates, calibrated using OxCal 4.1 to years BP (before 2000), for mammals from the Lateglacial Interstadial in the Dales caves. * Dates measured before the ultrafiltration method was adopted. ** New dates for specimens originally dated before ultrafiltration. All specimen numbers are prefixed by OxA-. Locations in Victoria Cave: A, B, C, D are chambers as in Figure 15.5; E is the entrance breccia (updated from Lord et al., 2007).*

inhibited re-colonisation by herbivorous animals and their predators, meaning that for two to three millennia the Dales may have had only a sparse, and perhaps seasonal, fauna. The palaeontological record resumes rather suddenly a little after 15 ka, when climate records show a rapid warming into the Lateglacial (Windermere) Interstadial (Table 15.5). This falls well into the range of radiocarbon dating, so a detailed chronology is established.

Some of the earliest dated specimens from the Lateglacial are the remains of brown bears, with mostly indirect evidence of the presence of wolves, starting from around 14.7 ka (Table 15.5) (Lord *et al.*, 2007, 2012). Brown bear, including some very young individuals, are represented by part-skeletons in several caves (Fig. 15.13). Of the seven bears identified from Victoria Cave, two are juveniles and one is clearly perinatal. Taken in conjunction with find-spots, which, when precisely known, are largely in dark, well-protected parts of the cave interior, it is likely that most of these bears died during hibernation. Brown bears directly dated to the Lateglacial Interstadial are known from Victoria Cave, Kinsey Cave, Sewell's Cave, and Conistone Dib Cave, with

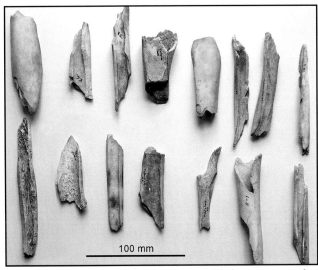

Figure 15.14. Lateglacial reindeer bones with fractures typical of predation or scavenging by wolves, from Victoria Cave (TO).

further specimens probably attributable to the Interstadial from Elbotlon Cave, and perhaps also from Moughton Fell Fissure and from Calf Hole if, as seems highly probable, an early identification of bison from this assemblage at the latter site is erroneous (Jones, 1894). A bear specimen from Raven Scar Cave, previously thought to be of Interstadial date, has been shown to date to the Early Holocene. Evidence of wolves is typically as heavily tooth-marked and splintered bones, mostly of reindeer, in entrance or talus locations, consistent with wolves using caves as dens (Fig. 15.14). Predators need prey, and assemblages from sites such as Victoria Cave and Sewell's Cave typically contain aurochs, reindeer and horse (Table 15.5). There is a need for more radiocarbon dates obtained directly from the bones of these animals; initial indications are that the reindeer components tend to be later in the Interstadial, representing the cooling oscillation of climate that preceded the short, cold Younger Dryas Stadial. There is a gap in the dated record from the Lateglacial Interstadial equivalent to the cold Older Dryas around 12,000 ka (Table 15.5).

The extent to which people played a role in the accumulation or movement of these animal bone assemblages is debatable. The presence of cut-marked bones (Fig. 15.15) and the occasional artefact shows that Upper Palaeolithic hunters were active in the Dales landscape at various times

during the Interstadial, the first of them equivalent of the Magdalenian hunters of Continental Europe. However, there is a distinct lack of evidence to show people using the caves for residence or even long-term shelter; there are no lithic scatters, nor concentrations of charred bones. Perhaps the numbers of bears and wolves were sufficient to deter competition for living space, and people may only have been present on the Dales uplands seasonally or intermittently. Although the record shows the Dales to have Upper Palaeolithic archaeology (see Chapter 16), the assemblages themselves are more a matter of palaeontology.

The Holocene

People became more active agents of bone deposition during the Holocene, and the cave record becomes more archaeology than palaeontology. There is a gap in the cave record for the earlier part of the Holocene, consistent with scree accumulation burying cave entrances during the cold Younger Dryas. However, a bear from Raven Scar Cave probably represents a hibernation death, and there are well-dated records from Kinsey Cave and The Cupcake. The source of bones at these last two sites appears to be fissures from the surface opening into the cave interior, thus acting as pit-fall traps. Pit-fall assemblages from the Dales range in date from the Last Interglacial to medieval times (Table 15.6). The record of capercaillie from Kinsey Cave is unexpected for a species well beyond its modern range, hinting at an early Holocene landscape very different to that of today. The same species has recently been recorded in an assemblage from Teesdale Cave, north of the Dales, for which reliable dating has yet to be established. Similarly unexpected is evidence that lynx persisted in the Dales into Anglo-Saxon times, a discovery that has important implications for understanding woodland clearance and disturbance (Hetherington *et al.*, 2005).

Shortly after 6000 years ago, the first domestic livestock were introduced into the Dales, together with the practice of entombing the dead within caves, commonly in association with bones of wild and domestic animals. Radiocarbon dates indicate that human and animal bones were moved around, re-associated and re-deposited over a period of centuries; bones found together do not necessarily represent people and animals that were contemporaneous.

On Gragareth, well-dated specimens of aurochs are recorded from both North End Pot and The Cupcake (Fig. 15.16). These mighty beasts appear from the cave record to have persisted in good numbers in the Dales for at least 2000 years after the introduction of domestic livestock. This raises

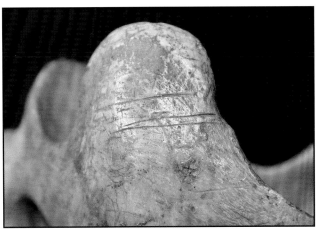

Figure 15.15. Cuts made by a stone blade on an atlas bone of a horse from the Lateglacial assemblage in Victoria Cave (TO).

site	age, ka	fauna
Raygill Fissure	127–114	mega-herbivores, carnivores
Stump Cross	95–80	reindeer, bison, carnivores
Ingleborough Cave	60–35	woolly rhinoceros
Elbolton Cave	c.14.5	mountain hare, brown bear
Conistone Dib Cave	13.5	brown bear
Kinsey Cave	11.6–9.0	roe deer, capercaillie
Cupcake	9.3	wild boar, aurochs, wolf
North End Pot	4.9–4.6	aurochs, red deer, black grouse, wolf
Rawthey Cave	1–0.7	roe deer, sheep, pig, dog

Table 15.6. Assemblages from recognised pit-fall sites in caves within the Yorkshire Dales.

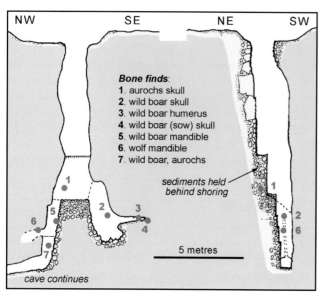

Figure 15.16. Intersecting profiles of the excavated Cupcake shaft on Leck Fell, with locations of major bone finds (survey by John Thorp).

Figure 15.18. A typical frog earth assemblage of small mammal bones, from Kinsey Cave (TO).

the obvious question of interbreeding between aurochs and domestic cattle, which DNA evidence indicates was negligible (Edwards *et al.*, 2007). A Neolithic farmer may not have been able to prevent a bull aurochs from mating with his domestic cattle, and the aurochs may have been regarded as a pest that was deliberately killed in some areas. Wolf is another species that causes debate. The specimens from Cupcake and North End Pot are clearly wolf, and there is convincing wolf from Shuttleworth Pot. However, the canid from Rawthey Cave is clearly a domestic dog, and there is no known unambiguous skeletal evidence of wolf in the Dales after the mid-Holocene. Wildcat is recorded from a few sites, though the difficulty of separating this species from feral domestic cat makes caution necessary (O'Connor, T, 2007). Among cat remains from the entrance scree at Victoria Cave, there are specimens that can be confidently attributed to both wildcat and domestic cat; these are not directly dated, though their stratigraphical position is consistent with a pre-Roman date. Archaeological assemblages from caves in the Dales commonly include bones of domestic livestock, whereas 'natural' traps such as fissures and shake-holes may be more likely to have acquired the bones of wild species. The Cupcake shaft, on Leck Fell, has recently yielded a remarkable collection of aurochs, wolf and wild boar bones (Thorp, 2011), the last an exceptionally large individual (Fig. 15.17).

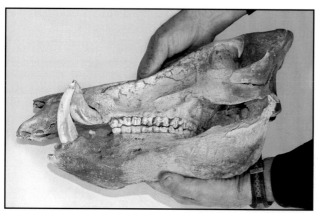

Figure 15.17. The complete skull of a wild boar, recovered from the Cupcake shaft on Leck Fell (photo: Peter Monk).

Several caves in the Dales and elsewhere in Britain have produced concentrations of very small bones, typically in discrete lenses or patches of sediment. Amphibian bones are generally conspicuous in these assemblages, giving them the epithet *frog earths* (Fig. 15.18). Regrettably, these deposits were noted but not retained in early cave excavations at Calf Hole, where *the top layer of 2 or 3 inches was of loamy clay, crowded with bones of small animals, frogs, rats, voles, &c.* (Jones, 1894). Similarities between assemblages are superficial, and it is likely that different *frog earths* have quite different taphonomic origins. Some may have originated with owls and other pellet-egesting birds roosting in the entrance zone of the cave. Few, if any, seem to be *in situ* death assemblages representing the past biota of the cave interior. The material associated with Neolithic activity in Kinsey Cave was predominantly frog and toad bones, with much crushing and splintering of the bones, which appear to be debris from a predator such as polecat or pine marten that habitually used the entrance zone of the cave. A similar assemblage has been identified in association with Neolithic and Bronze Age activity in Thaw Head Cave. Perhaps the human activity either opened up space that predators could exploit as a den, or served to attract mice and amphibians that then became prey. There is much that we still have to learn regarding the *frog earths*.

Apart from their intrinsic interest, one of the valuable aspects of these *frog earths* is the record that they provide of small species formerly present in the Dales, such as the hazel dormouse (*Muscardinus avellanarius*) from the Kinsey Cave assemblage, or birch mouse *Sicista* sp., from Chapel Cave, Malham (Derek Yalden, *pers. comm.*). A surprising number of them include abundant bones of water vole *Arvicola terrestris*, not generally thought of as a species of dry limestone uplands today. Water voles seem to have been widespread across the Dales into post-Roman times, and it may be that their restriction to waterside habitats is a relatively recent adaptation, possibly in response to competition from feral rabbits. Notably scarce in the *frog earth* assemblages, and from the cave palaeontology record in general, are records of bats. Bat bones are distinctly fragile, but so are those of small rodents and amphibians, which survive in at least some caves in a remarkably complete condition, so preservation alone is not an explanation (Fig. 15.19). Only a few positive identification have been made, mostly of *Myotis* species. Some of the caves that have become important roosting sites for bats today (see Chapter 14) may only have done so because cave exploration and excavation has opened up the entrances and main chambers to sizes amenable to bats. Part of the explanation for the near-absence of bats in cave palaeontology in the Dales may be that most caves, while attractive to voles and polecats, were unattractive to bats until substantially enlarged by people.

The present and the future

As the Holocene advanced, so human influence on bone deposition in caves became predominant. Palaeontological assemblages continue to be deposited, but their character reflects human impacts on the regional landscape. Bones of sheep and rabbits predominate, both of them alien species introduced to northern England as agricultural livestock, and now extensively managed and wholly feral respectively. Both species walk or fall into caves and fissures, and the past use of fissures and shake-holes for carcass disposal probably added to the deposition. As live animals, sheep and, especially, rabbits are a threat to the surviving cave palaeontology archive. Their trampling and burrowing can cause considerable damage, as in Victoria Cave (Murphy and Lord, 2003), and conservation measures should include the armouring of vulnerable *in situ* sediments. Badgers continue to use caves as setts, and their capacity for shifting earth and rocks makes it very difficult to protect sediments against their investigations. Cavers, too, shift remarkable quantities of sediment, but good liaison between cavers and cave palaeontologists can turn this to advantage: many of the important recent finds from Dales caves were by cavers and would not have been made otherwise (Murphy, 2002).

Figure 15.19. A remarkably well preserved skeleton of a newt, Triturus sp., which would be about 50 mm long if fully extended, found in Shuttleworth Pot, showing that small, delicate skeletons can survive in caves (photo: Dave Ramsey).

Figure 15.20. Ongoing erosion of in situ deposits in Victoria Cave, where cataloguing and conservation of the material has to be balanced against the need for reasonable access (TO).

Initial study of much of the most spectacular cave palaeontology in the Dales was undertaken a century or more ago, with all that implies in terms of records and the curation of materials. However, cave exploration is very active and recent finds at Shuttleworth Pot and Cupcake are important reminders that there is new material to be found and new information to be gained. The advent of compact digital cameras with a phenomenal capacity to record images in poor light may be one of the technological advances most useful to cave palaeontology. New finds can now be recorded *in situ*, and their images e-mailed to interested parties for record and advice in a matter of hours. Those *in situ* records, combined with more and more direct absolute dates, are one way forward for cave palaeontology in the Dales (Chamberlain, 2002). Another is to maintain the investigation of old assemblages, and to encourage their relocation and curation in the many collections into which they have been dispersed. The fact that new inferences are made regarding assemblages from Victoria Cave and Raygill Fissure over 130 years after their excavation is a reminder that, although cave palaeontology assemblages may be old, investigations of them are never finished.

References

Ashton, N, S G Lewis and C Stringer (eds), 2011. *The Ancient Human Occupation of Britain.* Elsevier: Amsterdam.

Baker, A, P L Smart and R L Edwards, 1996. Mass spectrometric dating of flowstones from Stump Cross Caverns and Lancaster Hole, Yorkshire: palaeoclimatic implications. *J. Quat. Sci.,* **11**, 107-114.

Bassinot, F C, L D Labeyrie, E Vincent, X Quidelleur, N J Shackleton and Y Lancelot, 1994. The astronomical theory of climate and the age of the Brunhes-Matuyama magnetic reversal. *Earth Planetary Science Letters,* **126**, 91-108.

Buckland, W, 1823. *Reliquiae Diluvinae; or Observations on the organic remains contained in caves, fissures and diluvial gravel and on other geological phenomena attesting the action of an universal deluge.* John Murray: London.

Busk, G, 1874. Notice of a human fibula of unusual form, Discovered in the Victoria Cave near Settle, in Yorkshire. *J. Anthropological Inst. G. B. and Ireland,* **3**, 392-395.

Caseldine, C J, S F McGarry, A Baker, C Hawkesworth and P L Smart, 2008. Late Quaternary speleothem pollen in the British Isles. *J. Quat. Sci.,* **23**, 193-200.

Chamberlain, A.T. 2002. A gazetteer of non-human vertebrate remains from caves in the Yorkshire Dales described in the scientific literature. *Capra,* **4** (www.capra.group.shef.ac.uk).

Collins, E R, 1959. The discovery of reindeer bones in Stump Cross Caverns, Greenhow Hill, Yorkshire. *Yorks. Archaeo. J.,* **40**, 160-162.

Coope, G R and R B Angus, 1975. An ecological study of a temperate interlude in the middle of the Last Glaciation, based on fossil Coleoptera from Isleworth, Middlesex. *J. Animal Ecology,* **44**, 365-390.

Currant, A and R M Jacobi, 2001. A formal mammalian biostratigraphy for the late Pleistocene of Britain. *Quat. Sci. Rev.,* **20**, 1707-1716.

Currant, A P and R M Jacobi, 2011. The mammal faunas of the British Late Pleistocene. 165-180 in Ashton *et al. op. cit.*.

Davis, J W, 1880. Report of the Raygill Fissure Exploration Committee, consisting of Prof. A.H. Green, M.A. F.G.S; Prof. L.C. Miall, F.G.S.; John Brigg, F.G.S; and James W. Davis, F.S.A., F.G.S., &c., (Reporter). *Proc. Yorks. Geol. Polytech. Soc.,* **7**, 300-305.

Davis, J W, 1882. On the exploration of a fissure in the Mountain Limestone at Raygill. *Rep. 51st Meeting Brit. Assoc. Advance. Sci.,* 645-646.

Davis, J W, 1884. Report of the Committee, consisting of Professor A.H. Green, Professor L.C. Miall, Mr John Brigg, and Mr James W. Davis (Secretary), appointed to assist in the exploration of Raygill Fissure, Yorkshire. *Rep. 53rd Meeting Brit. Assoc. Advance. Sci.,* 133-135.

Davis, J W, 1885. Report of the Committee, consisting of Professors A.H. Green and L.C. Miall and Messrs. John Brigg and James W. Davis (Secretary), appointed to assist in the exploration of the Raygill Fissure in Lothersdale, Yorkshire. *Rep. 54th Meeting Brit. Assoc. Advance. Sci.,* 240.

Davis, J W, 1886. On the exploration of the Raygill Fissure in Lothersdale, Yorkshire. *Proc. Yorks. Geol. Polytech. Soc.,* **9**, 280-281.

Davis, J.W. 1887. On the Exploration of the Raygill Fissure in Lothersdale, Yorkshire. *Rep. 56th Meeting Brit. Assoc. Advance. Sci.,* 469-470.

Dawkins, W B, 1872. Report on the results obtained by the Settle Cave Exploration Committee out of Victoria Cave in 1870. *J. Anthropological Inst. G. B. and Ireland,* **1**, 60-70.

Dawkins, W B, 1874. *Cave Hunting.* Macmillan: London.

Dawkins, W B, 1880. *Early Man in Britain and his place in the Tertiary Period.* Macmillan: London.

Dearne, M J and T C Lord, 1998. *The Romano-British archaeology of Victoria Cave Settle; researches into the site and its artifacts.* British Archaeological Reports British Series: Oxford.

Edwards, C J and 39 others, 2007. Mitochondrial DNA analysis shows a Near Eastern Neolithic origin for domestic cattle and no indication of domestication of European aurochs. *Proc. Roy. Soc. London,* **B274**, 1377-1385.

Farrer, J, 1862. *Notice of runic inscriptions discovered during recent excavations in the Orkneys.* John Murray: Edinburgh.

Gascoyne, M and D C Ford, 1984. Uranium series dating of speleothems: part II, results from the Yorkshire Dales and implications for cave development and Quaternary climates. *Cave Science,* **11**, 65-85.

Gascoyne, M, A P Currant and T C Lord, 1981. Ipswichian fauna of Victoria Cave and the marine palaeoclimate record. *Nature,* **294**, 652-654.

Gillieson, D, 1996. *Caves: Processes, Development and Management.* Blackwell: Oxford.

Gilmour, M, A Currant, R M Jacobi and C Stringer, 2007. Recent TIMS dating results from British Late Pleistocene vertebrate faunal localities: context and interpretation. *J. Quat. Sci.,* **22**, 793-800.

Hetherington, D A, T C Lord and R M Jacobi, 2005. New evidence for the occurrence of Eurasian lynx (Lynx lynx) in medieval Britain. *J. Quat. Sci.,* **21**, 3-8.

Jones, E, 1894. Exploration of the Calf Hole Cave at the Heights, Skyrethorns, near Skipton. *Rep. Meetings Brit. Assoc. Advance. Sci.,* 1894, 272-3.

Lambeck, K, 1993. Glacial rebound of the British Isles – II: a high-resolution, high-precision model. *Geophysical J. International,* **115**, 960-990.

Lewis, M, 2011. Palynology of hyaena (Crocuta crocuta) coprolites from the bone bed at Victoria Cave, North Yorkshire. *Proc. 1st Workshop AHOB3: Ancient Human Occupation of Britain, Dispersal of Early Humans: Adaptions, frontiers and new territories,* 23.

Lord, T C, T P O'Connor, D C Siebrandt and R M Jacobi, 2007. People and large carnivores as biostratinomic agents in Lateglacial cave assemblages. *J. Quat. Sci.,* **222**, 681-694.

Lord, TC, Lundberg, J and Murphy, P, 2012. A guide to work at Victoria Cave – from the 19th to 21st centuries. 84-97 in H J O'Regan, T Faulkner and I R Smith (eds.), 2012. *Cave Archaeology and Karst Geomorpholgy of North-West England.* Quaternary Research Association: London.

Lundberg, J, T C Lord and P J Murphy, 2010. Thermal ionization mass spectrometer U-Th dates on Pleistocene speleothems from Victoria Cave, North Yorkshire, UK: implications for palaeoenvironment and stratigraphy over multiple glacial cycles. *Geosphere,* **6**, 379-395.

Lyman, R L, 1994. *Vertebrate Taphonomy.* Cambridge University Press.

McFarlane, D A and D C Ford, 1998. The age of the Kirkdale Cave palaeofauna. *Cave Karst Science,* **25**, 3-6.

McFarlane, D A, J Lundberg and J Cordingley, 2005. A brief history of stalagmite growth measurements at Ingleborough Cave, Yorkshire, UK. *Cave Karst Science,* **31**, 113-118.

Meyer, M C, C Spötl and A Mangini, 2008. The demise of the Last Interglacial recorded in isotopically dated speleothems from the Alps. *Quat. Sci. Rev.,* **27**, 476-496.

Miall, L C, 1878. The geology, natural history and pre-historic antiquities of Craven in Yorkshire. 593-622 in T D Whitaker, *The History and Antiquities of the Deanery of Craven in the County of York.* Joseph Dodgson: Leeds and Cassell, Petter and Galpin: London.

Miall, L C, 1880. The cave and its contents. *Proc. Yorks. Geol. Polytech. Soc.,* **7**, 207-208.

Murphy, P. 2002. A gazetteer of non-human vertebrate remains from caves in the Yorkshire Dales referenced in caving club journals and allied literature. *Capra,* **4** (www.capra.group.shef.ac.uk).

Murphy, P J, 2011. A gazetteer of vertebrate remains from caves in the Yorkshire Dales referenced in caving club journals and allied literature. *Proc. Univ. Bristol Spel. Soc.,* **25**, 253-264.

Murphy, P and T C Lord, 2003. Victoria Cave, Yorkshire, U.K.; new thoughts on an old site. *Cave Karst Science,* **30**, 83-88.

Murphy, P J, R Smallshire and C Midgley, 2001. The sediments of Illusion Pot, Kingsdale, UK: evidence for subglacial utilisation of a karst conduit in the Yorkshire Dales. *Cave Karst Science,* **28**, 29-34.

O'Connor, A, 2007. *Finding Time for the Old Stone Age: a History of Palaeolithic Archaeology and Quaternary Geology in Britain, 1860–1960.* Oxford University Press.

O'Connor, T P, 2007. Wild or domestic? Biometric variation in the cat *Felis silvestris* Schreber. *Int. J. Osteoarchaeology,* **17**, 581-595.

Penkman, K E H and 7 others, 2011. A chronological framework for the British Quaternary based on *Bthynia* opercula. *Nature,* **476**, 446-449.

Plant, J, 1874. On bones of *Elephas Primigenius* from a cavern near Skipton. *Trans. Geol. Soc. Manchester,* **8**(3), 54.

Simms, M J, 1994. Emplacement and preservation of vertebrates in caves and fissures. *Zoological J. Linnean Soc.,* **112**, 261-283.

Sutcliffe, A J, 1960. Joint Mitnor, Buckfastleigh; a report on excavations carried out during 1939-41 by the late A.H. Ogilvie. *Trans. Torquay Nat. Hist. Soc.,* **13**, 3-28.

Sutcliffe, A J, 1985. *On the track of Ice Age mammals.* British Museum (Natural History): London.

Sutcliffe, A J, T C Lord, R S Harmon, M Ivanovich, A Rae and J W Hess, 1985. Wolverine in northern England at about 83,000 yr B.P.: faunal evidence for climatic change during Isotope Stage 5. *Quat. Res.,* **24**, 73-86.

Telfer, E S and J P Kelsall, 1984. Adaptation of some large North American mammals for survival in snow. *Ecology,* **65**, 1828-1834.

Telfer, M W, P Wilson, T C Lord and P J Vincent, 2009. New constraints on the age of the last ice sheet glaciation in NW England using optically stimulated luminescence dating. *J. Quat. Sci.,* **24**, 906-915.

Tiddeman, R H, 1873. The relation of man to the ice-sheet in the North of England. *Nature,* **9**, 14-15.

Tiddeman, R H, 1876. The age of Palaeolithic man. *Nature,* **14**, 505-506.

Tiddeman, R H, 1878a. On the age of the hyaena-bed at the Victoria Cave, Settle, and its bearing on the Antiquity of Man. *J. Anthropological Inst. G. B. Ireland,* **7**, 165-173.

Tiddeman, R H, 1878b. Fifth Report of the Committee … appointed for the purpose of assisting in the exploration of the Settle Caves (Victoria Cave). *Rep. 47th Meeting Brit. Assoc. Advance. Sci.,* 215-219.

Tiddeman, R H, 1879. Sixth Report of the Committee......appointed for the purposes of assisting in the exploration of the Settle Caves (Victoria Cave). *Rep. 48th Meeting of the Brit. Assoc. Advance. Sci.,* 377-380.

Turner, A, 2009. The evolution of the guild of large Carnivora of the British Isles during the Middle and Late Pleistocene. *J. Quat. Sci.,* **24**, 911-1005.

Vincent, P J, P Wilson, T C Lord, C Schnabel and K Wilcken, 2010. Cosmogenic isotope (36Cl) surface exposure dating of the Norber erratics, Yorkshire Dales: further constraints on the timing of the LGM deglaciation in Britain. *Proc. Geol. Assoc.,* **121**, 24-31.

Vincent, P J, T C Lord, M W and P Wilson, 2011. Early Holocene loessic colluviation in northwest England: new evidence for the 8.2 ka event in the terrestrial record? *Boreas,* **40**, 105-115.

Wilson, P, P J Vincent, M W Telfer and T C Lord, 2008. Optically stimulated luminescence (OSL) dating of loessic sediments and cemented scree in northwest England. *Holocene,* **18**, 1101-1112.

Cave archaeology

Tom Lord and John Howard

The limestones of the Yorkshire Dales contain a multitude of caves, rock shelters and natural shafts that have attracted not only people in the distant past but, in more recent times, archaeologists seeking evidence of their ancestors. Victoria Cave is the best known of the many Dales caves of archaeological significance, because of the large-scale excavations in the 1870s (Dawkins, 1872, 1874; Lord *et al.*, 2012). New data and interpretations have transformed ideas about the caves and their cultural history. As well as recent excavations, much entirely new information has come from looking again at the results of previous excavations, including a number of those that took place before the development of modern archaeology. Out of a total of nearly 80 cave excavations in the Dales, about 60 were before 1960; deposits in about 35 caves have been examined systematically.

People probably reached northern England on a number of occasions long before dates from Victoria Cave confirm Later Upper Palaeolithic presence about 12,500 BC. Any evidence that people explored the Dales before the Last Glacial maximum has been destroyed by successive glaciations. Ironically, during the Last Interglacial when deposits at Victoria Cave and Raygill Fissure reveal an abundance of big game (see Chapter 15), there is no unequivocal evidence for humans anywhere in Britain, which was then an island cut off from mainland Europe (Lewis *et al.*, 2011).

Radiocarbon dating of materials

All the cultural material from the Dales caves is derived from ages within the range that can be determined by radiocarbon dating (see Chapter 10). Furthermore, the modern methods that utilise accelerator mass spectrometry require only very small samples for analysis, thereby minimising damage to irreplaceable materials. There are currently about 90 radiocarbon dates on bone and antler from a total of 22 caves, rock shelters and shafts, so all the cave forms where cultural material has been found are represented. The results directly related to human presence consist of: 24 dates on human bone; 8 dates on bone or antler objects; and 16 dates for cut-marked, culturally smashed or modified animal bone. The other 40 or so dates are on large mammal bones that lack unequivocal human associations or got into a cave by natural processes such as carnivore actions or accidental death. These results provide a useful guide as to when caves were open. Dating of charcoal in cave sediments is invaluable for the Mesolithic and other periods with low rates of cultural deposition. Radiocarbon dating is bringing a new clarity to the cave record beyond the dreams of previous researchers (dates in this review were calibrated using OxCal 4.1 and have a 95% probability).

Cave archaeology, by Tom Lord and John Howard,
Tom Lord: Settle; tomlord@daelnet.co.uk
John Howard: Keighley: juliusagricola@tiscali.co.uk
Chapter 16, pages 239–251 in **Caves and Karst of the Yorkshire Dales**,
edited by Tony Waltham and David Lowe.
Published 2013 by the British Cave Research Association,
978-0-900265-46-4 and at www.bcra.org.uk

The first people in the Yorkshire Dales

Recent analysis of glacial erratics and loessic silts has shown that the much of the Dales limestone outcrops were ice-free by about 16,000 BC (see Chapter 3). Conditions were largely hostile to plants and animals for another 3000 years or so, until the beginning of the Lateglacial Interstadial. This was basically a period with warm summers and cold winters from 12,700 to 10,800 BC, interrupted by short, much colder events especially the severe Older Dryas cold event lasting a few hundred years around 12,000 BC. There is a gap in the dates for animal bones from the Dales caves around this time. The oldest dates for brown bears at Kinsey Cave and Victoria Cave are coincident with the onset of the Interstadial (see Chapter 15). All the dates for Later Upper Palaeolithic artefacts from the caves fall within the Interstadial, and these are supported by dates on bones attributable to carnivore actions (Table 16.1). Later Upper Palaeolithic artefacts are rare in the caves. They are overshadowed by evidence for brown bear hibernation, wolf scavenging and wolf denning. The entire archaeological record for Britain during the Lateglacial Interstadial might total little more than a few years or tens of years of occupation (Pettitt and White, 2012).

From Victoria Cave the date for a bevel-based reindeer antler rod (Lord, 2013) matches a dated cut-marked wild horse bone (Jacobi *et al.*, 2009) confirming human presence around 12,500 BC, during the first part of the Lateglacial Interstadial (Fig. 3.52). These two specimens could belong to one episode of activity. Their dates put the Yorkshire Dales firmly within the orbit of the Final Magdalenian settlement of northern Europe, when people first returned to areas previously abandoned for millennia during the Last Glacial Maximum. Magdalenian groups had arrived in southern Britain slightly before 12,700 BC (Jacobi and Higham, 2009), around the same time as the oldest dates for brown bears in the Dales caves. By the time Late Magdalenian people explored the Dales, generations of brown bears had already used Victoria Cave for hibernation, and bones of animals that

Figure 16.1. The entrances to Jubilee Cave, with Pen-y-ghent beyond; the flat terrace in front of the limestone scar was created by the debris excavated from the caves (photo: John Thorp).

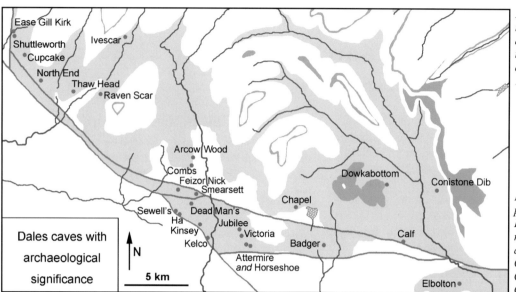

Figure 16.2. Caves in the Craven Dales with archaeological deposits that are described in this chapter; Rawthey Cave is 10 km north of the map area.

Figure 16.3. Refitted pieces of a Later Upper Palaeolithic bevel-based rod made from reindeer antler, found in Victoria Cave in 1870 in the Upper Cave Earth at the back of Chamber B.

had died in hibernation lay strewn about the cave where they had been fed upon and scattered by wolves (Lord *et al.*, 2007).

The conjoined pieces of the bevel-based rod of reindeer antler (Fig. 16.3) were found in 1870 but only identified in the 1920s (Breuil, 1921-22). The source of the reindeer antler could lie some distance away; radiocarbon dating has yet to confirm the presence of reindeer in the Dales at that time. The pieces of rod were found close to the back wall of the main chamber, Chamber A, some 30m in from the entrance, in a part of the cave that would have been in darkness during the Lateglacial.

The cut-marked wild horse atlas vertebra (Fig. 15.15) was also found close to the back wall of Chamber A in 1870. It records the removal of the head of a wild horse using stone tools (Lord *et al.*, 2007). It was probably carried into the cave by a wolf or a dog, and scavenged from an open air butchery site. Canid tooth marks overly the cut marks on the bone.

There are dated antler and bone objects (Lord, 2013) and scavenged cut-marked wild horse bones (Table 16.1) belonging to the second part of the Lateglacial Interstadial, after 12,000 BC. It is conceivable they only represent two episodes of human presence, with scavenged horse bones in a wolf den assemblage from Sewell's Cave revealing that people hunted wild horses (O'Connor and Evans, 2005).

A bilaterally barbed, antler point (Fig. 16.4) was found at the entrance to Victoria Cave in April 1870; it was described as a Neolithic bone harpoon (Dawkins, 1872, 1874) until Breuil (1921-22) compared it to the Final Palaeolithic barbed points from the Mas d'Azil in the French Pyrenees. A contemporary (Fig. 16.5) foreshaft of a composite-piece javelin head (Pettitt and White, 2012) was found by chance in 1931 (Jackson, 1945). It is engraved with a series of fine chevrons like the

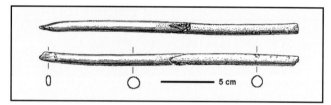

decorated Later Upper Palaeolithic wild horse mandible from Kendrick's Cave, North Wales (Sieveking, 1971). It was discovered in three pieces underneath calcite flowstone in the largely unexcavated passage beyond Chamber B, where more Later Upper Palaeolithic objects may await discovery (Fig. 16.6). It reveals another instance of exploring the dark inner areas of Victoria Cave and placing an object there in the Lateglacial, this time about 1500 years after the Final Magdalenian bevel-based rod was left in the cave. Dating suggests both objects were deposited during episodes of local hunting of wild horses (Table 16.1).

A bone point from Coniston Dib Cave, in Wharfedale, was dated before the development of improved dating methods (Hedges, 1992). It is identical to a find from Lynx Cave in North Wales dated 11,612 ± 210 BC (Blore, 2002, 2012). Both pieces were probably made from metatarsal bones of elk (*Alces alces*), which were hunted in lowland areas of northwest England during the second part of the Lateglacial Interstadial (Jacobi *et al.*, 2009).

specimen	location	calibrated age
Bevel-based rod of reindeer antler	Victoria Cave	12,521 ± 434 BC
Cut-marked atlas of wild horse	Victoria Cave	12,502 ± 438 BC
Tang of reindeer antler (artefact)	Kinsey Cave	11,359 ± 129 BC
Bone point (cf. elk, *Alces alces*)	Coniston Dib Cave	11,024 ± 223 BC
Decorated javelin foreshaft of reindeer antler	Victoria Cave	10,911 ± 203 BC
Bilaterally-barbed reindeer antler point	Victoria Cave	10,846 ± 153 BC
Mean of two dates for bones of wild horse associated with scavenged cut-marked bone in wolf den assemblage	Sewell's Cave	10,808 ± 148 BC

Figure 16.4. Later Upper Palaeolithic bilaterally-barbed point of reindeer antler, found beneath the scree at the entrance to Chamber A in Victoria Cave in 1870 (TL).

Table 16.1. Radiocarbon dates for human presence in the Lateglacial Interstadial.

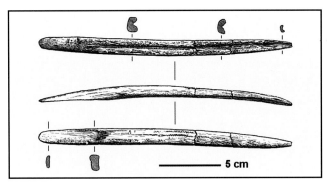

Figure 16.5. Later Upper Palaeolithic decorated foreshaft of a javelin head made from reindeer antler, found in Victoria Cave beneath flowstone in the largely unexcavated Chamber C in 1931.

There are very few Later Upper Palaeolithic stone tools from the Dales caves. Even including pieces with uncertain find histories, there are at most two from Raven Scar Cave, two from Kinsey Cave, and one from Victoria Cave. These stone tools are curved backed blades and knife points belonging to the second part of the Lateglacial Interstadial (Jacobi and Higham, 2011), and probably contemporary with the episodes of human represented by the dated antler and bone artefacts. Although small objects such as chipped stone tools would have been missed during excavations before the advent of diligent sieving, coarse sieves were in use by the 1930s, and the records from carefully excavated sites indicate that Later Upper Palaeolithic stone tools are genuinely rare in the Dales caves. Raven Scar Cave underwent a thorough excavation in the 1970s (Gilkes, 1976), but produced only two backed pieces (Fig. 16.7). Impact damage suggests these pieces may have been arrow tips.

The cave dates provide a basic chronology for Later Upper Palaeolithic activity in the Dales and northern England as a whole. Yet despite the considerable time span, there is nothing to indicate that human cave use was anything other than slight and intermittent; with possibly no more than three short events represented. Victoria Cave was explored on separate occasions, probably when people were in the area hunting wild horses, and so at times of the year when

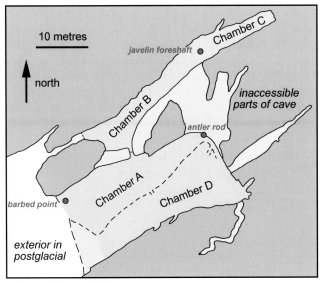

Figure 16.6. Victoria Cave before the excavations of 1870-78; the daylight entrance to Chamber D was originally blocked by sediment. Find spots are dated Later Upper Palaeolithic artefacts.

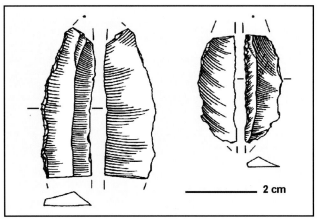

Figure 16.7. Later Upper Palaeolithic curved-backed flint blades, possibly arrow tips with impact damage, from Raven Scar Cave.

brown bears had vacated the cave. Anyone entering Victoria Cave would have encountered bones of brown bears that had died there, and had been fed upon and scattered by wolves. Just as wolves were attracted deep into the cave to get to the corpses of brown bears that had died in hibernation (Lord *et al.*, 2007), so might people have been after the marrow fat in the bones.

During the second part of the Interstadial bones of reindeer, wild cattle (aurochs) and wild horse were accumulated by wolves in Victoria Cave and Sewell's Cave (Lord *et al.*, 2007), suggesting that these large herbivores were present, and probably calving locally, during the spring and early summer when wolf pups are in dens. Their calves were attractive to humans as well as wolves, as calf skin provides soft leather. The presence of wild horse shows the uplands remained open ground providing good grazing when free from snow. The antler, bone and flint weapon heads found in the caves were designed to inflict wounds that bled copiously; they were used by small groups of mobile hunters looking to chance upon big game, and then get close to hit and wound an animal which weakened from bleeding could be tracked and killed. There is no evidence from the caves for human presence or wolf activity during the cold Younger Dryas Stadial that brought the Lateglacial Interstadial to an end around 10,800 BC.

Early Mesolithic, 9600 to 8000 BC

After a break of more than a thousand years during the cold Younger Dryas event, people returned to the Dales following the onset of rapid warming around 9,600 BC. Brown bears were probably already here by the time people arrived; there are dates for brown bear bones from Victoria Cave of 10,019–9406 BC and 9186–8806 BC. Brown bears could have been hunted in the Dales. A broad-blade flint microlith like those at Star Carr (near Scarborough) was found in Raven Scar Cave, along with brown bear remains dated 8294–7989. It is conceivable that the microlith got into the cave in the body of a brown bear wounded by an arrow. Early Mesolithic broad blade flint microliths of the Star Carr type are recorded from sites around Malham Tarn (Williams *et al.*, 1987).

There is scant evidence for Early Mesolithic activity in the caves. The only diagnostic artefacts are the Star Carr type microlith and possibly another piece from Raven Scar Cave, and a Deepcar type microlith from Jubilee Cave; perhaps add

Figure 16.8. Excavations at Victoria Cave in 1874, cutting through the great thickness of scree debris in order to explore the Hyaena Bone Bed for Palaeolithic tools.

Figure 16.10. Kinsey Cave, with the horizontal entrance excavated in the 1920s, below the blocked shaft into the main chamber (TL).

to these the distintive small blades and a stone bead from Chapel Cave, where fine sieving was used to ensure that small objects were not missed in the excavations (Donahue and Lovis, 2006). Early Mesolithic human remains have yet to be dated from the Dales caves; mortuary activity is an aspect of Early Mesolithic cave use in other limestone areas (Conneller, 2006) including those around Morecambe Bay (Smith, 2012).

The composite bone tool from the large rock shelter of Calf Hole (Jones, 1894) could belong to either Early or Later Mesolithic (Fig. 16.9). It consists of a wild boar canine set in a perforated haft of red deer antler. It was possibly a dual-purpose tool used in preparing arrow shafts: the hole in the haft being used to straighten the shafts after they were heated over a fire and the concave blade of the boars tusk used to smooth the shaft prior to heating and straightening.

Later Mesolithic, 8000 to 3800 BC

Later Mesolithic microliths are typically small geometric forms. These are found with lithic scatters throughout the Dales, but very few sites are dated, and the Later Mesolithic is a long period lasting about four thousand years. Current sea levels were reached by about 6000 BC and the loss of coastal lowlands could have encouraged greater use of the uplands. Cave use changes during the Later Mesolithic, as revealed by the cessation of mortuary activity in caves in southwest England and south Wales by about 6000 BC (Conneller, 2006). Three Dales caves have dated evidence for Later Mesolithic association unconnected with mortuary activity after 6000 BC. This might have been a relatively short event with cave use ending before 5000 BC.

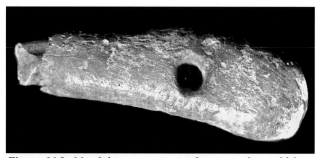

Figure 16.9. Mesolithic composite implement, with a wild boar canine set into a perforated handle of red deer antler; length is 19cm; found in Calf Hole, in Wharfedale, and photographed in the 1890s shortly before it was lost.

Recent excavation in the mouth of Chapel Cave found seventeen Later Mesolithic flint microliths and about eighty other non-diagnostic pieces of flint and chert. These occurred as discrete clasts in a sedimentary matrix that yielded a date of 5620–5424 BC on charcoal from near the top of the sequence (Donahue and Lovis, 2003). Analysis of the chert fragments indicate multiple possible sources including outcrops in Swaledale (Evans *et al.*, 2010). The cave was possibly visited by small task groups who had travelled some distance from their home settlements and used the cave to repair equipment (Donahue and Lovis, 2000). Chapel Cave is near to Malham Tarn, a unique upland lake that lies almost on the Pennine watershed; it would have been a permanent feature that was easily found in the largely wooded landscape of the Later Mesolithic. Groups travelling from settlements some distance away and meeting up at this upland lake might be one reason why Chapel Cave was used at this time.

That Later Mesolithic people explored caves is supported by charcoal dated about 5800 BC from the interior of the Arcow Wood Caves, and a piece of large red deer antler from inside Victoria Cave found mid-way in Chamber A in 1870 dated 5298–5057 BC. The latter find is so far the only piece of Later Mesolithic bone attributable to human deposition from a Dales cave, and currently the youngest evidence for Later Mesolithic cave use in the Dales. It also suggests the periwinkle (*Littorina* sp.) shell beads found during early work in Victoria Cave (Smith and Jackson, 1844) are Later Mesolithic. Periwinkle shell beads have been found in association with culturally smashed red deer bones in Three Holes Cave, Devon (Barton and Roberts, 2004) with dates matching the piece of red deer antler from Victoria Cave. The nearest source of periwinkle shells to Victoria Cave is Morecambe Bay, nearly 50 km away.

Presently there are no dates from the Dales caves for brown bears in the Mesolithic later than the specimen dated 8294–7989 BC from Raven Scar Cave. By the Later Mesolithic brown bears could have stopped using the Dales caves for hibernation (Lord *et al.*, 2007), and sites with old bear bones took on new cultural meanings. Brown bears had returned to Victoria Cave in the Early Mesolithic, adding more bones to those already there from the animals that died during the Lateglacial Interstadial. People might have come from the coast in the Later Mesolithic and put the shell beads

Table 16.2. Calibrated ages of Early Neolithic human bones from caves in the Craven Dales; the two dated bones from Kinsey Cave are probably from the same person (updated from Leach, 2008).

location	cave form	bone	structure	calibrated age
Kinsey Cave	rock shelter and chamber	femur	? whole body	3977–3800 BC
Kinsey Cave	rock shelter and chamber	mandible	? whole body	3961–3791 BC
Thaw Head Cave	small chamber	mandible, woman	whole body	3952–3716 BC
Arcow Wood Caves	multi- chamber	vertebra, adult	unknown	3943–3708 BC
Sewell's Cave	chamber, steep access	skull, man	skull	3942–3700 BC
Jubilee Cave	multi-chamber	tibia, man	whole body	3696–3529 BC
Cave Ha 3	rock shelter	tibia, man	whole body	3654–3522 BC
Lesser Kelco Cave	small chamber	skull, woman	skull	3650–3522 BC
Greater Kelco Cave	passage	femur, adult	unknown	3639–3381 BC
Cave Ha 3	rock shelter	mandible, child	whole body	3516–3111 BC

in Victoria Cave, perhaps because it was a special place that linked them to an ancestral past and a mythological present.

The dated Mesolithic animal bones from Kinsey Cave probably derive from animals that fell down a shaft into the main chamber (see Chapter 15). The bull aurochs dated 7501–7193 BC from the Cupcake shaft was possibly shot and wounded by an arrow before it fell to its death. Later Mesolithic stone tools found on the surface near large cave shafts suggests that people were attracted to these features (Thorp, 2013).

By 5000 BC there had been a change. Dates from Chapel Cave suggest Later Mesolithic abandonment after 5400 BC, with a break in cultural activity until the deposition of Early Neolithic human remains around 3600 BC. Dated Later Mesolithic charcoal and Early Neolithic human bone from the Arcow Wood Caves suggest a break from about 5800 BC to 3900 BC. The same sequence with a substantial break between Later Mesolithic cultural deposition and Early Neolithic mortuary activity was found at Three Holes Cave, Devon (Roberts, 1996; Berridge, 1996), so it appears to be more than a regional pattern.

In the Dales the emergence of rundkarren on limestone pavement as a result of extensive loessic colluviation during the cold event about 6200 BC (Wilson *et al.*, 2012) would not have gone unnoticed. The limestone outcrop with strange shapes to trap and break limbs would be good reason to avoid these areas. During the 6200 BC cold event it has been estimated for the Dales area that snow cover on ground above 380m lasted more than five months each winter for a period of one to two hundred years (Vincent *et al.*, 2011). Following this cold event, perhaps the areas of the Dales with new limestone pavements came to be regarded as places where dangerous spirits lived and were best avoided, with the result that the caves were abandoned more than a thousand years before the arrival of the first farming groups.

Early Neolithic, 3900 to 3200 BC

The Early Neolithic evidence from caves and rock shelters is very different to the sparse Mesolithic record. Cut-marked and culturally smashed animal bones provide unequivocal evidence for the deposition of processed animal remains, and these are mostly domestic cattle. Mortuary activity involving the corpse passing through multiple stages was widespread (Table 16.2). The dates from the Cave Ha 3 rock shelter for domestic cattle and sheep (Table 16.3) are comparable with dates for domestic cattle and sheep from Broken Cavern, Devon (Berridge, 1996); results from the two caves are as old as anywhere in mainland Britain (Tresset, 2003). This fits with suggestions for a rapid spread of farming groups from Northern France who brought with them novel technologies, domestic livestock, dairying, crop cultivation, and new mortuary practices (Collard *et al.*, 2010; Sheridan, 2007).

The new forms of deposition in caves and rock shelters began when Later Mesolithic hunter gatherers still lived in the Dales; currently the youngest dates for Later Mesolithic activity are from open sites on the gritstone uplands at the head of Nidderdale, 3944–3704 BC and 4232–3986 BC (Chatterton, 2007). Early farming groups were able to settle safely and so soon in the limestone areas of the Dales that had previously been abandoned by the native hunter-gatherers. An awareness of native beliefs might also explain why early farming groups went to the caves and put in cultural materials such as domestic animal bones. Maybe these were to win over the powerful local spirits believed in by the natives.

Caves located close together on Giggleswick Scar reveal contemporary Early Neolithic activity. Around 3900 BC part or the whole of an adult's body was placed in Kinsey Cave (Fig. 16.11); domestic cattle bones were smashed for marrow at the Cave Ha 3 rock shelter; and a man's skull was put in Sewell's Cave. This took place about the same time

Table 16.3. Sequence of the dated Neolithic materials recovered from the rock shelter of Cave Ha 3 in Giggleswick Scar (updated from Leach, 2008).

species	bone	evidence of activity	context	calibrated age
Domestic cow	Humerus, cut-marks and smashed open	on-site marrow extraction	natural alcove in back wall	3957–3715 BC
Domestic cow	Tibia, cut-marks and smashed open	on-site marrow extraction	natural alcove in back wall	3943–3699 BC
Domestic cow	Mandible, cut-marks	processed cow head left at site	stone paved area in front of rock shelter	3771–3645 BC
Sheep	Mandible	sheep head left at site	natural alcove in back wall	3765–3641 BC
Human adult	Tibia, whole body deposition	tibia smashed open around time of death; body later disarticulated	natural alcove in back wall	3654–3522 BC
Human child	Mandible, whole body deposition	body later disarticulated	natural alcove in back wall	3516–3111 BC
	Wood charcoal in thin, well-defined layer	on-site fires	tufa formed on back wall of rock shelter	2566–2211 BC

Figure 16.11. Two Early Neolithic skeletal mummies in Elbolton Cave (artist's reconstruction by Celia King).

as the beginning of Early Neolithic cave use in the Torbryan Valley, Devon (Berridge, 1996), but around 200 years before Neolithic mortuary activity is detected in the Mendip caves (Schulting *et al.*, 2010). The Giggleswick Scar caves retained specialist functions. Sewell's Cave was kept as a depository for human skulls; Lesser Kelco Cave served as a depository for human skulls and smashed domestic cattle bone. The skulls at these sites are not weathered suggesting they were deposited not long after death (Leach, 2008). At Cave Ha 3, a period when animal bones were smashed for marrow was succeeded by a period when human bodies were put in natural alcoves against the back wall of the rock shelter from about 3600 BC. Cave Ha 3 replicates the sequence at Broken Cavern, in the Torbryan Valley, where animal bone processing and deposition preceded mortuary activity (Berridge, 1996). Around 3600 BC a human skull and smashed domestic cattle bone were put into Lesser Kelco Cave. Sequences at Kinsey Cave and Greater Kelco Cave are disturbed and unclear.

The numbers of individuals represented at any one site are small; the body of one man, two children and possibly an infant lay in Cave Ha 3, and the skulls of two adults and two children in Sewell's Cave. The dates for Cave Ha 3 indicate that the whole bodies put there had died many generations apart. More dating is needed, but a pattern may be emerging of phases of Early Neolithic mortuary activity in caves, suggesting it was not an *ad hoc* practice when someone died, but was a behaviour triggered by external events, such as outbreaks of disease or adverse weather.

The man's skeleton from Cave Ha 3 shows that he suffered from osteoarthritis in his lower back, and his jaw was disfigured by disease. The elderly man whose body was put into Jubilee Cave suffered extreme osteoarthritis. The young woman whose body was put into Thaw Head Cave suffered disability, and possibly died giving birth. Whole bodies put into the caves during the Early Neolithic appear to represent deviant burials, where individuals are denied normal burial rites because of reasons connected with illness and disability or the manner of their death (Leach, 2008). Having chronic sickness or physical ailments could have identified individuals as having "malign souls" that might affect the well-being and health of domestic livestock and crops as well as other people (Hertz, 2004).

Such beliefs could have applied at Elbolton Cave, where three almost complete articulated skeletons were found (Jones, 1888, 1889, 1891); the two complete skulls have Neolithic cranial morphology. The bones exhibit canid tooth furrows, scoring and punctures which show that the bodies had been partly fed upon by dogs, foxes or wolves. This was probably supervised, because the feeding was halted before the major limb bones were damaged. The arrested feeding caused damage to the pelvic bones like that from the Early Neolithic barrow at Adlestrop on the Cotswolds, which is interpreted as evidence of excarnation (Smith, 2006). Care was taken to keep the partly de-fleshed corpses in an intact state in Elbolton Cave by packing them around with stones (Fig. 16.11). This might have been a deliberate attempt to preserve the body as a skeletal mummy, designed to keep the soul of that person tied to its bodily home (Taylor, 2002).

Early Neolithic mortuary activity in caves might have been concerned with keeping spirits (that were perceived as dangerous) physically tied to a marginal place – the cave being a space not in this world and not in the next world. It is entirely feasible that caves were sought out by the first farming communities in the Dales as places to tether dangerous spirits where they could do no harm to their crops, livestock and health. The need to look after and manage these spirits might then explain much of the archaeological record from caves and rock shelters for the next thousand years or so.

Later Neolithic, 3200 to 2600 BC

Caves used for mortuary activity in the Early Neolithic had objects placed in them during the Later Neolithic. At sites with skulls this practice might begin in the Early Neolithic by about 3600 BC. Pieces of Peterborough Ware pottery with a date range in northern England of 3600–2900 BC (Manby, 2007) are recorded from disturbed contexts at Sewell's and Lesser Kelco, two sites used as locales for Early Neolithic

Figure 16.12. The magnificent Cave Ha 1 rock shelter, excavated in 1873 by T McKenny Hughes after visiting the French Palaeolithic caves with Charles Lyell; the nearby, much smaller, Cave Ha 3 rock shelter contains Early Neolithic deposits (TW).

Figure 16.13. Later Neolithic mace head, made from the antler of a red deer, that was found on a ledge part way down the entrance shaft of North End Pot (photo: John Thorp).

skulls, and from Elbolton in a deep part of the cave with a skull (Jones, 1891). A wolf ulna dated 3635–3376 from Lesser Kelco is a possible Early Neolithic talisman. A possible Later Neolithic talisman, an aurochs toe bone, dated 3097–2914 BC (Lynch *et al.*, 2008) was found in Jubilee Cave, an Early Neolithic whole-body locale. At Thaw Head Cave, another Early Neolithic whole-body site, fragments of two Later Neolithic Grooved Ware jars date from after 3000 BC (Gilkes, 1995, 2001). The few Neolithic stone tools put in caves include special objects, but more precise dating is problematic, similarly with the deposition of Neolithic special objects in the grikes of limestone pavement (Lord, 2006). A culturally smashed piece of human femur from Greater Kelco Cave dated 2876–2620 BC might be the only bone from this person in the cave. It reveals unusual treatment of a body. Coincidently this person died about the same time as the oldest evidence for human bodies in cave shafts in the Dales.

Interest in cave shafts, the open potholes of the Dales, provides more evidence that cave use changed in the Later Neolithic. Disarticulated bones of two people, one dated 2886–2636 BC, were found in a deposit of human and animal bones at the base of the entrance shaft in North End Pot. Most of the bones were of wild animals, and the bone deposit extended to a depth of about 45m beneath the surface. The wild species are a wolf, adult and juvenile aurochs, red deer and black grouse; small pigs and a dog could be feral. It appears they all died after falling down the 20m-deep entrance shaft. The date for the skull of an aurochs bull, 2886–2640 BC (Lynch *et al.*, 2008) is identical to that for the human. At least part of the bone deposit might be cultural; perhaps an attempt by farmers to consign wild creatures to the underworld. Fossil pollen shows more intensive use of the uplands at this time (see Chapter 12). If the two people and all these animals were merely the victims of mischance, they were exceedingly unlucky. A Later Neolithic mace-head made from red deer antler (Fig. 16.13) was found on a ledge 10m down the entrance shaft, where its position indicated that it had been placed there intentionally (Gilkes and Lord, 1993).

Earlier Bronze Age, 2600 to 1400 BC

The deposition of pottery shows continued interest in caves and rock shelters previously used for mortuary activity in the Early Neolithic (Gilkes, 1973, 1995, 2001, 2003; Manby, 2007). Four of the eight sites with Beaker or other Earlier Bronze Age pottery, have dated Early Neolithic human remains – Lesser Kelco, Greater Kelco, Sewell's,

and Thaw Head. A fifth, Elbolton, was certainly used in the Early Neolithic for mortuary activity, and the other three (Attermire, Horseshoe and Raven Scar) have human bone as yet undated, but possible Early Neolithic. There is no evidence that Earlier Bronze Age pottery was put in caves as grave goods, although larger pots could have held cremations. A fairly complete Cordoned Barrel Urn and a cremated human mandible were found in Thaw Head Cave (Gilkes, 1995), and an unusual bone whistle from Raven Scar Cave seems to be Earlier Bronze Age (Gilkes, 1985).

Early Neolithic mortuary features and deposits of human and animal remains were rearranged during, or shortly before, the Earlier Bronze Age. At the Cave Ha 3 rock shelter a charcoal horizon dated 2566–2211 BC was sealed in the tufa that formed against the back wall of the rock shelter (Pentecost *et al.*, 1990). It post-dates the dismantling of Early Neolithic features at this site. Prior to the burning event, the skeletal remains of bodies put in natural alcoves against the back wall of the rock shelter had been disturbed, and jumbled up with older cut-marked and smashed animal bones, very likely moved from the front of the rock shelter (Table 16.3). Tufa then formed over the rearranged deposits. A key aspect of Earlier Bronze Age cave use might be the dismantling of Early Neolithic whole-body locales, and the taking down of skeletal mummies.

A startling find from the Earlier Bronze Age is the woman's skeleton dated to 2202–2031 BC from the Feizor Nick Caves (Smith *et al.*, 2007). A tiny gash in one of her back bones was shown to have been caused by a flint tipped projectile point. The woman had been shot by an arrow that had entered her body from the front, just below the rib-cage, and on passing through her stomach deflected off her backbone, where it severed a major artery, causing massive shock and bleeding. The trajectory of the arrow is consistent with her being shot from above as she lay on the ground. It is difficult to escape any conclusion other than this woman was deliberately shot in a manner intended to kill her. Furthermore, it may be that she was killed and her body left in the cave so that her soul would be stuck in a liminal place, forever between this world and the next (Taylor, 2002). The tiny gash in her backbone that provides evidence of her death opens to question the nature of dying of all the other people whose remains were placed into caves at various times.

Dates from cave shafts in the Dales reveal cultural deposition around the time the Feizor Nick woman was killed. Bones of a man from Shuttleworth Pot date from 2200–2026 BC. In the entrance shaft of North End Pot a layer of domestic animal bone, mostly juvenile cattle remains, dates from 2272–2035 BC (Lynch *et al.*,, 2008). Between 2300 and 2000 BC there was a marked climatic downturn with colder, wetter conditions and more flooding (Brown, 2008). Mixed farming in the Dales becomes less predictable and more hazardous during such periods, and hunger, crop failure and disease might underpin the unusual events that have been detected in the caves.

Cultural deposition in cave shafts occurred in the final part of the Earlier Bronze Age: a cut-marked small pig mandible from Shuttleworth Pot dates from 1884–1695 BC, and the body of man dated 1605–1307 BC lay in the talus beneath the now-blocked entrance shaft of Rawthey Cave (Chamberlain *et al.*, 1998).

Later Bronze Age, 1400 to 600 BC

There are very few Later Bronze Age artefacts, giving the impression that caves were rarely used at this time. Just one metal object from the entire Bronze Age is preserved from a Dales cave, and that is a Later Bronze Age pin from Raven Scar. The only pottery is a barrel-shaped jar from Thaw Head (Gilkes, 1995), and a fragment of a similar jar from Victoria Cave (Dearne and Lord, 1998). Two possible Later Bronze Age perforated bone buttons were found at the entrance to Victoria Cave. Dated bones include rare finds from Sewell's Cave, two lynx mandibles, probably deposited as skulls, with dates of 997–833 BC and 813–569 BC. From the scree at the entrance to Victoria Cave a culturally smashed red deer bone, dated 795–548 BC (Lord *et al.*, 2007), suggests a link between red deer hunting and deposition. A Later Bronze Age human bone is recorded from Badger Cave (Taylor, 2002).

A Later Bronze Age assemblage of human bones from the dark, inner part of Raven Scar Cave consist of the scavenged remains of young adults and children taken there and fed upon by a large carnivore (Leach, 2005). The Later Bronze Age pin was found in this part of the cave; it was possibly attached to clothing brought in with the scavenged body parts. One of the human arm bones dated 1048–896 BC has a metal blade mark made around the time of death. This suggests that at least one of these individuals was a victim of conflict. Many of the bones exhibit tooth marks and punctures made by a large carnivore. The animal was most likely lynx, as the tooth marks and manner of chewing are feline, rather than canid, and the many undigested bone fragments would be unusual for a canid. Lynx milk teeth and juvenile bone were found further in the cave.

Figure 16.14. *Excavations at Sewell's Cave 1933-34 by Tot Lord and the Pig Yard Club (from Raistrick, 1936).*

Figure 16.15. *Top of the sediment-filled shaft at North End Pot (TL).*

By contrast, the human remains in the entrance chamber at Raven Scar Cave consist mostly of loose teeth. Upper inner incisors are markedly over-represented. These teeth are single-rooted and are usually the first to fall out of human skulls. This is interpreted as showing that a number of human heads were placed in the cave entrance until they were entirely de-fleshed, or partially mummified by desiccating air currents, during which time many of the teeth fell out (Leach, 2005). The date of 1111–908 BC for a tooth is comparable to the result for the arm bone from the scavenged assemblage deeper in the cave, suggesting contemporary deposition. This then might be something very unusual: after lynx fed on human corpses, with at least one a victim of conflict, someone removed the heads, and preserved them in the cave before taking them away for use elsewhere. Scavenging is not typical lynx behaviour, so it was under human control and the animal was perhaps encouraged to feed on the corpses so as to give the preserved skulls magical qualities (Ogden, 2008). The lynx finds from Sewell's Cave suggest this elusive animal was imbued with special powers in the Later Bronze Age.

Iron Age, 600 BC to AD 100

The finds record suggests that caves were rarely used in this period. Diagnostic artefacts of any kind are simply not known. This appears to be a real phenomenon rather than the product of routinely describing Iron Age items as Romano-British. Non-perishable materials such as pottery might be lacking in any case, because it appears the Dales communities did not use pottery for much of the Iron Age (Harding, 2004). Dated charcoal provides the only evidence of Iron Age activity at the mouth of Chapel Cave.

Human and animal remains were placed in some caves. A culturally smashed human femur dated 511–376 BC was found mixed up with animal bones in Dead Man's Cave, behind Giggleswick Scar. Undated culturally smashed pieces of human bone from Raven Scar Cave and in the scree at the entrance to Victoria Cave might be Iron Age. The upper deposits in North End Pot (Fig. 16.15) contain Iron Age human and animal bones, showing that shafts continued to be a focus for whole-body deposition; the skull of a young adult was dated in the 1980s to 378 ± 380 BC (Gilkes and Lord, 1993), and there are also bones of a child. Represented among the animal bones are horses and dogs, species that are commonly associated with ritual Iron Age deposits (Green, 2001). Taken as a whole, the sequence at North End Pot is very like that from the Charterhouse Warren Swallet on Mendip (Audsley *et al.*, 1988; Levitan and Smart, 1989). Both shafts have dated Later Neolithic, Early Bronze Age and Iron Age bone deposits. Repeated synchronous deposition in the two shafts is further evidence that the North End Pot bone deposits are basically cultural in origin.

Romano-British, AD 100 to 450

There are two very different forms of deposition in the Romano-British period. The first continues the practice of whole-body deposition in cave shafts, a tradition in the Dales beginning in the Later Neolithic. This is represented by the body of a woman dated AD 63–240 from the talus deposits beneath the blocked shaft at Rawthey Cave (Chamberlain *et al.*, 1998). Within the talus, animal remains, especially horse, could also be Romano-British, but the deposit is very mixed, with material from the Earlier Bronze Age through to Mediaeval times, and there are bones of an adolescent person that have not yet been dated. The bodies of a number of Romano-British people and animals were put in the shaft at Dog Hole, at Haverbrack, near Morecambe Bay (Wilkinson *et al.*, 2011).

The second form of deposition is essentially novel, and generates the most prolific artefact horizon in the Dales cave record. The sites are concentrated in the fault scarps near Settle, with Victoria Cave and Attermire Cave having particularly rich assemblages (King, 2007, 1974, 1970; Henig and King, 2003; Chamberlain and Williams, 2001; Dearne and Lord, 1998; Branigan and Dearne, 1992; Jackson, 1962; Raistrick, 1939, 1936; Jackson and Mattinson, 1932; Poulton, 1881; Dawkins, 1874, 1872; Farrer and Denny, 1866; Smith, 1865; Denny, 1860; Farrer, 1857; Smith and Jackson, 1844, 1842). The cave distribution extends eastwards as far as Littondale, and northwest to the caves around Ingleborough, but there are far fewer artefacts in those caves. The deposits have a long history of investigation, beginning with work in Victoria Cave in 1837 (Lord, 2005). All the caves have deposition in the dark zones. Objects were sometimes placed in pools. Drip waters and calcite formations active during the Romano-British period added to their sense of other-worldliness. A small settlement beneath Attermire Scar (King, 1970) was possibly a service site for people visiting the caves nearby, and hints at the possibility of a managed commercial operation.

Figure 16.17. Replica of the Romano-British brooch of looped bronze wire, found in Attermire Cave; it is 46 mm long, possibly dates from late first century, and is a unique form of the bronze wire brooches found in caves above Settle (photo: John Whalley).

Materials such as iron and bronze are common, though rare in earlier deposits. There are iron weapons (Fig. 16.16), wheel fittings, tools, keys, lamp stands, and jewellery, bronze decorative pieces and fittings, delicate tools, cosmetic implements and jewellery, including many brooches (Fig. 16.17), and also bronze and silver coins. A medley of crafted objects made from bone and antler including the so-called "perforated bone spoons" whose purpose is still a mystery (Fig. 16.18), an elephant ivory sword pommel, beads and bangles made from glass and jet, and engraved intaglios from ring fittings (Fig. 16.19). There are pieces of pottery, but hardly ever evidence of whole pots, and from types normally found on Roman forts, villas or urban settlements, also palettes and counters made from broken pots, and bits of tiles and window glass. Stone spindle whorls were well made, along with palettes, polishers and more simple rubbing stones; the only quern stone is a flat type normally found on Roman settlements. Much charcoal is recorded with these assemblages, and the prominent layer at Chapel Cave was dated to the second century AD.

Victoria Cave has the largest animal bone assemblage; the cattle bones have cut-marks made by heavy cleavers, a butchery method more commonly found on Roman settlements; and there is a concentration of cut-marked juvenile sheep mandibles, possibly the result of cutting out their tongues for divination (Ryder, 1983). Waste pieces of crafted bone and antler from Victoria Cave suggests on-site bone working. A possible "head and hooves" horse burial from the scree outside Kinsey Cave was dated AD 127–324 (Lord *et al.*, 2007).

The date ranges of the large assemblage of pottery, jewellery and coins from Victoria Cave indicate that deposition began there by about AD 90 (Dearne and Lord, 1998), shortly after the Roman conquest of northern England in the early AD 70s. Garrisoning of the new northern forts by troops from the Balkan states of Dacia, Thrace and Illyria, is almost certain. An early second century AD bowl fragment from Victoria Cave has the name of its owner scratched on

Figure 16.16. An iron Roman short sword, a specialised military sword shorter than a gladius, found in Sewell's Cave; the blade is 34 cm long (TL).

Figure 16.18. Romano-British perforated bone spoon, 16 cm long, found in the dark, inner Chamber B of Victoria Cave in 1870.

Figure 16.19. Wax impression of the Romano-British red jasper intaglio found in Attermire Cave. It depicts a combination of the head of Minerva in a crested helmet, right, and a bearded Silenus, left, both Roman gods seen as protective and connected with salvation; the intaglio image is 11 mm high.

it, one Annamus – a name specific to the Roman province of Noricum, now part of modern day Slovenia and Austria (Tomlin and Hassall, 1998). Noricum was an Imperial mining district and an important producer of iron, silver, and lead. Men like Annamus would have been familiar with limestone landscapes in their homelands, and would have brought with them knowledge of mining and rituals connected with it. Finds of stamped pigs of lead from Nidderdale and Greenhow testify to lead production in the Dales soon after the conquest, and almost certainly organised by the Roman army (Bayley, 2002; Jones, 1986). Prospecting for metal ore and the getting of the ore from the shallow oxidised mineralised veins in the Craven uplands might have required the benefice of the underworld deities and involve propitiation (Henig, 1984).

Figure 16.20. A flooded part of Dowkabottom Cave, used in the Romano-British period when the water level was fluctuating (TL).

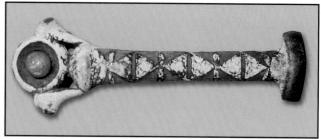

Figure 16.21. Bronze fitting, possibly from a Roman military harness of the late first century; it is 73 mm long and decorated with enamel and glass inlay, and was found in a small shaft on Ingleborough (photo: John Thorp).

Caves were widely regarded as entrances to the underworld in Roman times and an obvious place to make offerings to an underworld pantheon (Ogden, 2001; Flint et al., 1999).

Distinctive characteristics of the assemblages, notably the types of pottery, the presence of coins, and Roman military accoutrements, reveal that the Dales caves were used by people who were either part of the Roman army or closely connected with it, especially in the late 1st and 2nd centuries (Dearne and Lord, 1998). The 3rd and 4th century assemblages from the caves generally lack brooches and Roman military fittings, though how much this is due to changes in fashion and military organisation rather than changes in the groups who participate in cave activity is difficult to say. The dates of pottery from Victoria Cave suggest activity there continued throughout most of the Romano-British period.

Caves might provide access to underworld deities as well as those spirits of the dead inhabiting the underworld. Necromancy, the summoning up of the spirits of the dead, was an important aspect of cults connected with caves in the Celtic and classical world (Ogden, 2001; Flint et al., 1999). For the medley of immigrants connected with the Roman army, the caves would have given them an opportunity to access the underworld, and so contact the spirits of loved ones in distant homelands across the Roman Empire. The unprecedented scale of artefact deposition during the Romano-British period in the caves around Settle probably resulted from cult activity by ordinary migrants coming with the army from other parts of the Roman Empire and never returning home (Faulkner, 2001). These people went to the caves to reshape new cultural identities for themselves, away from the conventions of organised military religion (Irby-Massie, 1999).

Early Mediaeval, AD 400 to 1000

Materials from this time are scarce, and occur at fewer sites compared with the Romano-British period (King, 1974; Swanton, 1969). Attermire Cave has produced metalwork and some coins; single pieces of metalwork are recorded from Dowkabottom Cave and Victoria Cave; as well as two sites with no evidence of Romano-British deposition, Combs Cave and Smearsett Cave, on the west side of Ribblesdale. Dating of animal bones and charcoal has provided a little more context for Early Mediaeval cave use.

Greater Kelco Cave, a focus for Romano-British artefact deposition, was the scene of activity at the very beginning of the Early Mediaeval period when Giggleswick Scar lay on the boundary of a small, independent, Celtic kingdom (Wood, 1996). One of several culturally smashed red deer leg bones from Greater Kelco Cave was dated to AD 416–546. This suggests a link between red deer hunting and deposition as at Victoria Cave in the Later Bronze Age. Significantly the red deer date from Greater Kelco Cave matches the dates from the nearby Kinsey Cave for brown bear, AD 420–610 (Hammon, 2010), and lynx, AD 430–565 (Hetherington *et al.*, 2006), but these specimens lack cultural modification. The presence of brown bear and lynx points to an environment with significant amounts of woodland, and wild enough to be populated with large predators (Taylor, 2006). Set within a spectacular limestone landscape, it is easy to imagine how hunting red deer in this environment might involve atonement and deposition in a cave, especially if this was a high status activity.

Human remains are reported from Attermire Cave and Dowkabottom Cave in contexts likely to be post Romano-British (Farrer and Denny, 1866; Howson, 1850). Both caves have produced Early Mediaeval metalwork, and there are ninth century coins from Attermire Cave (King, 1974). These caves could have been re-used for mortuary purposes after the Anglo-Saxon conquest of the area in the seventh century, possibly fitting with such re-use of older earthworks (Semple and Williams, 2007), as illustrated by human remains dated AD 670–780 from a prehistoric cairn behind Giggleswick Scar near Feizor. A human tibia dated 560-655 AD suggests mortuary activity a little earlier at Kirkhead Cave, on the north side of Morecambe Bay (Smith, 2012).

Charcoal from the eighth or ninth century was dated from the Arcow Wood Caves in a context lacking cultural material. The nearby Combs Cave produced a small decorative piece of Anglo-Saxon metalwork.

Mid and Later Mediaeval, AD 1000 to 1500

Set against the more intensive use of the uplands during this period, especially monastic sheep management on the higher limestone ground, it is noticeable how few artefacts from this time have been found in the Dales caves. There are a few bits of pottery (Raistrick, 1936), an occasional metal or stone

Figure 16.22. Mediaeval ecclesiastical seal matrix, 55 mm high, carved in hard slate, found in Dowkabottom Cave and now lost (rubbing by Addison Crofton in about 1895).

object and some coins. Two objects are clearly Christian – part of a bronze cruciform pendant from Attermire Cave, and an ecclesiastical seal matrix in hard stone believed to have been found in Dowkabottom Cave about 1860, and now lost (Fig. 16.22). Both caves underwent deposition in the Early Medieval period, and it is tempting to regard Mediaeval Christian objects placed in them as attempts to counter older pagan associations.

Mediaeval Edwardian silver pennies are recorded from Attermire Cave and Ivescar Cave, in Chapel-le-Dale (Speight, 1892; Smith, 1865). The latter cave is especially wet, with a powerful stream after heavy rain. It is not a place to put coins intended to be recovered. On the reverse side the coins feature a design with a cross-like motif and twelve pellets. This Christian symbolism, the cross representing Jesus and the pellets standing for the twelve apostles, might explain why these coins were put in the two caves around AD 1400.

The youngest dates on animals that fell down the entrance shaft at Rawthey Cave suggest that the opening at the surface was finally blocked by about AD 1400 (Chamberlain *et al.*, 1998). This was possibly intentional to prevent sheep and other livestock falling down and being injured or killed. The blocking of cave shafts was probably a widespread practice on uplands used for grazing where livestock was no longer closely supervised.

Post-Mediaeval, AD 1500 onwards

A distinctive aspect of cave use after 1500 is the appearance of graffiti and other marks engraved into cave walls. These include ritual protection marks similar to those reported from Wookey Hole and other caves in Mendip (Binding and Wilson, 2010; Binding *et al.*, 2004). In Mendip, these are thought to date from the mid 16th to 18th centuries, a time when renewed belief in witchcraft and malevolent powers made people seek protection from them (Merrifield, 1987).

From the Dales there are examples of the conjoined **Vs** that resemble a single **W** (Fig. 16.23). The conjoined **Vs** stand for *Virgo Virginum*, meaning Virgin of Virgins. Inverted the conjoined **Vs** read as an **M** standing for Mary, mother of Jesus, and so the symbol cannot be turned back on the user. A crossed form of the letter **I** occurs with the conjoined **Vs** in Ease Gill Kirk Cave (Cordingley, 1999) suggesting, as in Mendip, that this mark was also intended as a protective symbol. The Kirk Cave is close to the Witches Holes, where it was said in 1820 that *witches ust ta meet yance a ear e thor holes, an mead a girt feast, an neabudy mud gang tull it, but sic as ther sels* (Balderston and Balderston, 1888). The need for the protective marks might have been to ensure that the growing numbers of paying visitors to the caves and their guides came to no harm. By the late 18th century, guided visits to the Dales caves were a routine part of the tourist experience (Hutton, 1781).

There is a heterogeneous quantity of post-Mediaeval objects in the collections from the caves, but these have not been studied properly. Compared to the mediaeval record there are fewer coins, which is surprising. The assemblage from Greater Kelco Cave includes an 18th century Jew's harp alongside small pieces of pottery that were deposited as single broken pieces.

Figure 16.23. *Conjoined Vs and a crossed **I**, possibly 17th or 18th century, carved into the limestone wall of Ease Gill Kirk Cave (photo: Dave Checkley).*

Through the millennia, people repeatedly used the Dales caves to access and mediate with the spirit world. Caves endured for a remarkably long time as places for these activities, and it is unlikely that there was any period in historic times when caves were not visited. Consequently, the archaeological deposits of the Dales caves are unique archives for understanding peoples' mythological landscapes and how they have evolved.

References

Audsley, A and 6 others, 1998 Charterhouse Warren, Farm, Swallet: exploration, geomorphology, taphonomy and archaeology. *Proc. Univ. Bristol Speleo. Soc.*, **18**, 171-239.

Balderston, R R and M Balderston, 1888. *Ingleton: Bygone & Present.* Edmondson: Skipton.

Barton, R N E and A J Roberts, 2004. The Mesolithic period in England: current perspectives and new research. 339-358 in A Saville (ed.), *Mesolithic Scotland and its Neighbours, the Early Holocene Prehistory Scotland, its British and Irish context, and some Northern European Perspectives.* Society of Antiquaries: Edinburgh.

Bayley, J, 2002. Non-ferrous metalworking in Roman Yorkshire. 101-108 in P Wilson and J Price (eds.), *Aspects of Industry in Roman Yorkshire and the North.* Oxbow: Oxford.

Berridge, P J, 1996. Later prehistoric and Romano-British evidence from the Torbryan Valley. 202-204 in D J Charman, R M Newnham and D G Croot (eds.), *Devon and East Cornwall Field Guide.* Quaternary Research Association: London.

Binding, C J and L J Wilson, 2010. Ritual protection marks in Wookey Hole and caves in the Cheddar Gorge, Somerset. *Proc. Univ. Bristol Speleo. Soc.*, **25**, 47-73.

Binding, C J, L J Wilson and T Easton, 2004. Ritual protection marks in Goatchurch Cavern, Burrington Coombe, North Somerset, with an appendix on the use of conjoined Vs to protect a dwelling. *Proc. Univ. Bristol Speleo. Soc.*, **23**. 120-133.

Blore, J D, 2002. *The Enigmatic Lynx.* Blore: Wallasey.

Blore, J D, 2012. *Lynx Cave, Denbighshire: 50 years of excavation, 1962-2012.* Blore: Wallasey.

Branigan, K and M J Dearne, 1992. *Romano-British Cavemen: Cave Use in Roman Britain.* Oxbow: Oxford.

Breuil, H, 1921-22. Observations on the pre-Neolithic industries of Scotland. *Proc. Soc. Antiquaries Scotland,* **8**, 261-281.

Brown, T, 2008. The Bronze Age climate and environment of Britain. *Bronze Age Review,* **1** (November), 7-22.

Chamberlain, A, B Sellars, P Murphy and A Goddard, 1998. The archaeology of Rawthey Cave, Sedbergh, Cumbria. *Archaeology North,* 14, 11-20.

Chamberlain, A T and J P Williams, 2001. A Gazetteer of English Caves, Fissures and Rock Shelters Containing Human Remains. *Capra,* 1 (www.capra.group.shef.ac.uk).

Chatterton, R, 2007. South Haw, Northern England. An upland Mesolithic site in context. 69-80 in C Waddington and K Pedersen (eds.), *Mesolithic Studies in the North Sea Basin and Beyond.* Oxbow: Oxford.

Collard, M, K Edinborough, S Shennan and M G Thomas, 2010. Radiocarbon evidence indicates that migrants introduced farming to Britain. *J. Archaeo. Sci.,* **37**, 866-870.

Conneller, C, 2006. Death. 139-164 in C Conneller and G Warren (eds.), *Mesolithic Britain and Ireland: New Approaches.* Tempus: Stroud.

Cordingley, J, 1999. More on those inscriptions and the letter I. *Craven Pothole Club Record,* 53, 50-51.

Dawkins, W B, 1872. Report on the results obtained by the Settle Cave Exploration Committee out of Victoria Cave in 1870. *J. Anthropol. Inst. G. B. and Ireland,* **1**, 60-70.

Dawkins, W B, 1874. *Cave Hunting: Researches on the Evidences of Caves Respecting the Early Inhabitants of Europe.* Macmillan: London.

Dearne, M J and T C Lord (eds.), 1998. *The Romano-British Archaeology of Victoria Cave, Settle: researches into the site and its artefacts.* British Archaeological Reports British Series, 278.

Denny, H, 1860. On the geological and archaeological contents of the Victoria and Dowkerbottom Caves in Craven. *Proc. Geol. Polytech. Soc. West Riding of Yorkshire,* **4**, 45-74.

Donahue, R E and W A Lovis, 2003. Initial evaluation of Graham Clarks's model of Mesolithic transhumance in northern England: a perspective from the Pennine uplands. *Proc. 6th Int. Conf. Mesolithic in Europe, MESO 2000 (Oxbow: Oxford).* 298-303.

Donahue, R E and W A Lovis, 2006. Regional settlement systems in Mesolithic northern England: scalar issues in mobility and territoriality. *J. Anthropol. Archaeo.,* **25**, 248-258.

Evans, A A, J L Langer, R E Donahue, Y B Wolframm and W A Lovis, 2010. Lithic raw material sourcing and the assessment of Mesolithic landscape organization and mobility strategies in northern England. *The Holocene,* **20**, 1157-1163.

Farrer, J W, 1857. Dowkerbottom Hole. *Proc. Soc. Antiquaries London,* **4**, 111-112.

Farrer, J W and H Denny, 1866. Further exploration in the Dowkerbottom Caves, in Craven. *Proc. Geol. Polytech. Soc. West Riding of Yorkshire,* **4**, 414-22.

Faulkner, N, 2001. *The Decline and Fall of Roman Britain.* Tempus: Stroud.

Flint, V, R Gordon, G Luck and D Ogden, 1999. *Witchcraft and Magic in Europe Vol. 2: Ancient Greece and Rome.* Athlone: London.

Gilkes, J A, 1973. The Neolithic and early Bronze Age pottery from Elbolton Cave, Wharfedale. *Yorks. Archaeo. J.,* **45**, 41-54.

Gilkes, J A, 1976. Excavations in a cave on Raven Scar, Ingleton, 1973-75. *Trans. Brit. Cave Res. Assoc.,* **3**, 95-99.

Gilkes, J A, 1985. A bone whistle from Raven Scar Cave, North Yorkshire. *Antiquity,* **59**, 124-5.

Gilkes, J A, 1995. Later Neolithic and Bronze Age pottery from Thaw Head Cave, Ingleton, North Yorkshire. *Trans. Hunter Archaeo. Soc.,* **18**, 1-11.

Gilkes, J A, 2001. Further finds of Grooved Ware from Thaw Head Cave, Ingleton, North Yorkshire. *Trans. Hunter Archaeo. Soc.,* **21**, 60-62.

Gilkes, J A, 2003. A sherd of Later Neolithic Grooved Ware from Lesser Kelcoe, Cave, Giggleswick, North Yorkshire, with a note on other finds of Grooved Ware from caves in the North of England. *Trans. Hunter Archaeo. Soc.,* **22**, 15-22.

Gilkes, J A and T C Lord, 1993. A Neolithic antler macehead from the North End Pot, Ingleton, North Yorkshire. *Trans. Hunter Archaeo. Soc.,* **17**, 57-59.

Green, M A, 2001. *Dying for the Gods: Human Sacrifice in Iron Age and Roman Europe.* Tempus: Stroud.

Hammon, A, 2010. The Brown Bear. 95-103 in T O'Connor and N Sykes (eds.), *Extinctions and Invasions: a Social History of British Fauna.* Windgather: Oxford.

Harding, D W, 2004. *The Iron Age in Northern Britain.* Routledge: Oxford.

Hedges, R E M, 1992. Radiocarbon dates from the Oxford AMS system. Archaeometry datelist 14. *Archaeometry,* **34**, 141-159.

Henig, M, 1984. *Religion in Roman Britain.* Batsford: London.

Henig, M and A King, 2003. Two Roman intaglios from Craven. *Yorks. Archaeo. J.,* **75**, 9-13.

Hertz, R A, 2004. Contribution to the study of the collective representation of death. 197-212 in A C G M Robben (ed.), *Death, Mourning and Burial: a Cross-cultural Reader.* Blackwell: Oxford.

Hetherington, D A, T C Lord and R M Jacobi, 2006. New evidence for the occurrence of Eurasian lynx (*Lynx lynx*) in medieval Britain. *J. Quat. Sci.,* **21**, 3-8.

Howson, W, 1850. *An Illustrated Guide to the Curiosities of Craven: with a geological introduction; notices of the dialect; a list of the fossils; and a local flora.* Whitaker: London.

Hughes, T M, 1874. Exploration of Cave Ha, near Giggleswick, Settle, Yorkshire. *J. Anthropological Inst. G. B. Ireland,* **3**, 383-387.

Hutton, J, 1871. *A Tour to the Caves in the Environs of Ingleborough and Settle in the West Riding of Yorkshire.* Richardson and Urquhart: London.

Irby-Massie, G L, 1999. *Military Religion in Roman Britain.* Brill: Leiden.

Jackson, J W, 1945. A lance-point of Upper Palaeolithic type from Victoria Cave, Settle, Yorkshire. *Antiquaries J.,* **22**, 147-148.

Jackson, J W, 1962. Archaeology and Palaeontology. 252-346 in C H D Cullingford (ed.), *British Caving*. Routledge Kegan Paul: London.

Jackson, J W and W K Mattinson, 1932. A cave on Giggleswick Scars near Settle, Yorkshire. *The Naturalist*, 1, 5-9.

Jacobi, R M and T F G Higham, 2009. The early Lateglacial re-colonization of Britain: new radiocarbon evidence from Gough's Cave. *Quat. Sci. Rev.*, 28, 1895-1913.

Jacobi, R and T Higham, 2011. The Later Upper Palaeolithic recolonisation of Britain: new results from AMS radiocarbon dating. 223-247 in N Ashton, S Lewis and C Stringer (eds.), *The Ancient Human Occupation of Britain*. Elsevier: Amsterdam.

Jacobi, R M, T F G Higham and T C Lord, 2009. Improving the chronology of the human occupation of Britain during the Late Glacial. *Proc. Workshop 14 (Commission XXXII) of 15th U.I.S.P.P. Congress*, Mainz and Bonn, 7-25.

Jones, E, 1888. On the recent exploration of a cave at Elbolton, near Thorpe. *Proc. Yorks. Geol. Polytech. Soc.*, 11, 86-90.

Jones, E, 1889. On further exploration of a cave at Elbolton near Thorpe, in Craven. *Proc. Yorks. Geol. Polytech. Soc.*, 11, 307-310.

Jones, E, 1891. Exploration of the Elbolton Cave. *Proc. Yorks. Geol. Polytech. Soc.*, 12, 105-107.

Jones, E, 1894. Exploration of the Calf Hole Cave at the Heights, Skyrethorns, near Skipton. *Report 64th Meeting Brit. Assoc. Advancement Science*. John Murray: London.

Jones, R F J, 1986. Rome in the Pennines. *British Archaeological Reports, British Series*, 158, 229-236.

King, A, 1970. Romano-British metalwork from the Settle district of West Yorkshire. *Yorks. Archaeo. J.*, 62, 410-417.

King, A, 1974. A review of archaeological work in the caves of North-West England. 182-200 in A C Waltham (ed.), *The Limestones and Caves of North-West England*. David and Charles: Newton Abbot.

King, A, 2007. Reports on Romano-British and other objects from Attermire Cave, Settle, Yorkshire. *Cumberland Westmorland Antiquarian Archaeo. Soc. Extra Series*, 33, 249-272.

Leach, S, 2005. Heads, shoulders, knees and toes. Human skeletal remains from Raven Scar Cave in the Yorkshire Dales. *British Archaeological Reports International Series*, 1383, 59-68.

Leach, S, 2008. Odd One out? Earlier Neolithic deposition of human remains in caves and rock shelters in the Yorkshire Dales. 35-56 in E M Murphy (ed.), *Deviant Burial in the Archaeological Record*. Oxbow: Oxford.

Levitan, B M and P L Smart, 1989. Charterhouse Warren Farm Swallet, Mendip, Somerset: radiocarbon dating evidence. *Proc. Univ. Bristol Speleo. Soc.*, 18, 390-394.

Lewis, S G, N Ashton and R Jacobi, 2011. Testing human presence in the Last Interglacial (MIS 5e): a review of the British evidence. 125-164 in N Ashton, S Lewis and C Stringer (eds.), *The Ancient Human Occupation of Britain*. Elsevier: Amsterdam.

Lord, T C, 2005. The discovery of Victoria Cave. *North Craven Heritage Trust J.*, 5-6.

Lord, T, 2006. How old are limestone pavements? *Proc. North Craven Historical Research Group Workshop: Re-thinking Craven's Limestone Landscape*, 47-51.

Lord, T C, 2013. The chronology of the Later Upper Palaeolithic recolonisation of Yorkshire: new results from AMS radiocarbon dating of objects from caves in the Yorkshire Dales. *Prehistoric Yorkshire*, 50, 14-18.

Lord, T, J Lundberg and P Murphy, 2012. A guide to work at Victoria Cave, from the 19th to 21st centuries. 84-97 in O'Regan *et al., op. cit.*.

Lord, T C, T P O'Connor, D C Siebrandt and R M Jacobi, 2007. People and large carnivores as biostratinomic agents in Late Glacial cave assemblages. *J. Quat. Sci.*, 22, 681-694.

Lynch, A H, J Hamilton and R E M Hedges, 2008. Where the wild things are: aurochs and cattle in England. *Antiquity*, 82, 1025-1039.

Manby, T G, 2007. Edenside Tarn and the Neolithic pottery of North-Western England. Cumberland Westmorland Antiquarian Archaeo. Soc. Extra Series, 33, 61-97.

Merrifield, R, 1987. *The Archaeology of Ritual and Magic*. Guild: London.

O'Connor, T and J G Evans, 2005. *Environmental Archaeology: Principles and Methods*. Sutton: Stroud.

Ogden, D, 2001. *Greek and Roman Necromancy*. Princetown University Press.

Ogden, D, 2008. *Night's Black agents*. Hambledon Continuum: London.

O'Regan, H J, T Faulkner and I R Smith, (eds.), Cave Archaeology and Karst Geomorphology in North West England. Quaternary Research Association: London, 186pp.

Pentecost, A, P M Thorpe, D D Harkness and T C Lord, 1990. Some radiocarbon dates for tufas of the Craven District of Yorkshire. *Radiocarbon*, 32, 93-97.

Pettitt, P and M White, 2012. *The British Palaeolithic: Human Societies at the Edge of the Pleistocene World*. Routledge: London.

Poulton, E B, 1881. A preliminary account of the working of Dowkerbottom Cave, in Craven, during August and September, 1881. *Proc. Geol. Polytech. Soc. West Riding of Yorkshire*, 7, 351-368.

Raistrick, A, 1936. Excavations at Sewell's Cave, Settle, W. Yorkshire. *Proc. Univ. Durham Phil. Soc.*, 9, 191-204.

Raistrick, A, 1939. Iron Age settlements in West Yorkshire. *Yorks. Archaeo. J.*, 34, 115-150.

Roberts, A J, 1996. The Early Holocene period and Mesolithic archaeology. 201-202 in D J Charman, R M Newnham and D G Croot (eds.), *Devon and East Cornwall Field Guide*. Quaternary Research Association: London.

Ryder, M L, 1983. *Sheep and Man*. Duckworth: London.

Schulting, R J, P J Gardiner, C J Hawkes and E Murray, 2010. The Mesolithic-Neolithic human bone assemblage from Totty Pot. *Univ. Bristol Speleo. Soc.*, 25, 75-95.

Semple, S J and H M R Williams, 2007. *Early Medieval mortuary practices. Anglo-Saxon Studies in Archaeology and History*, 14. Oxbow: Oxford.

Sheridan, J A, 2007. From Picardie to Pickering and Pencraig Hill? New information on the 'Carinated Bowl Neolithic' in northern Britain. 441-492 in A W R Whittle and V Cummings (eds.), *Going over: the Mesolithic-Neolithic transition in North-West Europe*. Oxford University Press.

Sieveking, A, 1971. The Kendrick's Cave mandible. *British Museum Quarterly*, 35, 230-250.

Smith, C R and J Jackson, 1842. Roman remains discovered in the caves near Settle in Yorkshire. *Archaeologia*, 29, 384-385.

Smith, C R and J Jackson, 1844. Caves in which Romano-British remains have been discovered near Settle, in Yorkshire. *Collectanae Antiqua*, 2, 69-72.

Smith, H E, 1865. The limestone caves of Craven and their ancient inhabitants. *Trans. Historical Soc. Lancashire Cheshire*, 5, 199-230.

Smith, I R, 2012. Kirkhead Cavern, Kent's Bank Cavern and Whitton's Cave near Allithwaite – geology, sediments and archaeology. 84-97 in O'Regan *et al., op. cit.*.

Smith, M J, 2006. Bones chewed by canids as evidence of human excarnation: a British case study. *Antiquity*, 80, 671-685.

Smith, M J, M B Brickley and S L Leach, 2007. Experimental evidence for lithic projectile injuries: improving recognition of an under-recognised phenomenon. *J. Archaeo. Sci.*, 34, 540-553.

Speight, H, 1892. *The Craven and North-West Yorkshire Highlands*. Elliot Stock: London.

Swanton, M J, 1969. A rune stone from Victoria Cave, Settle, Yorkshire. *Mediaeval Archaeology*, 13, 211-214.

Taylor, T, 2002. *The Buried Soul: How Humans Invented Death*. Beacon: Boston, USA.

Taylor, T, 2006. From wildness to wildscape: questions from archaeological theory. *Proc. North Craven Historical Research Group Workshop: Re-thinking Craven's Limestone Landscape*, 27-28.

Thorp, J, 2013. The lithic associations of caves and potholes: the occurrence of lithic artefacts in, and adjacent to, the caves and potholes of the Yorkshire Dales. *Prehistoric Yorkshire*, 56-62.

Tomlin, R S O and M W C Hassall, 1998. Victoria Cave. Roman Britain in 1997, Inscriptions. *Brittania*, 29. 439.

Tresset, A, 2003. French Connections II: of cows and men. 18-30 in I Armit, E Murphy, E Nelis and D Simpson (eds.), *Neolithic Settlement in Ireland and Western Britain*. Oxbow: Oxford.

Vincent, P J, T C Lord, M W Telfer and P Wilson, 2011. Early Holocene loessic colluviation in northwest England: new evidence for the 8.2 ka event in the terrestrial record. *Boreas*, 40, 105-115.

Wilkinson, D M, H J O'Regan and J Thorp, 2011. Dogs, scouts and cavers: a history of the archaeological excavation at Dog Hole Cave, Haverbrack, Cumbria, North West England. *Cave Karst Science*, 38, 125-130.

Williams, D J, J A Richardson and R S Richardson, 1987. Mesolithic dates at Malham Tarn and Great Close Mire, North Yorkshire. *Proc. Prehistoric Soc.*, 53, 363-383.

Wilson, P, M W Telfer, T C Lord and P J Vincent, 2012. Loessic sediments in North West England. 143-150 in O'Regan *et al., op. cit.*.

Wood, P N, 1996. On the Little British Kingdom of Craven. *Northern History*, 32, 1-20.

Index to localities

with site locations by National Grid Reference

All NGRs are approximate, and SD unless stated otherwise

Many caves and landforms are on private land, and inclusion in this listing does not indicate or imply any right of access.